HANDBOOK OF WORKED EXAMPLES IN STRUCTURAL ENGINEERING

Inder Jit Handa, P.E.

Consulting Engineer

PRENTICE-HALL, INC. Englewood Cliffs, New Jersey 07632

Library of Congress Cataloging in Publication Data

Handa, Inder Jit.
Handbook of worked examples in structural engineering.

Bibliography: p.
Includes index.
1. Structural engineering—Problems, exercises, etc.
I. Title.
TA640.4.H36 624.1'076 80-29067
ISBN 0-13-382903-0

Printed in the United States of America

10 9 8 7 6 5 4 3 2 1

PRENTICE-HALL INTERNATIONAL, INC., *London*
PRENTICE-HALL OF AUSTRALIA PTY. LIMITED, *Sydney*
PRENTICE-HALL OF CANADA, LTD., *Toronto*
PRENTICE-HALL OF INDIA PRIVATE LIMITED, *New Delhi*
PRENTICE-HALL OF JAPAN, INC., *Tokyo*
PRENTICE-HALL OF SOUTHEAST ASIA PTE. LTD., *Singapore*
WHITEHALL BOOKS LIMITED, Wellington, *New Zealand*

To my wife "RAJI"

".....And the hail and the snow,and the rain fell,and the floods came,and the wind blew,and beat upon the house,but it did not fall,because it had been founded on the rock."

Inder.

Contents

MEET THE AUTHOR

Inder Jit Handa, P.E. has spent most of his career (24 years) either in design of institutional, commercial or residential buildings and supervision of its construction or in hydraulic structures including bridges and sanitary structures. At present, associated with N.Y.C. firm of bridges and other structures, he has filled about five notebooks, each of 300 pages, with problems he faced in structural engineering. With the problems he has recorded their solutions so he would never have to work them out again. A licensed engineer in New York, Mr. Handa is a 1955 Civil Engineering graduate from the Government School of Engineering, Nilokheri, India, obtained his B.S.C.E. from the University of Louisville in 1965, M.S.C. (Structures) from the University of Toledo, M. Engineering from the University of Louisville and he is a member of the A.S.C.E., A.C.I. and A.I.S.C.

PREFACE

This book is intended primarily to serve as a guide and reference source for structural engineers by presenting detailed solutions to a vast number of practical problems in structural engineering. The problems included in this book are typical ones which have arisen in the design practice of the author during the last twenty-four years. It is hoped that the information presented in this book will demonstrate the method of analysing the problem in order to arrive at the correct solution.

A book containing a very wide area of structural engineering possesses many important advantages. It offers a unified, integrated treatment of the material, presenting all relevant definitions, concepts, and equations in one simple, practical self-contained volume. Since the structural engineer requires intimate familiarity with a wide variety of subjects, if he is compelled to refer to several books for review and application, the absence of a uniform and consistent approach would be a source of difficulty and confusion.

In chapters like Foundation Engineering, Elastic and Plastic Design of Steel Structures, the material is presented in a manner that seeks to make the subject as readily comprehensible as possible, and to minimize the mathematical work entailed in the design.

The sections have been written by the author in ready-to-use form where possible in specific areas of analysis, design and construction. Portions of the book were submitted to persons associated with Structural Engineering by Chuck Iossi, Engineering Editor of Prentice Hall so that they might criticize the material. The comments and criticism have been very helpful to the author. It was impractical to adopt all the suggestions regardless of their merits.

The author is indebted in the writing of this book to the many individuals who have encouraged him in the pursuit of engineering knowledge. The reader will notice the slightly unusual dedication. It is to acknowledge the help of my daughter Benita Handa, who had offered her services to type the manuscript and correct the language.

Lastly and by no means least, the author is very much indebted and thankful to his wife Raji, who has been a continuous source of inspiration throughout his career and has stood steadfastly with every initiative and venture of the author.

In the Appendix, the author has listed many of the organizations that were consulted or provided material for this book.

Inder Jit Handa

October 1, 1980
New York City

1

FOUNDATION ENGINEERING

SIX BASIC STEPS TO CHOOSE THE TYPE OF FOUNDATION

1) Collect approximate information concerning the nature of the superstructure and the loads to be transmitted to the foundation.
2) Determine the subsurface condition in general.
3) Match the above information with customary types of foundation to judge whether or not these could be constructed under the existing conditions,whether they could carry the required loads and whether they might experience deterimental settlement. In this way the unsuitable types of foundation may be eliminated.
4) Make detailed studies and tentative designs of the most suitable types.These must be carried far enough to determine the approximate size of footing,length and number of piles,etc.Also, be able to estimate refined estimates of settlement to predict the behavior of the structure.
5) Finally,prepare an estimate of cost of each promising type of foundation and choose the type most acceptable as to performance and cost.
6) Make a detailed structural analysis and design of its various parts to meet local building code requirements,with the knowledge you possess of statics,strength of materials,and principles of Reinforced Cement Concrete designs.

SQUARE FOOTING DESIGN

This footing is subjected to bending in all directions,its ratio of maximum vertical shear to maximum bending moment is very high, it is not reinforced in diagonal tension,and it carries a heavy load concentrated in a small area.As a result,the footing require two way reinforcement,its depth is usually governed by the punching shear.

EXAMPLE 1-01

Given:- Design a square, isolated footing of reinforced concrete to carry a load of 361 Kips delivered to a 16" x 16" tied column. Follow ACI 318-77 with intermediate grade steel. Soil bearing pressure is assumed to be 6 Kips/sq.ft. Use deformed bars without end hooks, design and details are required and that the load given, exists at the bottom of the column, assume that the dowelling is rquired. Column concrete fc' 4000 psi; footing concrete fc' 3000; Fy 40000 psi.

Design Criteria:- Footing should be safe, simple and economical. This should be proportioned to produce substantially equal settlements of supported columns. Also the bond stress is often the controlling criterion in selecting the reinforcement.

Solution:-A) Estimate the footing weight and determine the plan of the footing. The total weight of the footing may be estimated and added to the column load or as an alternative, the effect of these loads in term of unit soil pressure be estimated. Let us assume the thickness of footing 2' i.e. 300 psf is the weight of the footing.

Net Soil pressure, p = 6000-300 = 5700 psf
Column weight = 361 Kips
Est. weight of footing = 19 Kips
Total load = 380 Kips
Total load with Load Factor = 380 x 1.4 = 532 Kips
Contact Area = 532/(6.0x1.4) = 63.3 sq.ft
Hence provide 8' x 8' x 2'-0" footing.
Soil pressure with L.F = 361x1.4/8x8 = 7.89 K/sq.ft
Net Soil pressure = 7.89 ÷ 1.4 = 5.63 < 6.0 O.K

B) With a footing depth 2'-0" with 3" clear cover for placement on earth, with bars in two directions, d for the upper layer will be 19".

Effective Soil pressure p = $361 \times (1.4+1.7)/2 \div (8\times8) = 8.74^{k}/\square'$

Punching shear around the col. determines necessary depth. This is calculated around a perimeter d/2 from the col. face.

perimeter $b_o = 4(16 + 2\times 19/2) = 140''$ or $35'' = 2.92'/\text{side}$

$V_u = 8.74(8^2 - 2.92^2) = 485.39K$

$v_u = V_u/\phi b_o d = 485.39/0.85\times140\times19 = 215\ \text{PSI} < 4\sqrt{3000}$ o.K.

Beam type shear/ft width of footing on plane

$d = 21''$ from col.

$V_u = 8.74\times1(4-0.67-1.75) = 13.83^K$

$v_u = 13.83/0.85\times12\times21 = 64\ \text{Psi} < 2\sqrt{3000} = 109\ \text{Psi}$ ok.

Check M_u@ col.face $= 8.74(4-0.67)^2/2 = 48.51$ kft/ft

$M_u/\phi b d^2 = 48.51\times12000/0.9\times12\times21^2 = 122$

then from table of flexural strength coefficients k for rectangular section from ACI Design Handbook S.P.17, 1973, for $f_c' = 3000$ P.S.I & Fy = 40000 Psi, $\rho = 0.003$ & $\rho_{min.} = \frac{200}{F_y} = 0.005$

provide $\rho_{min.}$ $\therefore A_s = 0.005\times12\times21 = 1.26\square''$

use #9 @8" c/c = 1.500" in both directions.

The transfer of stress at the base of the col. is necessary by the use of dowel of the same size and number as the main reinforcement. These dowels must be lapped to the main steel for a distance of 20 dia. bar size for Fy 40000 psi and embedded into footing for anchorage length.

$l_d = 0.04 A_b F_y / \sqrt{f_c'} = 0.04 \times 1.128 \times 40000 / \sqrt{3000} = 32.99$ Say $33''$

Since footing extend 28" beyond the face of the col., so anchorage length in footing $= 24 - 3 - 2 \times 1.128 = 18.74'' = 18.75''$

Anchorage length in col. $= 20 \times 1.128 = 22.75''$

Total anchorage length $= 18.75 + 22.75 = 41.5'' > 33''$ ok

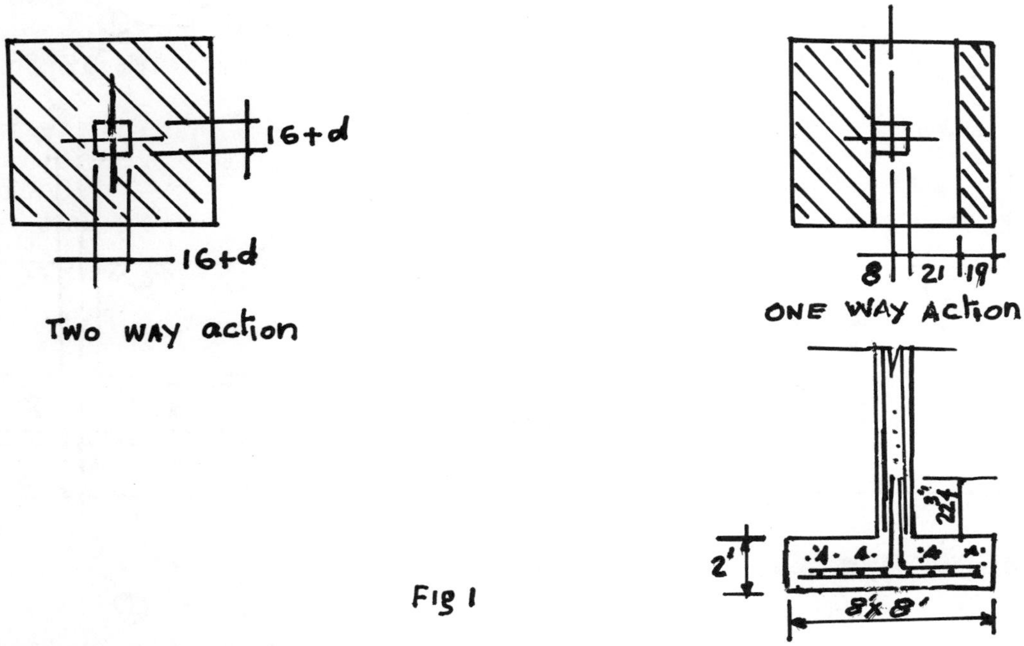

Fig 1

RECTANGULAR FOOTING DESIGN

It is not always possible to construct square footing to carry the column load. Property lines, equipment interference, etc. may restrict one dimension. The problem is similar to square footing and equations can be used to find depth for punching shear. This depth should be checked for wide beam shear which may control if L/B approaches 2 and/or the use of alternative soil pressure with edge forces is used for a footing on cohesive soil.

EXAMPLE 1-02

Given:- The reinforced concrete footing shown is 28 ft. long and 6 ft. wide. The total soil pressure acting upward on the bottom of the footing is 6550 psf. Find the correct column load assuming that the footing pressure is uniform. The footing is a total of 4 ft. thick and is conventially reinforced. Also design the reinforcing steel. Use ACI 318-77. Assume concrete = 150 pcf and Average Load factor = 1.65. See Fig. 2

Description of Approach:- For uniform soil pressure, the centroid of the footing must be made coincident with the resultant of the loads. The Net Soil pressure that produces max.

bending and shear stress is found. This Net Soil pressure will help in finding point of zero shear and load in each column. With max. moment, the reinforcing steel in both the direction can be found.

Design Criteria:- Uniform Soil pressure under total load

Solution:- Assume $F_y = 40000$ psi, $f'_c = 3000$ Psi

$$\text{Footing width} = 6' = \frac{P_1 + P_2}{P_{net} \times L_{gth}}$$

where P_{net} Service load $= 6550 - 4 \times 150 = 5950$ psf

$$\therefore 6' = 1.65(P_1+P_2)/(5950 \times 1.65) \times 28 = \frac{P_1+P_2}{5950 \times 28}$$

Thus $P_1 + P_2 = 6(5950 \times 28) = 999.6^k$ —— (1)

Also C.G. of the footing must coincide with resultant of forces.

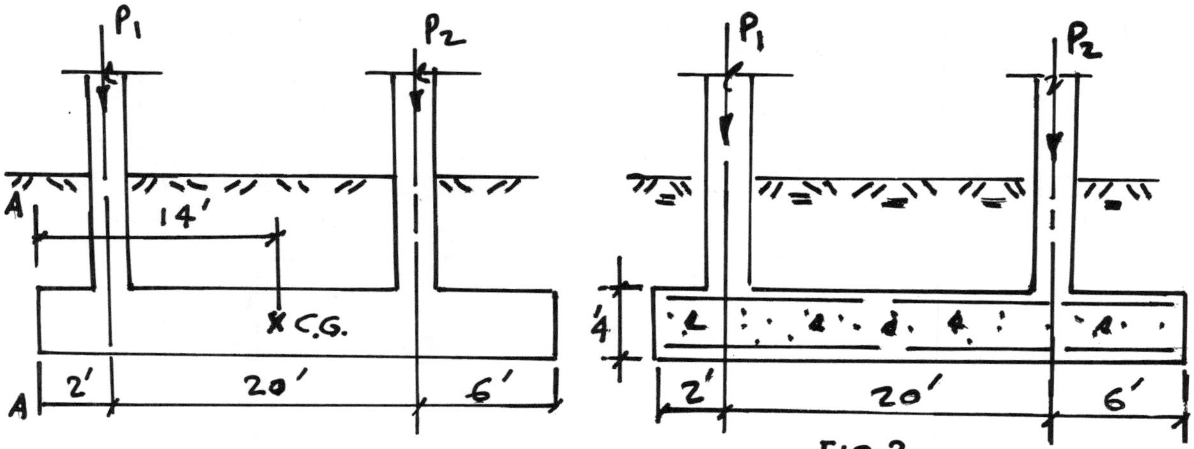

Fig 2

Also $P_1 \times 2 + P_2 \times 22 = 999.6 \times 14$

$\therefore \quad P_1 + 11 P_2 = 6997.2$ —— (2)

From (1) & (2) $P_1 = 399.8^k$; $P_2 = 599.8^k$

Net Soil pressure that produces max. bending & shear stress

$= (599.8 + 399.8)/6 \times 28 = 5.95^k/\square'$

Load factor $P_{net} = 5.95 \times 1.65 = 9.818^k/\square'$

Net upward soil pressure $= 9.818 \times 6 = 58.908^k/\text{Ft.}$

$℄ V @ P_1 = 58.908 \times 2 - 399.8 \times 1.65 = -541.86^k$

$℄ V @ P_2 = -58.908 \times 6 + 599.8 \times 1.65 = +636.24^k$

Point of zero shear from ℄ col. $P_1 = 20\left(\frac{541.86}{1178.10}\right) = 9.2'$

Max. +ve Moment for bottom steel $= 58.908 \times 5^2/2 = 736.3'^k$

effective $d = 44''$, $M/\phi b d^2 = 736.3 \times 12000/(0.9 \times 72 \times 44^2) = 70$

Use $P_{min} = 0.002$ ∴ A_s (Bott.) Long'l $= 0.002 \times 72 \times 44 = 5\square''$ Use 5-#9

Max −ve Moment for top steel $= 58.908 \times (11.2)^2/2 - 399.8 \times 1.65 \times 9.2$

$= 2375.77'^k$

$M/\phi b d^2 = 227$; use $P = 0.006$ from Table

∴ A_s (Top) Long'l $= 0.006 \times 72 \times 44 = 15\square''$, Use 10-#11 $= 15.6\square''$

To find transverse reinforcement, width of band around cols. to be found thus sizes of the cols. for load P_1 and P_2.

$P_{1(u)} = 599.7^k$ & $P_{2(u)} = 899.7^k$

Also $P_u = 0.85\phi\left[0.85 f'_c (A_g - A_{st}) + F_y A_{st}\right]$

Also Assume A_{st} Col. $= 0.04 A_g$

For P_1 $\therefore 599.7 = 0.85 \times 0.7[0.85 \times 3(A_g - 0.04A_g) + 40 \times 0.04A_g]$

$= 0.595[4.05A_g]$

$\therefore A_g = 249 \square''$ use $16'' \times 16'' = 256 \square''$

Similarly for P_2, $A_g = \dfrac{899.7}{0.595 \times 4.05} = 373$

use $20'' \times 20'' = 400 \square''$

P_{net} Col. 1 $= \dfrac{599.7}{6} = 99.95\ ^k/Ft$

$M_U = \tfrac{1}{2} \times 99.95 \times 2.33^2 = 271.3\ ^{\prime k}$

$M_U/\phi bd^2 = \dfrac{271.3 \times 12000}{0.9 \times 72 \times 44^2} = 26$ use $\rho_{min} = 0.002$

$\therefore A_s$ (Transverse), Col. 1 $= 0.002 \times 76 \times 44 = 6.7 \square''$

use 12 - #7, c/c @ $6\tfrac{1}{4}''$

P_{net} Col. 2 $= \dfrac{899.7}{6} = 149.95\ ^k/Ft.$

$M_U = \tfrac{1}{2} \times 149.95 \times 2.17^2 = 353\ ^{\prime k}$

$M_U/\phi bd^2 = \dfrac{353 \times 12000}{0.9 \times 72 \times 44^2} = 19.2$ use $\rho_{min} = 0.002$

$\therefore A_s$ (TRANSVERSE) Col. 2 $= 0.002 \times 126 \times 44 = 11 \square''$

use 19 - #7, c/c @ $6\tfrac{1}{2}''$

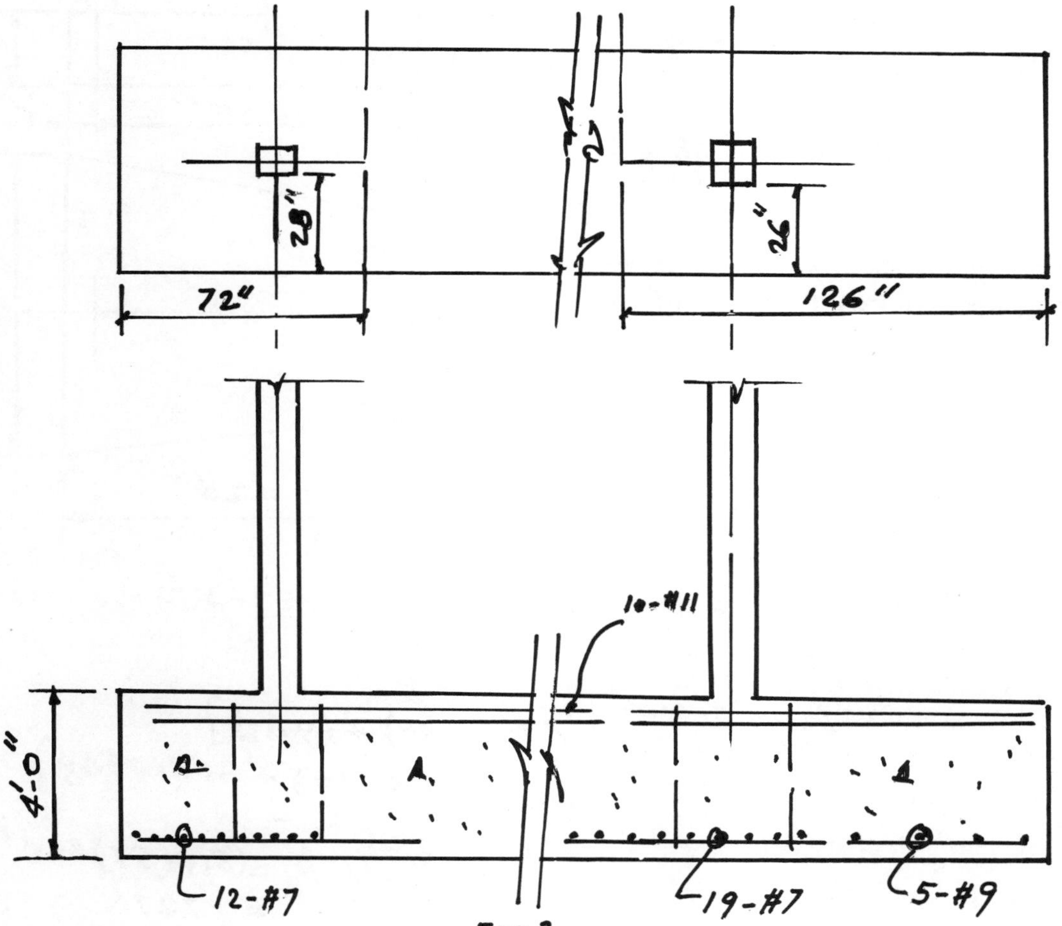

Fig 3.

TRAPEZOIDAL FOOTING DESIGN

It is nothing but another type of combined footing.

EXAMPLE 1-03

Given:- Design a trapezoidal reinforced concrete footing (two-way) to support two column loads. One column supports 411 kips and the other supports 514 kips. They are 18 ft. apart center to center. The allowable bearing pressure is 4.0 ksf. The footing can extend only one foot beyond the centerline of each column measured parallel to aline between columns. Maximum length of the footing is then 20 ft. Use $f'_c = 3000$ psi and $f_y = 60,000$ for the footing itself. Average Load factor for two column is 1.65. Use ACI 318-77 Code.

Solution:-

Locate the resultant col. load by summation of Moments about z in fig 1-3

$\Sigma M_z = 411 \times 1 + 514 \times 19 = 925\,x$

$\therefore x = 11'\text{-}0''$

Assume a footing thickness 4'-0"

its weight = 600 psf.

Allowable soil pressure

$= 4000 - 600 = 3400$ psf

$\therefore$ footing area $= \dfrac{925000}{3400}$

$= 272\ ft^2$

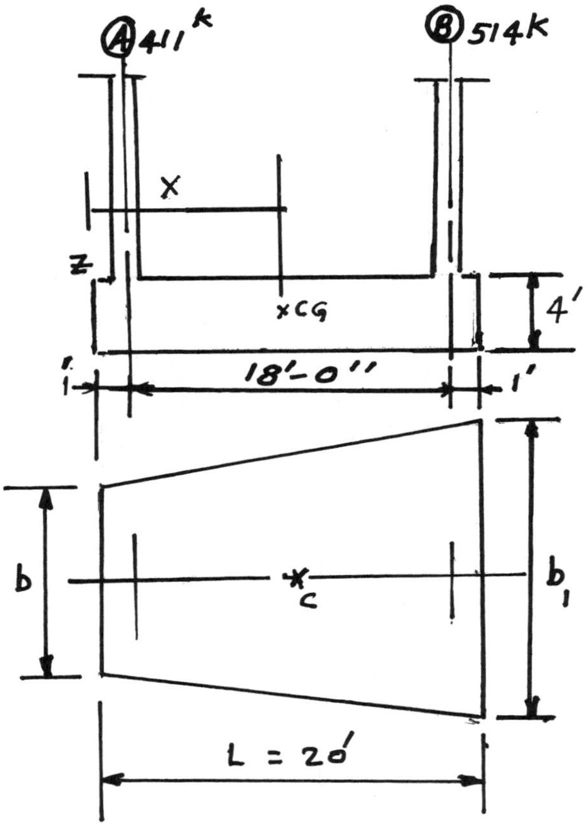

Fig 1-3(a)

Assume a trapezoidal shape whose Area $A = (b_1 + b)\,L/2$

$\therefore b_1 + b = \dfrac{2A}{L} = 27.2\ ft$

The c.g of trapezoidal area and the resultant force of the cols. are to coincide

$$c = \frac{L(2b + b_1)}{3(b + b_1)}$$

$$11' = \frac{20(b + 27.2)}{3 \times 27.2}$$

$b_1 = 17.68$ ft

$\therefore b = 9.52$ ft

Use $b_1 = 17'\text{-}9''$, $b = 9'\text{-}9''$

Actual area provided $= 275\ ft^2$

Hence net soil pressure

$= 925/275 = 3.36\ kft^2$

Col. size $P = 0.85\phi[0.85 f'_c(A_g - A_{st}) + f_y A_{st}]$

Assume $A_{st} = 0.04\,A_g$

$\therefore P = 0.85 \times 0.70[0.85 \times 3(A_g - .04A_g) + 60 \times .04A_g]$

$= 2.89\,A_g \quad \therefore A_g = \dfrac{P}{2.89}$

with load factor, $P_A = (411 + 41) \times 1.4$ & $P_B = (514 + 51) \times 1.4$

$= 581\ K \qquad = 727\ K$

A_g col. A $= 581/2.89 = 201\,\square''$ use 16"x16"
A_g col. B $= 727/2.89 = 252\,\square''$ use 18"x18"

The shear & diagonal tension :-

ONE WAY action

$V_A = 581 - 1.65 \times 3.36 \left(\frac{9.75+11.88}{2}\right) \frac{64}{12}$
$= 261.22$ K

$v_A = \frac{V}{\phi b_w d} = \frac{261.22 \times 1000}{0.85 \times 64 \times 44}$
$= 109 \approx 2\sqrt{3000}$
ok

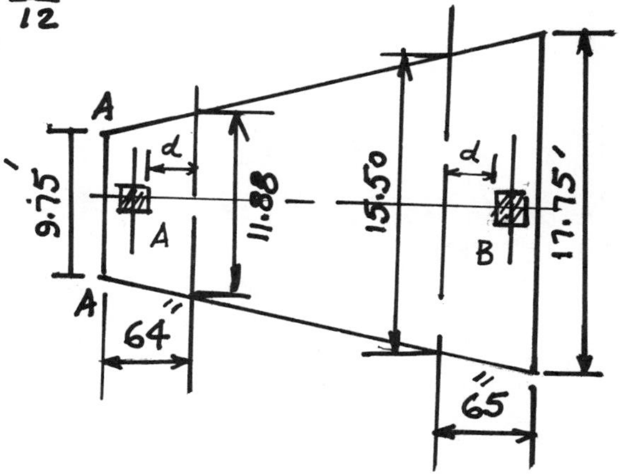

Similarly
$V_B = 727 - 3.36 \times 1.65 \left(\frac{15.5+17.75}{2}\right) \times 65/12$
$= 227.75$ K

$v_B = \frac{V_B}{\phi b_w d} = \frac{227.75}{0.85 \times 65 \times 44} = 93$
< 109 ok

TWO WAY action
at a distance d/2 from face

$v_A = \frac{V_A}{\phi b_o d}$

$V_A = 581 - 3.36 \times 1.65 (42 \times 60)/144$ K
$- \left(\frac{42 \times 60}{144}\right) 4' \times 0.15 \times 1.65 = 464$

$v_a = 87 < 4\sqrt{3000} = 218$ ok

Again $v_B = \frac{V_B}{\phi b_o d}$

$V_B = 727 - 3.36 \times 1.65 (43 \times 62)/144$
$- \frac{43 \times 62}{144} \times 4 \times 0.15 \times 1.65$
$= 608.47$ K

$v_B = 110 < 4\sqrt{3000} = 218$ ok

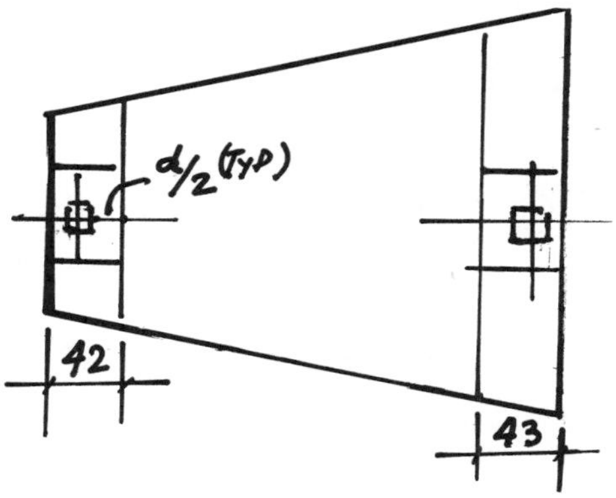

Fig 1-3 (b)

Longitudenal Bending moment

Point of zero shear from AA

Max. $M_x = -581(x-1) + 3.36 \times 1.65 \left(9.5\frac{x^2}{2} + 0.2\frac{x^3}{3}\right)$
$= -581x + 581 + 31.12x^2 + 0.369x^3$ — (1)

$\frac{dM_x}{dx} = -581 + 62.24x + 1.107x^2$
$0 = 62.24x + 1.107x^2 - 581$
or $x^2 + 56.22x = 524.84$ or $x = 8.15'$

$M_{max} = -581(8.15-1) + 31.12(8.15)^2 + 0.369(8.15)^3 = -2062.6'^K$

For plotting moment diagram, find moment for x = 1', 2', 4', 6' & 8.15' with above equation (1).

$M_1 = 31.49'^K$; $M_2 = -455.04'^K$; $M_4 = 1221.96(-)$; $M_6 = -1707.98'^K$
& $M_{8.15} = -2062.6'^K$.

Let us also find steel in columns

$$A_{st} = \frac{P}{0.85\times0.7} - 0.85f_c'A_g/(f_y - 0.85f_c')$$

$$= 1.67P - 2.55A_g/(60 - 0.85\times3)$$

$$= 1.67P - 2.55A_g/57.45$$

$$\therefore A_{stA} = \frac{1.67\times581 - 2.55\times16\times16}{57.45} = 5.52\,\square''$$

$$\& \quad A_{stB} = \frac{1.67\times727 - 2.55\times18\times18}{57.45} = 6.75\,\square''$$

Provide 12-#7 in Col. A & Col. B = 7.2 > 5.52 or 6.75 ok

To determine steel area in footing

width b @ C.G $= 9.75 + (\frac{4}{20}\times8.15)\times2 = 13.01'$

LONGITUDINAL TOP BARS

$M_u/\phi bd^2 = (2062.6\times12000)/0.9\times13.01\times12\times44^2$

$= 90.5$

p frm ACI Tables = 0.0023 which is $< \frac{200}{f_y}$

Use $p_{min} = 0.0033$

$A_s = 0.0033\times13.01\times12\times44 = 22.66\,\square''$

Use 15-#11 = 23.4 □'' > 22.66 ok

$l_d = 1.4\times0.04\times1.56\times60000/\sqrt{3000} = 95.76''$ Say 8'-0''

TRANSVERSE BOT. BARS

Col. A; $w_A = 64''$, P_{net} in upward directions $= \frac{581}{(9.75+11.88)/2}$

$= 53.72\,K/\square'$

$M_U = \frac{1}{2}(53.72)(4.87 - 0.67 + \frac{1.06}{2})^2 = 600.9'K$

$p = (600.9\times12000)/.9\times11.88\times12\times44^2 = 29$

use $p_{min} = 0.0033 \therefore A_s = 0.0033\times11.88\times12\times44$

$= 20.69\,\square''$ use 10-#14 $= 22.25\,\square''$

$l_d = 0.04\times2.25\times60000/\sqrt{3000} = 99.6$ Say 8'-4''

Col. B; $w_B = 65''$, P_{net} in upward directions $= \frac{727}{(15.5+17.75)/2}$

$= 43.72\,K/\square'$

$M_U = \frac{1}{2}(43.72)(7.75 - .75 + \frac{1.43}{2})^2 = 1302'K$

$p = 48$, use $p_{min} = 0.0033$; $A_s = 0.0033\times15.5\times12\times44 = 27\,\square''$

use 13-#14, $l_d = 8'$-4''

Nominal longitudenal bars #4@12'' o/c are placed in the bott. of footing in order to space and held in position stirrups & transverse reinforcement.

Transfer of stress @ base of col. Dowels are to be provided and embedded into footing through bond.

For Col. A & #7 ϕ bar $L_1 = 20\phi = 15''$ for compression Length & for critical tension compression splice $L_2 = 30\phi = 23''$

$\therefore L_1 + L_2 = 15 + 23 = 38 <$ eff. d of 44''

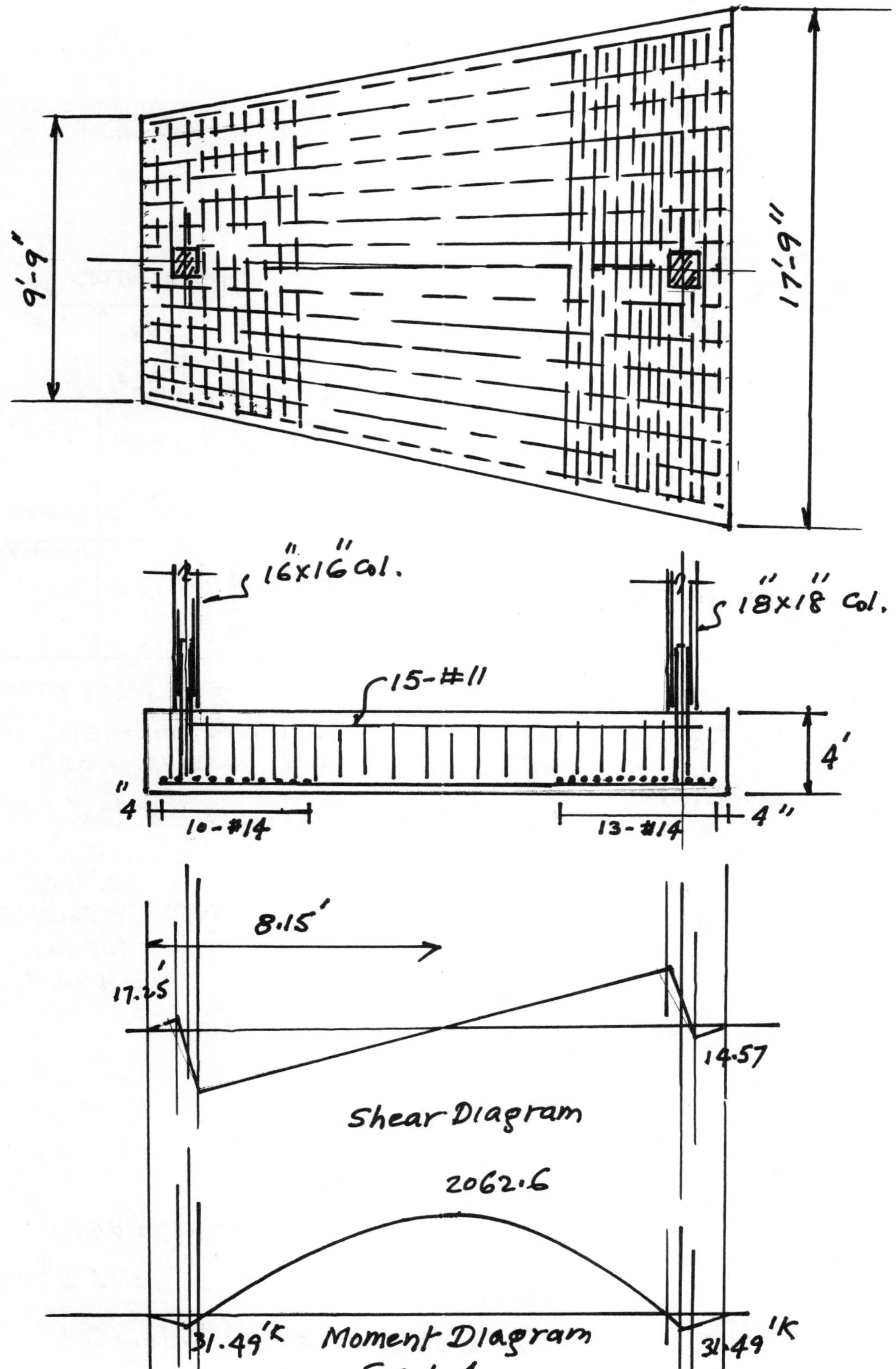
9'-9"
17'-9"
16"x16" Col.
18"x18" Col.
15-#11
4'
4"
10-#14
13-#14
4"
8.15'
17.25'
14.57
Shear Diagram
2062.6
31.49'K
Moment Diagram
31.49'K

Fig 1-4

SHEET PILING DESIGN

EXAMPLE 1-04

Given:- Determine the diagrams for pressure, shear, and moment acting on the sheet piling per foot of wall length (straight wall of piles) and the requirement for the anchor unit. Determine where the anchor unit should be placed and what you want to specify for it.

Solution:-

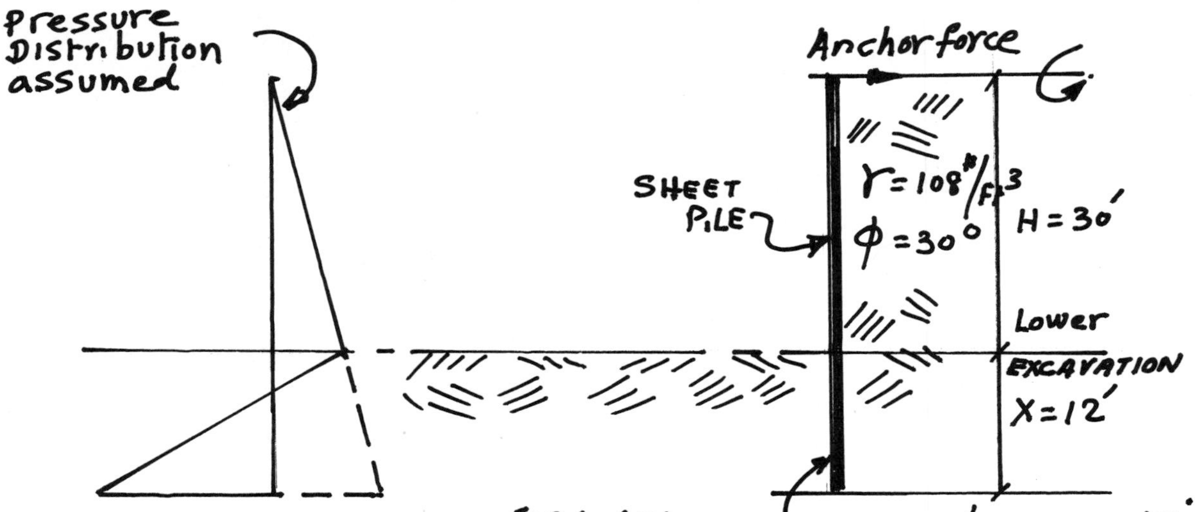

Fig 1-4(a) Z of STL = 29,000 ksi

To calculate the soil pressure for maximum moment, we have to find the coefficient of active and passive earth pressure respectively.

p_a = Coefficient of active earth pressure $= \gamma \tan^2(45-\phi/2)$

$= 108 \tan^2 30$

$= 36^{\#}/cft$

p_p = coefficient of Passive earth pressure $= \gamma \tan^2(45+\phi/2)$

$= 108 \tan^2 60$

$= 324^{\#}/cft$

$a' = p_p - p_a = 324 \times 12 - 36 \times 42 = 2376^{\#}/sft$

$a = p_a H = 36 \times 30 = 1080^{\#}/sft$

$y = \dfrac{a}{p_p - p_a} = \dfrac{1080}{324-36} = 3.75'$

$P_a = \frac{1}{2} \times 1080 \times 30 = 16200^{\#}/\square'$

$P_a' = \frac{1}{2} \times 1080 \times 3.75 = 2025^{\#}/\square'$

$P_p = \frac{1}{2} \times 2376 \times 8.25 = 9801^{\#}/\square'$

Tie Rod Tension:- $T = (16200 - 2025) - 9801 = 8424^{\#}$

$T_{design} = 8424 \times 1.3 = 10952^{\#}$

Max. moment. Let pt of zero shear be at x' below G.L

$\frac{1}{2}(36)x^2 = 8424$

$x = \sqrt{468} = 21.63'$

∴ Max Mom:

$8424 \times 21.63 = +182000'\#$

$\frac{1}{2}(36)(21.63)^2 \times 7.21 = -\underline{60718}$

$121282'\#$

Section modulus $Z = \frac{121282 \times 12}{24000} = 60.5\ IN^3/FT$ WIDTH of WALL

∴ USE U.S STEEL BP12-53 $Z = 67.0\ IN^3$

TIE ROD use 8'-0 spacing, $T = 8 \times 10{,}952 = 87.616K$

$F_b = 22Ksi$

Area of Tierod $= \frac{87.616}{22} = 3.97\square''$

Use $2\frac{1}{4}''$ upset to $2\frac{3}{4}''$, Net Area $= 4.62\square''$

WALES

$M = \frac{1}{9}(10.952)8^2 = 77.8'K$

$F_b = 22Ksi$

$S_{reqd} = \frac{77.8 \times 12}{22} = 42.4^3$ Use 2-12 ⊔ 25 $= 47.8^3$

Deadmen:-

$f'_c = 3000psi$, $f_y = 40000\ Psi$

$\gamma = 108\ \#/ft^3$, $K_p = 3.0$, $K_a = 0.333$

$T = \frac{1}{F_S}\frac{1}{2}\gamma(K_p - K_a)H^2$

$10952 = \frac{1}{1.5} \times \frac{1}{2} \times 108(3.0 - 0.33)H^2$

∴ $H^2 = 114$, $H = 10.67ft$ use 11'

Max Mom Longitudinal $= 1/9\ 10.952 \times 8^2 \times 1.4$

$= 108.9'k$

$d = \sqrt{\frac{M_u}{K\phi b}} = \sqrt{\frac{108900 \times 12}{385 \times 0.9 \times 120}} = 5.6$

Use $t = 12$, $d_{eff} = 9''$

Check Shear $v = \frac{V_u}{\phi bd} = \frac{61.32 \times 1000}{0.9 \times 10 \times 12 \times 9} = 63$

$< 2\sqrt{f'_c} = 109$ ok

∴ for $\frac{M}{\phi bd^2} = \frac{108.9 \times 12000}{0.9 \times 12 \times 10 \times 9^2} = 148$

$p = 0.0038$ frm ACI Tables

$A_s = 0.0038 \times 120 \times 9 = 4.1\square''$

use 10 - #7 $= 6.0\square''$

Max. Mom. Transversly $= \frac{1}{2}(10.952)\frac{10}{4} \times 1.4$

$= 19.17'K$

for $\frac{M}{\phi bd^2} = 26$ use $p_{min} = 0.0015$

$A_s = 0.0015 \times 9 \times 12 = 0.162\square''$, use #10 @ 12"

Bearing Plates

$$A = \frac{87.616}{1.125} = 77.6\,\square''$$

$$1.125 = 0.375 f'_c$$

Use $9.5'' \times 9.5'' = 90.5\,\square''$

$3''\phi$ Hole $= 7.0$

$$83.5 > 77.6\,\square'' \text{ ok}$$

$$M = \tfrac{1}{2}(1.125)(4.75)^2 = 12.72''k$$

$$S_{req'd} = \frac{12.72}{22} = 0.579 \text{ IN}^3 = \frac{bd^2}{6}$$

$$d = \sqrt{0.366} = 0.605 \quad \text{Use } 3/4'' \text{ PL}$$

Location of deadman

$$\tan 30^\circ = \frac{42}{x}$$

$$\therefore x = \frac{42.0}{0.577} = 72.9' \quad \text{Say } 73'$$

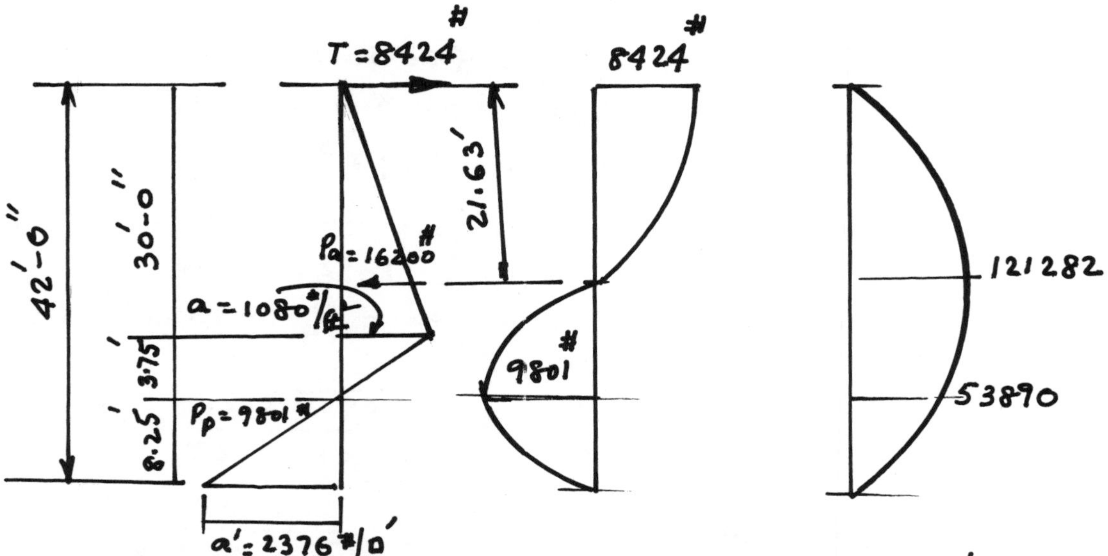

Pressure Diagram Shear Diag. Moment Diag.

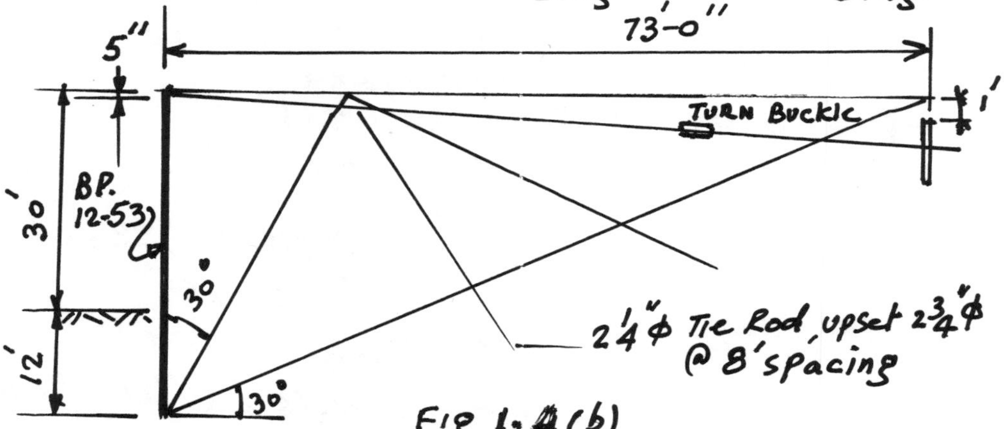

Fig 1.4(b)

CRIB WALL DESIGN

EXAMPLE 1-05

Given:- For the Crib Wall described below, determine the existing safety factor against sliding.

The precast concrete crib elements are 8" x 8" square and form 8" x 8" squares. Centerline dimensions are used. As a second part of this problem, determine the value of theta (   ) such that the safety factor is just exactly 2.50 by either increasing from 10 or by decreasing it.

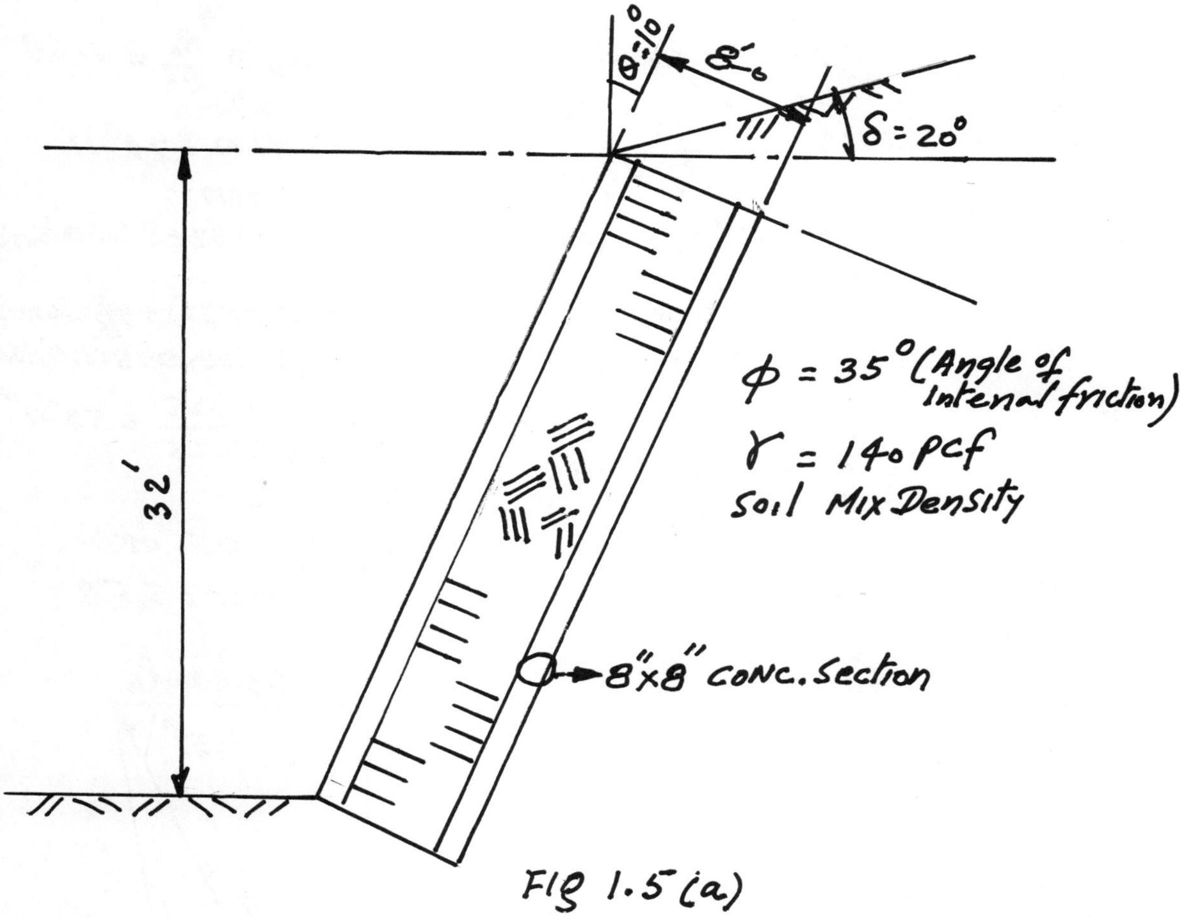

FIG 1.5 (a)

Solution:-

$$FC = 32'$$

$$CJ = 8\cos\theta\tan\delta = 2.86'; \quad AE = 32\tan\theta = 5.68'$$

$$EF = 8\cos\theta = 7.86'; \quad FG = (AE + EF)\tan\theta = 2.39'$$

$$GJ = FG + FC + CJ = 37.25'$$

$$H = GJ = 37.25'$$

$$K_A = \left[\cos\phi / \left(1 + \sqrt{\sin\phi(\sin\phi - \cos\phi\tan\delta)}\right)\right] = 0.344$$

$$P_A = \frac{K_A(\gamma H)^2}{2} = 33.4 \text{ kips}$$

weight of soil (within the hatched portion); consider 1 ft section.

Δ BJC = $\frac{1}{2} \times 7.86 \times 2.86 \times 1 \times 140$ = 1580 Lbs

$\square$ BCEF = $7.88 \times 32 \times 1 \times 140$ = 35300#

Δ BAE = $\frac{1}{2} \times 5.68 \times 32 \times 1 \times 140$ = 12740#

Δ AFG = $\frac{1}{2}(AE + EF) \times FG \times 1 \times 140$

= $\frac{1}{2} \times 13.54 \times 2.39 \times 1 \times 140$ = 2270#

$\therefore G$ = 51890# or 51.89k

Locating C.G of whole hatched portion

$(51.89)x = 1.58 \times 2.62 + 35.3 \times 3.94 + 2.27 \times 4.51 + 12.74 \times 9.77$

$x = 5.35'$

$R = \sqrt{P_A^2 + G^2} = 61.82^k; \ \alpha = \sin^{-1} \frac{51.89}{61.82} = 57^\circ$

$R_N = R \sin(\alpha + 10) = 56.91^k; \ R_S = R \cos(\alpha + 10) = 24.14$

Existing Factor of Safety against sliding $= \tan\phi \frac{R_N}{R_S} = 1.64$

b) F.S. = $\tan\phi \ R_N/R_S$ where F.S = 2.5; $\tan\phi = 0.7002$

$R_N/R_S = 3.5713$ or $\frac{R\sin(\alpha+\theta)}{R\cos(\alpha+\theta)} = 3.5713 \therefore \alpha + \theta = 74^\circ\text{-}21'$

After number of trials, it is found $\theta = 16^\circ$, then

H for P_A = $0.344 \times \frac{140}{2}\left[32\tan\theta + 8\cos\theta\right]\tan\theta + 32 + 8\cos\theta\tan\delta]$

= 39.10 k

G = $140[(\frac{1}{2} 8\cos\theta \times 8\cos\theta\tan\delta) + (8\cos\theta \times 32) + \frac{1}{2} 32\tan\theta \times 32) + \frac{1}{2}(32\tan\theta + 8\cos\theta)(32\tan\theta + 8\cos\theta)\tan\theta]$

= 62.25 K

R = $\sqrt{H^2 + G^2} = 73.25^k; \ \alpha = \sin^{-1}\frac{62.25}{73.25} = 58^\circ\text{-}21'$

R_N = $R\sin(58^\circ\text{-}21' + 16^\circ\text{-}0') = 70.5k$

R_S = $R\cos(58^\circ\text{-}21' + 16^\circ\text{-}0') = 19.78k$

F.S = $\tan\phi \ R_N/R_S = 0.7002 \times \frac{70.5}{19.78} = 2.5$ ok

HENCE θ should be increased to 16° to get 2.5 F.S.

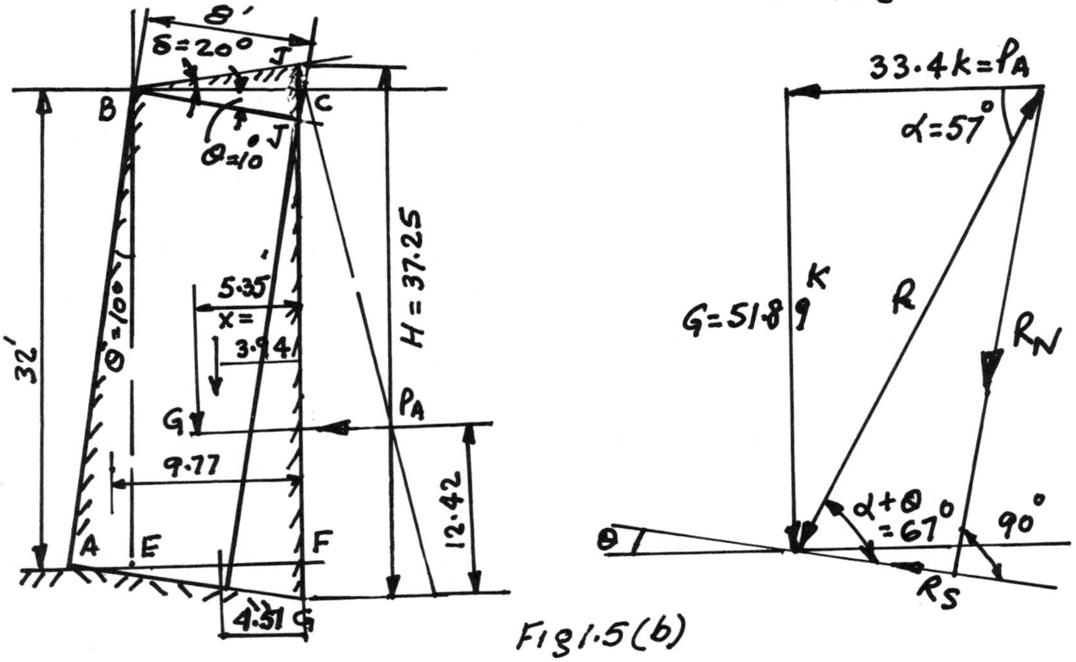

Fig 1.5(b)

LOAD ON TUNNEL SUPPORT IN RUNNING GROUND

ARTICLE 1-06

The term running ground applies to all those soils located above the water table which have a stand-up time equal to zero. Clean gravel and clean coarse sand belong to this category. Since these materials have no cohesion at all they start to run on every surface with a slope angle of more than about 34 as soon as the lateral support is removed. They are also unable to abridge a gap in the roof support if the width of the gap is greater than a few times the diameter of the largest grains.

In spite of the extraordinary mobility of running ground the load on the roof of tunnel supports in running ground does not exceed a small fraction of the weight of the ground located above the roof. If the depth of the overburden is greater than about 1.5 times the combined width and height of the tunnel, the load is practically independent of the depth. (In circular tunnel supports height of tunnel is taken as zero.) The cause of this phenomenon is commonly known as arch action.

The term arch action indicates the capacity of the ground located above the roof of the tunnel to transfer the major part of the total weight of the overburden onto the ground located on both sides of the tunnel. The body of soil which transfers the load is referred to as the ground arch.

In order to investigate the cause of arch action and the laws which determine the load on the roof support in running ground, numerous model tests have been made with perfectly cohesionless sand. These test results led to the following general conclusions regarding the prerequisites for arch action and the factors which determine the load on the roof support in flat-roof tunnels through cohesionless sand located above the water table.

(a) The arch action is the inevitable consequence of the local stress relaxation produced by mining operations. The mechanics of the arch action are illustrated in Figure 1. In this figure the ground arch is represented by the area a c d b. The ground arch has a width B_1. While the tunnel is being excavated and the support installed, the mass of sand constituting the ground arch tends to move downward into the tunnel. The downward movement is resisted by the friction along the vertical boundaries a c and b d of this mass. The friction forces transfer the major part of the weight of the overburden, with height H, on the material located on both sides of the tunnel and the roof support carries only the balance, equivalent to a height H_p.

(b) The thickness D of the ground arch is roughly equal to 1.5 B_1. Above the ground arch the pressure conditions in the sand remain practically unaffected by the tunnel operations.

(c) A very small downward movement of the crown of the ground arch suffices to reduce the load on the support of the intradosof the arch to a value H_p min. which is very much smaller than the thickness D of the ground arch. If the

crown of the ground arch is allowed to subside still more, the load on the roof support again increases and approaches a value H_p max. which, however, is also much smaller than D.
(d) As time goes on the load on the tunnel roof increases by about 15% of the load which acted on the roof immediately after arching became effective. However, the support service period is so short, that this increase can be disregarded.
(e) As the depth of the overburden on a tunnel with a given cross section increases from zero, the roof load increases. As the depth H approaches a value equal to about 1.5 times the width of the ground arch, the load becomes practically independent of depth.
(f) The value increases approximately in direct proportion to the width B_1 of the ground arch, everything else being equal. This relation can be expressed by the equation.

$$H_p = C \times B_1 \quad \text{wherein } C \text{ is a constant.}$$

The value of C depends on the degree of compactness of the sand and on the distance d, through which the crown of the ground arch subsided while the tunnel was mined and the roof support was being installed. The model tests have furnished the following information concerning the influence of these factors on the load:

Dense Sand	H_p min. $= 0.27\ (B+H_t)$	for a yield of	$0.01\ (B+H_t)$
	H_p max. $= 0.60\ (B+H_t)$	for a yield of	$0.015\ (B+H_t)$
Loose Sand	H_p min. $= 0.47\ (B+H_t)$	for a yield of	$0.02\ (B+H_t)$
	H_p max. $= 0.60\ (B+H_t)$	for a yield of	$0.15\ (B+H_t)$

The weight acting on the roof per unit of length of the tunnel is $Q_h = wH_pB$ wherein w is the unit weight of the sand.
The above equations show that the load on the roof of a tunnel assumes its minimum value if the roof subsides by an amount ranging between about 1 percent of the sum of width and height of tunnels in dense sand and about 2 percent of this sum for tunnels through loose sand. ($H_t = 0$ for circular section) The distance through which the sand located above the tunnel really subsides depends on the degree of cohesion of the ground, on the method of mining, the skill and care of the miners and various other factors.
Since running ground requires breasting on account of lack of cohesion the vertical compression of the block of ground located ahead of the working face is almost eliminated by the lateral support. It is inevitable that a certain amount of material runs into the tunnel while breasting boards are being manipulated. This process also causes the sand located above the tunnel to settle through a distance of at least a few percent of the height of the working face. In any event the subsidence of the sand located above the tunnel is likely to be somewhat greater, and not smaller, than the yield required to reduce the roof load to the minimum value, H_p min. The corresponding load is somewhat greater than H_p min. However, the difference cannot be very important.
In circular tunnels the width of the zone of arching is considerably reduced by the absence of vertical walls and the pressure on the roof is further reduced by the roof being arched. Therefore, the load on the roof of such tunnels can safely be estimated by introducing the value $H_t = 0$ into equa-

tions shown.
If we use a condition of loose sand for a maximum condition, then $H_p = 0.60\ (B) \quad B = 20$ ft.
$= 0.60\ (20) = 12.0$ ft.
This could be increased to account for mining inaccuracies, slight fabrication inaccuracies, care with which steel supports are set, and degree of cohesion of the ground. Further since means of identifying the ground, through bore logs, is not always indicative of the actual conditions encountered, an additional allowance should be made in the loading the tunnel supports is to be designed for.

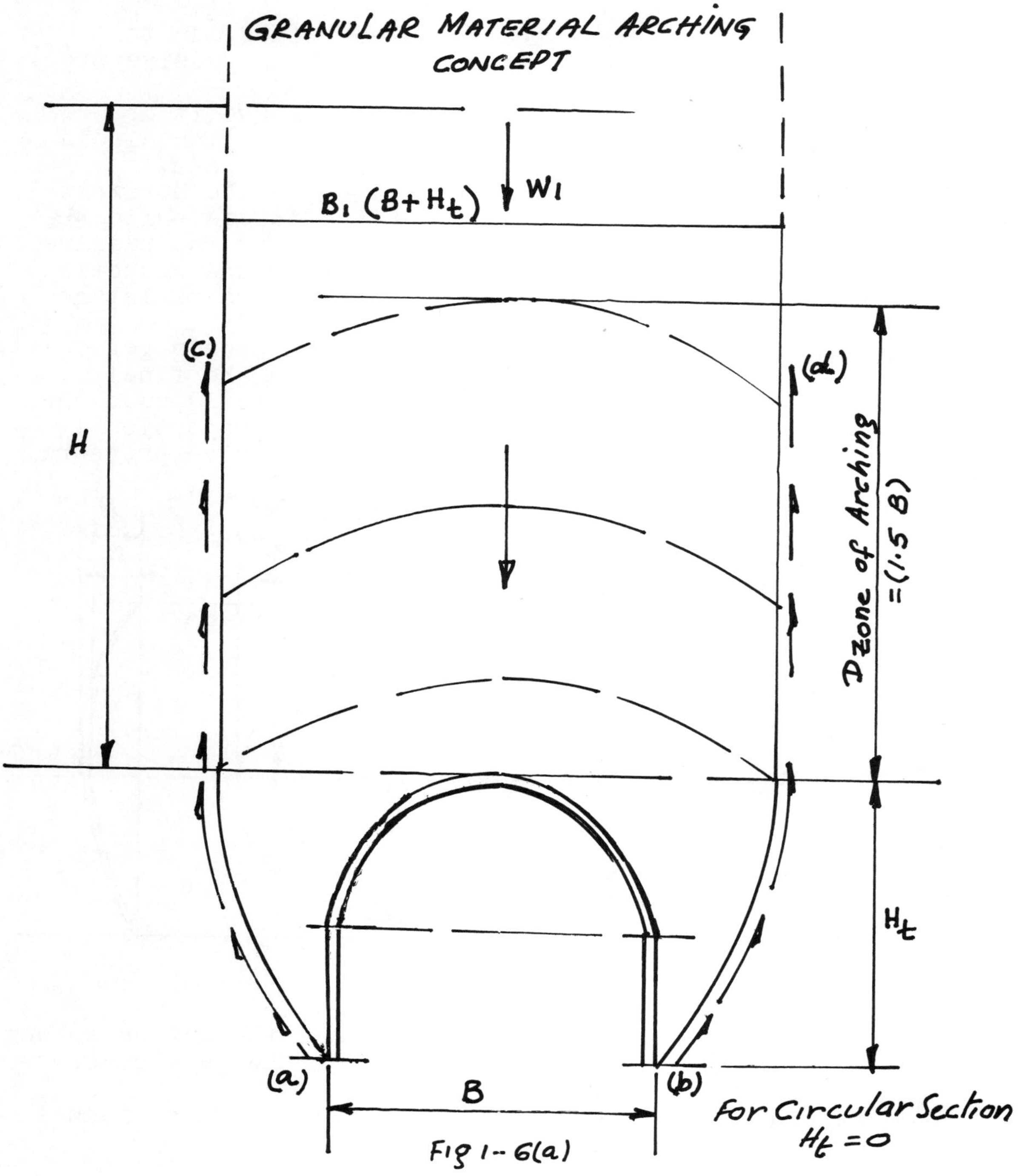

Fig 1-6(a)

The difference between the vertical and active horizontal loading is greater in non-plastic soils than in silt or soft clay and also varies in the amount of earth cover over the tunnel.

For large earth covers the vertical loads are much greater than the active lateral pressure resulting in large moments. It is desirable to consider the relieving effect of the lateral passive soil pressures produced by the tunnel deformation caused by the active loads. The amount of this passive resistance that may be developed will depend on the horizontal deformation of the tunnel and on the resistance of the soil to being compressed. The measured lateral deflections of tunnels are usually less than the computed values due to assumed active forces so it is apparent that the passive pressures are brought into play.

In order to determine the lateral passive pressure it is necessary to determine the deflection, at the horizontal diameter of the tunnel, due to the assumed active forces.

If we let d_1 represent the lateral deflection at the horizontal diameter of the tunnel due to all the active forces while d_2 represents the deflection at the same point after the passive pressures were applied, then d_3 would represent the reduction in the maximum deflection due to the final passive resistance of the soil ($d_3 = d_1 - d_2$).

Let K represent the soil constant, pressure in pounds per sq.ft. to compress the soil 1 inch. Then d_2k would be the final maximum intensity of the passive pressure that would push the tunnel back through a maximum distance d_3. By proportion it can be shown that $P_2 = kd_2$, P_2 being maximum passive pressure to push tunnel back the distance d_2.

LATERAL PASSIVE PRESSURE

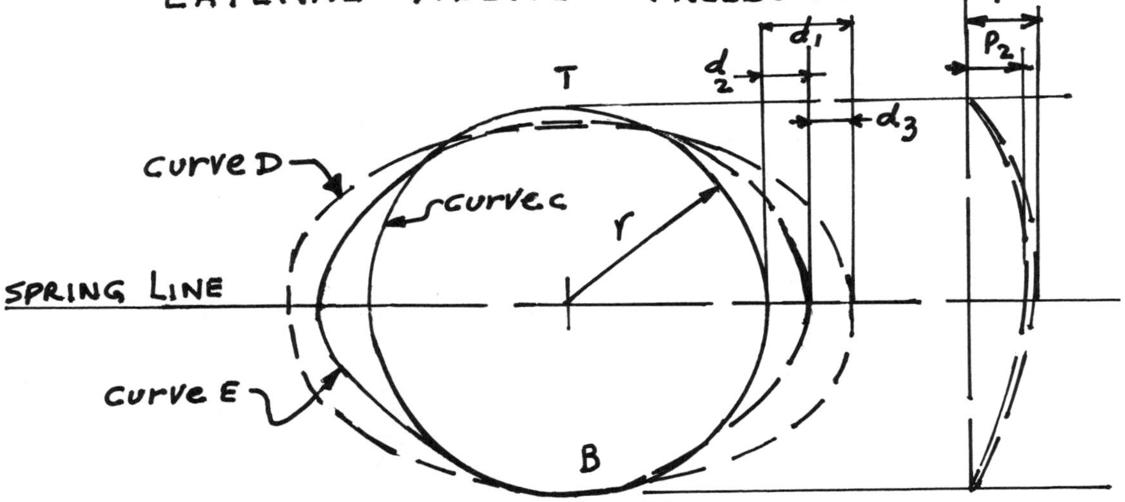

Fig 1-6(b)

Curve C - Undeformed tunnel.
Curve D - Tunnel after deformation due to all the active forces.
Curve E - Final position of the tunnel after the passive pressures are brought into action.
d_1 - Lateral deflection at the spring line of the tunnel due to all the active forces.

d_2 - Lateral deflection at the spring line after passive pressures are brought into action.

p - Pressure curve whose ordinates vary approximately as the lateral deflection of the tunnel with the maximum ordinate $= p$ representing the lateral pressure to bring tunnel back to its original position.

The maximum intensity, p, of a lateral pressure which varies as the deflection caused by a uniform vertical loading, w, must be equal to 1.28w in order that the lateral pressure would cause the same horizontal deflection (inward) as the vertical loading does (outward).

The lateral pressure causes moments at the top and bottom of the tunnel of $-.182pr^2$. As the final passive pressure, whose maximum intensity is p_2, would vary proportionately to that whose maximum intensity is p, then due to such final pressure, $M_T = M_B = -.182 P_2 r^2$. This minus sign denotes compression at intrados of tunnel. For P_2 in pounds per sq. ft. and r in feet, M would be in foot pounds.

Substituting for P_2, its equivalent Kd_2 and for d_2 its equivalent $\frac{pd_1}{(Kd_1+p)}$, then

$$M_T = M_B = -.182Kd_2r^2 = -.182\,Kr^2\left(\frac{pd_1}{Kd_1+p}\right)$$

Since $p = 1.28\,w$ and for any deflection d_1, the value of

$$w = \frac{d_1 EI}{144r^4} \text{ then}$$

$$p = \frac{1.28 d_1 EI}{144 r^4} = \frac{0.0089\,EId_1}{r^4}$$

This would be a constant for any tunnel ring having a maximum deflection due to all the active forces.

At the spring line, moments due to the passive pressures resulting from a deflection d_1,

$$M = +.208Kr^2\left(\frac{d_1 p}{Kd_1+p}\right)$$

The plus sign denotes tension at intrados of the tunnel.

The thrusts at the top and bottom of the tunnel

$$H_T = H_B = 0.59Kr\left(\frac{pd_1}{Kd_1+p}\right)$$

Adding passive moments and thrusts to active moments and thrusts algebraically will give final moments and thrusts in the lining. The maximum passive pressure intensity could be found from,

$$P_2 = K\left(\frac{pd_1}{Kd_1+p}\right)$$

the value of K can be determined by knowing the assumed active forces and the horizontal deflection which should represent the horizontal distortion of one half of the tunnel after it began to press against the soil.

GRILLAGE FOUNDATION DESIGN

EXAMPLE 1-07

Given:- Below is a description of a grillage foundation subject to a gravity loading of 110 kips. CHECK ALL STRESSES. Make any assumptions necessary and pass on the general

acceptability of the system.
Each I beam is a 6" I 12.5 #/ft. of A-36 steel with $F_y = 33.0$ ksi. They are 6" apart measured from web centerlines at both levels and the system is doubly symmetrical about the axes. The concrete pad is thin and acts merely to transmit the load and pressure and to distribute it more uniformly. The concrete pad and the rigid 16" x 16" steel bearing plate are not to be analyzed.

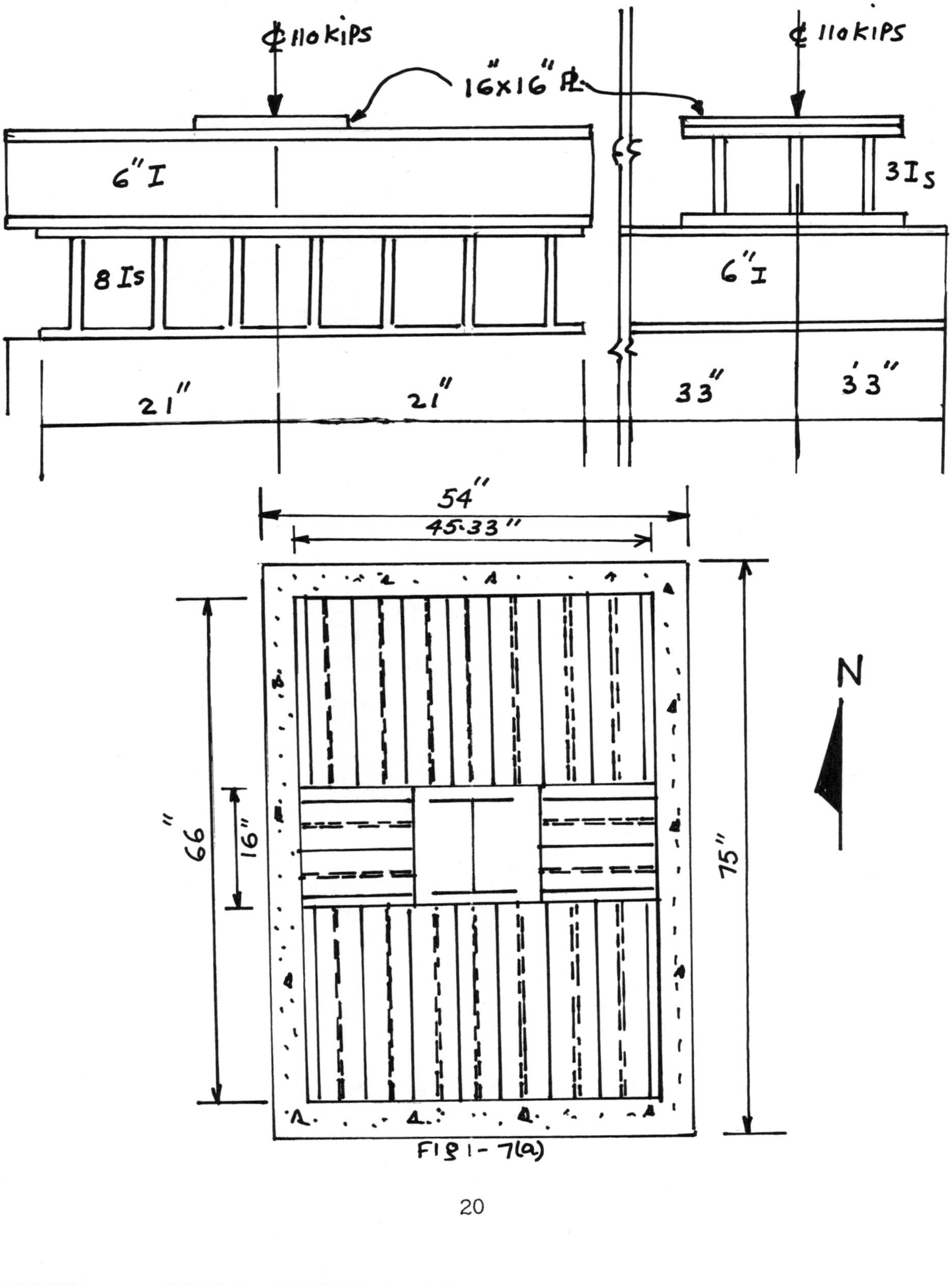

FIG 1-7(a)

Solution :- Properties of 6"I 12.5 $d = 6.0"$; $t_f = 0.359"$
$t_w = 0.23"$, $b_f = 3.33"$
$S_x = 7.3$; $I_x = 21.8 \text{ in}^4$

$F_y = 33$ ksi, $F_v = 13$ ksi, $F_b = 20$ ksi. Size of ℙ = 16"×16"

Length upper Tier beam = 45.33"

Length lower Tier beam = 66.00"

Load upper Tier $= \frac{110 \times 144}{16 \times 16} \times 1.33 = 82.2^k/ft$

Load Lower Tier $= \frac{110 \times 144}{45.33 \times 66} \times 5.5 = 29.2^k/ft$

Check upper Tier

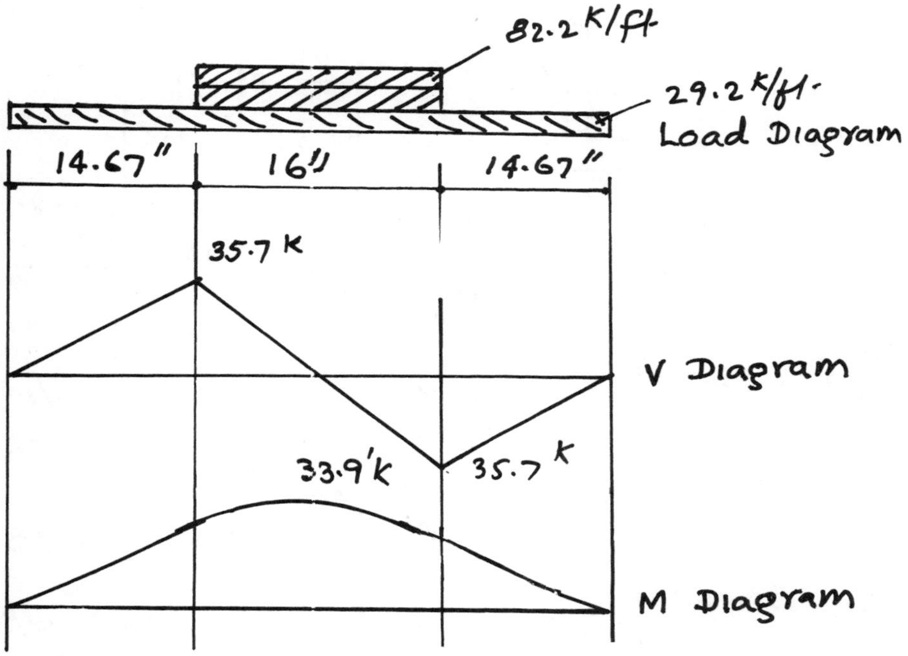

Upper Tier
fig 1-7(b)

Flexural requirement for 3 Beams

Shear $= 29.2 \times \frac{14.67}{12} = 35.7^k$

Moment $= \frac{29.2}{2}\left(\frac{14.67+8}{12}\right)^2 \quad \frac{82.2}{2}\left(\frac{8}{12}\right)^2 = 33.9'^k$

Shear for one beam $= \frac{35.7}{3} = 11.9^k$

$f_v = \frac{V}{A_w} = \frac{11.9 \times 1000}{5.282 \times 0.23} = 9.8$ ksi

$\frac{f_v}{F_v} = \frac{9.8}{13.0} = 0.75 < 0.85$ ok

Also $f_v = \frac{VQ}{It}$ where $Q = 3.33 \times 0.359 \times 2.821 + 2.641 \times 0.23 \times 1.320 = 4.16$

$= \frac{11.9 \times 1000 \times 4.16}{21.8 \times 0.23} = 9.85$ ksi < 13 ksi ok

Moment for one beam $= \frac{33.9}{3} = 11.3'^k$

$F_b = 11.3 \times 12000 / 7.3 = 18.480$ ksi < 20 ksi ok

Web crippling

$$f_b = \frac{P}{(b+2k)t} = \frac{110}{3(16+2\times0.75)\times0.23}$$
$$= 9.15\ ksi < 25\ ksi\ \ ok$$

Web buckling

$$P_{cr} = \frac{\pi^2 EI}{(0.5L)^2}$$

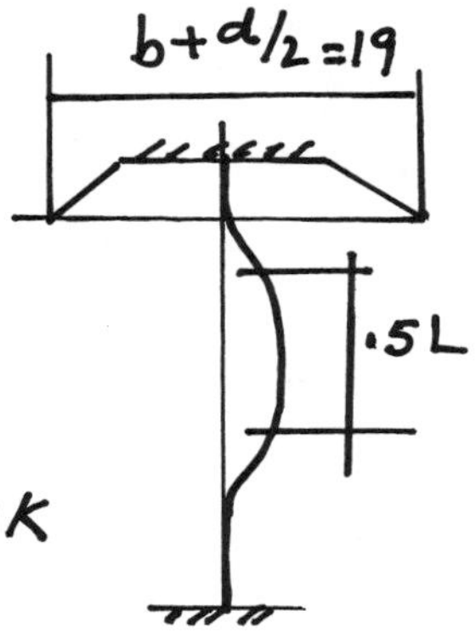

I of Average width for vertical web buckling = $b+d/2$ @ the applied load concentration

$$I = \frac{1}{12}\times19\times0.23^3 = 0.0193\ in^4$$

$$L = 6 - 2\times0.359 = 5.282''$$

$$P_{cr} = \frac{4\times\pi^2\times29000\times0.0193}{(5.282)^2} = 791.54^K$$

$$F.S = \frac{791.54}{36.67} = 21.59 > 2.0^+\ ok$$

Check lower tier beams, length 66"; 8 - 6I12.5

$$\text{Moment/Beam} = \frac{WL}{8} - \frac{WL'}{8} = \frac{110}{8\times2}\left[\frac{66}{4} - \frac{16}{4}\right] = 86''^K$$

$$F_b = \frac{86}{7.3} = 11.76 < 20.0\ ksi\ \ ok$$

$$\text{Load bottom tier} = \frac{110\times144}{45.33\times66}\times\frac{45.33}{12} = 20^{K}/ft$$

$$V = 20\times(33-8)/12 = 41.7^K$$

$$V_{for\ one\ beam} = \frac{41.7}{8} = 5.21^K$$

$$f_v = \frac{VQ}{It} = \frac{5.21\times4.16}{21.8\times0.23} = 4.32^{ksi} < 13^{ksi}\ ok$$

WEB Crippling

It is checked by using the width of flange of an upper tier beam as the length in bearing against the lower tier beams. Since flange of the upper beam tier is not rigid, k distance is not taken into consideration.

$$f_b = \frac{110}{3.33\times0.23\times24} = 5.97^{ksi} < 25^{ksi}\ ok.$$

where 24 is number of intersection of upper & Lower Beams.

Web buckling:- Since the direct compression is assumed to be distributed over top tier which is quite safe. Since the space between beams is ordinarily filled with concrete. Hence it is safe. In General, if web meets the buckling requirement in the upper Tier, no need for investigation in lower tier.

OCTAGONAL FOUNDATION DESIGN

EXAMPLE 1-08

Given:- Design the size of Octagonal Foundation for vertical pressure vessel as per sketch.

Solution:-

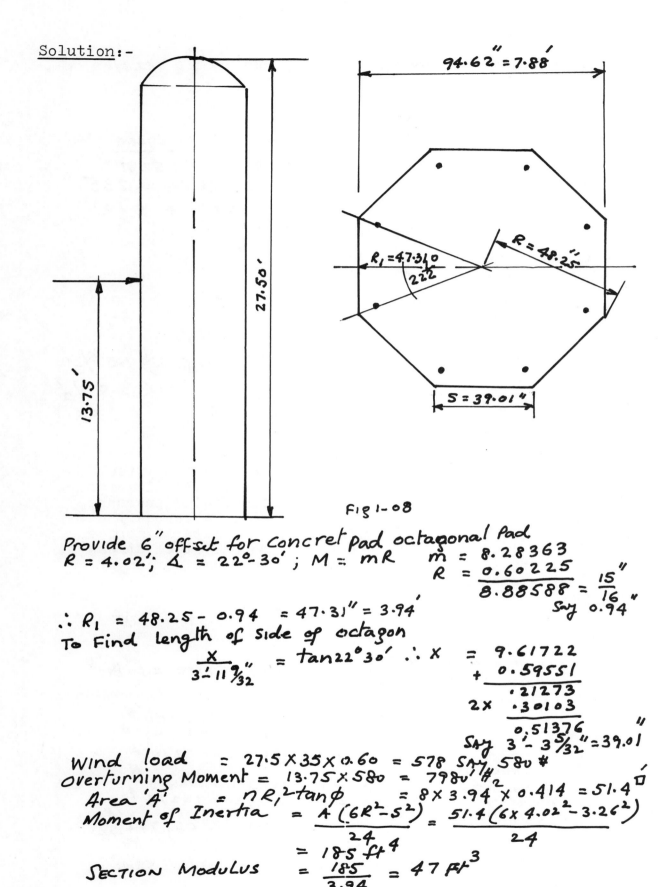

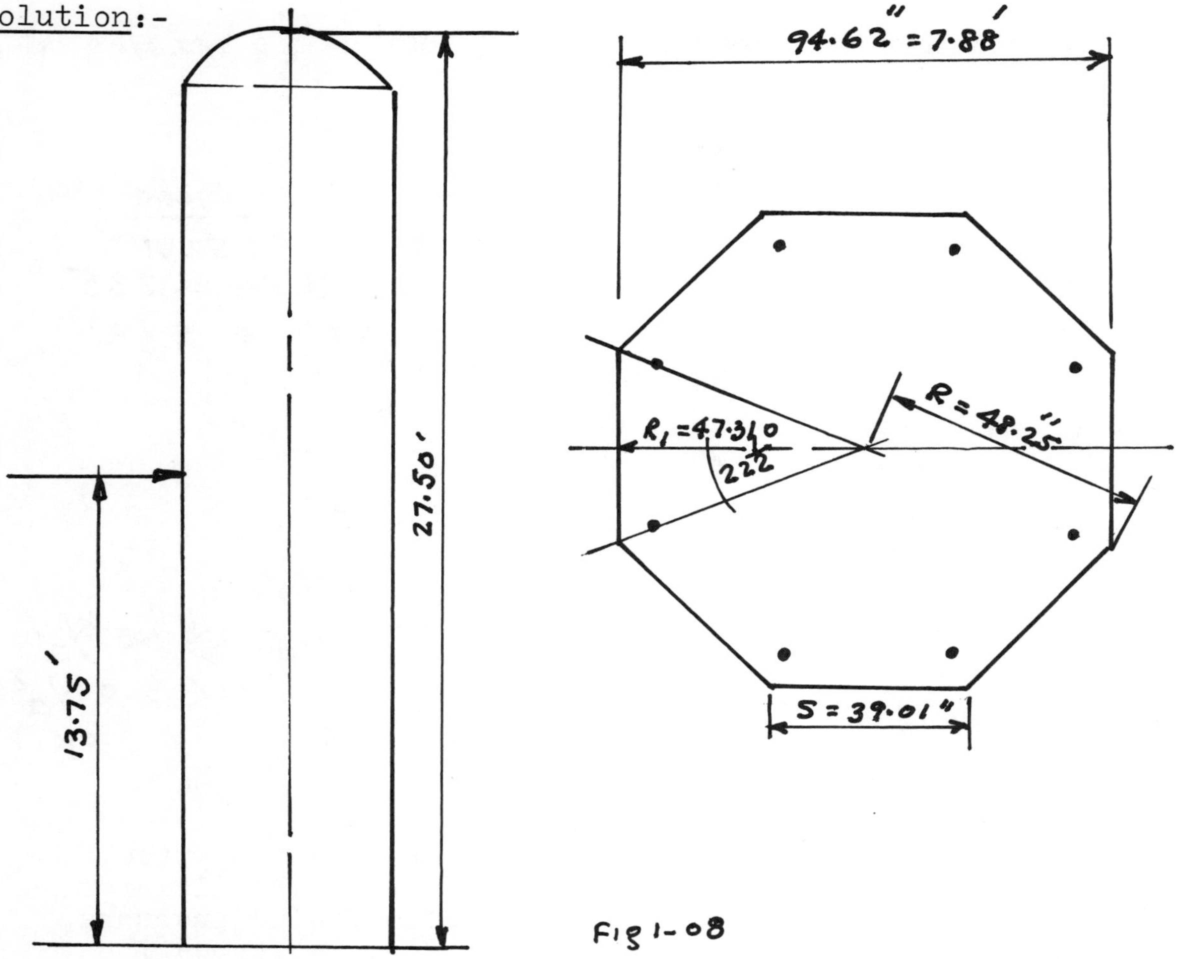

Fig 1-08

Provide 6" offset for concret pad octagonal pad

$R = 4.02'$; $\Delta = 22^\circ\text{-}30'$; $M = mR$

$$\begin{aligned} m &= 8.28363 \\ R &= 0.60225 \\ \hline & 8.88588 = \tfrac{15}{16}" \text{ Say } 0.94" \end{aligned}$$

$\therefore R_1 = 48.25 - 0.94 = 47.31" = 3.94'$

To Find length of side of octagon

$$\frac{x}{3'\text{-}11\tfrac{9}{32}"} = \tan 22^\circ 30' \quad \therefore x = 9.61722$$

$$\begin{aligned} & 9.61722 \\ + & \; 0.59551 \\ \hline & .21273 \\ 2\times & \; .30103 \\ \hline & 0.51376 \end{aligned}$$

Say $3'\text{-}3\tfrac{5}{32}" = 39.01"$

Wind load $= 27.5 \times 35 \times 0.60 = 578$ Say $580\#$

Overturning Moment $= 13.75 \times 580 = 7980'\#$

Area 'A' $= nR_1^2 \tan\phi = 8 \times 3.94^2 \times 0.414 = 51.4^{\square'}$

Moment of Inertia $= \dfrac{A(6R^2 - S^2)}{24} = \dfrac{51.4(6 \times 4.02^2 - 3.26^2)}{24}$

$= 185 \text{ ft}^4$

Section Modulus $= \dfrac{185}{3.94} = 47 \text{ ft}^3$

weight of vessel empty = 8281 # 8281

weight of vessel full

$\frac{\pi}{4}(5.54)^2 \times 27.5 \times 62.4 = 41500$ #

weight of foundation =

$51.4 \times 3.5 \times 150$ = 27,000 # 27000

76781 # 35281 #

e (vessel empty) = 8281 ÷ 35281 = 0.235

e (vessel full) = 8281 ÷ 76781 = 0.107

e ÷ h = 0.235 ÷ 7.88 = 0.0298

e ÷ h = 0.107 ÷ 7.88 = 0.0136

compression over the whole BASE

Max. soil pressure

Direct load = $\frac{76781}{51.4}$ = 1.49 k/□'

overturning = $\frac{8281}{47}$ = 0.18 k/□'

1.67 k/□' > 1.5 k/□'

< 3.0 k/□'

OK

NOTE: complete design is not given. as next example of stack is fully solved.

EXAMPLE 1-09

Given:- Design foundation for ground supported A-36 Steel stack 100 ft. high with the profile as shown. The diameter of the vessel is 54" and 60" with insulation, wind pressure 30 psf, siesmic coefficient 10 percent. Allowable bearing pressure on soil is 4500 psf with or without lateral forces. Foundation is to be 3000 psi concrete. Normal steel stress 22000 psi. Normal stress increased 1/3 for combination of vertical and lateral forces.

Solution:-

Vertical load (V)

Empty vessel (a) = 106526 #

vessel operating (a+b) = 122726 #

vessel under test (a+c) = 197226 #

Lateral loads Wind (d) = $30 \times 5 \times 0.6 \times 1.2 \times 100$ = 10800 #

overturning moment

Hh_1 = 10800×50 = 540000 '#

Hh_2 = 10800×54.5 = 588600 '#

Hh_3 = 10800×56.5 = 610200 '#

Seismic load (e)

vessel Empty = 0.10×106526 = 10653 #

vessel operating = 0.10×122726 = 12273 #

overturning moment

Hh_2 = 12273×54.0 = 662742 '#

Hh_3 = 12273×56.0 = 687288 '#

ANCHOR BOLTS

Assume 16 Anchor bolts on dia of circle = $58\frac{1}{2}$''

Bolt Tension $F = \frac{4M}{DN} - \frac{V}{N} = \frac{4 \times 540000}{4.88 \times 16} - \frac{106526}{16} = 21006$

Req'd net area of bolt $= \frac{21006}{15000} = 1.4 \square''$

use $1\frac{5}{8}''\phi$ bolt - Area $= 1.515 \square''$, allowable load $= 22.7K$

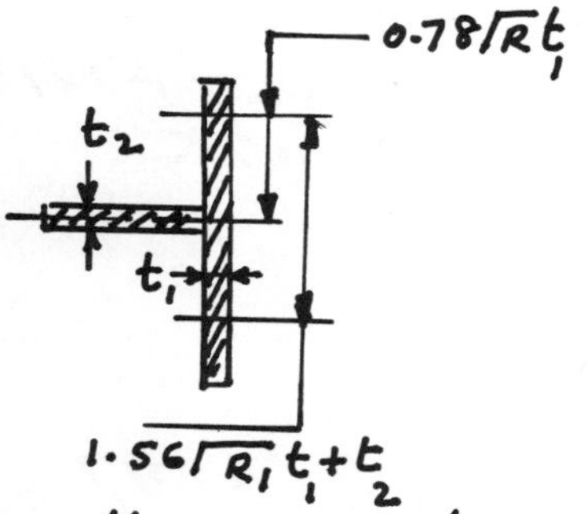

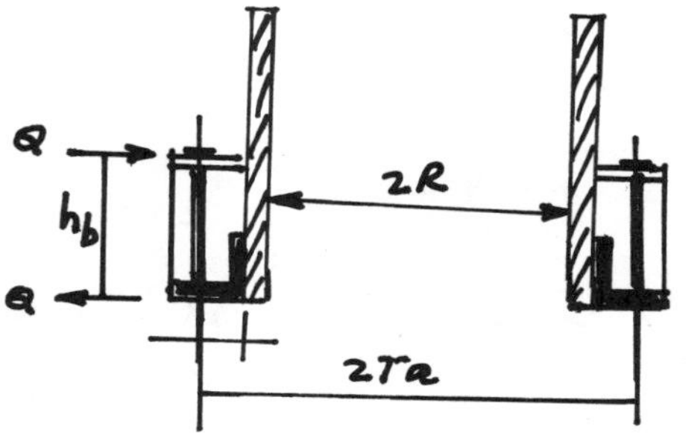

Length $A_1 = 12\frac{1}{2}''$, $B = 24\frac{1}{2}''$

size of sleeve $= 3\frac{1}{2}''\phi \times 18''$ Lg

Base ring for Anchor bolt, $Q = \frac{Fe}{h_b} = \frac{21006 \times 2}{12.5} = 3361$

Max. compression B.M $= CQr_a = 0.258 \times 3361 \times 29.25$

$= 25363''\#$

$S_x = \frac{25363}{10000} = 2.53 \text{ in}^3$

$b_{ring} = 8''$

$\therefore \frac{bd^2}{6} = 2.53$, $d = \sqrt{\frac{2.53 \times 6}{8}} = 1.38''$ use $1\frac{1}{2}''$

Max. compression on concrete $= \left[\frac{V}{\pi D} + \frac{4M}{\pi D^2}\right] \div B$

$= \left[\frac{122726}{\pi \times 54} + \frac{54000 \times 12}{\pi \times 54^2}\right] \div 8 = 178.8 \#/\square''$

ALLOW. Max Comp. on concrete for $f_c' = 3000$ Psi

$= \phi(0.85 f_c') \times 1.33 = 3052$ Psi

Hence the bearing on concrete is very small & so solution is adequette.

Pedestal:-

Anchor bolt circle	=	$58\frac{1}{2}''$
Sleeve dia	=	$3''$
Vertical bar, say 2 @ 3/4	=	$1\frac{1}{2}''$
Cover 2 @ 2"	=	$4''$
		$67''$ use $72''$ across flats

Vertical reinforcement.

$h = 72''$, $d_{eff} = 69\frac{1}{2}''$

width of rectangular beam $= \frac{5}{8}(72) = 45''$

Weight of Pedestal $= 28.27 \times 45 \times 150$

$= 19085\#$

Empty vessel + wind V $= 106526 + 19085 = 125611\#$

Moment @ tension steel $= 588600 + 125611 \times 33.5$

$= 4796500''\# = 400'K$

For $b = 45$; $d = 69\frac{1}{2}''$, $F = 18.37$

$K_U = \frac{M_U}{F} = \frac{400}{18.37} = 21.77$

$A_s = \frac{400}{2.96 \times 69.5} = 1.94 \square'$

2. Check for condition of vessels operating with seismic load

$V = 122776 + 19085 = 141861^{\#}$

M about tension steel $= 6627462 + 14186 \times 33.5 = 948.317K$

$K_U = \frac{948.317}{21.77} = 43.56$

$A_S = \frac{948.317}{2.46 \times 69.5} = 4.6 \square''$

less $\frac{V}{F_y} = A_s = \frac{141861}{60000} = \frac{2.36 \square''}{2.24 \square''}$ use 4-#7

Base Slab

$M_{seismic} = 687288'^{K}$, $F_1 = 4500$ Psi

D = Req'd Dia. across FLAT $= 2.6 \sqrt[3]{\frac{M}{F_1}} = 2.6 \sqrt[3]{\frac{687288}{4500}} = 13.5'$

Similarly

$D = 1.25 \sqrt{\frac{V}{F_2 - G}}$ where $V = 197226^{\#}$, $F_2 = 4500$ Psi

Wt/$\square'$ of Base & Earth

$G = 2 \times 150 + 4.0 \times 100 = 700^{\#}$

$D = 1.25 \sqrt{\frac{197226}{4500 - 700}} = 9.0'$

Use $D = 13'\text{-}6''$

Check Base Pressure

WT of operating vessel	$= 122726^{\#}$
WT of Pedestal	$= 19085^{\#}$
WT of footing 2' thick $151 \times 2 \times 150$	$= 45300^{\#}$
WT of earth on footing $(151 - 28.27) 4 \times 100$	$= 49092^{\#}$
	$V = 236203^{\#}$

Overturning Moment Seismic $= 687288''^{\#}$

$\frac{e}{D} = \frac{2.91}{13.5} = 0.216$

$L = 3.13$

$F = \frac{LV}{A} = \frac{3.13 \times 236203}{151} = 4896 > 4500$ N.G

F.S against overturning $= \frac{D}{2e} = \frac{13.5}{2 \times 2.91} = 2.32 > 2$

Let us consider empty vessel + wind load to get lower F.S.

From figure 1.09 (b), For $\frac{e}{D} = 0.216$ for axis // to side of octagon, $L = 3.13$, $K = 0.303$

Max Base pressure $F = \frac{3.13 \times 22003}{151} = 4560 \simeq 4500$ ok

$KD = 0.303 \times 13.50 = 4.09'$

Moment/ft width about the edge of Pedestal.

	SHEAR	ARM	Moment
2744×3.75	10290	1.88	19345
$1756 \times \frac{1}{2} \times 3.7$	3292	2.50	8230
Less Footing/Earth 700×3.75	-2620	1.88	-4950
	10962		22625
Use 0.85 of above value for design	9317		19231'#

t_{base} assumed $= 24$, $d_{eff} = 20''$

$K_U = \frac{19.23}{0.144} = 133.54$

$a_U = 2.89$

$A_S = \frac{19.23}{2.89 \times 20} = 0.33 \square''$

Use #6 @ 12" $= 0.44 \square''$

$U = \frac{V}{\Sigma_0 d} = \frac{9317}{\pi \times 0.75 \times 20} = 197$

$U_{all} = 9.5\sqrt{f_c'}/D = 694 > 197$

(Diagram of Example 1-09 and figure to determine the base pressure of Octagonal Foundation on next page)

a) Lateral Load acts at right angles to diagonal from one corner to the opposite corner, gives maximum intensity of base pressure acting at farthest corner from diagonal.

b) Lateral Load acts parallel to one side to be used for design of slab.

CANTILEVER RETAINING WALLS

EXAMPLE 1-10

Given:- Design a reinforced concrete wall to retain an earth bank 14 ft. high. The top surface is horizontal and supports a surcharge of 455 psf. The soil weighs 130 pcf and its angle of internal friction is 35, the coefficient of friction of the soil and concrete is 0.5. The allowable soil presume is 4000 psi, $f_c' = 3000$ psi and $f_y = 6$ 0000 psi. The base of the structure must be set 4 ft. below ground level to clear the frost line and the factor of safety against sliding and overturning should have a maximum value of 1.5.

Solution:- In retaining wall the resultant is permitted to intersect the base near the forward edge of the middle third. Trial Section has usually the following relationship.

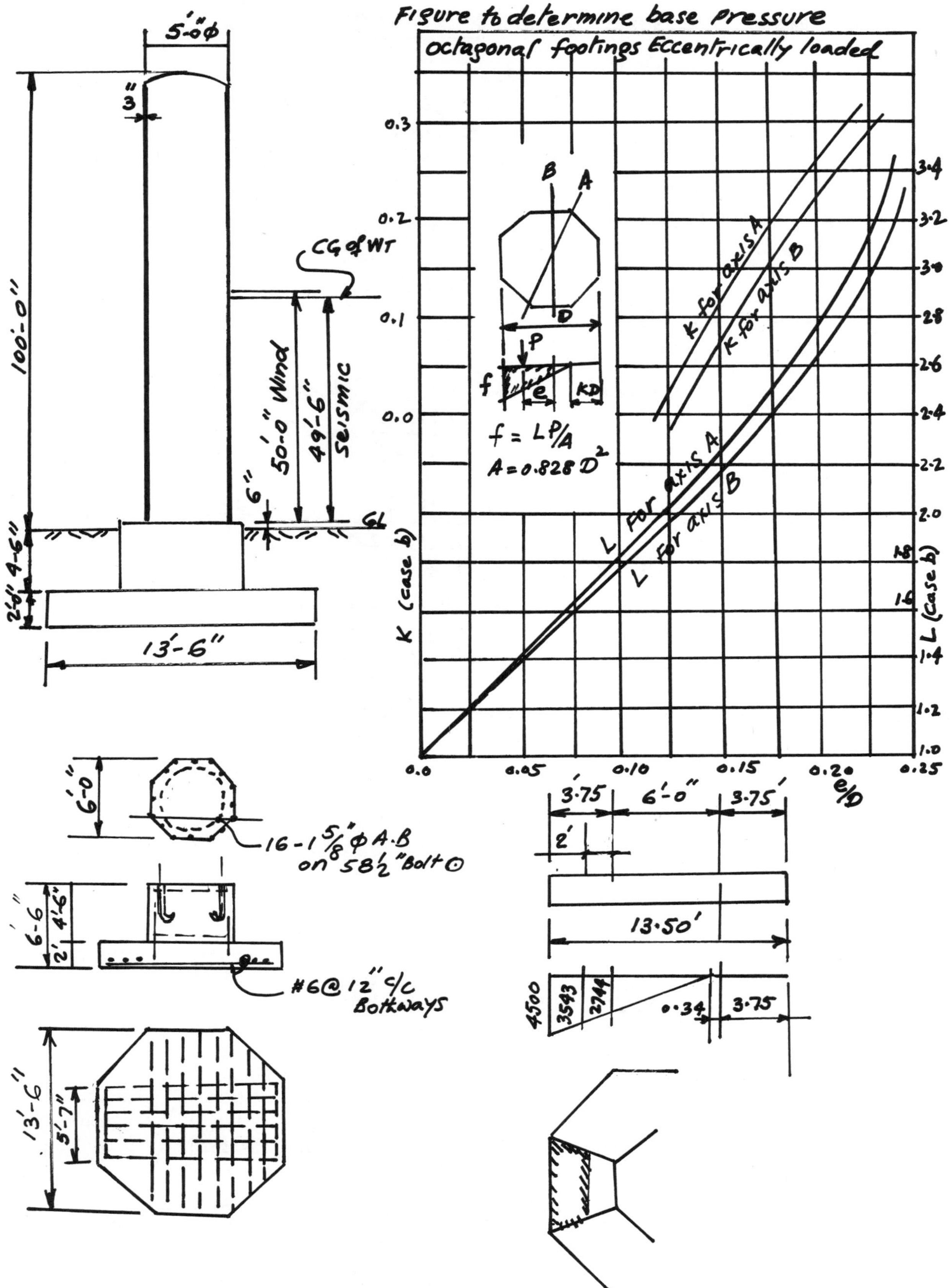

Figure to determine base pressure
octagonal footings Eccentrically loaded
5'-0"φ
3"
100'-0"
CG of WT
50'-0" Wind
49'-6" seismic
6"
GL
4'-6"
2'-0"
13'-6"
0.3
0.2
0.1
0.0
B
A
D
P
f
e
KD
f = LP/A
A = 0.828 D²
K for axis A
K for axis B
L for axis A
L for axis B
K (case b)
L (case b)
3.4
3.2
3.0
2.8
2.6
2.4
2.2
2.0
1.8
1.6
1.4
1.2
1.0
0.0
0.05
0.10
0.15
0.20
0.25
e/D
6'-0
16-1 5/8"φ A.B on 58 1/2" Bolt ⊙
6'-6
4'-6"
2'
#6@12" c/c Bothways
13'-6"
5'-7"
3.75
6'-0"
3.75'
2'
13.50'
4500
3543
2744
0.34
3.75

Fig. 1-09

$a = 0.60y \quad ; \quad b \geq 8''$

$c = d = b + 0.045y$

$f = \frac{a}{3} - \frac{c}{2}$

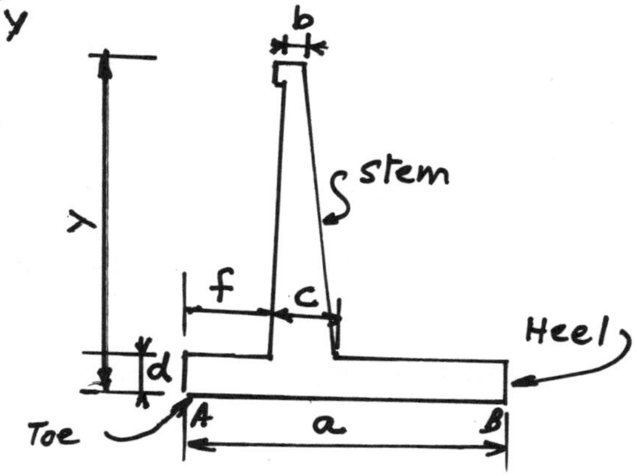

We know that resultant earth pressure T

$$T = \frac{1}{2} C_a w y (y + 2h)$$

& Moment $\quad M = \frac{1}{2} C_a w y^2 (y + 3h)$

where C_a, the coefficient of active earth pressure

h, the equivalent height of surcharge

w the unit weight of earth

Then $h = \frac{455}{130} = 3.50'$; $\sin 35° = 0.574$, $\tan 35° = 0.700$

$C_a = \frac{1 - \sin\phi}{1 + \sin\phi} = 0.271$

$\therefore \quad T_{AB} = \frac{1}{2} \times 0.271 \times 130 \times 18 (18 + 2 \times 3.5) = 7898'\#$

$M_{AB} = \frac{1}{6} \times 0.271 \times 130 \times 18^2 (18 + 3 \times 3.5) = 54219'\#$

Stability of retaining wall:

	Force	ARM	Moment ft lbs
$W_1 = 1.5 \times 11 \times 150 =$	2475	5.5	13613
$W_2 = 0.67 \times 16.5 \times 150 =$	1658	3.33	5521
$W_3 = 0.50 \times 0.83 \times 16.5 \times 150 =$	1027	3.95	4057
$W_4 = 1.25 \times 1.13 \times 150 =$	212	3.75	795
$W_5 = 0.5 \times 0.83 \times 16.5 \times 130 =$	890	4.23	3764
$W_6 = 6.5 \times 16.5 \times 130 =$	13943	7.75	108058
$W_7 = 2.5 \times 3 \times 130 =$	975	1.50	1463
	Σ_F 21180		Σ_M 137271
		Less O.T Mom.	54219
			83052 '#

$\therefore x = \frac{83052}{21180} = 3.92 \quad \therefore e = 5.50 - 3.92 = 1.58 \text{ ft}$

Since the criteria is to pass resultant through middle third $\therefore$ P_a for 1' LGTH $= \frac{\Sigma V}{BL}\left(1 \pm \frac{6e}{B}\right) = \frac{21180}{11}\left(1 \pm \frac{6 \times 1.58}{11}\right)$

$= 3581, 270$ psf.

Check $\quad x = \frac{11}{3}\left(\frac{3581 + 2 \times 270}{3581 + 270}\right) = 3.92'$ ok

Factor of Safety against overturning

$$= \frac{137271}{54219} = 2.53 > 1.5 \text{ ok}$$

Check against sliding

Friction A to C $= \frac{1}{2}(3581 + 2184) \times 3 \times 0.7 = 6053$

" C to B $= \frac{1}{2}(2184 + 270) \times 8 \times 0.5 = 4908$

Passive Earth pressure $= \frac{1}{2}\left(\frac{1 + \sin\phi}{1 - \sin\phi}\right) \times 130 \times (2.75)^2$

$= \frac{1814}{12775}$

∴ Factor of Safety against Sliding

$$= \frac{12775}{7898} = 1.62 > 1.5 \text{ ok}$$

Hence trial section is ok for stability.

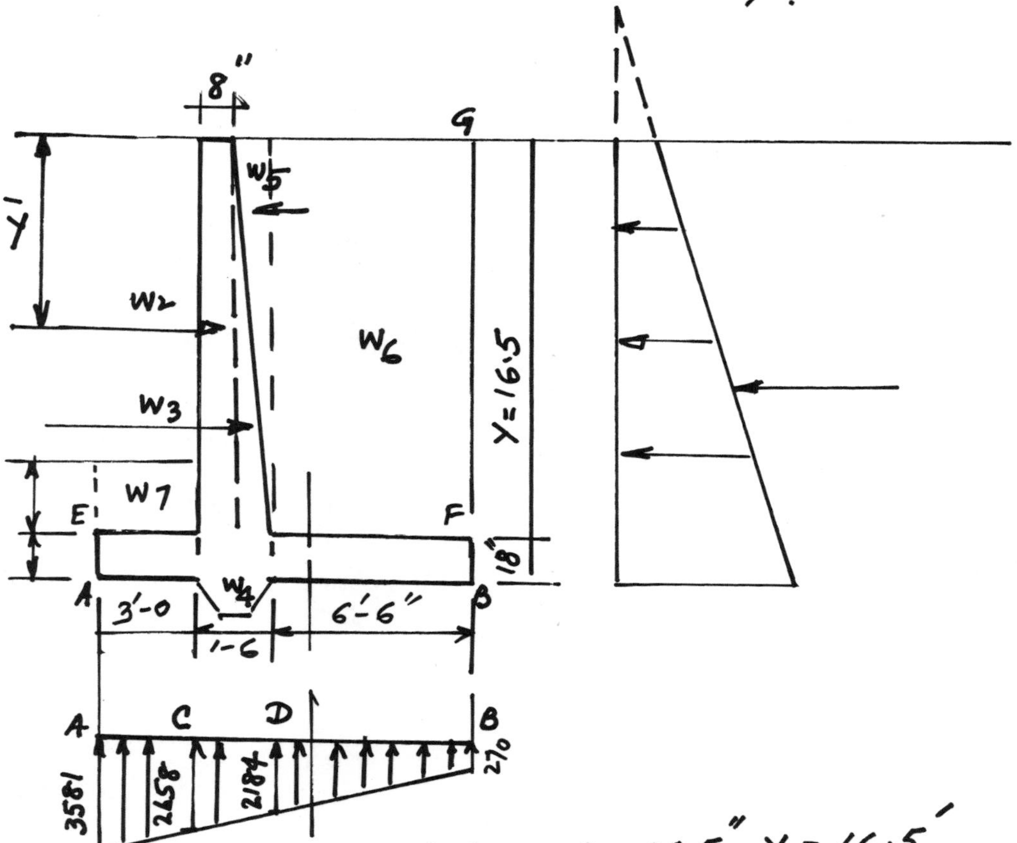

Reinforcement in wall stem, $d = 14.5''$, $Y = 16.5'$

Design loads $U = 1.4D$ to cause greater moments

$T_{EF} = \frac{1}{2} \times 35.2 \times 16.5\,(16.5 + 2 \times 3.5) = 6824\#$

& $6824 \times 1.4 = 9554\#$

$M_{EF} = \frac{1}{6} \times 35.2 \times (16.5^2)(16.5 + 3.5) \times 1.4 = 752664'\#$

$A_s = \frac{M_U}{\phi f_y (d - a/2)}$ where $\phi = .90$ $a = \frac{A_s f_y}{0.85 f'_c b}$

$b = 12$, $d = 14.5$, $a = 2.00$ in

$A_s = \frac{'(752)}{0.90 \times 60(14.5 - 1.00)} = 1.03 \text{ in}^2$ use #7@7"

$v_U = \frac{9554}{0.85 \times 12 \times 14.5} = 64 < 2\sqrt{3000} = 110$ ok

Moments at bar cut offs can be interpolated from table 14-22 by st line interpolation from CRSI handbook. Theoretical cut off point is 11'-7"

$M = 198744$ "#, $d = 4.5 + 10 \frac{11.58}{16.5} = 11.52$ in

$$As = \frac{198.744}{0.9 \times 60 \times (11.52 - 1.00)} = 0.349 \text{ in}^2$$

use #7@14"

Horizontal bars in stem

see table 14-8 CRSI, L Bars are 18-#5, 6 of which are located in footing

$A_s = (18-6)0.31 = 3.72 \text{ in}^2$

$$p_T = \frac{3.72}{\frac{1}{2}(8+18)(16.5)12} = 0.0014 < 0.002$$

Provide $A_s = 0.002 \times 16.5 \times 12 = 0.396 \square''$

Design of HEEL

surcharge upto G.

$p = 16.5 \times 130 + 1.5 \times 150 = 2370$ psf

$V = 6.5[2370 - \frac{1}{2}(2184 + 270)] \times 1.4$

$= 10402$ #

$M = 12 \times 6.5^2[\frac{1}{2} \times 2370 - \frac{1}{6}(2184 + 2 \times 270)] \times 1.4$

$= 536200$ "# $= 536.2$ kip in

$d = 18 - 3 - \frac{1}{2}(0.875) = 14.5$

$a = 2$

$$As = \frac{536.2}{0.9 \times 60 \times (14.56 - 1)} = 0.732 \quad \text{use \#7@7''}$$

$$v = \frac{10.402}{0.85 \times 14.50 \times 12} = 70 < 2\sqrt{f_c'} = 110 \text{ ok}$$

Design of Toe

$V = 3(\frac{1}{2}(3581 + 2658) - 1.5 \times 150) \times 1.4 = 12159$ #

$M = 12 \times 3^2[\frac{1}{6}(2658 + 2 \times 3581) - \frac{1}{2} \times 225] \times 1.4 = 230529$ "k

use #5@7"

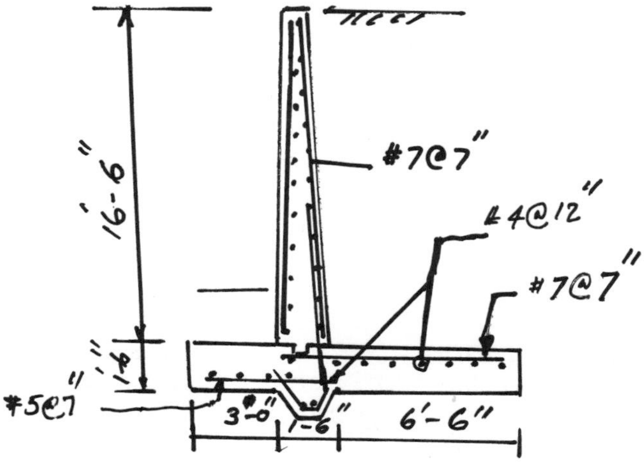

DESIGN OF CONCRETE FOUNDATION PIERS OR CAISSONS

These are large underground concrete filled shafts or wells used to support buildings, bridges and other structures. Such caissons may range in size up to 15 ft. diameter and 200 ft. deep or to reach suitable bearing. In ancient times and for many years, one of the most elementary methods is to excavate an open well, line it with timber, then fill it with concrete. The caissons were used in India in 19th century, where bridge piers were constructed by sinking a brick caisson and the divers inside the caisson brought up the mud in bucket.

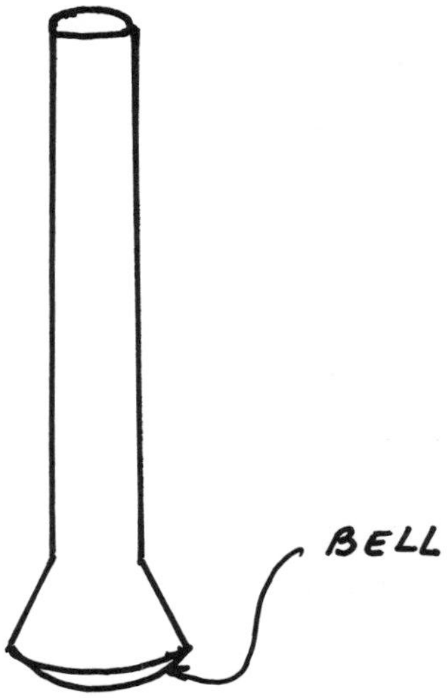

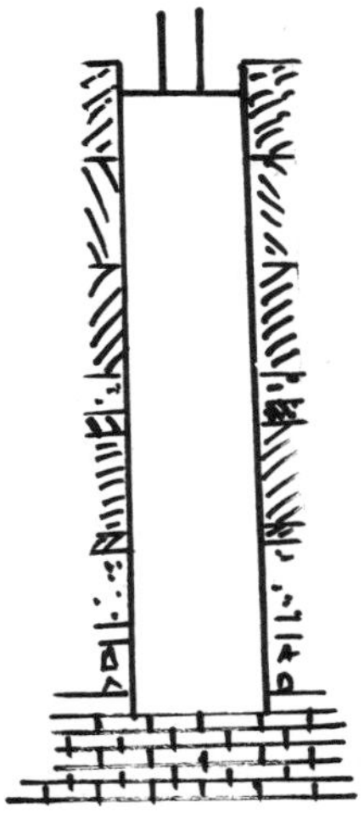

SUPPORT CONDITIONS FOR CAISSONS

1) For the caisson which is actually forced into the ground, skin friction becomes part of the design and it may be necessary to calculate additional weight necessary to force into the ground. 2) Lateral support of caisson in light of possible eccentricity. 3) Height to diameter restriction 12-30. 4) In deep caisson, the dead weight of the concrete is important and is considered to be about the same as that of the soil which was excavated.

DESIGN CONSIDERATIONS

It involves a number of factors relating to soil mechanics and construction procedures. 1) Depth of caisson. 2) Type of bottom bearing soil. 3) Construction sequence. 4) Possible future construction on adjacent properties. 5) Lateral pressures on caissons by neighboring excavations. 6) Type of excavation (hand or drilled). 7) Type of lining (temp. or perm.) 8) Type of foundation under other parts of structure. 9) Tolerance for construction are closely related to design, 1% eccentricity i.e. yields 8% stress increase. 10) Economical combination of shaft diameter and concrete strength. 11) Available bearing pressure of bottom of caisson.

Lateral loads on caisson. When horizontal force on the structure must be resisted by caisson, sound engg. judgement is needed. It is necessary to determine the passive resistance of the soil, distribution of soil pressures and variation of moments and shears in caisson.

DESIGN PROCEDURE

It was developed by Reese and Matlock and applies to short and long caissons. The method is basedon the relationship where is soil modulus (force per unit of length of pile and per unit of deflection, psi)

X the distance down from the surface, inches.

K a coefficient having units (lbs. per cubic inch) which depends on the type of cohesive or cohesionless soil.

A thorough soil testing program should be carried out before completing design.

EXAMPLE 1-11

Given:- A caisson 106' deep having a diameter of 6'; Concrete strength 5000 psi; modulus of elasticity of concrete K assumed coefficient of soil modulus variation 5lbs/cu.in. Forces acting on the top of caisson are shown. Determine Maximum Bending moment in the caisson using the method of Reese and Matlock.

Solution:-

RELATIVE stiffness factor(T) $= \left(\frac{EI}{R}\right)^{0.2} = \left(\frac{4\times10^6 \times \frac{\pi}{4} \times 36^4}{5}\right)^{0.2}$ $= 254$

Depth coefficient max (Z) $= \frac{L}{T} = \frac{1275}{274} = 5$

Moment due to H - M_H $= A_M H_T$ From fig 15 of Reese and Matlock paper, the value of A_M can be read directly and curve for M_H constructed, Max $M_H = 0.78 \times 60 \times 254 = 990$ ft-kips.

Similarly curve for M_m (Moment due to M_T) can be read from figure 2.0 of reference

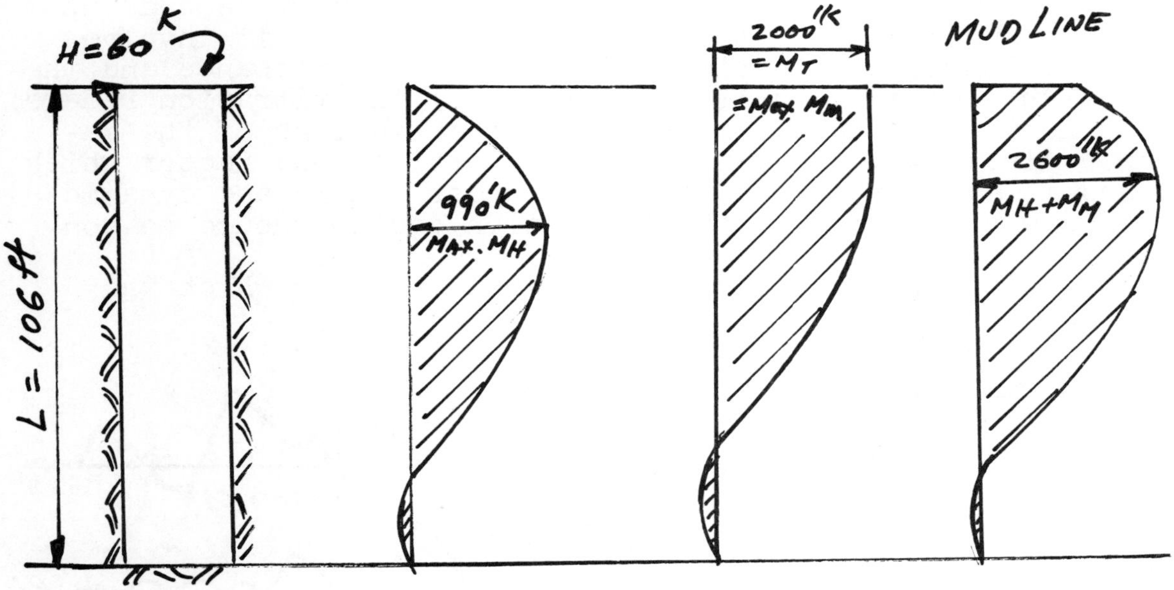

DYNAMIC FOUNDATION DESIGN

(Reciprocating Machine Foundation Design)

This design includes studies of response of foundations to the dynamic loading and transmission of wave energy through the soil so as not to cause harmful effects to the machines, structures or people in the vicinity.

The following questions must be answered by the design procedure: a) What should be considered failure of chosen design function and limits on the design criteria. b) What is the relation between applied loads and quantities significant to the design criteria. c) How are significant quantities and errors involved in evaluation. d) What sort of factor of safety do we apply while designing.

DESIGN CRITERIA

While considering the foundation represented by the rigid block supported on soil, when acted upon by dynamic loads, the rigid block may vibrate in any of the six freedoms shown in sketch.

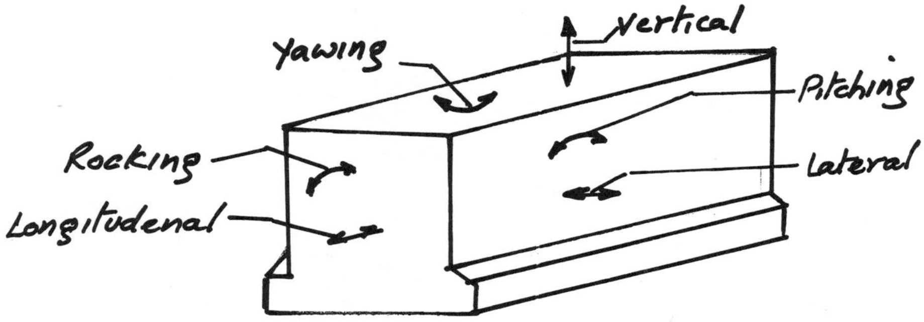

But usually the condition of failure of vibrating foundations is when the motion of machinery exceeds a limiting value of velocity or acceleration of the foundation. The design criteria for steady state vibration of the machinery depends upon the prime function of entire installation. Thus it involves consideration of the initial cost, cost of maintenance and the cost of the replacing unit. Amplitude of the vibration refers to the horizontal motion measured on the bearings of the machine. Also the introduction of the service Load Factor which is used to evaluate the performance under static and dynamic loadings with regards to the foundation design should be considered.

The following figure shows the pattern of motion which the rigid block may follow.

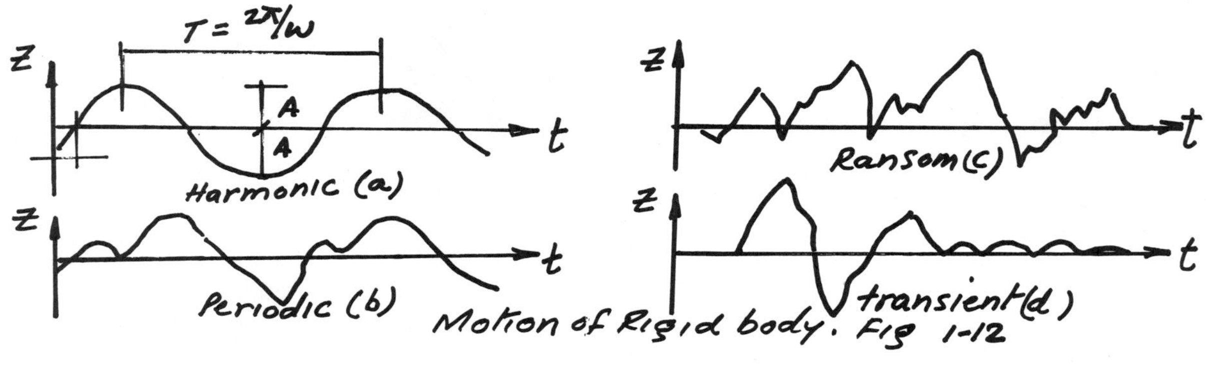

1) Rotating machinery

where Q - sinusoidal loading
W - frequency rad./sec.
- eccentric mass
e - eccentric radius from center of rotation to C.G. of rotating mass
f - frequency of rotation

2) Reciprocating machinery

Internal combustion engine, steam engine, machinery involving crank mechanism produce reciprocating forces.

$$z_c = r\omega^2 \cos \omega t$$
$$z_p = r\omega^2\left(\cos \omega t + \frac{r}{L}\cos 2\omega t\right)$$
$$z_p = (m_{rec} + m_{rot})\, r\omega^2 \cos \omega t + m_{rec}\frac{r^2}{L}\omega^2 \cos 2\omega t$$
$$F_y = m_{rot}\, r\omega^2 \sin \omega t$$

where L = Length of connecting rod, r = Length of crank; z_c = acceleration of crank pin in vertical direction, z_p = acceleration of wrist pin in vertical direction, F_z = Total vertical force, F_y = Total Horizontal force; m_{rot} = Total rotating mass; m_{rec} = Total reciprocating mass

In figure 1-12(a), displacement $z = A\sin(\omega t - \phi)$

A = max. displacement, ω = radian/unit time, ϕ = phase angle of curve. Also $f = \frac{\omega}{2\pi}$, $T = \frac{1}{f} = \frac{2\pi}{\omega}$, $f_n = \frac{\omega_n}{2\pi} = \frac{1}{2\pi}\sqrt{\frac{K}{m}}$

$$z_s = \frac{W}{K}, \quad f_n = \frac{1}{2\pi}\sqrt{g/z_s}$$

where f_s = frequency of oscilation. T = period of vibration

z_s = static displacement, W = weight on spring

Relation between static displacement and natural frequency for spring mass system.

z_s, in	f_n cycles/sec
0.001	99.0
0.01	31.3
0.10	9.9
1.00	3.13

EXAMPLE 1-12 Design of Pump Foundation

Given:- Design a foundation for the basic layout of the compressor and its drive motor with a dimension as shown. The total weight of the compressor and the motor is 10900 lbs. The compressor has a bore of 14.5 in., a stroke of 9.0 in. and its operating speed 450 r.p.m. It developes the following unbalanced forces.

Vertical		Horizontal	
Primary	9180 lbs.	Primary	310 lbs.
Secondary	2200 lbs.	Secondary	0 lbs.

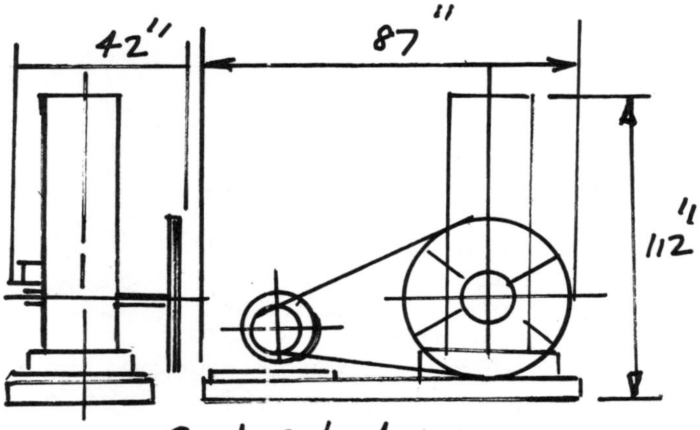

Single cylinder Compressor
Fig1-12(e)

Solution:- The vertical primary and secondary forces produce a periodical vertical force.

$$F_Z = (m_{rec} + m_{rot}) r\omega^2 \cos\omega t + m_{rec}\frac{r^2}{L}\omega^2 \cos 2\omega t$$

where $\omega = 2\pi f$

$$\therefore F_Z = 9180 \cos\omega t + 2200 \cos 2\omega t$$

Since the compressor is to be supported by a foundation block resting directly upon the soil.
Soil test results are v_s (shear wave velocity) = 806 ft./sec.
Unit weight γ = 100 lbs./cft, G (shear modulus) = 14000 lbs/in
ν (poisson ratio) = 1/3

Design proceedure:- acceptable limit of motion (criteria for failure) vertical motion = Horizontal motion.

Reference # M.P. Blake Pg 111-114, 450 r.p.m operating speed gives in case B amplitude of 0.0021 for foundation soil system.

$\therefore$ Area req'd to limit state displacement caused by Q_0 = 11400 lbs to a value of 0.002 in

$$Z_s = \frac{(1-\nu)Q_0}{4Gr_0} \text{ or } 0.002 = \frac{2}{3} \times 11400/(4 \times 14000 \times r_0)$$

r_0 = 67.9 in = 5.66 ft say 6'-0"

$\therefore$ Base area = 113 ft² & Z_s again = 0.0019 in

Hence 16'×7'×3'-0 block is ok

WT of footing = 50400 lbs $\therefore$ Total oscilating weight including machinery = 61300 lbs. FROM Richard Hall & Wood (1970) equivalent damping ratio 'D' = 0.60 for

$$\text{mass ratio } B_Z = \frac{(1-\nu)}{4}\frac{W}{\gamma r_0^3} = \frac{2/3 \times 61300}{4 \times 100 (6)^3} = 0.473.$$

Max Dynamic vertical displacement @ resonance frequency

$$Z = Z_s \frac{1}{2D\sqrt{1-D^2}} = 0.0019 \frac{1}{2 \times 0.6\sqrt{1-(0.6)^2}} = 0.00198 \text{ in}.$$

$$f_n = \frac{1}{2\pi}\sqrt{\frac{K_Z}{m}} \text{ where } K_Z = \frac{4Gr_0}{1-\nu} = 3/2 \times 4 \times 14000 \times 72 = 6.048 \times 10^6 \text{ \#/"}$$

$$\therefore f_n = \frac{1}{2\pi}\sqrt{6.048 \times 10^6 \times 386/61300} = 31.1 \text{ CPS} = 1864 \text{ CPM} > 450, \therefore F_S = \frac{1864}{450} = 4.20$$

Determination of Natural Frequency of Structural Members Supporting Variable Speed Pumps

Note:- If the frequency of the impulses is very large (1000 cycles per minute), the supporting structure is likely to have a natural frequency so much lower that the two will not vibrate in harmony. The danger zone to watch lies in a range of 200 - 500 cycles per minute. It is advisable to keep the natural frequency of the foundation low enough so as not to exceed 30 - 50% of the machine frequency or so high as to exceed this frequency by 200 - 300%.

Safe limit recommended for preventing the occurence of resonance.

Machine	Supporting Members
	Low 200-300 cycles/min.
600 cycles/minute	
	High 1200-1800 cycles/min.

Pump & Motor Data

Pump No.	WT of Motor & Magnetic Dr.	R.P.M Rev/min.	R.P.S Rev/sec.	Remarks.
1	14,900 #	588	9.8	Variable speed
2	6,800 #	588	9.8	Constant speed
3	28,000 #	506	8.5	Variable speed
4	12,000 #	506	8.5	Constant speed

EXAMPLE 1-13

Given:- The members to be investigated for Canaveralejo Sewage pumping station 1) Steel plate 2) Rolled beam 3) Concrete beam

Solution:- 1) Steel plate, no analysis of the natural frequency is needed because the weight of the motor is uniformly distributed and immediately transferred into a supporting steel member beam.

2. Steel Beam W 24×145, $I = 4561\ \text{in}^4$, $WT = 145\ \#/\text{ft}$.

$$f_{sb} = \frac{1}{2\pi}\sqrt{\frac{Kg}{W}} \quad \text{where } k = \frac{48EI}{L^3} = 7.47\times10^5$$

Length $L = 17.2$ ft

$$\therefore f_{sb} = \frac{1}{2\times\pi}\sqrt{\frac{7.47\times10^5\times386}{14900}} = 22.1\ \text{c/s or } 1320\ \text{c/M}.$$

3. Concrete beam 24×36"

To find M

Pump #1		7450 #
#2	,	3400 #
Conc. BMS 2'×3'×17.2'	,	13500 #
STL. BM 145×17.2		2500 #
		28850

$$\therefore M = \frac{28850}{386} = 75.0.$$

$$f_{cb} = \pi^2 \sqrt{EI/ML3}$$

$$= 3.14^2 \sqrt{\frac{3\times10^6 \times 94000}{75\times12.2\times12^3}} = 204 \text{ Cycles/Se.}$$

TYPICAL PUMP FOUNDATION

supporting motor of 800 r.p.m in chlorine contact tank of Ches. Elizabeth Sewage treatment plant, Va.

Assume WT of Pump = 23K

Add 15% Impact for Vibration = 3.5K

Total weight = 26.5K Say 27K

Size of Pad 4×4 = 16 □″

$P = 27/16 = 1.7^K/□'$

Check Shear, $d = \dfrac{1.7\times1.4\times1000}{0.9\times12\times109} = 2 < 6''$ ok

MOMENT/FT $= 1.7\times1.4\times0.83 = 1.97'^K$ "

Use MIN. STEEL $A_S = 0.002\times12\times6 = 0.144$ □″

Use #4@9″ = 0.27 > 0.144 ok

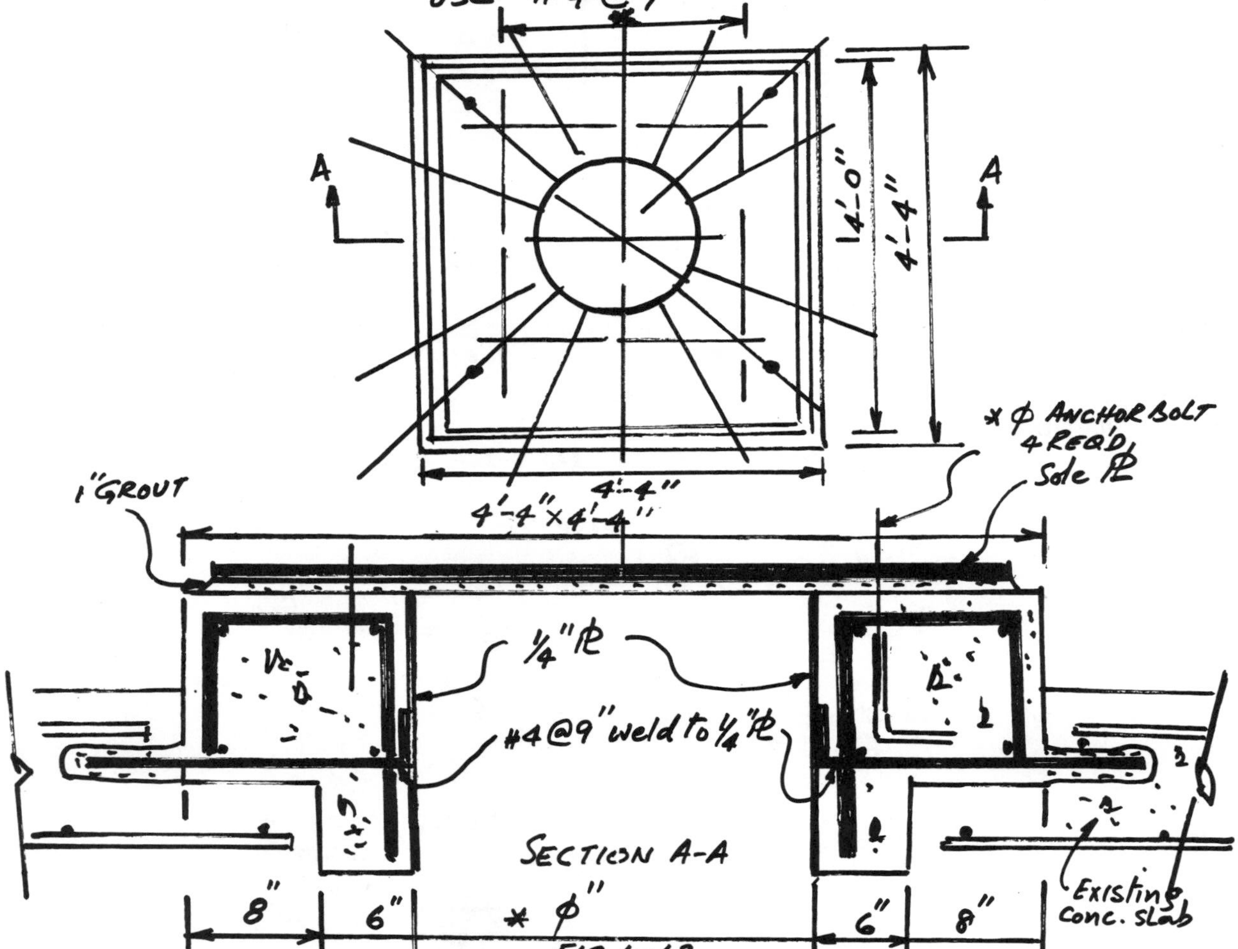

FIG 1-13

DESIGN OF PILE FOUNDATION

The complete procedure for the design of pile foundation can be summarised by the following steps:

1. Calculate the loads - 2 types: one for bearing capacity and the other for settlement analysis. The total load acting on the piles should include the weight of the pile cap and the soil above it. Also the additional load on piles due to negative skin friction if the ground is filled or to be filled.
2. Sketch a soil profile showing the soil stratification and superimpose the outlines of proposed foundation and sub-structure.
3. Establish the water table and study the possibility of lowering the water table for bridge foundation. The depth of the scour should be established.
4. Determine the type and length of the piles.
5. Determine the pile capacity.
6. Establish the pile spacing.
7. Check stresses in the lower strata.
8. Analyze the settlement.
9. Design the pile cap.
10. Check the uplift and lateral load.
11. Establish the pile load test criteria.

The bearing capacity of a single pile is controlled by the structural strength of the pile or the supporting strength of the soil and the smaller of the two is to be used for the design.

A. Structural strength of the pile as pile capacity.
   1. Severe damage due to overdriving should be avoided. Hence limitations are: Timber piles $\leq$ 25 tons/pile
      Concrete piles $\leq$ 65 tons/pile
      Steel pile up to the full allowable stress.
   2. To avoid overstress in pile under the design load, follow the codes of various cities and the National Building Code.
   3. To avoid buckling failure of the pile, the total load should not exceed the critical buckling load divided by an appropriate factor of safety.

B. Supporting strength of the soil as pile capacity.
   1. Point - bearing piles

$$Q_{ult} = \pi R^2(1.3cN_c + \gamma DN_q + 0.6\gamma RN_\gamma)$$

or $$Q_{ult} = \pi R^2(\gamma DN_q + 0.6\gamma RN_\gamma) + 2\pi Rhf_s$$

where Qult = ultimate bearing capacity of single pile
R = Radius of pile tip
C = Cohesion of soil
D = Total penetration of the pile from the ground surface to the pile tip
γ = Unit-weight of soil-use buoyant weight for the portion below the ground water
N_c, N_q, N_γ = Terzaghi's bearing capacity factors, depending upon the of the soil
h = Depth of penetration of the pile tip in the supporting layer of the granular soil

$fs = r\,(D-h/2)\tan\phi$ where ϕ is the angle of Internal friction of the supporting soil

2. Pedestal type - bearing pile
   The capacity of the pile is increased as a result of the increased base area and the increased density of the soil.
3. Friction pile in granular soil

$$Q_{ult} = 2\pi RL(\gamma Z + q)K\tan\phi$$

where R = average radius of pile
- L = total length of embedment of pile
- γ = unit-weight of soil-use buoyant weight
- Z = depth of the center of gravity of the embedded portion of the pile
- q = permanent surcharge load
- K = coefficient of the lateral earth pressure usually K 1.75
- ϕ = angle of the internal friction of soil

The bearing capacity of the pile group.

$$Q_g = SLP + q_{ult}A - \gamma LA$$

where Qg = upper limit of the pile group capacity is always ultimate capacity of the single x the number of piles in group
- S = shear resistance of the soil along the vertical surface of the block
- L = length of the pile embedment
- p = perimeter of the area enclosing all the piles in the group
- q_{ult} = ultimate bearing capacity of the soil at the pile tip level
- A = area enclosing all the piles in the group
- γ = unit weight of the soil within block L x A

Stress on the lower strata
Use 60 degree rule approximate method as explained in the figure.

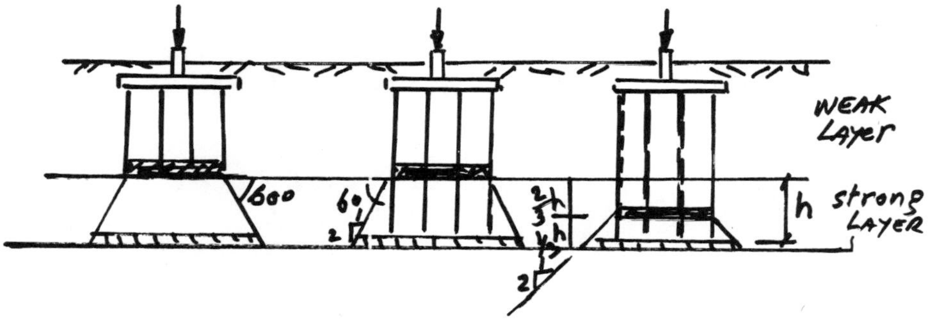

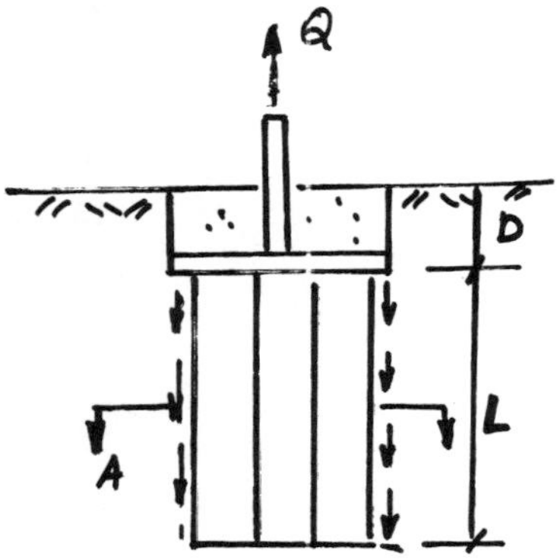

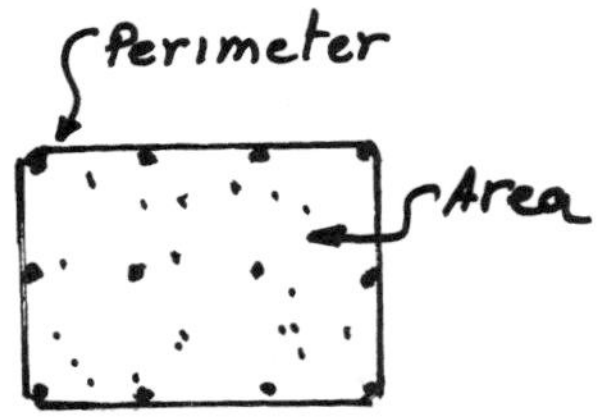

Fig. a: For Point-Bearing Pile
b: For Friction Pile — Rigid footing and load is uniformly distributed
c: For Friction Pile — Where load is assumed to spread out from a depth L/3 measured from tip of pile

Uplift

When the piles are required to resist uplift force in excess of the dead load of the structure, take the following steps:

1. Anchor the piles into the cap sufficiently and tie the cap with columns.
2. Reinforce the concrete piles with longitudinal steel for the full net uplift.
3. The uplift capacity of piles in soft clay must be determined by pull test.

The total uplift resistance of a pile group is the smaller of the following two values:

1. Uplift resistance of single piles x number of piles in the group.
2. Uplift resistance of the entire group, which is composed of three parts:
   a: The weight of the pile cap plus the weight of the soil above it.
   b: The weight of the block of soil
   c: The frictional resistance along the perimeter of the block sp(L D)

EXAMPLE 1-14

Given:- This practical problem of piling was used in metallizing facilities of raw ore handling in the mid-west. We had to design a stock piling platform for material of unit weight of 0.150 k/c ft. and of the X-section shown below. Also this area was situated in Zone 2 of earthquake region. Loader's wheels are placed 8' apart and carry 31 k load.

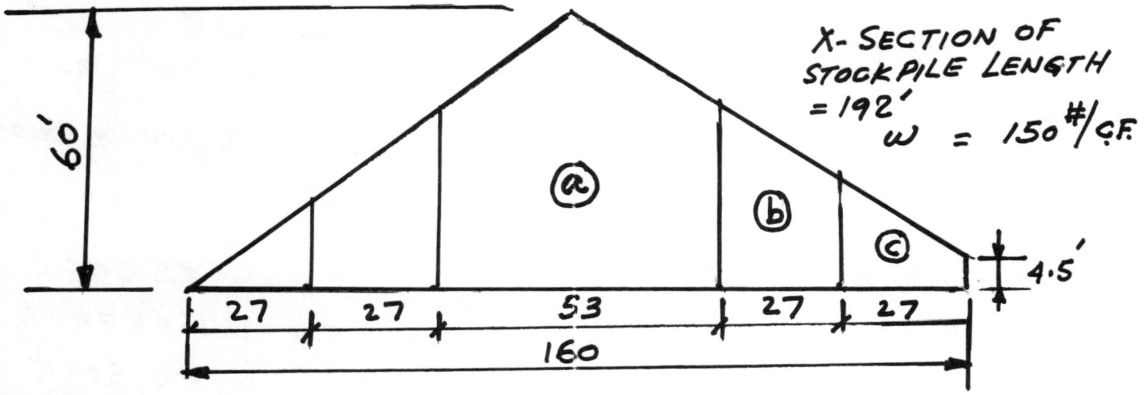

Solution:-

Assume the slab is 2' thick

Safe load/pile = 140k or 70 tons (cast in place conc.)

Load in area (a) Av. Height is 51'

= $52 \times 192 \times 51 \times 0.150 + 52 \times 192 \times 2 \times 0.150$
= $79{,}390^K$

No of Piles = 79390/140 = 567

Load in Area (b) Av. Height = 34′+2′(Slab) = 36′

= $2(27 \times 192 \times 36 \times 0.150) + 2(27 \times 108 \times 36 \times 0.150)$
= 87480^K

No of Piles = 87480/140 = 625

spacing of Piles in area (a)

$$S_a^2 = \frac{140}{0.150 \times 53} = 17.6$$

S_a = 4.28′ ∴ use spacing 4′-6″

∴ No of Piles in 52′ side = 12
No of rows of Piles in 192′ side = 43

Total No of Piles in area (a) = 12×43 = 516

Again ~~spacing of Piles~~ in area (b)

$$S_b^2 = \frac{140}{0.15 \times 36} = 2.5, \quad S_b = 5.08''$$

Use spacing = 5′-6″

∴ No of Piles in area (b) = 5×47×2 = 470
5×20×2 = 200

Total No of Piles in area (b) = 670

Again spacing of Piles in area (c)

$$S_c^2 = \frac{140}{0.150 \times 17} = 56$$

S_c = 7.45 use spacing 8′-0″

∴ No of Piles in area (c) 4×27×2 = 216
4×8×2 = 64
280

THUS Total Piles of 70 TON = 1466

STRESSES in Pile due to Earthquake Zone 2.

Assumptions:- Load being granular and not a cohesive one
Horizontal force due to Earthquake Zone 2
= 10% superstructure load

Superstructure load

Weight of slab = 300×160×2.12×0.150 = 15300K

Weight of stockpile = $\frac{160 \times 60}{2} \times 230 \times 0.150$ = 165000K

Total = 180,300K

Horizontal force = $180300 \div \frac{1}{10}$ = 18030K

Lever arm = 20′

$M = 18030 \times 20 = 360\,600\ '^{k}$

M due to Earthquake $= 0.075 \times 360{,}600 = 27000\ '^{k}$

M on one pile $= \dfrac{27000}{1466} = 18.42\ '^{k}$

Section modulus of Pile

$$S = 0.098175\ \frac{d^4 - d_1^4}{4d}$$

$$= 0.098175\ \frac{10 - d_1^4}{10}$$

Since pile is $\frac{1}{4}$" thick, $d_1 = 9.5$

$$\therefore\ S = 0.098175\ \frac{10^4 - 9.5^4}{10} = 18.6\ in^3$$

$$\therefore \text{ stress in pile} = \frac{18.42 \times 12}{18.6} = 11.88\ ksi$$

Pile supported mat foundation
Assumption:

a: Horizontal load to exceed 10% vertical capacity.
b: May increase pile load 1/3 for loads of short duration.
c: Reduce effective pile load by 8 tons due to the down drag.

Pile 4.5' on center bothway

10"ϕ pile of max. load 70^T or 140^k, $f'_c = 3000\ psi$, $f_s = 20000\ psi$

$W_1 = 0.150 \times 53 \times 4.5 \times 4.5 = 162^k$

$w' = 162/(4.5)^2 = 7.94\ ^k/ft^2$

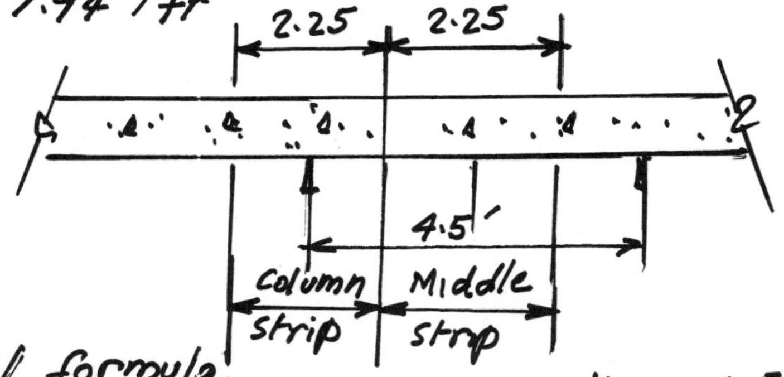

Design by empirical formula

Sum of +ve and -ve moments where $W = 162^k$, $L = 4.5\,ft$

$M_0 = 0.09\ WLF\left(1 - \dfrac{2c}{3L}\right)^2$

c = 10" for col w/o capital & = d of pile = 10"

$F = 1.15 - \dfrac{c}{L} = 1.15 - \dfrac{0.83}{4.5} = 0.97$ use 1

$M_0 = 0.09 \times 1.62 \times 4.5 \times 1\left(1 - \dfrac{2 \times .83}{3 \times 4.5}\right)^2 = 52\ '^{k}$

$t_1 = 0.028\,L\left(1 - \dfrac{2c}{3L}\right)\sqrt{\dfrac{w'}{f'_c/2000}} + 1.5 = 1.75 < 4"$ ok

Use t = 24"

For interior panel w/o drop panel

Col. strip $= +M = M_c = 0.22\,M_o = 11'^K$

$-M = -M_c = 0.46\,M_o = 23'^K$

Mid strip $\pm M = 0.16\,M_o = 8'^K$

To check shear requirement, $v = \dfrac{V}{b_o d}$

Thus $d = \dfrac{V}{v\,b_o} = \dfrac{140000}{2\sqrt{f_c'} \times \pi(10+d)} = \dfrac{140000}{110 \times 31\pi} = 13''$

t by checking punching shear

$Area = \pi r l - \pi 5^2 \times 1.4 = \pi\left[(t+5)(1.4t+7) - 35\right]$

$= \pi\,(1.4t^2 + 14t)$ $\quad r = t+5''$

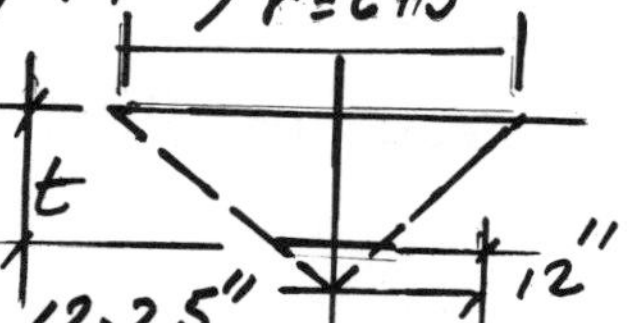

$\therefore \pi(1.4t^2 + 14t) \times 110 = 140000$

$t = 12.7 \quad \therefore d = 12.7 + 12 = 24.7 > 24$

$\therefore$ use $d = 28''$, $d_{eff} = 16 - (3 + 0.75) = 12.25''$

$\therefore$ As for $+M_c = \dfrac{11 \times 12}{20 \times 0.9 \times 12.25} = 0.6\,\square''$, #6@8"

$-M_c = \dfrac{23 \times 12}{20 \times 0.9 \times 12.25} = 1.28\,\square''$, #7@5½"

$+M_m = \dfrac{8 \times 12}{20 \times .9 \times 12.25} = 0.44\,\square''$, #5@8"

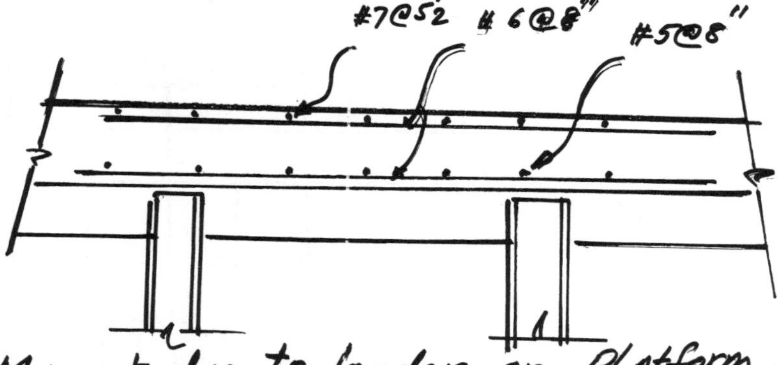

Check Max. Moment due to loader on platform.

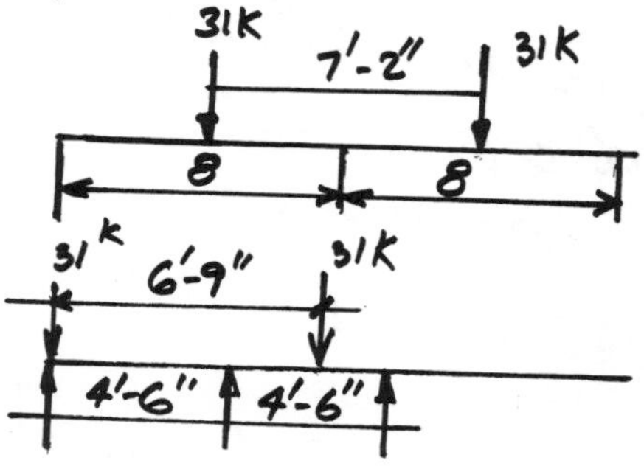

I

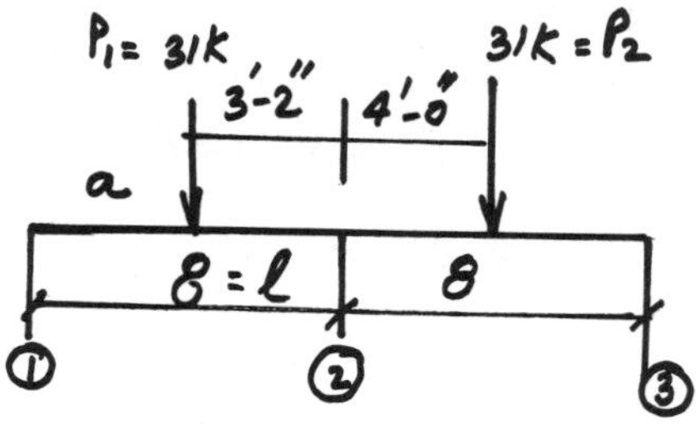

II

$$-M = \frac{P_1 ab}{4l^2}(l+a) + \tfrac{3}{32}P_2 l$$

$$= \frac{31\times4.83\times3.17}{4\times8^2}(8+4.83) + \frac{3}{32}\times31\times8 = 46.6'^{K}$$

$$+M_{2-3} = \frac{13}{64}Pl = \frac{13}{64}\times31\times8 = 50.4'^{K}$$

$$-M_{1-2} = \frac{Pab}{4l^3}\left(4l^2 - a(l+a)\right)$$

$$= \frac{31\times4.83\times3.17}{4\times8^3}\left(4\times8^2 - 4.83\,(8+4.83)\right) = 49'^{K}$$

$-M$ for 2' col. strip $= \frac{46.6}{8}\times2 = 11.6'^{K}$

$+M$ for 2' col. strip $= \frac{50.4}{8}\times2 = 12.6'^{K}$

Load Dist. factor $= \frac{8^3}{8^3+8^3} = 0.5$

Load for ea. direction $= \frac{31}{2} = 15.5^{K}$

Distribution E $= 4 + 0.06\times8 = 4.48'$ For wheel load

$-M = \frac{0.088\times2\times15.5\times8}{4.48} = 4.9^{K}\,FT/FT = 9.8^{K}/FT^2$

$+M = \frac{0.173\times15.5\times4.5}{4.48} = 2.69^{Kf}/FT = 5.38^{K}/FT^2$

∴ Design of slab ok for ore pile not as critical as for wheel load.

Design of retaining wall 4'-6" HIGH for 5'-0" tire of loader at the end of base slab of Iron oxide ore pile. $\angle\beta$ of ore pile = 35°

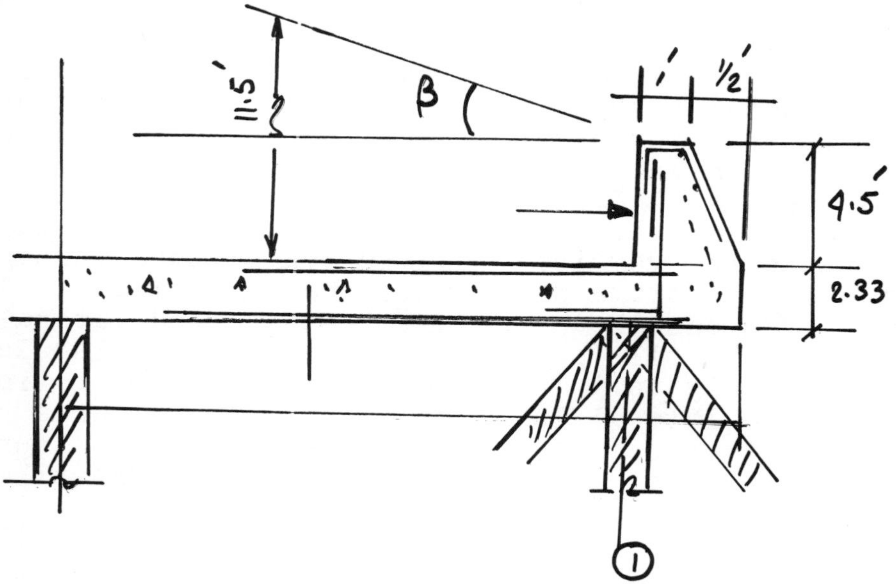

$$\text{Load/ft} = \begin{array}{l} 1 \times 4.5 \\ 0.5 \times 4.5 \times 0.5 \end{array} \quad \begin{array}{l} = 4.5 \\ = 1.12 \\ \hline 5.62 \times 0.15 = 0.84^{k}/_{1} \end{array}$$

$$\bar{X} = \frac{4.5 \times .5 + 1.12 \times 1.17}{5.62} = 0.634'$$

$$\cos\beta = \cos\phi = \cos 35 = 0.819$$

$$P_a \text{ by Rankin's formula} = \frac{1}{2} r h^2 \left(\cos\beta \, \frac{\cos\beta - \sqrt{\cos^2\beta - \cos^2\phi}}{\cos\beta + \sqrt{\cos^2\beta - \cos^2\phi}} \right)$$

$$= \frac{1}{2} r h^2 \cos\beta$$

$$= \frac{1}{2} \times 150 \times (13.83)^2 \times 0.819 = 11.75^{k}/_{1}$$

$$V_{Pressure} = 8 \times 8 \times 0.15 = 9.6^{k}/_{1}$$

$$R_{@ \text{Pile } ①} = \frac{1}{8} \left[(9.6 \times 4) + (11.75 \times 3.83) + (0.84 \times 8.63) + (3.32 \times 4.7) \right]$$

$$\text{where slab weight} = 9.5 \times 2.33 \times 0.15 = 3.32^{k}/ft$$

$$= 13.3^{k}$$

Design of stem

$$M = 11.75 \times 1.5 = 17.63'^{k} \;\&\; M_U = 17.63 \times 1.7 = 29.97'^{k}$$

THEN Being ρ min.
use $As = \#7 @ 9''$

LATERAL LOAD ON PILES

All structures are inevitably subjected to a certain amount of horizontal force due to the wind, earth pressure. The amount of lateral force carried by each pile depends upon the structural framing which brings the lateral force down to the bottom of the columns. It is unsafe to assume that the frictional resistance exists between the bottom of the pile cap and the soil because the vertical load is transmitted through the piles to the lower strata and not to the soil immediately below the pile cap. Unless the structure is supported laterally by other means, the pile should be designed to resist lateral load. It is commonly felt that the basement floor or tie beams to distribute the lateral load (horizontal) to a large number of piles. The allowable lateral load on a given pile foundation depends on the type of pile, soil embedment of the pile head, nature of the lateral load and the amount of lateral movement acceptable, which is 1/4" for building and 1/2" for miscellaneous structure.

General Solution:- To find the moments and displacement of laterally load plumb piles based on the Winkler's method of beam on elastic foundation which is given by Malock and Reese who assumed a linear relation $E_s = kx$

Procedure:- 1, Assume a value of k, the constant of soil modulus in P.S.I

2, Compute $T = \left(\frac{EI}{k}\right)^{1/5}$ where T = stiffness factor of soil, E = modulus of elasticity, I = Moment of Inertia of Pile section.

3, compute $Z_{max} = \frac{L}{T}$ where L = length of Pile

4, for value of x, determine A_y, B_y, A_m, B_m.

5, Calculate deflection $Y = A_y\left[\frac{P_t T^3}{EI}\right] + B_y\left[\frac{M_t T^2}{EI}\right]$

6, Calculate moments $M = A_m\left[P_t T\right] + B_m\left[M_t\right]$.

EXAMPLE 1-15

Given:- Find the resistance to lateral load about the major axis of 10 BP42, A36 Steel, 50 ft. long embedded full length in uniform medium sand N 20. The head of the pile is restrained by a rigid cap. Allowable lateral displacement 1/4".

Solution:-

Limitation of deflection

1, $E_s = 35$ Psi/inch $= 30\times10^6$/cu.ft

2, Allowable δ ie $Y = 1/4"$ & $x = 0$

3, $Y = A_y\left[\frac{P_t T^3}{EI}\right]$

$T = \left[\frac{EI}{k}\right]^{1/5} = \left[\frac{30\times10^6\times210.8}{35}\right]^{1/5} = 44.8"$

To find A_y, $Z_{max} = \frac{L}{T} = \frac{720}{44.8} = 16.1$

$x = 0$, $\therefore \frac{x}{T} = 0$

From Fig for $\frac{x}{T} = 0$, $Z_{max} = 16.1$

$A_y = 2.3$

4, $0.25 = 2.3\left[\frac{P_t\times44.8^3}{30\times10^6\times210.8}\right]$

$\therefore P_t = 7600$ lbs

Limitation of moments

1, $M = \left[A_m P_t T\right]$

2, $M_{cap} = f_{all}\times S$

3. $f_{all} = 15000$#/□"

4, $M_{cap} = 15000\times43.4 = 65000$ in lbs

5, $T = 44.8"$ & $Z_{max} = 16.1$

6, $A_m = 0.75$ @ $Z = 1.3T = 1.3\times44.8 = 58$#

7, $P_t = \frac{M}{A_m T} = \frac{65000}{0.75\times58} = 14940$ lbs

ESTABLISHING AND/OR PROVING LOAD CARRYING CAPACITY

A. The Dynamic Formula and Curves

1. Fundamental principles and statement of the basic dynamic formula. (See fig. no. 1-16)

a. The physics of the problem is based upon Newton's Second Law; i.e., if an unbalanced force acts upon a body, the body will accelerate and the acceleration will be directly proportional to the force and in the same direction of the force. In addition the concept of impulse; i.e a force acting through a time interval, momentum; i.e., the mass and the velocity of a body, and the conversation of momentum; i.e., the total momentum of colliding bodies as unaltered by the collision, all form the basis for the derivation and application of the dynamic pile driving formula. Also included is the consideration as to whether the system is perfectly elastic or inelastic; i.e., the coefficient of restitution equals one for the perfectly elastic condition or for the perfectly inelastic condition the coefficient of restitution equals zero. Assuming no losses in the system, if it were perfectly elastic the ram would rebound to the height from which it fell. If it were perfectly inelastic the ram would move with the pile.

b. The application of these laws begin with the definition of the momentum of the falling ram; i.e., the weight of the ram times its velocity divided by the acceleration due to gravity. Considering losses due to compression of the ram, pile cap and pile, restitution, movement of the pile, the momentum of the ram at the end of the period of restitution is equal to the initial momentum minus the impulse force of compression and the impulse force of restitution. As a result, the momentum of the pile, assuming that the pile is able to move, is equal to the impulse force of compression plus the impulse force of restitution. With this basic understanding of what is taking place, based upon the principles of physics, the load carrying capacity of the pile may be derived. This derivation of the load carrying capacity is given by the following formula:

$$R_U = \frac{ef\, W_r h}{s + \frac{1}{2}(C_1 + C_2 + C_3)} \times \frac{W_r + e^2 W_p}{W_r + W_p}$$ -- for drop hammers & single acting hammer

$$R_U = \frac{12\, ef\, E_n}{s + \frac{1}{2}(C_1 + C_2 + C_3)} \times \frac{W_r + e^2 W_p}{W_r + W_p}$$ — for double & differential acting hammer

The former equation expresses the general condition that exists when the ram (Wr) falls a height (h) and strikes the pile (Wp). There is a temporary compression of the pile head and cap (C_1), the pile (C_2), and the ground (C_3). The ram (Wr) rebounds in the semi-elastic collision (e) and the pile (Wp) moves the set distance (s) plus one-half the sum of (C_1) plus (C_2) plus (C_3). The driving force has a mechanical efficiency of (ef). As a result of this collision the pile (Wp) indicated a certain resistance of ultimate carrying capacity. (Ru).

2. Review of Basic Soil Types

a. Cohesive Soils - silts and clays: Consideration for the pile foundation design must be bearing capacity and settlement.

b. Cohesionless Soils - gravels, sands and silts: Consideration for pile foundation design must be bearing capacity.

c. The differing consideration is settlement or consolidation of the subsurface soils below the tip based upon the principle of pore pressure; i.e., the rate of the dissipation of water from within the voids formed by the soil grains.

3. General conditions where the dynamic formula does not apply would be foundations consisting of fine-grained soils; i.e., silts and clays.

a. Governing Conditions:

1. The physical characteristics of the soil below the pile tips over a large area must be known in order to determine the amount of settlement which will result from the induced stress of the pile group.

2. The reduced value of friction that must be used when the pile is used in a group.

3. The soil structure and hydrostatic conditions induced temporarily while driving.

4. Other short or long term adjustments in bearing value such as adhesion and ground water conditions.

b. Laboratory undisturbed tests aid in evaluating these limitations. Shear tests such as triaxial compression tests are used for determining the shear strength and bearing capacity and consolidation tests which determine the physical characteristics of the underlying compressible strata enable the designer to estimate the total settlement and the time in which this settlement will occur.

4. General condition where formula does apply would be foundations consisting of granular soils; i.e., silts, sands and gravels.

a. These soil types dissipate pore pressures readily; i.e., the water is able to escape from the voids in the soil structure and consolidation is considered instantaneous.

b. Exceptions which have to be considered for these cohesionless soils are:

1. Cases where coarse grained granular soil's capacity decreases due to internal readjustment.

2. Cases where uniform sands under the water table go "quick" during driving but firm up after excess pore pressures are allowed to dissipate.

c. Criteria for evaluating these exceptions would be to resume driving 24 hours later and determine the change in driving resistance.

5. Use of the Dynamic Formula: From the basic dynamic formula, final sets are plotted against ultimate driving resistances or against working loads at any selected factor of safety. These curves (see fig. no.   ) can be plotted readily by

assuming several different driving resistances and solving for the corresponding values of the set. These curves show graphically the resistance to be expected for the entire range of values of the set and are especially interesting as they show what may be expected as driving becomes harder and approaches the penetration for the design capacity.

6. Modifications of the Dynamic Formula

a. The basic changes in the dynamic formula involve assumptions as to what values are to be used for the efficiency of the system, whether the system is perfectly elastic or inelastic, or more realistically somewhere between the two extremes, and impact losses.

b. The number of modifications of the basic dynamic formula are as numerous as the variable conditions for which the formula is to be used. A leading text on the subject numbers twenty-one. To name a few would be the Hiley Formula, the Pacific Coast Uniform Building Code Formula, the Navy McKay Formula, the Èngineering News Formula, the United States Steel Formula, the Bureau of Yards and Docks Formula and the Goodrich Formula.

c. Probably the best known variation of the basic dynamic formula is the Engineering News Formula. In this modification the impact loss is entirely neglected, the mechanical efficiency of the system is taken as 100% and the elastic loss of the cap pile and soil are represented by constant term equal to unity. The height of fall (HO is taken in feet and multiplied by 12 and the factor of safety of 6 is assumed.

$$R_a = \frac{2 W_r H}{S + 1.0}$$

This formula was again modified by single acting, double acting and differential steam hammers. For single acting hammers

$$R_a = \frac{2 W_r H}{S + 0.1}$$

and for double acting hammers

$$R_a = \frac{2 E_n}{S + 0.1}$$

This second example; i.e., the Pacific Coast Uniform Building Code Formula is of specific interest in that Section V cities this formula as being in reasonable agreement with the test failure load for displacement piles. This formula assumes the mechanical efficiency to be 100% and considers the elastic losses to be equal to twice the average elastic loss taking into account the full length of the pile. Fixed values of the coefficient of restitution are also assumed. As a result the following formula is arrived at and it is suggested that a safety factor of 4 be applied to obtain a safe working load.

$$R_U = \frac{12 W_r H \dfrac{W_r + K W_p}{W_r + W_p}}{S + \dfrac{24000 R_U L}{AE}}$$

The addition of the factor (K) is a constant equal to 0.25

for steel piles and 0.10 for other types of piles. All weights are measured in tons.

B. The Empirical Formula

1. Derivation: These formulas are derived from model tests, experience and specific local foundation conditions.

2. Number of Empirical Formulas: A leading authority in the field cites seven or more different empirical formulas for the many different foundation conditions, among them the Wilcoxen Formula, the Simplex Formula and the Trautwine Formula.

3. Example of the Empirical Formula: The Wilcoxen Formula is based on model tests with a factor of safety of 6. The working load (R) is determined by the weight of the ram (Wr) times its fall (H) divided by the set value (S) with an exponent (N) ranging from 0.6 to 1.0 as the foundation soils become stiffer or denser.

$$R_a = \frac{W_r H}{S^N}$$

C. The Static Formula

1. Derivation: The static formula is nothing more than an equation whereby the ultimate capacity is equal to the resistance (R) that can be developed in skin friction and end bearing (R). Many of the leading texts give average adhesion values for cohesive soils, average friction values for cohesionless soils and indicate what modifications are necessary for an approximation of the load carrying capacity of the pile.

$$R_U = f_U A_S + R_t$$

2. Number of Static Formulas: Taking the theoretical concepts of the science of Soil Mechanics such as lateral earth pressure and bearing capacity in both cohesive and cohesionless soils, the simplified equations stated above can be elaborated into an equation of many terms containing the many variations considered to have a substantial effect upon the end result. Without too much trouble, five to ten static formulas may be easily located.

3. Example of Static Formula: The Howe Formula includes such terms as the cross-sectional area of the pile (A), the length of the pile times the square root of 2 (L1), the unit weight of the soil (w), the strength parameter for cohesionless soils; i.e., the angle of internal friction (ϕ) and an adhesion value (f). These terms are combined to give the ultimate capacity in the following form:

$$R_U = \frac{A L_1 w}{144}\left(\frac{1+\sin\phi}{1-\sin\phi}\right)^2 + 4 L_1 f \sqrt{\frac{A}{144}}$$

D. Pile Load Tests

1. Principle of the Pile Load Test: The principle of the pile load test is rather simple in that selected piles in a proposed foundation design are tested by applying either vertical or lateral loads in such a manner so as to simulate as much as possible the design conditions. The total test load is generally taken two to three times the design working load.

The use of the pile load test is expensive, approximately $2000 per test, and normally only on major projects is it economically feasible to check the design arrived at through the science of Soil Mechanics. However, on these major projects it is found that by verifying the design capacity indicated by the dynamic formula, many times a substantial savings can be made when the results of the pile load test indicate that the pile was over-driven. On minor projects the above-mentioned dynamic formula is the chief tool for evaluating the design.

2. Limitations of the Pile Load Test: The pile load test is governed primarily by the principles of economics since pile load test procedures usually require a minimum of 24 hours with personnel available throughout the test. As a function of time, the tests are most satisfactory in cohesionless soils where the pore pressures can be readily dissipated.

DERIVATION OF DYNAMIC PILE DRIVING FORMULA

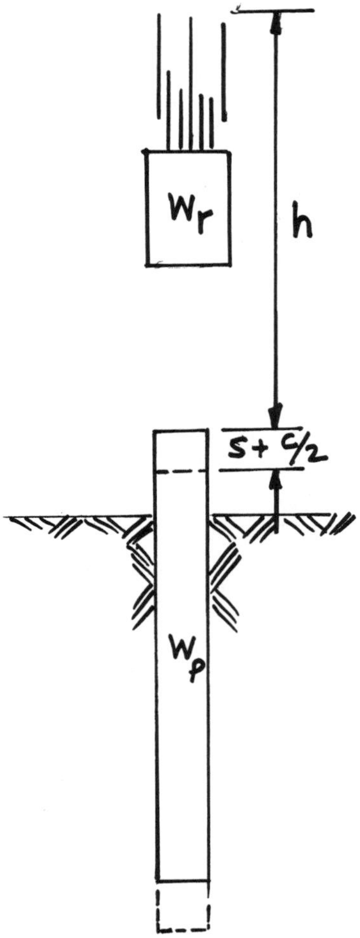

PHYSICS

Newton's second law

$$F = ma$$

$$\text{Impulse} = \int_{t_2}^{t_2} F\,dt$$

$$\text{Momentum} = mV$$

Conservation of momentum

Impulse A = − Impulse B

$$\text{or } m_A V_{A2} - m_A V_{A1} = -(m_B V_{B2} - m_B V_{B1})$$

$$= m_A V_{A1} + m_B V_B = m_A V_{A2} + m_B V_{B2}$$

APPLICATION

$$\text{momentum of Ram} = \frac{W_r V}{g}$$

momentum of Ram at end of period of restitution is

$$\frac{W_r V_r}{g} = \frac{W_r V}{g} - I_c - eI$$

and the momentum of the piles

$$\frac{W_p V_p}{g} = I_c + eI.$$

From this is derived

$$R_U = \frac{e_f W_w h}{s + \frac{1}{2}(C_1 + C_2 + C_3)} \times \frac{W_w + e^2 W_p}{W_w + W_p}$$

For drop hammer and single acting hammer.

CONDUIT UNDERGROUND DESIGN

The design of Pipe (Conduit Underground) requires consideration of its structural capacity to carry the load to which it will be subjected in service. Structural design consists of two major phases: 1. determination of loads on the structure and 2. determination of supporting strength or the ability to carry the load with an adequate and realistic factor of safety. Loads on conduit consist of 1. earth load including lateral earth pressure, plus, 2. the effect of surface - traffic loads both static and dynamic.

EXAMPLE 1-16

Given:- A 10" Reinforced Concrete Pipe having a 6" sidewalk is to be installed as a projecting conduit in a class A bedding on a foundation of ordinary soil and covered with an embankment of 7.83'. The unit weight of the soil cover is 130 pcf. Determine the required strength of the pipe which will not develop a crack wider than 0.1 inch. Assume impact factor for the truck loading as 1.5.

Solution:-

For 10" conduit of Low. Grade

Minimum height of 7.83'

Assume $\gamma_{sd} = 0.4$

$p = 0.7$

$\gamma_{sdp} = 0.28$

$H = 7.83 + \frac{1.08}{4} - 1.08$

$= 7.02'$

$B_c = 1.08'$

w = unit weight of soil backfill = 130 pcf

$\frac{H}{B_c} = \frac{7.02}{1.08} = 6.5$

C_c = Load coeff 10.00 for clay

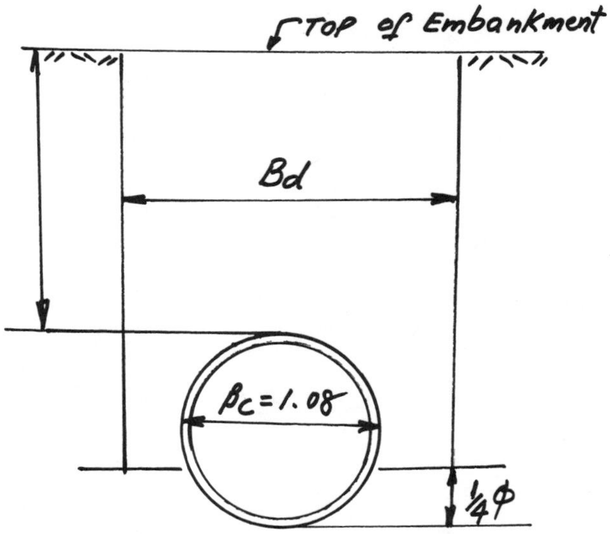

Morston's formula

$W_c = C_c w B_c^2 = 10.0 \times 130 \times 1.08^2 = 1516 \#/\text{ft}$

where W_c = Total load on horizontal plane through the top of the conduit between side of ditch.

Surface loads

$W_T = \frac{1}{A} I_c C_T P$

where W_T = Average load on conduit due to truck wheel load.

A = effective length :- length of pipe over which the average live load produces the same effect on stress or deflection as does the actual load which is of varying intensity along the pipe usually $A = 3$

I_c = Impact factor for truck loading $= 1.5$

C_T = Load coefficient - represent the fractional part of the wheel load P which is applied directly above the center of area, the load transmitted to the section is maximum. The value is 4 times influence coefficient from table 4 (Gaylord & Gaylord) Pg 25-14 for one quadrant for the area $X = \frac{B_c}{2} = \frac{1.08}{2} = 0.54'$

$$Y = A/2 = 3/2 = 1.5'$$

$$m = \frac{X}{H} = \frac{0.54}{7.02} = 0.077 \text{ Say } 0.1$$

$$n = \frac{Y}{H} = \frac{1.5}{7.02} = 0.212$$

$\therefore$ Influence coefficient $= 0.00957$ by interpolation

Hence $C_T = 4 \times 0.00957 = 0.03828$

$P = 16000$ Lbs

$\therefore W_T = \frac{1}{3} \times 1.5 \times 0.03828 \times 16000 = 306 \text{ \#/Lft}$

Total load $= 1516 + 306 = 1822 \text{ \#/Lft}$

q = ratio of total lateral pressure to total vert. load

$$= \frac{mK}{C_c}\left(\frac{H}{B_c} + m/2\right)$$

where K = ratio of lateral unit pressure to vert. unit pressure. From chart Pg 127/Conc. Pipe Hand Book $= 0.37$

Assuming concrete craddle projection bedding class A

m = fractional part of vert. height of conduit over which lateral pressure acts $\approx$ projection ratio $p = 0.70$

r_{sd} = Settlement ratio $= 0.4$

$r_{sdp} = 0.7 \times 0.4 = 0.28$

$\frac{H}{B_c} = \frac{7.02}{1.08} = 6.5$

$C_c = 10$

$q = \frac{0.10 \times 0.37}{10}(6.5 + 0.05) = 0.0242$

From Page 123 Pipe Handbook

$N' = 0.505$

$x' = 0.811$

$L_f = \frac{1.431}{N' - x'q} = \frac{1.431}{0.505 - (0.811 \times 0.0242)} = 2.94$

Req'd ultimate strength in bearing

$= \frac{1822}{2.94} \times 1.5 = 930\ ^{\#}/Lft$

From table 18 for A.S.T.M spec. #C14-59 for 10"φ Pipe permissable strength in bearing = $2.8\ ^{K}/Lft$.

Use C14-59, 10"φ standard strength conc. sewer pipe.

2

ELASTIC DESIGN OF STEEL STRUCTURES

ELASTIC DESIGN

If a structure is considered to fail when the computed stress at any point within the structure reaches the yield point, then one might design the structure so that the computed stress under the working load never exceeds a certain fraction of yield point. The safety factor would be the reciprocal of this fraction. This method of design based upon the working stress and upon the elastic behavior throughout the structure up to the point of failure is called Elastic Design.

EXAMPLE 2-01

Given:- The stress-strain curve of the material (compressive) is given below for the stub column of an aluminum alloy. Use the tangent modulus concept E , solve for the critical buckling load (Euler load) P_c for the frame and the material below. Use the 8 WF and its accompanying specifications. Length LC = 13.5 ft.

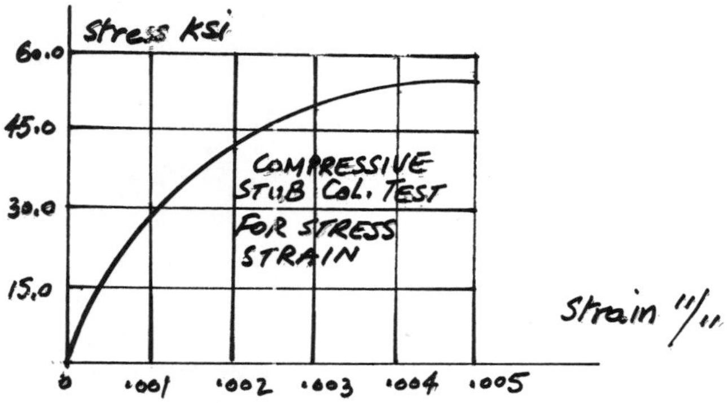

Solution:- $P_c = \dfrac{\pi^2 EI}{(0.82L)^2}$

$$\sigma_{cr} = \frac{P_c}{A} = \frac{\pi^2 EI}{(0.82L)^2 \times A} = \frac{\pi^2 EI}{\left(\frac{0.82L}{r}\right)^2}$$

using the tangent modulus concept

$$\sigma_{cr} = \frac{\pi^2 E_t}{\left(\frac{0.82L}{r}\right)^2}$$

$$\frac{\sigma_{cr}}{E_t} = \frac{\pi^2}{(0.82L/r)^2} = \frac{9.87}{\left(\frac{17625}{4.04}\right)} = 0.00226$$

using r of y-axis

From graph $\sigma_{cr} = 27.8$ ksi

$P_c = \sigma_{cr} A = 27.8 \times 9.12 = 253^k$

$E_t = 12300$

then in $P_c = \dfrac{\pi^2 EI}{(0.82L)^2}$

$45000 > E > 31000$

$908 > P_c > 626$

σ_{cr}	E_t	σ_{cr}/E_t
6.25	45,000	0.000139
11.10	33,600	0.000331
15.0	31,000	0.000480
23.0	17,275	0.001332
30.0	9,380	0.003200
31.45	7,433	0.004230
32.30	6,283	0.005140
35.0	4,925	0.007110
36.9	4,200	0.008790

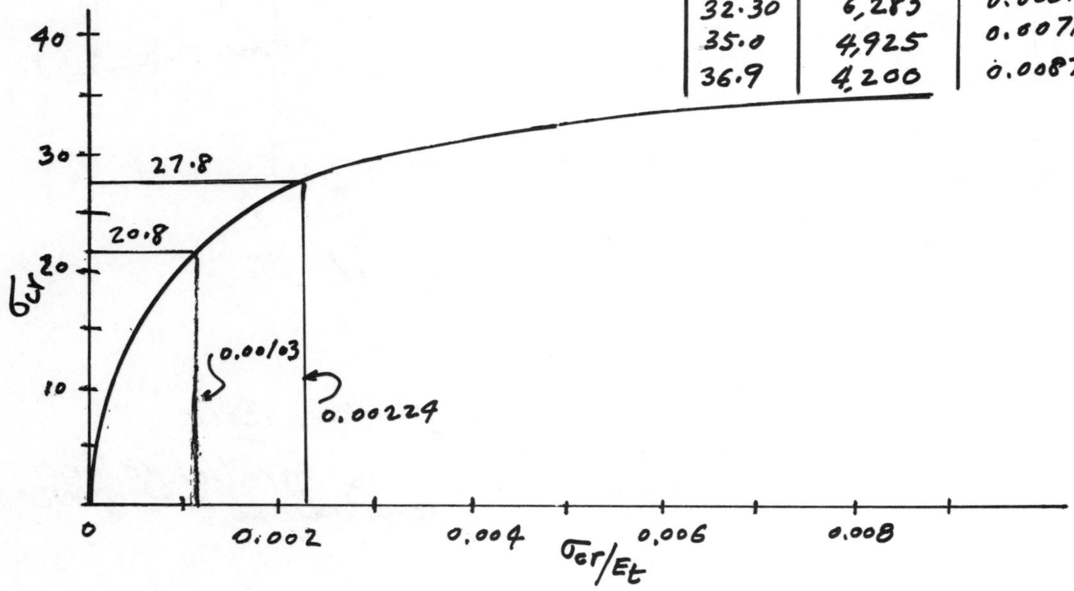

EXAMPLE 2-02

Given:- For the problem described below, compute the rigid body collapse load P . The column A is supported about its weak Y-Y axis as shown by a P beam, continuous longitudinally as shown, which is an W 8X31 with its Y-Y axis vertical. The W 8X31 beam is in turn supported vertically by rigid frames that are assumed not to deflect laterally. Note that the cross-section of member A (the column) is not defined. This fact is not necessary for the computation of the rigid body collapse load P .

Determine the rigid body collapse load.

Determine the flexural stiffness (spring constant) of the W 8X31.

Determine some acceptable cross-section for the column A (ASTM A-36) such that the Euler buckling load of the column is at least 1.3 times the rigid body collapse load.

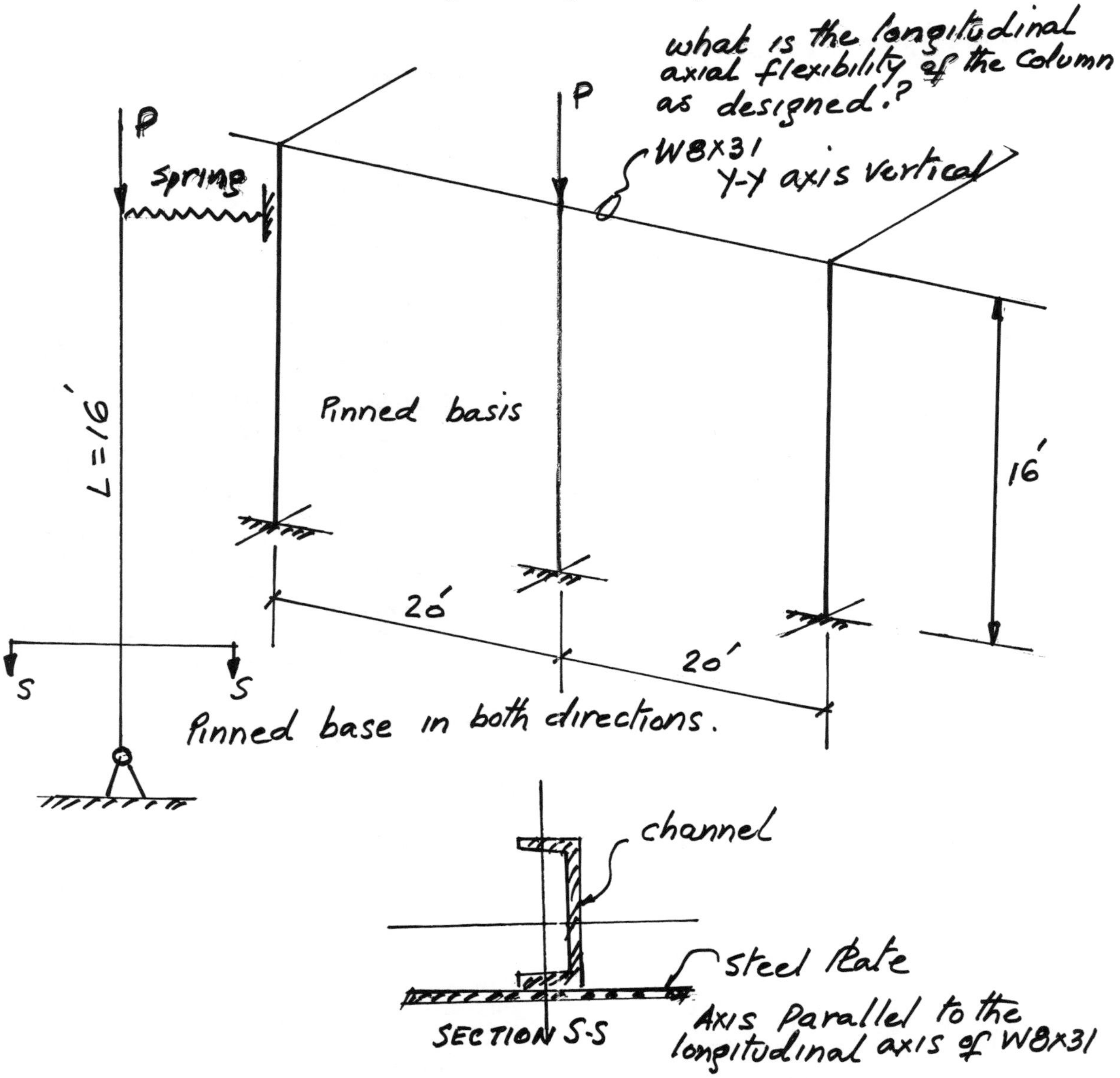

Solution:-

Ist choice

Both ends pinned W8X31

$\Delta = \frac{PL^3}{48EI}$

$K = \frac{F}{x} = \frac{P}{PL^3} 48EI_{xy}$

$= \frac{48EI_{xy}}{L^3}$

$= \frac{48 \times 29000 \times 37}{(40 \times 12)^3}$

$= 0.465$ K/" — flexural stiffness of Beam.

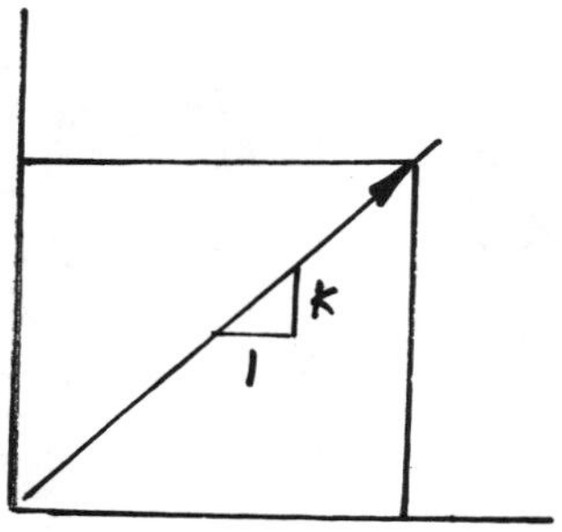

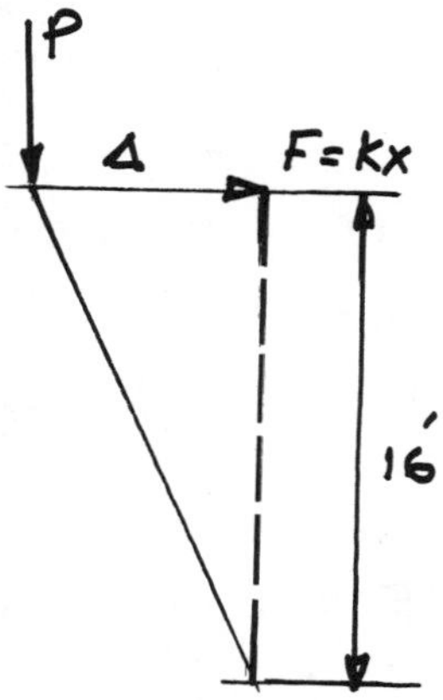

Taking moment

$F \times L = P_R x$

$(Kx) L = P_R x$

$KL = P_R$

$P_R = 0.465 \times 16 \times 12 = 89.3^k$

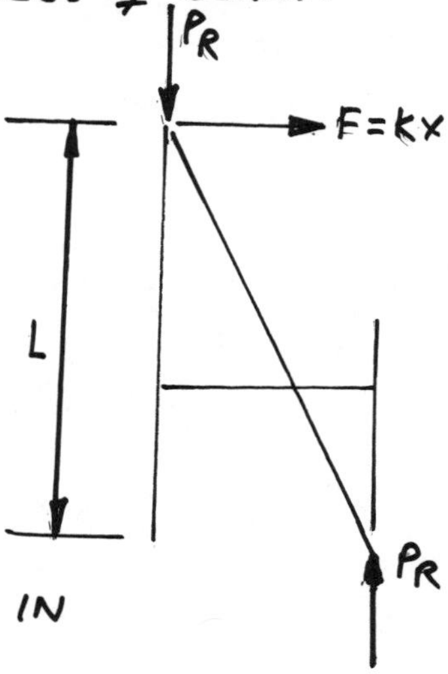

Rigid body collapse load

$P_E = 1.3\ P_R = 1.3 \times 89.3 = 116^k$

$= \frac{\pi^2 EI}{L^2}$

$I = \frac{P_E L^2}{\pi^2 E} = \frac{116 \times 16 \times 16 \times 12^2}{3.14^2 \times 29 \times 10^3} = 14.95$ IN

$\therefore I_{req'd} = 14.95\ IN^4$

TRY 6 [8.2 , $I_y = 0.70$

$\therefore I_{PL} = 14.95 - 0.70 = 14.25\ IN^4$

Use 6" PL, Solve for t $\quad I = \frac{1}{12} t b^3 = 14.25$

$= \frac{1}{12} t\, 6^3 = 14.25, \quad t = \frac{14.25 \times 12}{6 \times 6 \times 6} = 0.79$

use 7/8" thick PL.

2nd choice

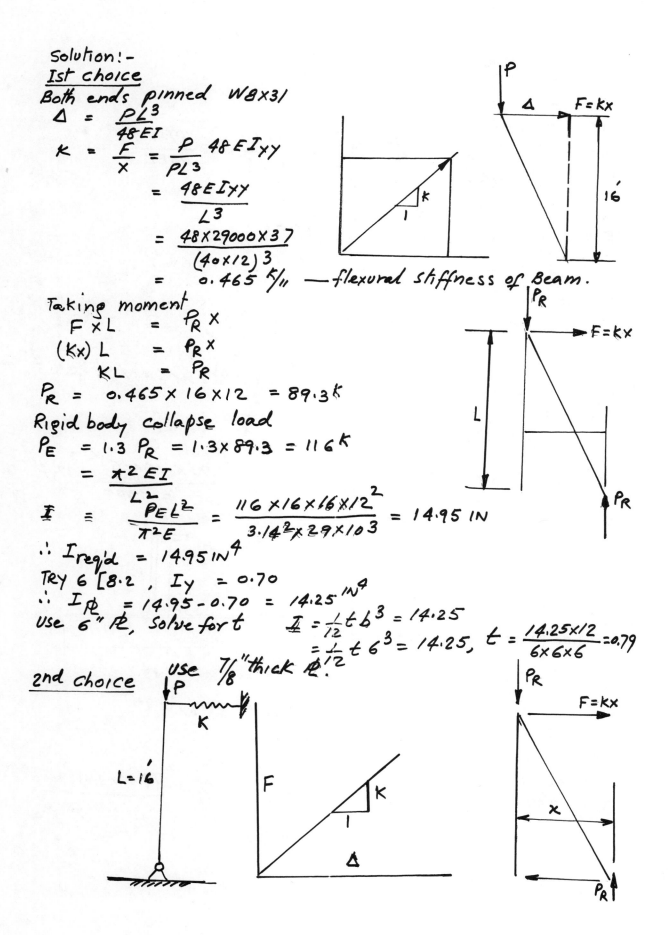

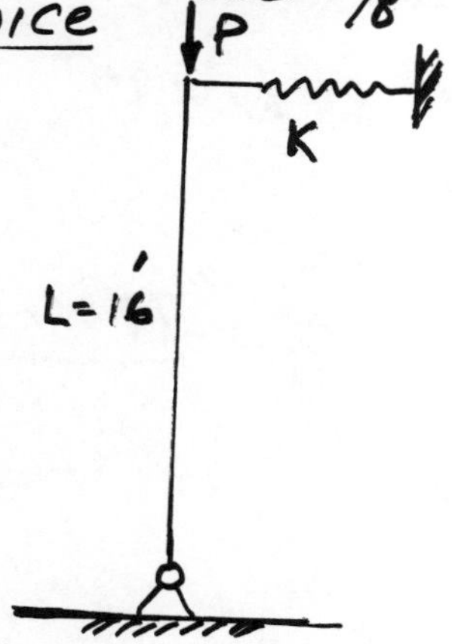

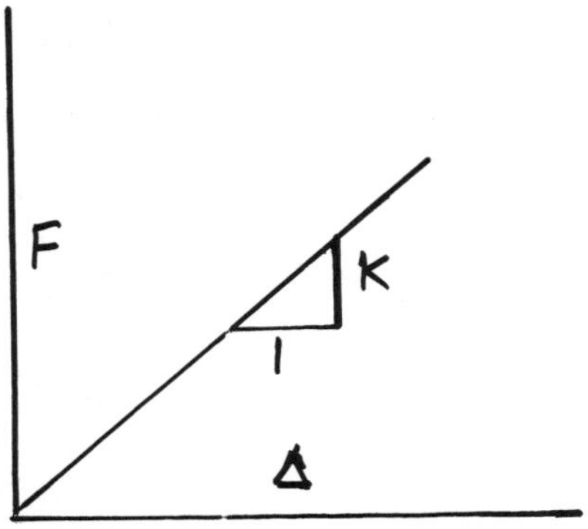

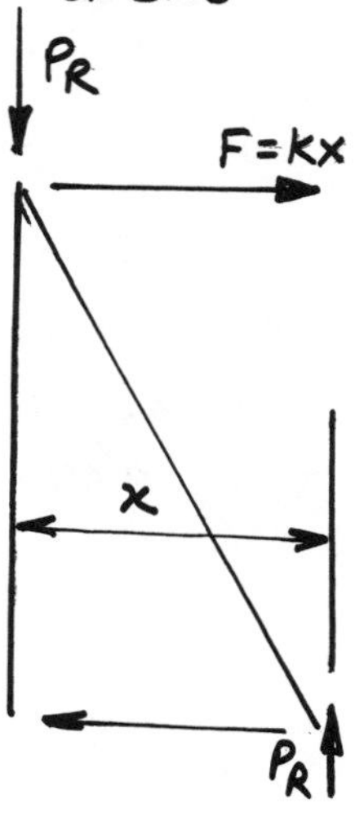

$F = Kx$

$x = F/K$

$x = \Delta$

For pin ends $\Delta = \dfrac{PL^3}{48EI}$

For pinned & fixed end $\Delta = \dfrac{7PL^3}{768EI} \simeq \dfrac{PL^3}{110EI}$

For fixed ends $\Delta = \dfrac{PL^3}{192EI}$

For this problem use $\Delta = \dfrac{PL^3}{120EI}$

$E = 29\times10^3$ ksi, $I_{YY} = 37.0\ in^4$

$K = \dfrac{F}{x} = \dfrac{120EI}{L^3} = \dfrac{120\times29\times10^3\times37}{(40\times12)^3} = 1.162\ ^k/in$

= flexural stiffness of Beam

Taking moment in free body, $FL = P_R x$

$KxL = P_R x$

$P_R = KL$

$= 1.162\times16\times12 = 223.5^k$

Rigid body collapse load

$1.3\times P_R = 290^k$

$\sigma = \dfrac{P_E}{A} = \dfrac{\pi^2E}{(\frac{KL}{r})^2}$

$\therefore P_E = \dfrac{\pi^2EI}{(KL)^2}$ & $I = \dfrac{P_E(KL)^2}{\pi^2E} = \dfrac{290\times(12\times16)^2}{\pi^2\times29000} = 37.4\ in^4$

Try 9[20.0 & PL $\frac{1}{4}\times12\times192''$

About Y-Y axis

	A	Y	AY	AY²	Io
9]20	5.86	6.00	35.16	210.96	2.4
PL	3.00	6.00	18.00	108.00	36.0
	8.86		53.16	318.96	38.4

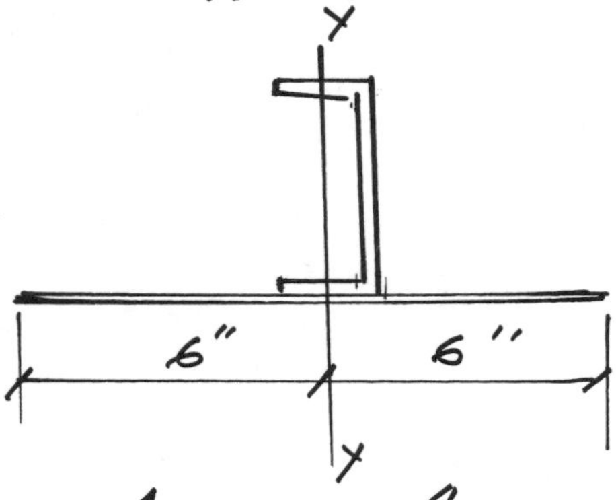

$\bar{y} = \dfrac{53.16}{8.86} = 6.0''$

$I = 38.4\ in^4 \simeq 37.4\ in^4$

$\Sigma Ay\bar{y} = 318.96$

About X-XIS, I_o 9]20 is 60.6 in^4 ok

Longitudenal flexibility

Longitudinal stiffness $= K = \dfrac{F}{x} = \dfrac{F}{\Delta} = \dfrac{AE}{L} = \dfrac{(5.86+3.0)29000}{12\times16}$

$= 1388\ ^k/in$

EXAMPLE 2-03

Given:- For the following frame, compute the correct values of K and 1/K using the Aisc allignments charts (and in Beedle). Note that AISC only allows Sidesway Uninhibited, wheras the first part of this problem is for the Sidesway Prevented. All joints are rigid except as noted. Bases are fixed and pinned as noted. EI of each particular member is constant.

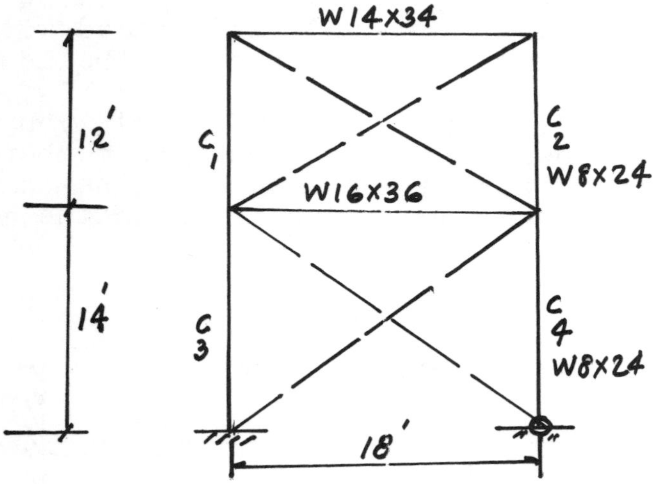

Compute: (A) Sidesway Prevented: K for C1, C3 and C4.
(B) Sidesway Permitted: K for C1, C3 and C4.
(C) Compute $1/K^2$ for (A) and (B) above.

stiffness $= M/\theta = \frac{4EI}{L}$, use relative stiffness $\frac{I}{L} = I = I_x$

Col.	I_x	L	I_x/L	Beam	I_x	L	I_x/L
W8x24 C_1	82.5	144	0.573	W14x34	339.2	216	1.570
W8x24 C_2	82.5	144	0.573	W16x36	446.3	216	2.066
C_3	82.5	168	0.491				
C_4	82.5	168	0.491				

$G = \Sigma \frac{I_c}{L_c} / \Sigma \frac{I_B}{L_B}$

$G_1 = 1.0$ (Fixed end)

$G_6 = 10.0$ (Pinned end)

$G_2 = G_5 = \frac{1.064}{1.570} = 0.515$

$G_3 = G_4 = \frac{0.573}{2.066} = 0.365$

sidesway prevented

K_{C1} for G_2 & G_3 = 0.67

K_{C3} for G_1 & G_2 = 0.73

K_{C4} for G_5 & G_6 = 0.81

sidesway Permitted

K_{C1} = 1.13

K_{C2} = 1.23

K_{C4} = 1.78

$1/K^2$	sidesway Permitted	sidesway Prevented
C_1	0.784	2.23
C_2	0.661	1.37
C_4	0.316	1.235

EXAMPLE 2-04

Given:- This is a problem in torsion wherin one is to use the approximate approach to analysis as indicated for tubes and closed sections.
Use the 7th Edition of the AISC building specifications, where the tube sections are given.
Use the allowables (in shear) given in the code and assume that the material is ASTM A-36 at F_y = 36.0 ksi.
The closed section is to be supported as shown below, torsionally and flexurally fixed at both ends and loaded with a vertical loading parallel to and at the surface of the long face of the tube.
For this section given below (all at ASTM A-36), you are to compute the maximum allowable load P which the member will support as shown. Compute moments and shears in the conventional manner and analyze torsional shear according to the method for the closed section.

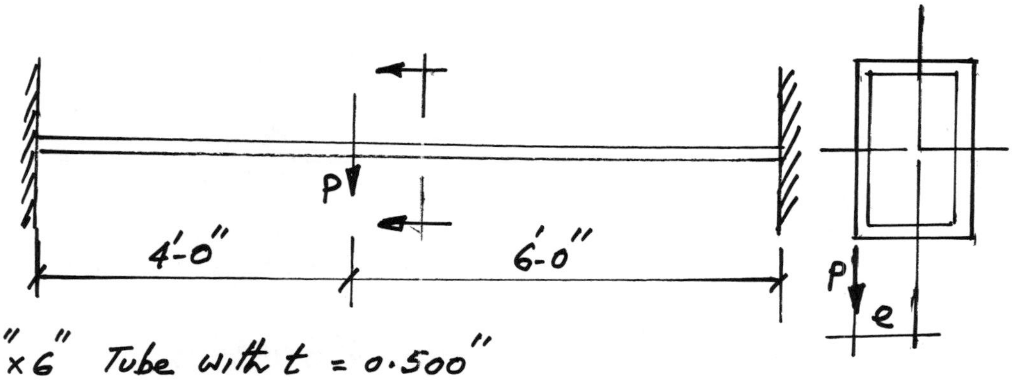

Tube 12"×6" Tube with t = 0.500"

F_v for A_{36} = 14500 P.S.I ; $M_z = P \times e$

G = 12×10^6 P.S.I

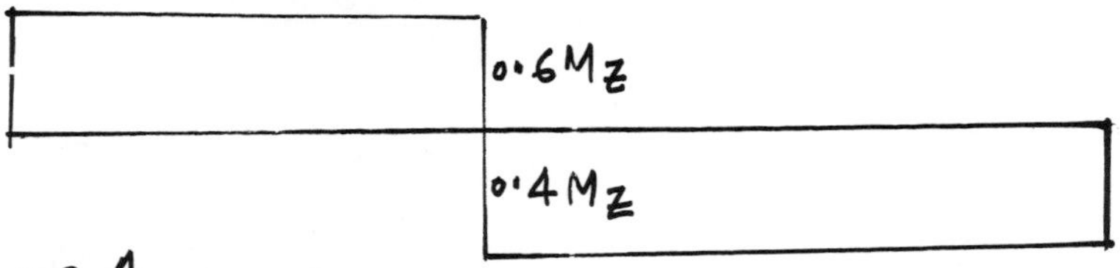

$M_z = q \times 2A$

$A = 12 \times 6 = 72 \square''$, $e = 3''$ & $q = vt$

$M_z = \frac{1}{2} \times 14.5 \times 2 \times 72 = 1044'^{\#}$

$\frac{6}{10} Pe = \frac{6}{10} \times P \times 3 = 1044$

$\therefore P = \frac{1044 \times 10}{3 \times 6} = 580^k$

EXAMPLE 2-05

Given:- This is another problem in torsion wherin one is to use an exact approach (with an assumed distribution of twist) to the analysis as indicated for the W open sections in the text, Beedle, et al.

Use all the allowables in the AISC assuming that the material is ASTM A-36, F = 36.0 ksi.

The W section is to be supported as shown below, which is the same as was used for example 2-04 with the tube, torsionally and flexurally fixed at both ends and loaded with a force parallel to the web and acting at the eccentricity given.

For the section and loading, etc given, compute the magnitudes of all the stresses at the two most severely stressed cross-sections; they are the left end and the point of loading. Compute the conventional flexural and shear stresses. Also compute the torsional stresses, shear and longitudinal, due to both resistances to the applied torque.

Section: W18X45
Loading: DL @ 45 plf
LL: P = 21.0 kips
e = 3.73 in.

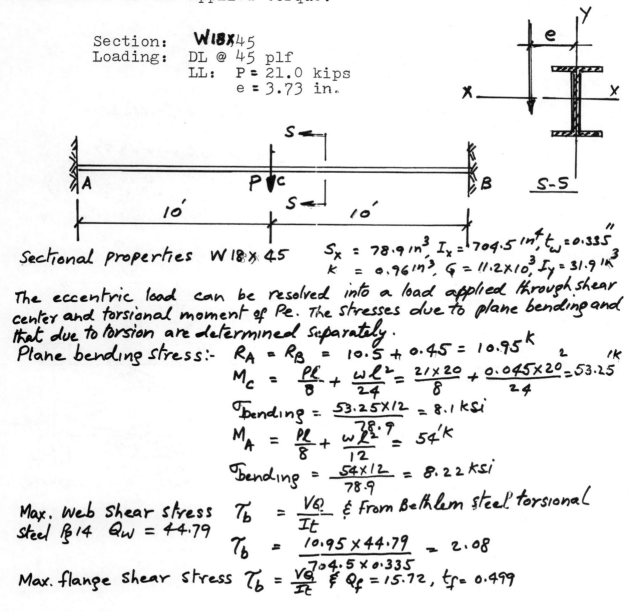

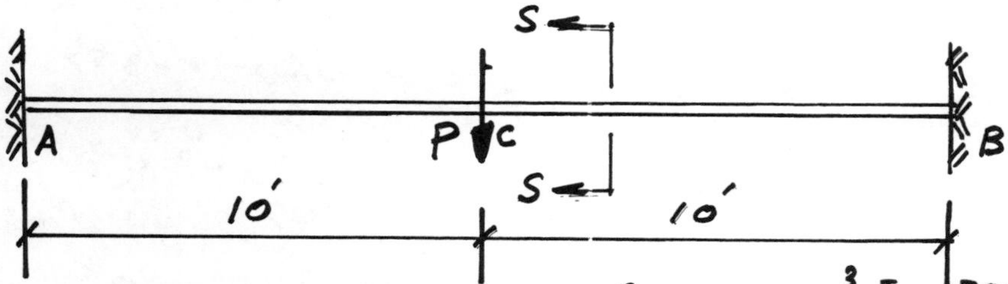

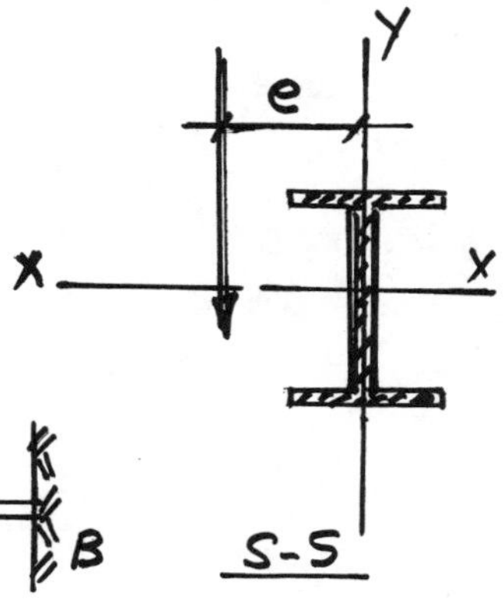

Sectional properties W18X45 $S_x = 78.9\ in^3$, $I_x = 704.5\ in^4$, $t_w = 0.335''$
$k = 0.96\ in^3$, $G = 11.2\times10^3$, $I_y = 31.9\ in^3$

The eccentric load can be resolved into a load applied through shear center and torsional moment of Pe. The stresses due to plane bending and that due to torsion are determined separately.

Plane bending stress:- $R_A = R_B = 10.5 + 0.45 = 10.95^k$

$$M_c = \frac{Pl}{8} + \frac{wl^2}{24} = \frac{21\times20}{8} + \frac{0.045\times20^2}{24} = 53.25^{1k}$$

$$\sigma_{bending} = \frac{53.25\times12}{78.9} = 8.1\ ksi$$

$$M_A = \frac{Pl}{8} + \frac{wl^2}{12} = 54^{1k}$$

$$\sigma_{bending} = \frac{54\times12}{78.9} = 8.22\ ksi$$

Max. Web shear stress $\tau_b = \frac{VQ}{It}$ & From Bethlem steel torsional steel pg 14 $Q_W = 44.79$

$$\tau_b = \frac{10.95\times44.79}{704.5\times0.335} = 2.08$$

Max. flange shear stress $\tau_b = \frac{VQ}{It}$ & $Q_f = 15.72$, $t_f = 0.499$

$$\tau_b = \frac{10.95 \times 15.79}{704.5 \times 0.499} = 0.491 \text{ ksi}$$

Torsional stresses:-

$$M_z = KG\beta_{max}\frac{\pi}{L}\cos\left(\pi\frac{z}{L}\right) + EI_y\frac{d^2}{4}\beta_{max}\cos\frac{\pi z}{L}\left(\frac{\pi}{L}\right)^3$$

At the end $z = 0$

$$\therefore M_z = 0.96 \times 11.2 \times 10^3 \beta_{max}\frac{\pi}{20 \times 12} + 29 \times 10^3 \times 31.9 \times \frac{17.36^2}{4}\beta_{max}\left(\frac{\pi}{20 \times 12}\right)^3$$

where $M_z = 21 \times 3.73/2 = 39.17''^K$

$$39.17 = 139.5\,\beta_{max} + 152.5\,\beta_{max} = 292\,\beta_{max}$$

$$\therefore \beta_{max} = \frac{39.17}{292} = 0.134 \text{ radians}$$

$$M_T^z = KG\beta_{max}\frac{\pi}{L}\cos\left(\pi\frac{z}{L}\right)$$

@ $z = 0$

$$M_T^z = 0.96 \times 11.2 \times 10^3 \times 0.132 \times \frac{\pi}{20 \times 12} = 18.6''^K$$

$$M_w^z = 39.17 - 18.6 = 20.57''^K$$

stress due to st. Venant

a) $$v_s = M_z^T t/k_t = \frac{18.6 \times 0.335}{0.96} = 6.5^K/_{''^2}$$

b) stress due to warping

From table 3,4 of A.I.S.C Journal Jan, 1966 Page 43, 44

$\omega_{max} = 32.45 \text{ in}^2$, $C_w = 2.374 \text{ in}^6$, $S_w = 73.16 \text{ in}^4$, $\lambda = 0.01237 \text{ in}^{-1}$

Let $r = \lambda l = 0.01237 \times 20 \times 12 = 2.97$

η with $z/l = \frac{120}{240} = 0.5$, proceed to curve where $r = 2.97$

η @ left $= 0.310$

M_w due to flang bending for $z = 0$, $= \frac{1}{\lambda}\eta M = \frac{1}{0.01237} \times 0.31 \times (-21 \times 3.73)$

$= -1968 \text{ K in}^2$

normal bending stress $$\sigma_s = \frac{M_w}{S_w} = \frac{-1968}{73.16} = -26.9 \text{ ksi}$$

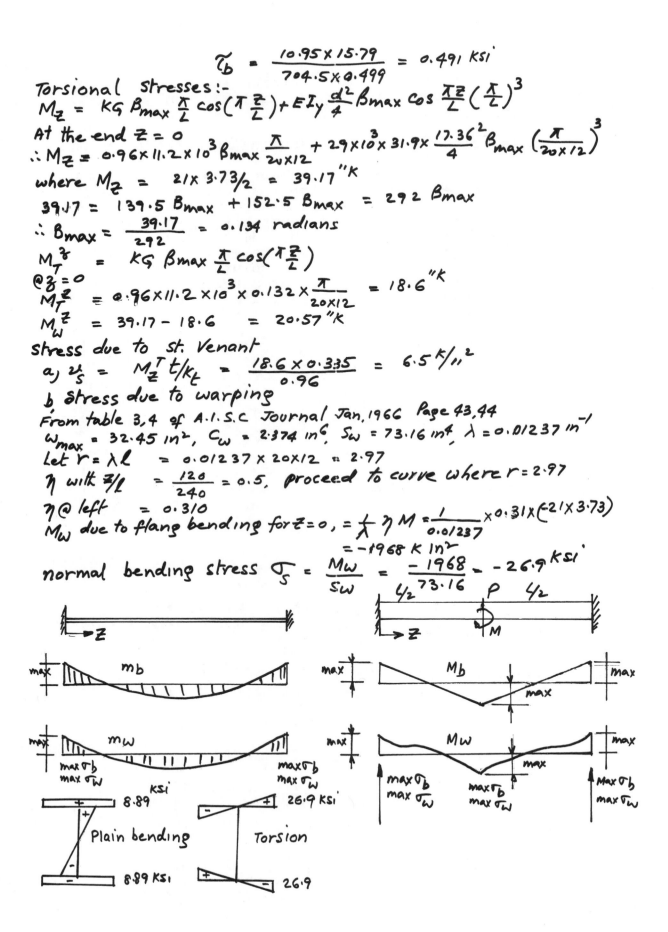

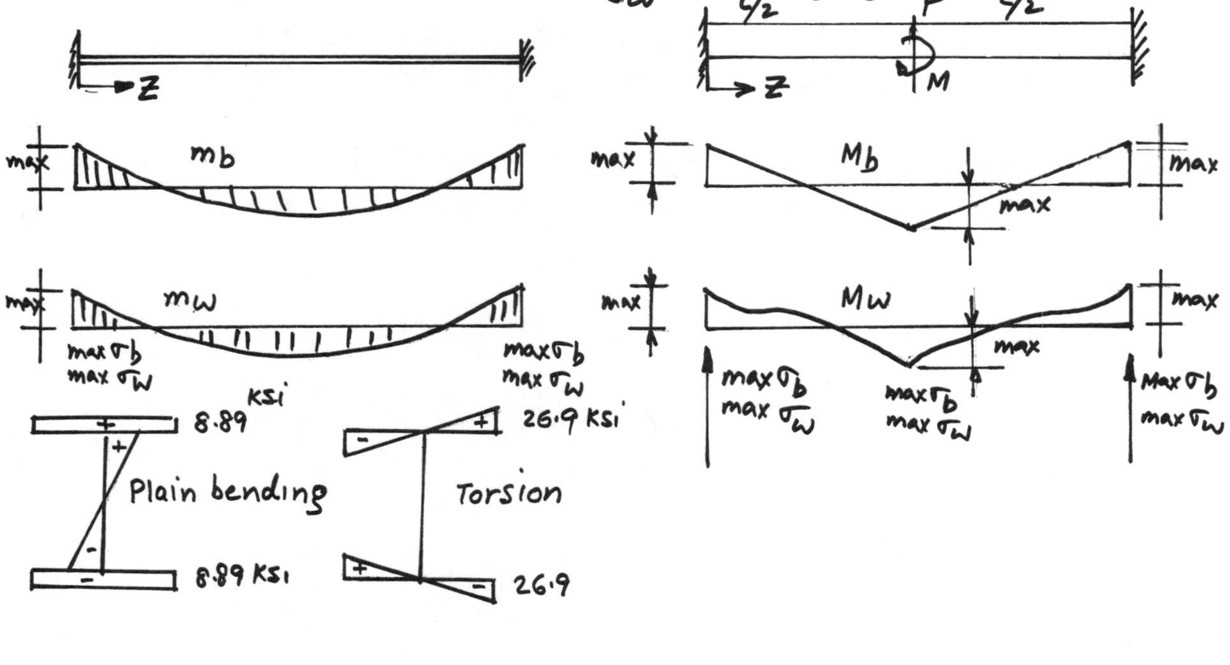

EXAMPLE 2-06

Given:- This is the analysis of the design of a multi-cell box girder subject to conventional forces as well as a severe torsional moment.

* Analyze the continuous box girder to determine a preliminary design of the sections. Moments, shears, and preliminary sections, plate thicknesses, etc. are to be produced. The section chosen is then to be checked for all stresses and torsional effects are to be included.

This is a two-span continuous girder of steel (ASTM A-36) where each span is 175.0 ft. long. LL = 5.0 k/ft. DL to be estimated. EI and loading are constant. Use AISC 7th Edition Part I for guidance in your analysis.

It is not recommended that a variable EI solution be used, but a variation of plate girder stiffness transversely is in order. You may use any number of cells that you wish, but it is suggested that a 4-cell system be selected for simplicity. The structure is to be welded. If the torsional analysis indicates that redesign is needed, it is not necessary for you to do so. Note the difference in support conditions. Assume that the transverse spacing of support points at Sections A and C is 22.0 ft. total; thus, the eccentricity of the loading from its support in Section B is 11.0 ft.

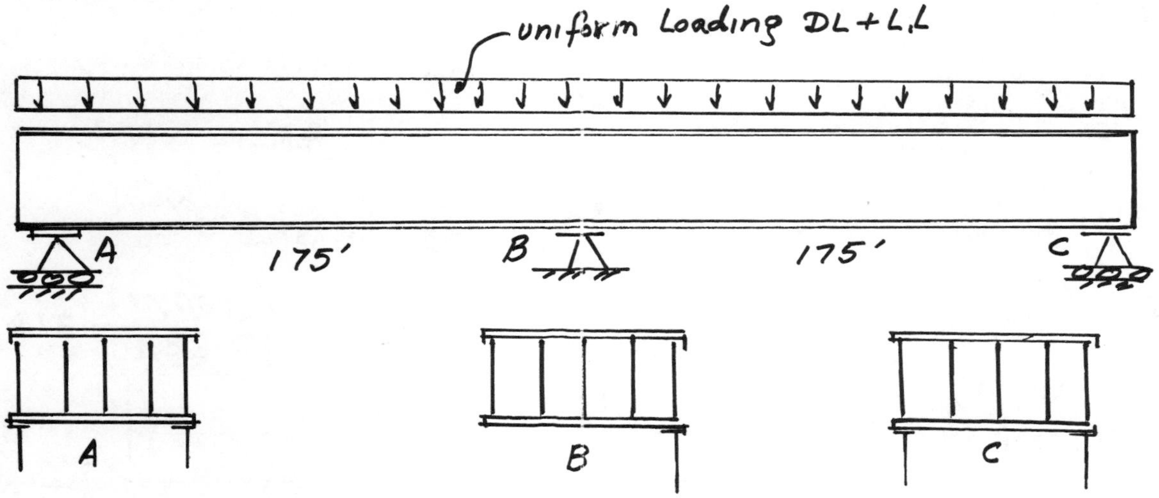

LOAD DISTRIBUTION PROCEDURE FOR A BOX GIRDER BRIDGE

Assumption made:

1. Because of its flexural rigidity, the concrete roadway slab acts as a transverse diaphragm. The slab may be replaced by an equivalent diaphragm at the middle span and the effective width of the slab is 50% of the slab length.
2. Since the torsional rigidity of the slab is small, it is ignored compared with the flexural and torsional rigidity of the box girder.
3. There is no flexural restraint developed between the roadway slab and the girder web.
4. Principal of super position is applicable.
5. The load distribution coefficient can be closely approximated by determining percentage carried by each girder

where a unit load is applied at mid span of the bridge at the point under consideration. The load distribution coefficients can be found with the above assumption in mind. However, due to the lack of time, the dead load (for the slab, steel and diaphragm) can be taken as per the Grinter text page 143:

$w, k/ft = 10L + 1000 = 10 \times 175 + 1000 = 2750\ \#/' = 2.75\ k/'$

$(D.L + L.L)/Ft = 5 + 2.75 = 7.75k$

Shear Diagram

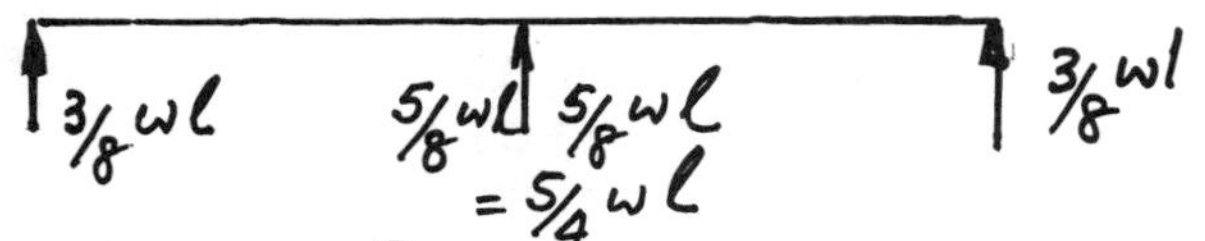

Moment Diagram

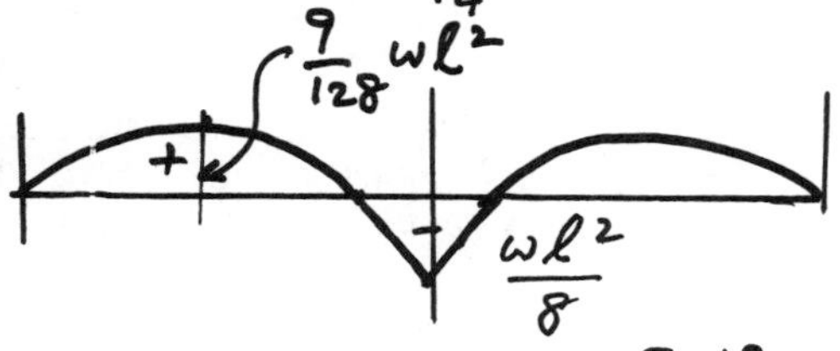

$+M = \frac{9}{128} wl^2 = 16600'k$

$-M = \frac{wl^2}{8} = 29500'k$

Depth span ratio as per AASHTO $= \frac{L}{125} = \frac{175 \times 12}{125} = 84''$

preliminary design:- Let $h_{web} = 84''$

for no reduction of stress $h/t = 162$ (A.I.S.C 1.10.6)

$\therefore t_w = \frac{84}{162} = 0.518$

$Max\ t_w = \frac{84}{320} = 0.262$ (A.I.S.C 1.10.2)

Usually $t_w = 0.375''$ is used

$\therefore$ Size of web Plate $= 84 \times 3/8$ & $A_w = 31.5 \square''$

$\frac{h}{t} = 84/3/8 = 224$

Preliminary FLANGE Design, $A_f = \frac{M}{F_b h} = \frac{29500 \times 12}{22 \times 84} = 190 \square''$

At Support A & C

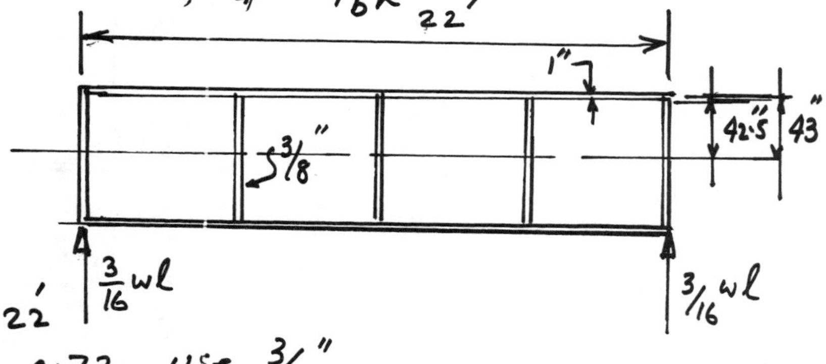

Length of flg Pl $= 22'$

$t_{flg} = \frac{190}{22 \times 12} = 0.72$ use $3/4''$

Check local buckling $\frac{b}{t} = \frac{1}{2} \times \frac{66}{3/4} = 44 > 42$ N.G

Use $t_{flg} = 1''$, $\therefore \frac{b}{t} = \frac{1}{2} \times \frac{66}{1} = 33 < 42$ ok

Moment of Inertia of girder $= .5\left(\frac{bh^3}{12}\right) + Ay^2_{FLG}$

$$M.I = \frac{5 \times .375 \times 84^3}{12} + 2 \times 264 \times 1 \times (42.5)^2$$

$$= 1043500 \text{ IN}^4$$

F_b allowable = 22 ksi

$$S_m \text{ furnished} = \frac{1043500}{43} = 24200 \text{ in}^3$$

$$S_m \text{ req'd} = \frac{29500 \times 12}{22} = 16091 \text{ in}^3$$

So preliminary section is too big

Location of Flange splices:- Since for the span of this length usually length of Plate is 40-50′ max and also usually flange splice are located @ 1/4 Point of girder which gives moment curve as a parabolic. The moment @ quarter point can therefore be assumed as 3/4 of midspan moment. Using these moment, final girder section can be obtained.

$$M = 3/4 \times 29500 = 22125$$

Final section selected $h_w = \frac{L}{28} = \frac{175 \times 12}{28} = 75''$

$$t_w = 3/8''$$

$$\frac{h_w}{t_w} = 75 \times \frac{8}{3} = 200 > 162 \quad \therefore \text{ check reduction of stress}$$

$t_f = 1''$, $b_f = 66$ ie width of one cell.

$$M.I \text{ of Final section} = 5 \times 3/8 \times \frac{75^3}{12} + 2 \times 264 \times 38^2 = 716349 \text{ IN}^4$$

$$S_m \text{ furnished} = 716349/38.5 = 18600 \text{ IN}^3 > 16091$$

$$\text{Bending stress @ Top \& BOT FLG} = \frac{22125 \times 12}{12600} = 14.25 \text{ ksi}$$

$$\text{Resisting moment @ splice Point} = \frac{22 \times 22125}{14.25} = 34200^k > 29200$$

Hence no splice is req'd.

Only bottom welding of FLG PL is enough.

$$\text{Bending stress @ max. +ve Moment} = \frac{16600 \times 12}{18600} = 10.7 \text{ ksi}$$

$$\text{Bending stress @ max. -ve moment} = \frac{29600 \times 12}{18600} = 19.0 \text{ ksi}$$

Reduced allowable compressive bending stress in flange due to possible lateral displacement of web in compression region.

$$\sigma_b \le \sigma_B \left[1.0 - 0.0005 \frac{A_w}{d_f} \left(\frac{d_w}{t_w} - \frac{24000}{\sqrt{\sigma_B}}\right)\right] \quad \text{AISC 1.10.6}$$

$$\le 22 \left\{1.0 - 0.0005 \times \frac{28.125}{264} (200 - 164)\right\} = 22 > 19 \text{ ok.}$$

Intermediate stiffeners:- These will be the plates welded to only one side of web. The design will be with reference to art. 1.6.8 AASHTO Specifications:-

Stiffener spacing:-

Shear @ ℄ bearing $= \frac{3}{8}wL = 254^K$

Unit shearing stress $f_v = \frac{V}{t b_{,}} = \frac{254}{0.275 \times 75} = 9\,ksi < 14\,ksi$

Max stiffner spacing
1) 12'
2) unsupported depth of web = 6'-3"
3) $\frac{12000}{\sqrt{f_v}} t_w = \frac{12000}{\sqrt{9000}} \times \frac{3}{8}'' = 3'-11\frac{1}{2}''$ ←

No of stiffener $= \frac{175}{3.96} \simeq 45$ equally spaced @ 3'-10"

Size of stiffener width $= 2 + \frac{h}{30} = 2 + \frac{77}{30} = 4.57''$ Say 5"

Min Thickness = $\frac{5}{16}''$

$I_{min} = dt^3 J/_{11}$ where d = stiffener spacing $47\frac{1}{2}''$

$t = 0.375''$

$J = 3.75\left(\frac{77}{75}\right)^4 = 5.0\ in^4$

$I_{min} = \frac{75(0.375)^3 \times 5}{} = 1.83\ in^4$

$I_{furnished} = \frac{bd^3}{3}'' = \frac{5}{16} \times \frac{5^3}{3} = 13\ in^4 > 1.83$

use $5 \times \frac{5}{16}''$ ℄.

Size of weld:- There is no stress in the fillet weld connecting intermediate stiffener to the web, size of the fillet weld will be normal. For $\frac{3}{8}''$ ℄, minimum weld is $\frac{3}{16}''$ use $\frac{3}{16}''$ fillet weld each side. Transverse fillet weld should not be used on a tension flange & so bottom edge of stiffener will be tightly fitted ($\frac{1}{16}''$ max Gap) to upper surface of bott flange. A seal weld be used to fasten upper edge of stiffener to upper flange.

Bearing stiffener @ ends of girder A & C

V = 254k, Area req'd for comp. stress $= \frac{254}{22} = 11.55\ in^2$

Area req'd for bearing on flange $= \frac{254}{27} = 9.41\ in^2$

use 2- ℄ $10 \times \frac{5}{8}''$ one each side Gross area = $12.5\ \square$

net area for Bearing = $11.25\ in^2$ (1" less for copes)

There will be 4 fillet welds which must develop shear between web & stiffeners.

Stress in weld $= \frac{254}{4 \times 75} = 0.85^K/in$ use $\frac{1}{4}''$ for $\frac{5}{8}''$ Plate.

Bearing stiffener @ center support B

$V = \frac{5}{4} wL = \frac{5}{4} \times 7.75 \times 175 = 1690^{k}$

Area req'd for comp. stress $= \frac{1690}{22} = 76.82 \text{ in}^2$

Area req'd for bearing on flange $= \frac{1690}{27} = 62.6 \text{ in}^2$

Try 8 - 12"x1" Pℓ, check width thickness ratio $\frac{12}{1} < 16$ ok

Check compressive stress

$I = 4\left(1 \times \frac{(24.375)^3}{12}\right) = 4800 \text{ in}^4$

$A_{eff} = (8 \times 12 \times 1) + 25 \times \frac{3}{8} \times \frac{3}{8} = 99.5 \text{ in}^2$

$r = \sqrt{\frac{4800}{99.5}} = 6.95 \text{ in}$

$l = 75 \times \frac{3}{4} = 56.25''$

$\frac{l}{r} = \frac{56.25}{6.95} = 8.1$

$\therefore F_a = 21.25 \text{ ksi}$

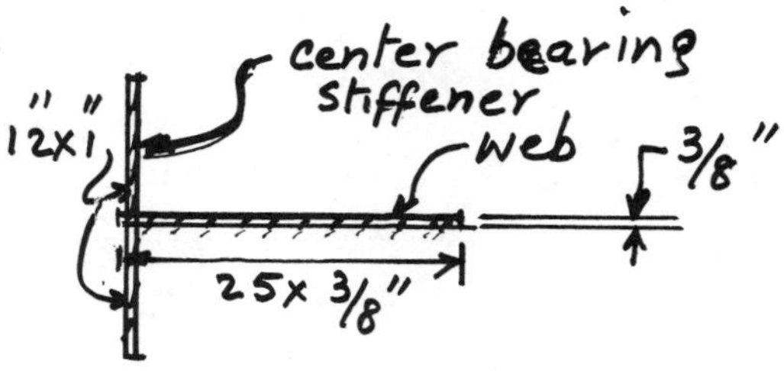

effective Area

Actual comp. stress in stiffener $= \frac{1690}{99.5} = 17.0 < 21.25$ ok

Flange web weld: The flanges will be connected to the web Plate by fillet weld on each side of web. The welds will be continueous & will be designed to carry Longitudinal shear @ the Junction of flange & web.

Top & Bot. Flange $q = \frac{VQ}{I} = \frac{254 \times 264 \times 38}{716349} = 3.56^{k}/\text{in}$

Leg size of fillet weld $w = \frac{3.56}{0.6} = 6$

use 3/8" continueous weld on each side.

Design of end bearing

Bearing Area $= \frac{254000}{600} = 423 \square''$ use $21 \times 21 = 441 \square''$

Assume $1\frac{1}{4}''$ thick & casting shown as minimum.

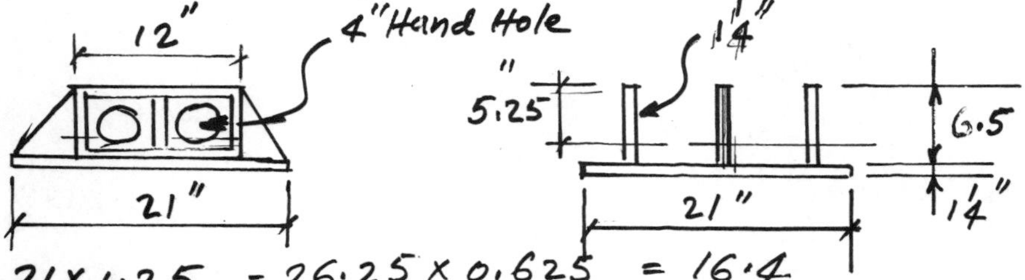

Centroid

$21 \times 1.25 = 26.25 \times 0.625 = 16.4$

$3 \times 6.5 \times 1.25 = 24.4 \times 4.5 = 109.8$

$50.65 \qquad 126.2$

$\bar{x} = \frac{126.2}{50.65} = 2.5$

Bending moment $= 600\,(.5 \times 21)\,\frac{5}{2} = 157500''\#$

M.I $\quad \frac{1}{12} \times 21 \times 1.25^3 = 3$

$26.25 \times 1.82^2 = 84$

$3 \times \frac{1}{12} \times 1.25 \times 6.5^3 = 86$

$24.4 \times 1.75^2 = 76$

$\qquad\qquad 249$

$$S_c = \frac{157500 \times 5.25}{249} = 3320\ \#/\square''$$

Design of Central Bearing

$$\text{Bearing Area} = \frac{169000}{600} = 287''^{\square}$$

use $54 \times 54 \times 1.25''$

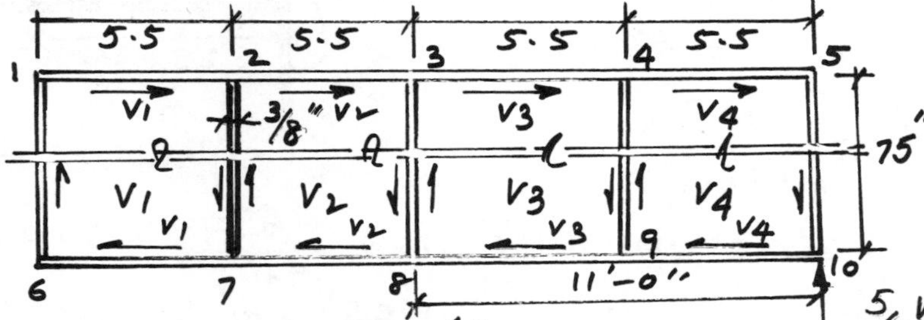

Torque $= 1690 \times 11 = 18590$ 'K

Assume $Q_1 = Q_2 = Q_3 = Q_4 = Q$

A_{Poly} = Same for all $= 5.5 \times 6.42 = 35.30\,\square''$

∴ unknown are V_1, V_2, V_3, V_4 & Q

1, 2, 6, 7	The shear in line	2, 7	$V_1 - V_2$
2, 3, 8, 7		3, 8	$V_2 - V_3$
3, 4, 9, 8		4, 9	$V_3 - V_4$
4, 5, 10, 9		5, 9	$V_4 - V_1$

This obeys the equilibrium condition.

Joint action of 4 Quad is given by

$$M_t = v_1 \times 2A_{Poly_{1,2,6,7}} + v_2 \times 2A_{Pol_{2,3,8,7}} + v_3 \times 2A_{Poly_{3,4,9,8}} + v_4 \times 2A_{Poly_{4,5,10,9}}$$

$$18590 = 2A_{Poly}(v_1 + v_2 + v_3 + v_4) = 2 \times 35.3\,(v_1 + v_2 + v_3 + v_4)$$

$$v_1 + v_2 + v_3 + v_4 = \frac{18590}{70.6} = 264 \quad \text{— ①}$$

mutual Compatability

$$2QG = \frac{1}{A_{Poly}} \sum \frac{v_n\, a_n}{t} = \frac{12}{35.3}\left[v_1\left(\frac{5.5}{1} + 6.25 \times 8/3 + \frac{5.5}{1} + 6.25 \times 8/3\right) - (6.25 \times 8/3)\, v_2\right]$$

$QG = 15.05\, v_1 - 5.67\, v_2$

$QG = 7.52\, v_1 - 2.84\, v_2$ — ②

Simily $QG = 7.52\, V_2 - 2.84\, v_3$ — ③

$QG = 7.52\, V_3 - 2.84\, v_4$ — ④

$QG = 7.52\, V_4 - 2.84\, v_1$ — ⑤

Solving equations ① — ⑤ simultaneously

$\therefore$ $v_1 = v_2 = v_3 = v_4 = 0.224\,QG$

$4 \times 0.224\,QG = 264, \quad QG = 294$

$\therefore\ Q = \dfrac{294}{12 \times 10^6} = 24.5 \times 10^{-6}\ in^{-1}$

& $v_1 = v_2 = v_3 = v_4 = 0.224 \times 294 = 65.8^{K}/ft = 5.48^{K}/in$

$\tau_{1-2} = \dfrac{65.8}{1 \times 12} = 5.48\ ksi$

$\tau_{1-6},\ \tau_{2-7} = \dfrac{65.8}{3/8 \times 12} = 14.6\ ksi$

$\tau_{7-6} = \dfrac{65.8}{1 \times 12} = 5.48\ ksi$

Allowable $\tau = \dfrac{F_y}{\sqrt{3} \times 1.4} = 14.7\ ksi$

Resultant horizontal shear $= (5.48 \times 66)4 = 1444^{K}$.

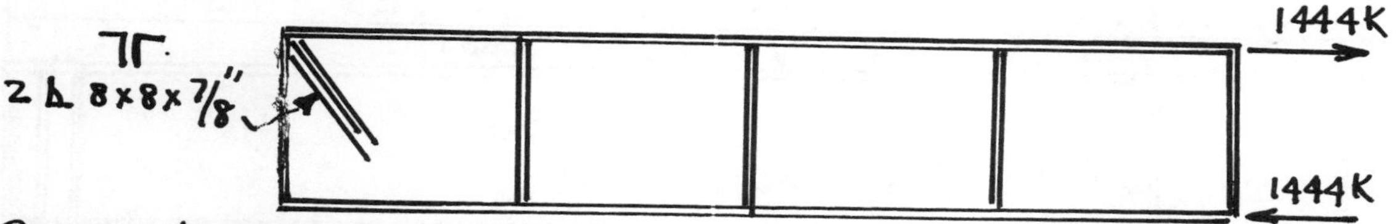

Since torsion is constant, shear of 1444^{K} exists on each foot length of X-Section.

Diaphragms are provided to resist this shearing action. Diaphragms plates @ load point location maintain the shape and cut down on effect of warping. They act as transverse load distribution and act as bearing & web stiffener. Diaphragms are welded in field.

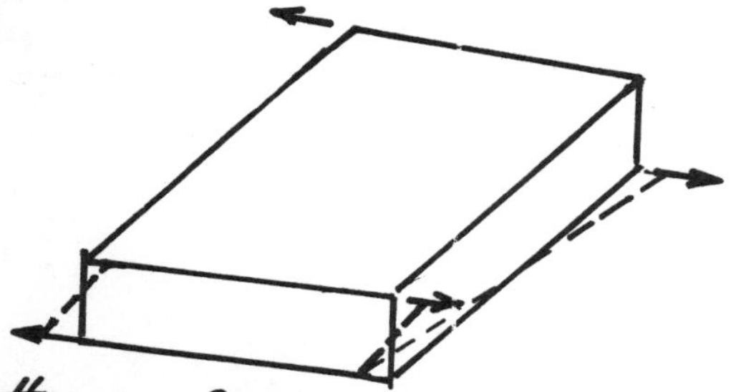

Warping is there Beam Type

f_{b} beam $= \dfrac{1444}{264 \times 1} \times 3/2 = 8.2$

In one cell $v_H = 66 \times 5.48 = 361^{k}$

$v_v = 75 \times 5.48 = 411^{k}$

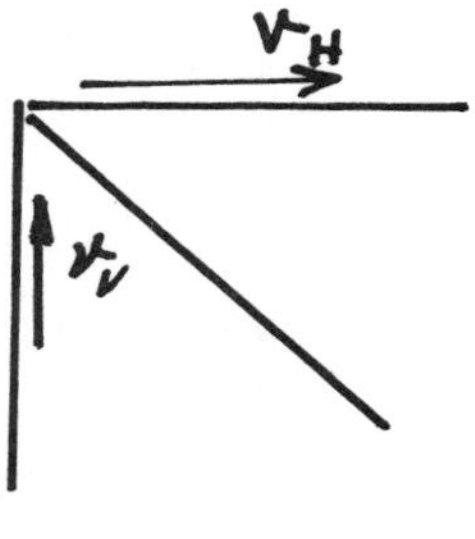

Comp. force for diaphragm $= \sqrt{361^2 + 411^2} = 547^{k}$

Length $L = \sqrt{66^2 + 75^2} = 99.5''$

Try $F_a = 21$ ksi

$$A = \frac{547}{21} = 26.05\,\square'' \text{, use 2 Ls } 8\times8\times7/8'' \text{, B to B } 1/4''$$

$$A = 26.46,\ r = 3.46$$

$$f_a = \frac{547}{26.46} = 20.06 \text{ ksi}$$

$$\frac{l}{r} = \frac{99.5}{3.46} = 28.6$$

$$\therefore F_a = 20.08 \text{ ksi} > 20.06 \quad \text{ok}$$

Hence use diaphragm of X-bracing type of 2 Ls $8\times8\times7/8''$ T

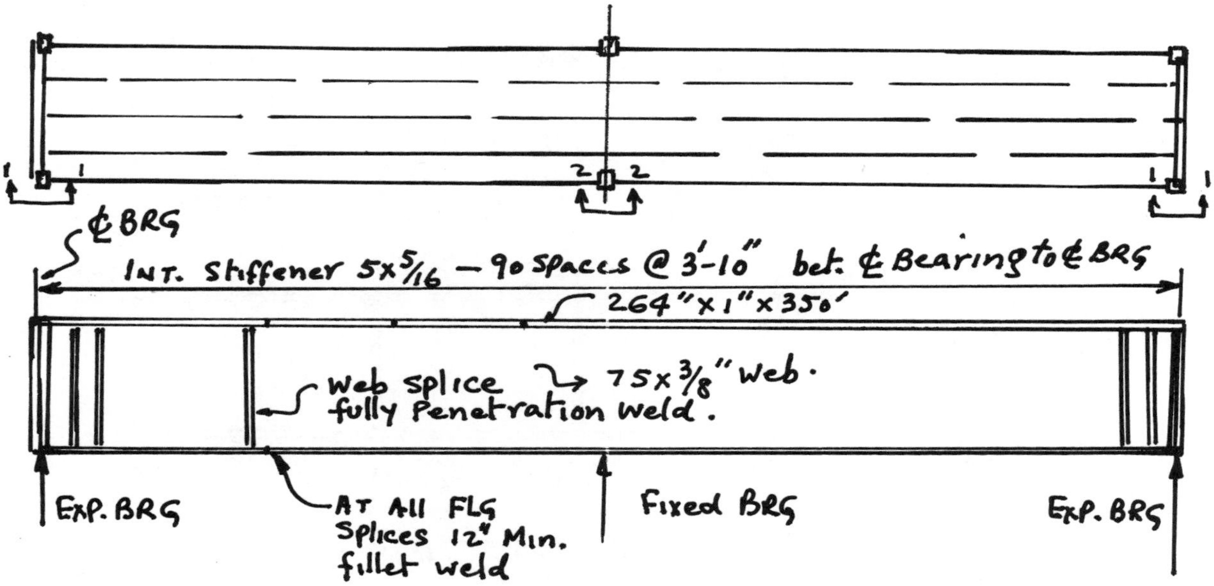

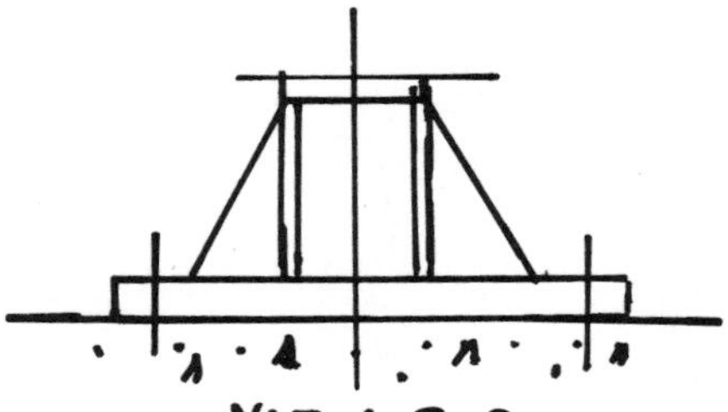

VIEW 2-2

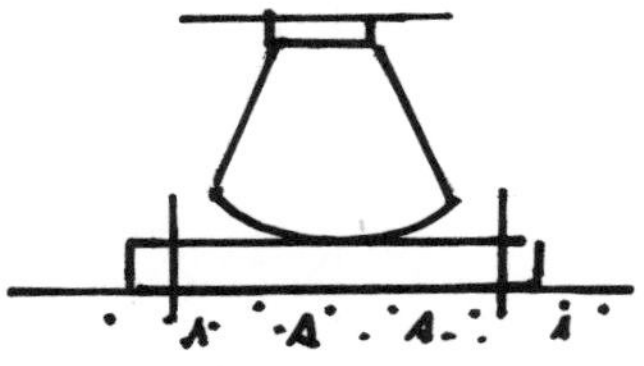

VIEW 1-1

EXAMPLE 2-07

Given:- (A) Check the following column situation according to the 7th Edition AISC Specifications:

W21x73: This is a compact section.

ASTM A-36: $F_y = 36$ ksi

Total height of column: 20 ft.

Bracing is parallel to the strong X-X axis and is 6' from the top and 6' from the bottom, leaving 8 ft. unbraced in the middle section.

Bracing is also parallel to the weak Y-Y axis and here is only at the top and bottom of the column.

Axial load is 30 k and moment about the strong axis (M_x) only is 255 ft. kips.

The design procedure is elastic and conventional. The column is pinned at the bottom and the top, the forces are constant and sidesway is permitted.

(B) Check the same column if an additional moment (M_y) of 25.5 ft. kips. is added about the weak axis. All other forces continue to act, otherwise select the proper section.

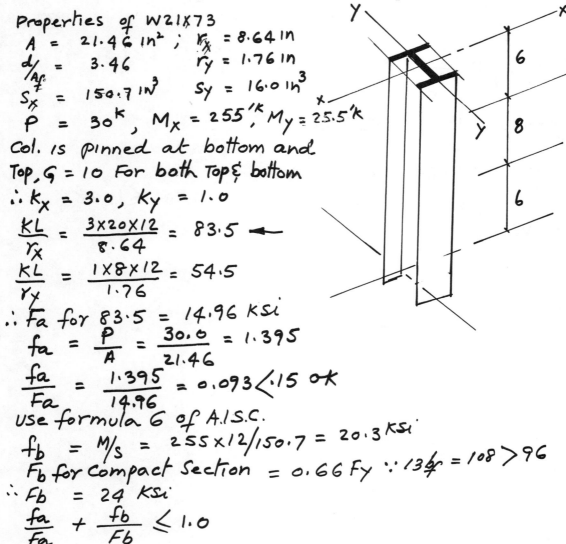

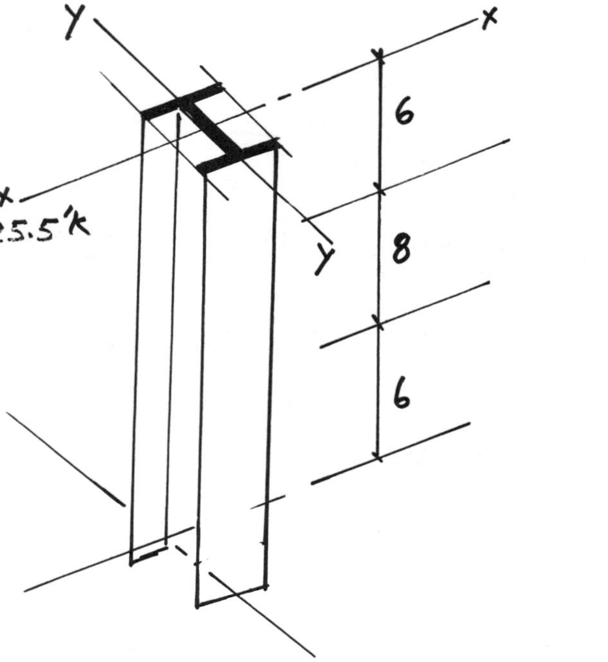

Properties of W21X73

$A = 21.46 \text{ in}^2$; $r_x = 8.64 \text{ in}$

$d/A_f = 3.46$ $\quad r_y = 1.76 \text{ in}$

$S_x = 150.7 \text{ in}^3$ $\quad S_y = 16.0 \text{ in}^3$

$P = 30^k$, $M_x = 255'^k$, $M_y = 25.5'^k$

Col. is pinned at bottom and Top, G = 10 For both Top & bottom

$\therefore K_x = 3.0$, $K_y = 1.0$

$$\frac{KL}{r_x} = \frac{3 \times 20 \times 12}{8.64} = 83.5 \longleftarrow$$

$$\frac{KL}{r_y} = \frac{1 \times 8 \times 12}{1.76} = 54.5$$

$\therefore F_a$ for $83.5 = 14.96$ ksi

$$f_a = \frac{P}{A} = \frac{30.0}{21.46} = 1.395$$

$$\frac{f_a}{F_a} = \frac{1.395}{14.96} = 0.093 < .15 \text{ ok}$$

Use formula 6 of A.I.S.C.

$$f_b = M/S = 255 \times 12/150.7 = 20.3 \text{ ksi}$$

F_b for Compact Section $= 0.66 F_y \because 13\frac{b}{f} = 108 > 96$

$\therefore F_b = 24$ ksi

$$\frac{f_a}{F_a} + \frac{f_b}{F_b} \leq 1.0$$

$$\frac{1.395}{14.96} + \frac{20.3}{24} = .939 < 1 \quad \text{ok.}$$

B) $M_y = 25.5'^k$, $f_{by} = \frac{25.5 \times 12}{16} = 19.12$ ksi

$F_{by} = 0.66 F_y = 24$

$$\frac{f_a}{F_a} + \frac{f_{bx}}{F_{bx}} + \frac{f_{by}}{F_{by}} \leq 1$$

using properties of W21X73

$$\frac{1.395}{14.96} + \frac{20.3}{24.0} + \frac{19.12}{24.0} = 0.093 + 0.846 + 0.797 = 1.736 > 1$$

No. Good.

Try W 24X100, properties are $A = 29.43\ in^2$, $r_x = 10.08$ in

$d/A_f = 2.58$, $r_y = 2.63$ in

$S_x = 248.7\ in^3$, $S_y = 33.9\ in^3$

$F_{bx} = F_{by} = 24.0$ ksi

$f_{bx} = \frac{255 \times 12}{248.7} = 12.30$ ksi

$f_{by} = \frac{25.5 \times 12}{32.9} = 9.03$ ksi

$f_a = \frac{30}{29.43} = 1.02$ ksi

$\frac{KL}{r_x} = \frac{3 \times 20 \times 12}{10.08} = 71.5 \leftarrow \quad \frac{KL}{r_y} = \frac{1 \times 8 \times 12}{2.63} = 36.5$

$\therefore F_a = 16.27$ ksi

In formula $\frac{f_a}{F_a} + \frac{f_{bx}}{F_{bx}} + \frac{f_{by}}{F_{by}} \leq 1$

$$= \frac{1.02}{16.27} + \frac{12.30}{24.0} + \frac{9.03}{24.0}$$

$$= 0.063 + 0.512 + 0.376 = 0.951 \leq 1 \quad \text{ok}$$

Use W 24X100

EXAMPLE 2-08

Given:- Compute and plot all critical points needed to define the load-deflection curve for the following structure:

Use all E = 30,000 ksi

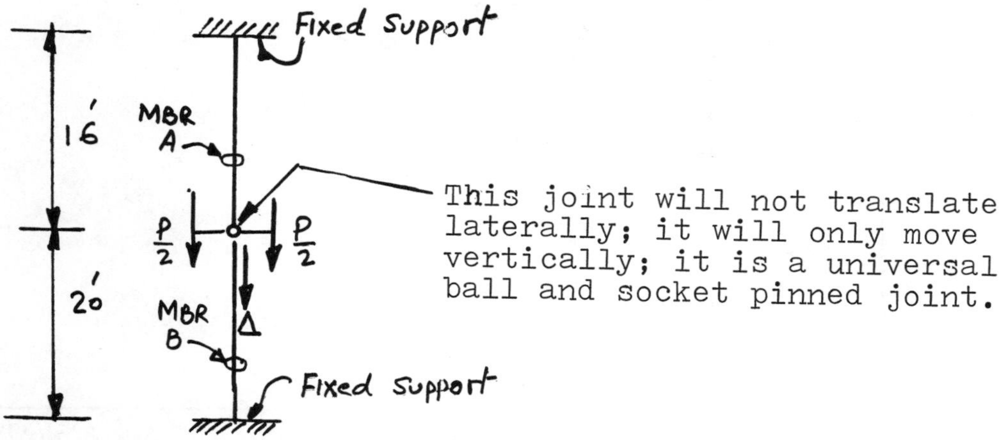

Member	Section	A in²	ry in	Iy in⁴	Fy ksi
A	W12X65	19.11	3.02	174.6	42.0
B	W12X120	35.31	3.13	345.1	42.0

K = 0.7 in both cases

Methods of failure

1, General yielding
1, MBR A, $P_y = 42 \times 19.11 = 803^k$
2, MBR B, $P_y = 42 \times 35.31 = 1482^k$

2, Buckling
1, MBR A is in tension, so no Buckling
2, MBR B $P_{E_B} = \dfrac{\pi^2 E A_B}{(\frac{KL}{r})^2} = \dfrac{9.85 \times 30000 \times 35.31}{(\frac{0.7 \times 20 \times 12}{3.13})^2} = 3630$

$\therefore 1482 < 3630$

$\therefore$ MBR B will not fail due to Buckling. MBR A will yield 1st.

$P_A + P_B = P$ & $\Delta = \dfrac{PL}{AE}$

$\Delta_A = \Delta_B = \dfrac{P_A L_A}{A_A E} = \dfrac{P_B L_B}{A_B E} \therefore P_A = \dfrac{P_B L_B}{A_B E} \times \dfrac{A_A E}{L_A} = \dfrac{A_A}{A_B} \times \dfrac{L_B}{L_A} \times P_B$

$= \dfrac{19.11}{35.3} \times \dfrac{20}{16} \times P_B = 0.676 P_B$

$\therefore 0.676 P_B + P_B = P$

$P_B = \dfrac{P}{1.676} = 0.597P$

& $P_A = 0.676 \times 0.597P = 0.403P$

Hence when P_A reaches its yield pt, Load $P = \dfrac{803}{0.403} = 1990^k$

when P_B reaches its yield point, Load P corresponds to

$$= \frac{1432}{0.597} = 2480^K$$

when $P = 1990$, $P_B = 1990 - 803 = 1187$

∴ MBR A will not carry any further load

$$\Delta_A = \Delta_B = \frac{P_A L}{A_A E} = \frac{803 \times 16 \times 12}{19.11 \times 30 \times 10^3} = 0.269$$

Additional deflection in MBR B due to $1480 - 1187 = 293^K$

$$\Delta_B = \frac{293 \times 20 \times 12}{35.31 \times 30 \times 10^3} = 0.066$$

∴ Total $\Delta = 0.269 + 0.066 = 0.335''$

$P_U = 1480 + 803 = 2283$ K

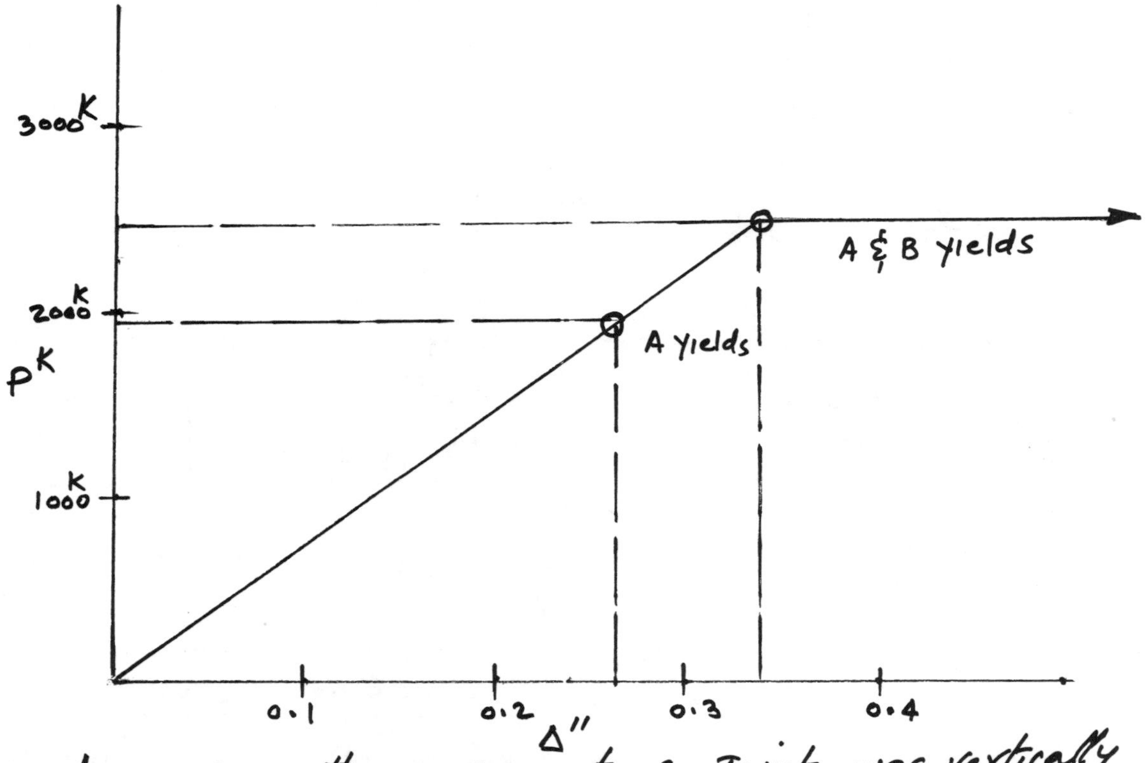

In above case, the movement of Joint was vertically and load deflection curve is plotted. Here the deflection is due to elastic shortening first and a linear one.

EXAMPLE 2-09

Given:- Consider the following simple span plate girder which is loaded as noted: LL = 2.50 kips/ft. uniform, full-span
DL = selected dead weight of girder.
Concentrated loads are shown.

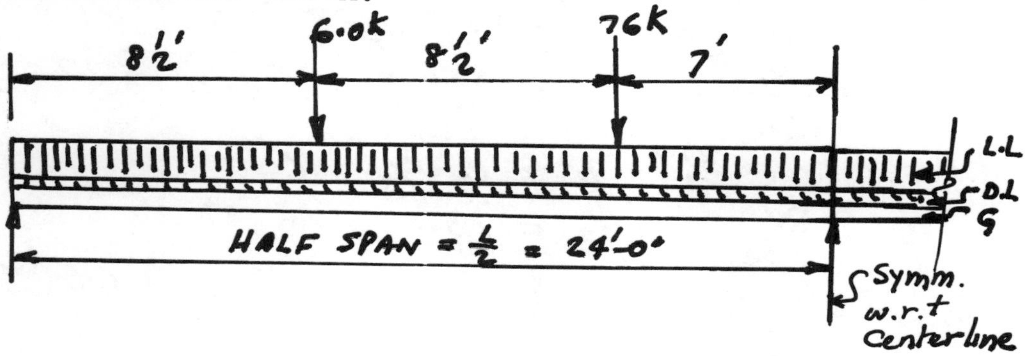

You are to design and select a built-up plate girder with a single web only and flanges; that is, no box girders. Use the moments and shears indicated by the above and use the general requirements of the AISC 7th Edition and select the preliminary section. Lateral bracing exists at the 76 kip load points and at the supports. The material is to be ASTM A-36 steel. The out-to-out depth is to be limited to no more than 6 ft. 6 in. Include your preliminary selection of welding, bracing, etc.

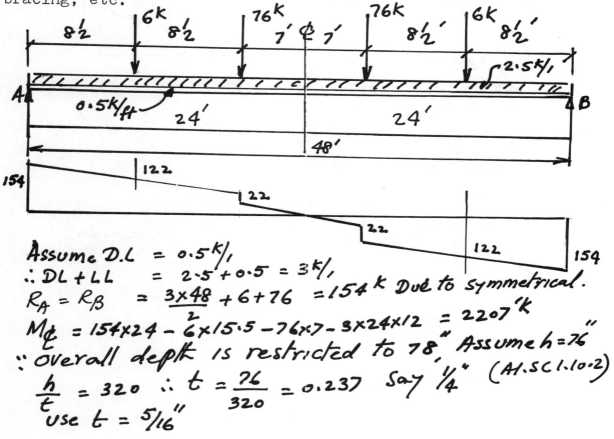

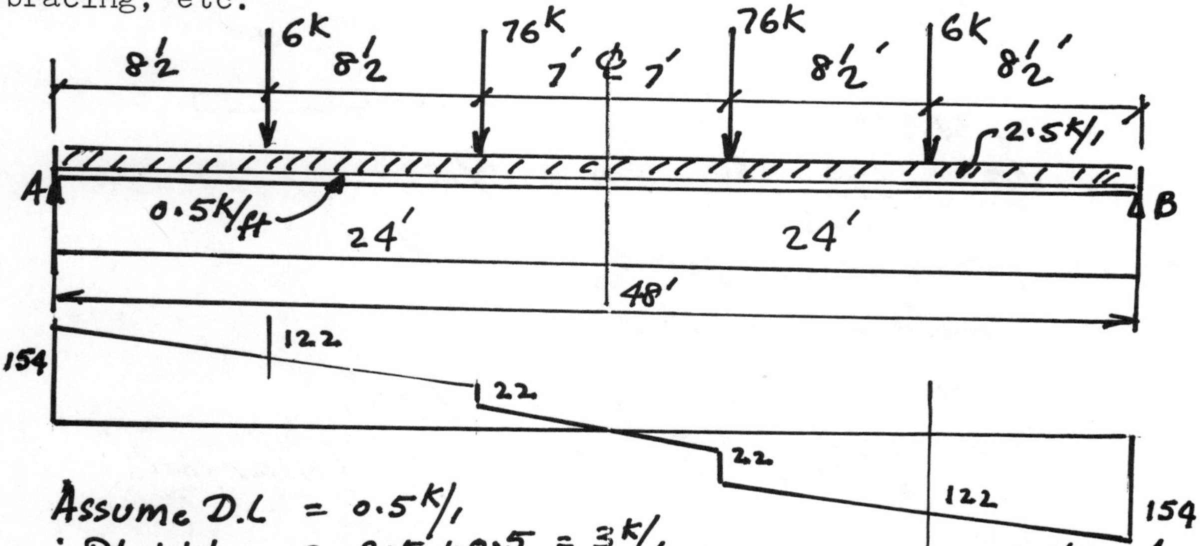

Assume D.L $= 0.5^{k}/'$

$\therefore$ DL + LL $= 2.5 + 0.5 = 3^{k}/'$

$R_A = R_B = \frac{3\times48}{2} + 6 + 76 = 154^{k}$ Due to symmetrical.

$M_{℄} = 154\times24 - 6\times15.5 - 76\times7 - 3\times24\times12 = 2207'^{k}$

$\because$ overall depth is restricted to 78", Assume h = 76"

$\frac{h}{t} = 320 \quad \therefore t = \frac{76}{320} = 0.237$ Say 1/4" (AISC 1.10.2)

use t = 5/16"

$A_w = 76 \times 5/16 = 23.75\ \square''$

$\frac{A_w}{6} = \frac{23.75}{6} = 3.96\ \square''$ Say $4''$

$F_b = 22$ ksi

$\because\ M = F_b\left(A_f + \frac{A_w}{6}\right)h$ or $\frac{M}{F_b h} = A_f + A_w/6$

$\therefore\ A_f = \frac{M}{F_b h} - \frac{A_w}{6} = \frac{2207 \times 12}{22 \times 76} - 4.0 = 12$

Choose $t_f = 3/4''$, $b = 12 \times 4/3 = 16''$

$\frac{b}{t} = \frac{8}{3/4} = 32/3 = 10.57 < 16$ ok

Shear stress in web $= \frac{V}{A_w} = \frac{154}{23.75} = 6.5^{\text{ksi}} < 14.5$ ok

DESIGN OF WELDS

Sec.	A in²	Y	Ay²	I_o	I_g in⁴
76×5/16	23.75				11431
16×3/4	12.0	38 3/8	3022×12 =36264	1	36265
16×3/4	12.0				47696

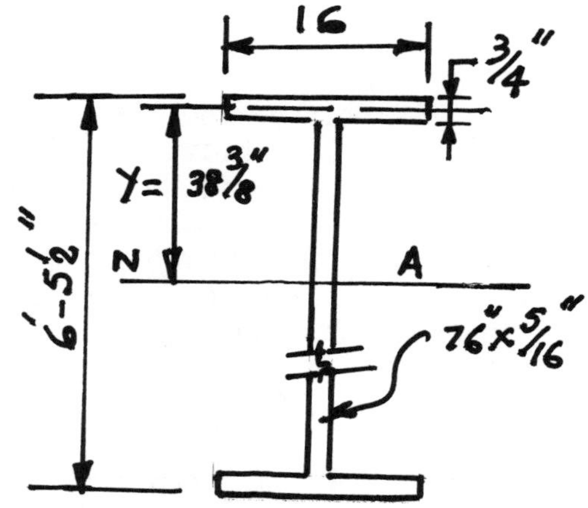

$Q = 12 \times 38.375 = 460.0$

$q = \frac{VQ}{I} = \frac{154 \times 460}{47696} = 1.42^{k}/''$

Pg AISC, Min. weld for $3/4''$ ℞ $= 1/4''$

$\therefore$ Use $1/4''$ weld double fillet

length of weld $= \frac{1.42 \times 12}{2.4} = 7.10''$

Use $7\frac{1}{4}''$ of $1/4''$ double fillet weld per linear foot.

EXAMPLE 2-10

Given:- Shown below is a single span portal frame. It is pinned at both column bases in all design cases and the joonts between the column and the beam are as indicated:

Loadings: Wind Load 600 plf on the vertical surface.
Dead weight of the frame itself as determined by the designer.
Live load of 1000 plf of beam length along the span.

This is an elastic design under AISC 7th Edition Specifications using ASTM A-36 steel. Use constant EI members; however, the column may differ from the beam if desired. The ratio of I_B to I_C should probably be less than 2.0 and greater than 1.0.

In each requirement below, it is required that the analysis be done, the sections be chosen and checked, and the connections be designed and detailed.

Assume that the columns are pinned at the bases and that the beam-to-column connection is structurally rigid. Sidesway is then resisted by the cross-bracing shown in red. The sidesway bracing is assumed to be of sufficient stiffness that there is no sidesway at all.

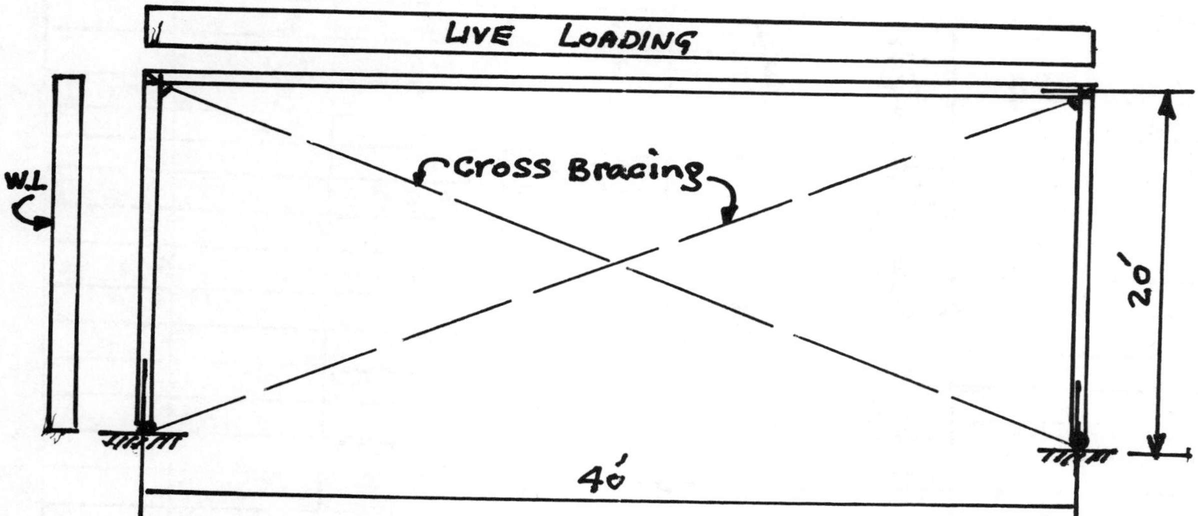

Solution:- Try W12x72 for beam & W10x66 for columns.

$$\frac{I_B}{I_C} = \frac{597.4}{382.5} = 1.496 \text{ Say } 1.5$$

$$\therefore I_B = 1.5 I_C$$

Relative stiffness

$$K_{AB} = \frac{I_C}{20} \times 40 = 2$$

$$K_{BC} = 1.5\frac{I_C}{20} \times 40 = 3$$

$$K_{CD} = \frac{I_C}{20} \times 40 = 2$$

Fixed End Moment

$$M_{AB} = +\frac{w\ell^2}{12} = \frac{0.6 \times 20^2}{12} = +20'K$$

$$M_{BA} = -20'K$$

$$M_{BC} = +\frac{w\ell^2}{12} = \frac{1.072 \times 40^2}{12} = 143'K, \quad M_{CB} = -143'K$$

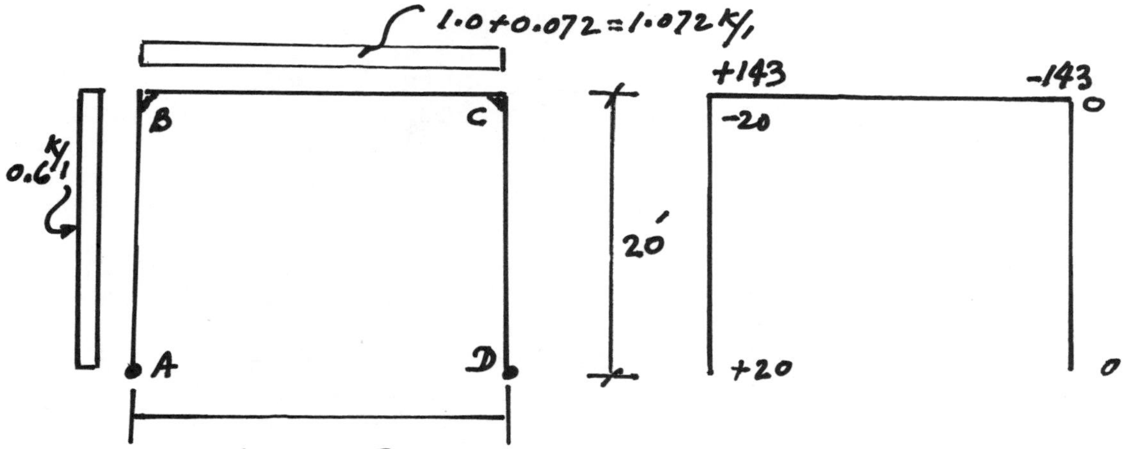

$M_{CD} = M_{DC} = 0$

For distribution of F.E.M, K_M for $AB = 2 \times \frac{3}{4} = 1.5$

$CD = 1.5$

Moments are distributed by moment distribution method

J_T	A	B		C		D	
MBR	AB	BA	BC	CB	CD	DC	
K	2	2	3	3	2	2	
K_M	1.5	1.5	3	3	1.5	1.5	
OR	3	3	6	6	3	3	
D.F	–	1	2	2	1	–	
F.EM	+20	-20	+143	-143	–		
	-20	-41	-82	+95	+48		
		-10	+47.5	-41			
		-12.5	-25.0	+27.3	+13.7		
			+13.7	-12.5			
		-4.6	-9.1	+8.3	+4.2		
			+4.2	-4.6			
		-1.4	-2.8	+3.1	+1.5		
		-89.5	+89.5	-67.4	+67.4		

$R_A \times 40 - 42.88 \times 20 + 12 \times 10 = 0$

$R_A = 18.44^k$

$R_D = 24.44^k$

$H_A \times 20 - 12 \times 10 - 89.5 = 0$

$H_A = 10.48^k$

$H_D = 12 - 10.48 = 1.52^k$

$F_1 = \frac{10.48 \times \sqrt{5}}{2} = 11.7^k (T) +$

$F_2 = 1.52 \times \sqrt{5}/2 = 1.7^k (C) -$

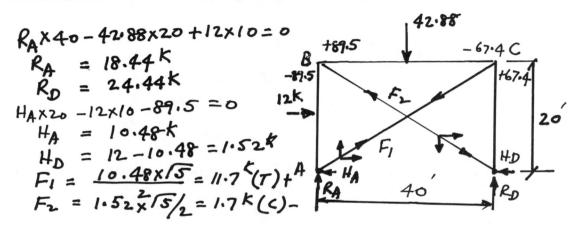

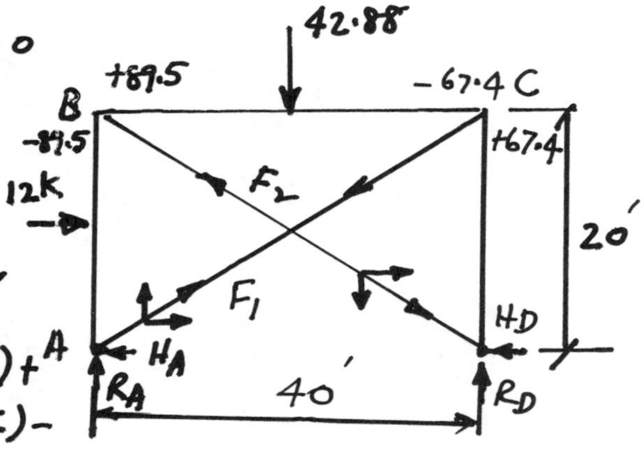

Check W12x72

$l_b = 480'' > 13\, b_f = 13 \times 12.04 = 156.5$ — NON COMPACT

To find F_b, check formula 4, 5 of AISC

By formula 4, $\frac{ld}{A_f} = 480 \times 1.52 = 730$

$\therefore F_b = \frac{12000}{730} = 16.4$ ksi

By formula 5, $F_b = 22000 - \frac{0.679}{1.75}\left(\frac{480}{3.04}\right)^2$

$= 21.04$ ksi ← use

$M_{max} = \frac{wl^2}{8} - \left(\frac{89.5+67.4}{2}\right) = \frac{1.072 \times 40^2}{8} - 78.45 = 135.95^{1k}$

$f_b = \frac{135.95 \times 12}{97.5} = 16.7$ ksi

$f_a = \frac{10.48}{21.16} = 0.480$ ksi

$\frac{kl}{r_x} = \frac{1 \times 40 \times 12}{5.13} = 93.5, \quad F_a = 13.78$

$\frac{f_a}{F_a} + \frac{f_b}{F_b} \leq 1 \; ; \; \frac{0.480}{13.78} + \frac{16.7}{21.4} \leq 1$ or $0.827 \leq 1$ ok

Use W12x72

Check W10x66, properties $A = 19.41\ in^2$, $r_x = 4.44\ in$, $\frac{d}{A_f} = 1.37$

$S = 73.7\ in^3$, $r_y = 2.58\ in$

When $k = 2$, $\frac{kL}{r_x} = \frac{2 \times 12 \times 20}{4.44} = 108.5$

$F_a = 11.88$ ksi

$f_a = \frac{18.44}{19.41} = 0.95, \quad f_b = \frac{89.5 \times 12}{73.7} = 12.2$

from formula (4) $\frac{ld}{A_f} = 240 \times 1.37 = 330, \quad \frac{f_a}{F_a} = \frac{0.95}{11.88} = 0.08$

$F_b = \frac{12000}{330} = 37.2 > 22$ use 22

$\therefore \frac{f_a}{F_a} + \frac{f_b}{F_b} \leq 1 \; ; \; 0.08 + \frac{12.2}{22} \leq 1$ or $0.08 + 0.556$

$= 0.636 \leq 1$ ✓

Design of Bracing due to sidesway.

Assume Connection @ intersection offers no lateral support.

$L_d = \sqrt{40^2 + 20^2} = 44.7'$ or $536.4''$

Max $\frac{L}{r}$ for Tension member $= 300$

$r_{min} = \frac{536.4}{300} = 1.788''$, Try 2 Ls 4x4x5/16 ~~7F~~ 3/8''.

$A = 4.80\ \square''$, $r = 1.80$ in.

With intermittent weld @ $24 \times \frac{1}{4} = 6''$
Pg 5-43 AISC,

$$P = \frac{\pi^2 E A}{(L/r)^2} = \frac{\pi^2 \times 28.2 \times 10^3 \times 4.8}{(536.4/1.80)^2}$$

(Comp. Buckling Load) = 15.7 > 1.7 ok

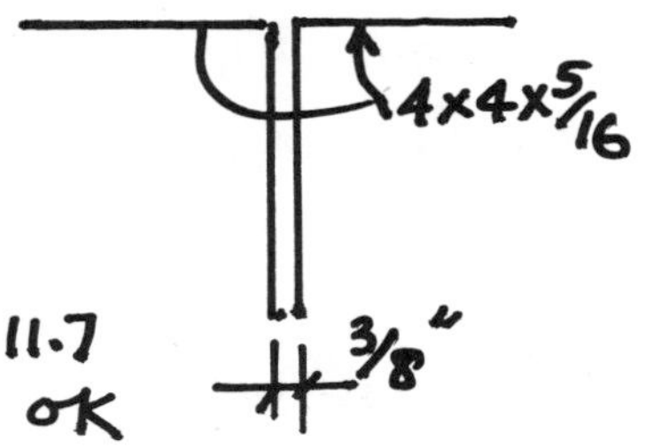

Allowable Tension Load
= 22 × 4.80 = 105.6 > 11.7 ok

To safeguard against temp. adjustment, bolt holes are slotted @ the lower end of Δ, Bolts in the slotted holes are eventually welded to angles.

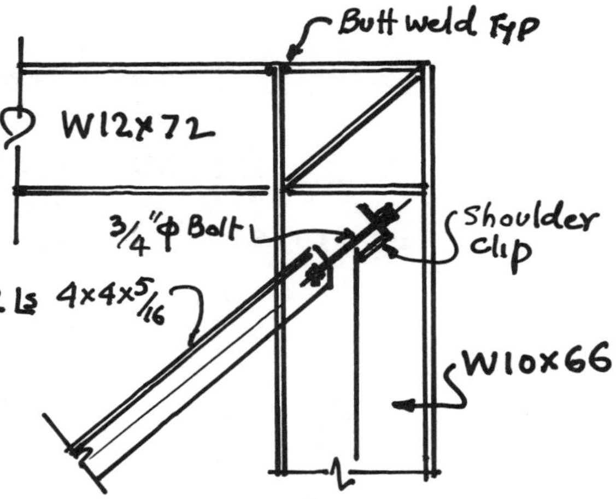

change in length due to sway of Panel.

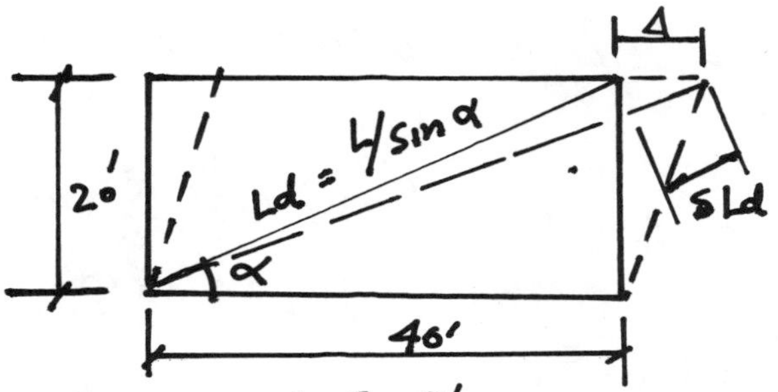

$\delta L_d = \Delta \cos\alpha$

Unit strain $= \frac{\delta L_d}{L_d} = \Delta \frac{\cos\alpha}{L_d}$

Force in diagonal $= AE \frac{\cos\alpha}{L_d} \Delta$

Contribution of bracing for shear resistance

$$R_h = AE \cos^2\alpha \sin\alpha \frac{\Delta}{h}$$

where $\cos\alpha = \frac{2}{\sqrt{5}}$, $\sin\alpha = \frac{1}{\sqrt{5}}$

$$R_h = 4.80 \times 29 \times 10^3 \times \left(\frac{2}{\sqrt{5}}\right)^2 \times \left(\frac{1}{\sqrt{5}}\right) \frac{\Delta}{h}$$

$$= 49700 \frac{\Delta}{h} \text{ kips}$$

If $\frac{\Delta}{h}$ is Limited to 0.001

$\therefore R_h = 49.7$ & $\Delta_{max} = 20 \times 12 \times 0.001 = 0.240''$

Design of 90° knee

It is design of knee Joint @ B & C transmiting shear, thrust & moment.

Shearing stress in the knee web is obtained by assuming B.M & thrust in the members are resisted by flanges only while web resists shear only.

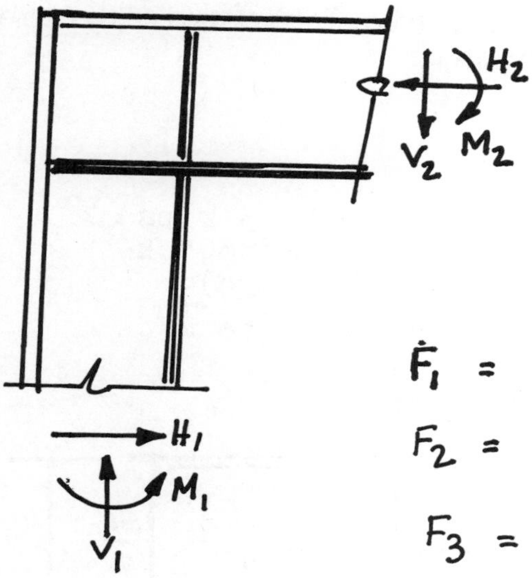

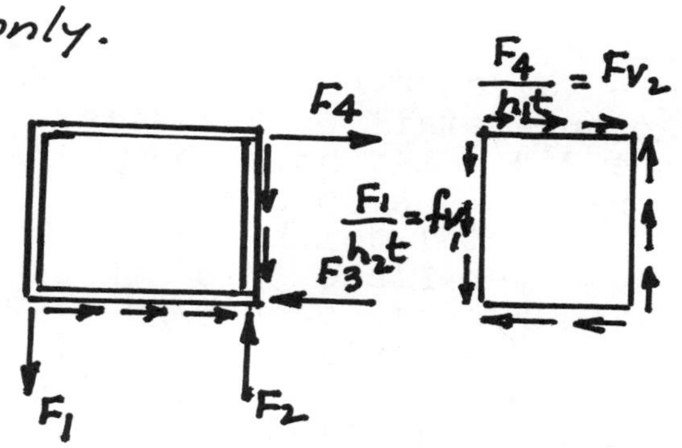

$$F_1 = \frac{M_1}{h_1} - \frac{V_1}{2} = \frac{-89.5}{10.31} - \frac{18.44}{2} = -17.97^k$$

$$F_2 = \frac{-89.5}{10.31} + \frac{18.44}{2} = 0.47^k$$

$$F_3 = \frac{M_2}{h_2} + \frac{H_2}{2} = \frac{-67.4}{12.25} + \frac{1.52}{2} = -4.70^k$$

$$F_4 = \frac{-67.4}{12.25} - \frac{1.52}{2} = -6.22^k$$

$$F_{v_1} = \frac{-17.97}{12.25 \times 0.430} = -3.41 < 14.5 \text{ ok}$$

$$F_{v_2} = \frac{-6.72}{10.31 \times 0.457} = -1.32 < 14.5 \text{ ok}$$

Hence no diagonal stiffeners are required. Just Butt welding the flange web of frame is enough.

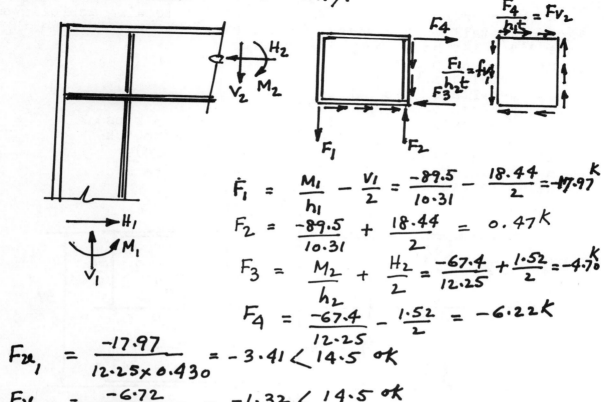

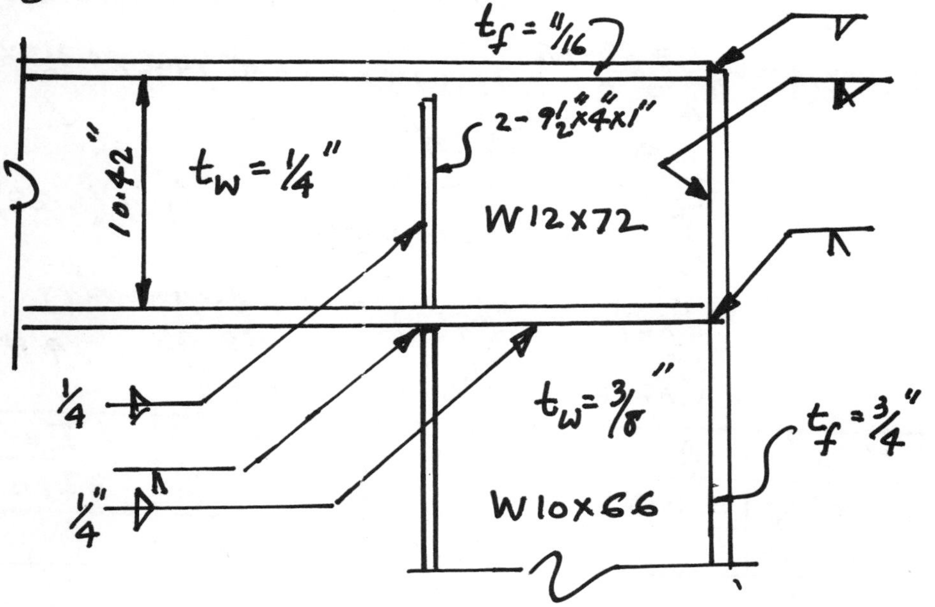

EXAMPLE 2-11

Given:- Given a plate girder section and its loading as follows: Design and detail (plate sizes, welds, etc.) the reinforcement for the 20" x 24" hole shown in the web.

Section: ASTM A-36 Steel
Total depth 4'-3"
Web Plate 5/16" thick
Flanges each 5/8" x 12"

Forces: Shear on section at ℄ of hole: V = 20.5 kips
Moment on section at ℄ of hole: M = 8860" k

Specifications: AISC 7th Edition Part I (Elastic)
F_y = 36.0 ksi Assume fully braced.

Check all stresses etc.

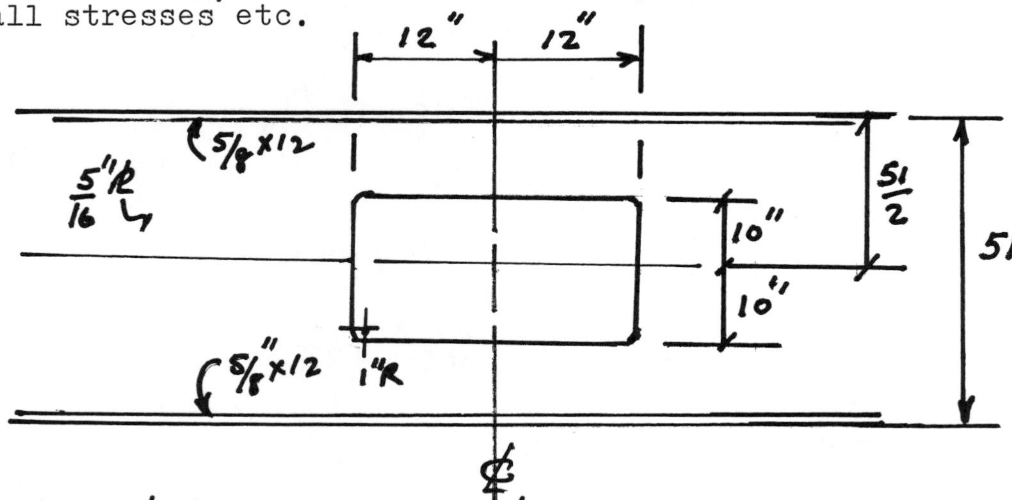

To find centroid X_G of Tee Section

$$\bar{Y} = \frac{2(5.843 \times 0.625 \times 0.313) + 15.5 \times 0.313 \times 7.75}{2(5.843 \times 0.625) + (15.5 \times 0.313)}$$

$$= 3.28''$$

$$I_X = 2\left(\tfrac{1}{3} \times 5.843 \times 0.625^3\right) + \tfrac{1}{3} \times 0.313 \times 15.5^3$$

$$= 388.95 \text{ in}^4$$

$$I_X = I_{XG} + Ay^2$$

$$I_{XG} = I_X - Ay^2 = 388.95 - 12.11\,(3.28)^2 = 258.45 \text{ in}^4$$

$I_{XG(1)} = I_{XG(2)}$ Due to symmetry.

$$(I/c)_{(1)} = (I/c)_2 = \frac{258.45}{3.28} = 79 \text{ in}^3$$

SECTION	A IN²	Y IN	Ay² IN⁴	Io	Ig IN⁴
49.75x 5/16	15.55			3210	3210
12x0.625	7.5	25.19	7.5x1263		9480
12x0.625	7.5				12690

D/d M.I of opening 5/8x20 − 208

12482 IN⁴

Applied forces @ ℄ $V_x = 20.5^k$; $M_x = 8860''^k$ constant over 24"

$V_A + V_B = V_x$ & $V_A = V_B = \frac{25.5}{51} V_x = \frac{V_x}{2} = 10.25^k$

∵ Hole is centered over N.A of Girder.

Consider section LL critical for moments

From Pg 160 of formulas for stress and strain By Roark

$$S_a = \frac{M_A}{I/c} + \frac{V_A x \left[\frac{I_1}{I_1 + I_2}\right]}{(I/c)_1} \text{ ---- compression}$$

$$S_b = \frac{M_A}{I/c} + \frac{V_B x \left[\frac{I_1}{I_1 + I_2}\right]}{(I/c)_2} \text{ --- Tension}$$

Also $S_a + S_b \leq 0.6 \times F_y = 0.6 \times 36 = 21.6$ ksi

Due to Symmetry $S_a = S_b$; $I_1 = I_2 = I_{XG(TEE)} = 258.45 \text{ IN}^4$

$M_A = 8860''^k$, $I_g = 12482 \text{ IN}^4$; $V_A = V_B = 10.25^k$

$(I/c)_1 = (I/c)_2 = 79 \text{ in}^3$

$$\therefore S_a = S_b = \frac{8860}{\frac{12482}{25.5}} + \frac{10.25 \times 12 \times \left[\frac{258.45}{258.45 + 258.45}\right]}{79}$$

$$= 19.1 < 21.6 \text{ ok.}$$

∴ No reinforcement is needed due to stress.

Check stem of tee which is subjected to compression against local buckling.

$\frac{b_f}{t_f} \leq \frac{3000}{\sqrt{36000}} = 16$; $\frac{6}{0.625} = 9.6 < 16$ ok

$\frac{b_s}{t_s} \leq 21$; $\frac{15.5}{.313} = 49.6 > 21$, N.G. Hence web needs stiffener plate. As per 1.9.2 of AISC $\frac{b_s}{t_s} \leq \frac{8000}{\sqrt{36000}} = 42$ & $\frac{b_f}{t_f} \leq 16$

∴ $b_s = 42 \times 5/16 = 13.125$ & $b_f = 6"$, $t_f = 5/8"$ to get $b_f/t_f = 9.6 < 16$ ok

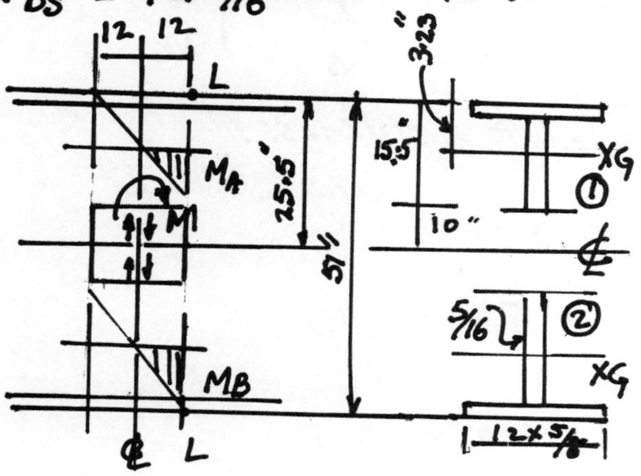

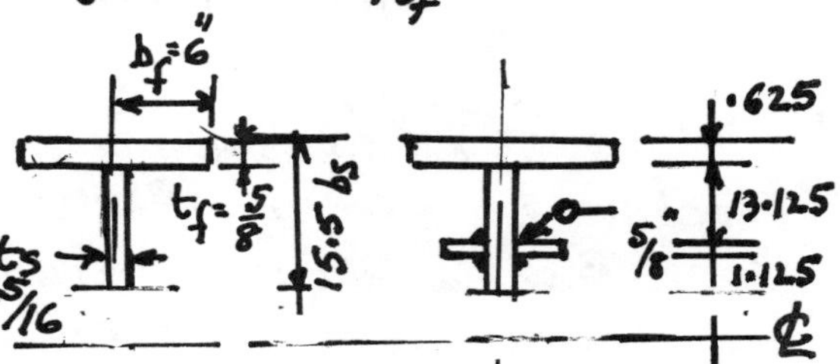

EXAMPLE 2-12

Given:- This is a semi-rigid connection design problem in which the beam, the column, the bracing, and the connection are all to be designed using a combination of the beam-line semi- graphical approach and the semi-rigid connection analysis process. The only assumptions made for purposes of problem-simplification are such that the charts for F are not needed since they are not readily available. Use ASTM A-36 and AISC Specifications Part I Elastic.

Connection: Use p = 0.50 and F = 0.79 based on an assumed ratio (K_B/K_C) = 1.20 Use it.

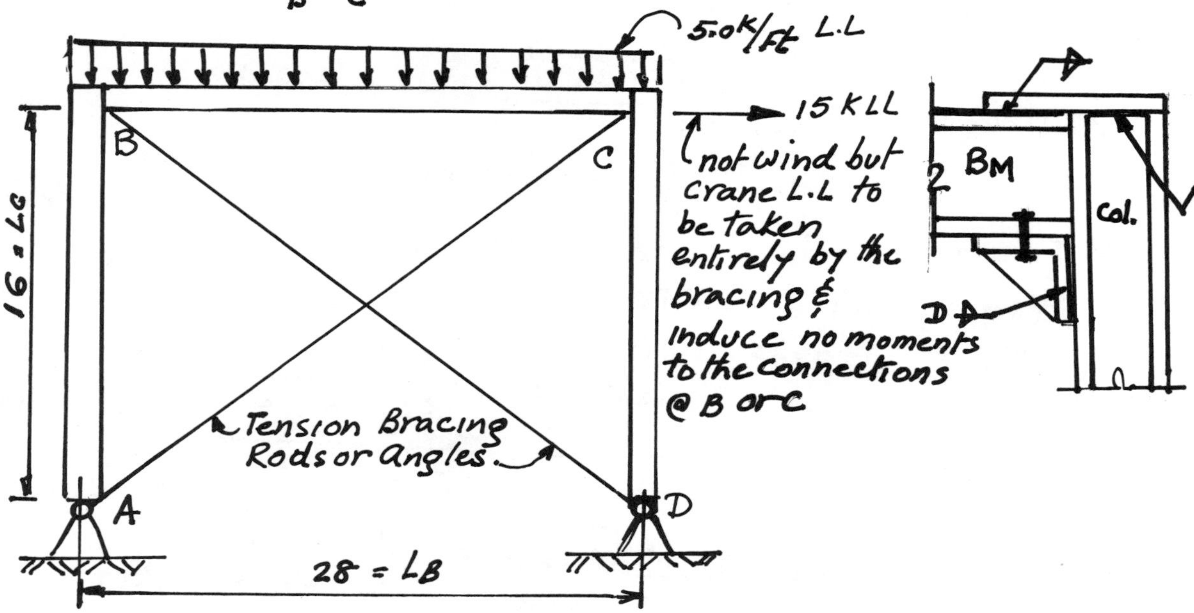

Use Beam Line approach with computed JE for the connection. Design the beam, column (selecting it for required K if at all possible), connection (see detail) at B and/or C, and select a bracing for whatever you consider proper.

Dead load of beam = 0.1 K/ft

Live load = 5.0 K/ft ∴ Total load = 5.1 K/ft.

To do the analysis of Portal frame first determine relative I_B & I_C. $\frac{K_B}{K_C} = 1.2$ where $K_B = \frac{I_B}{L_B}$ & $K_C = \frac{I_C}{L_C}$

$$\therefore \frac{I_B}{I_C} = 1.2\frac{L_B}{L_C} = 1.2 \times \frac{28}{16} = 2.1 \text{ or } I_B = 2.1 I_C$$

Structur & Loading along with relative stiffness.

Pinned Portal frame

Semi rigid connections @ B & C

Relative stiffness

$$AB = \frac{I_C}{16} = 7.0 = K_{AB}$$

$$BC = \frac{2.1 I_B}{28} = 8.4 = K_{BC}$$

$$CD = \frac{I_C}{16} = 7.0 = K_{CD}.$$

Fixed end moments

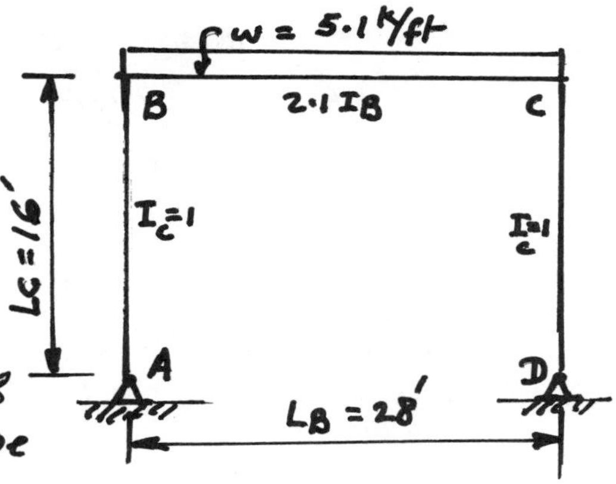

$M_{AB} = M_{BA} = 0$

$M_{BC} = + \dfrac{wL_B^2}{12} = \dfrac{5.1 \times 28^2}{12} = 333.2'^k$

$M_{CB} = -333.2'^k$

$M_{CD} = M_{DC} = 0$

No sidesway because
1) symmetric loading
2) L.L on side taken up by bracing

Moment-distribution is By slope deflection method.

$M_{AB} = +7(-2\theta_A - \theta_B)$; $M_{BA} = +7(-2\theta_B - \theta_A)$

$M_{BC} = +333.2 + 8.4(-2\theta_B - \theta_C)$; $M_{CB} = -333.2 + 8.4(-2\theta_C - \theta_B)$

$M_{CD} = +7(-2\theta_C - \theta_D)$; $M_{DC} = +7(-2\theta_D - \theta_C)$

Joint conditions:- $M_{AB} = 0$; $M_{BA} + M_{BC} = 0$; $M_{CB} + M_{CD} = 0$; $M_{DC} = 0$

Shear conditions:- $H_A + H_B = 0$

& $M_B = 0 = M_C$

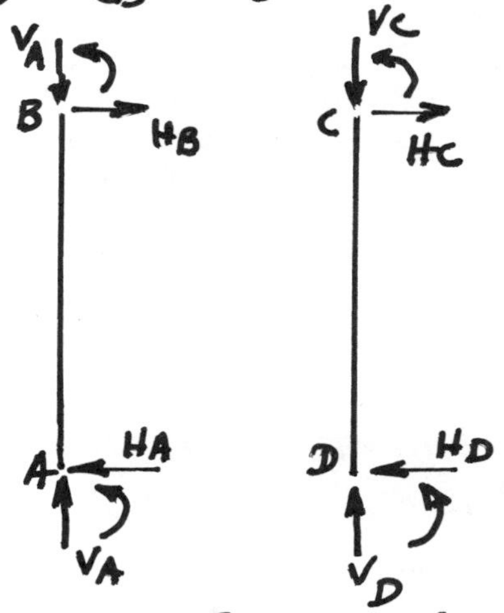

Thus $\left(\dfrac{M_{AB} + M_{BA}}{16}\right) + \left(\dfrac{M_{DC} + M_{CD}}{16}\right) = 0$

$\therefore -\theta_A - \theta_B - \theta_C - \theta_D = 0$

Final slope deflection equations to be solved are

$$-14\theta_A - 7\theta_B = 0$$
$$-7\theta_A - 30.8\theta_B - 8.4\theta_C = -333.2$$
$$-8.4\theta_B - 30.8\theta_C - 7\theta_D = +333.2$$
$$-7\theta_C - 14\theta_D = 0$$
$$-\theta_A - \theta_B - \theta_C - \theta_D = 0$$

$\theta_A = -8.814$; $\theta_B = +17.629$; $\theta_C = -17.63$; $\theta_D = 8.814$

& $M_{AB} = 0$, $M_{BA} = -185.11$; $M_{BC} = 185.11$; $M_{CB} = -185.11$;

$M_{CD} = +185.11$; $M_{DC} = 0$

Also note $-\theta_A = +\theta_D$; $\theta_B = -\theta_C$; $\theta_A = \frac{1}{2}\theta_B$; $\theta_D = \frac{1}{2}\theta_C$

$M_B = M_C$; $M_A = M_D = 0$

Determine $\theta_B = \theta_C$ for Beam by conjugate beam method

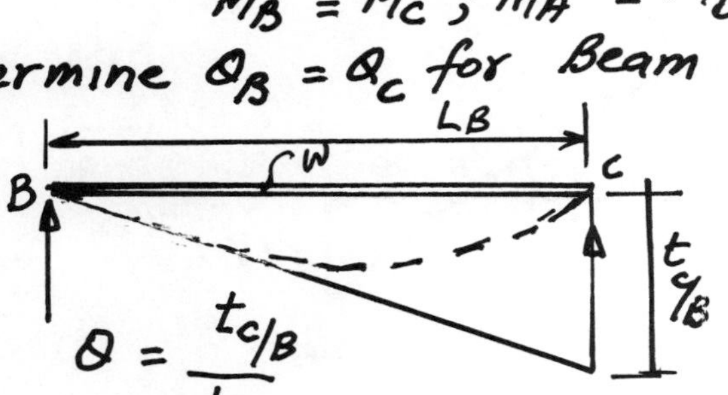

$\theta = \dfrac{t_{c/B}}{L_B}$

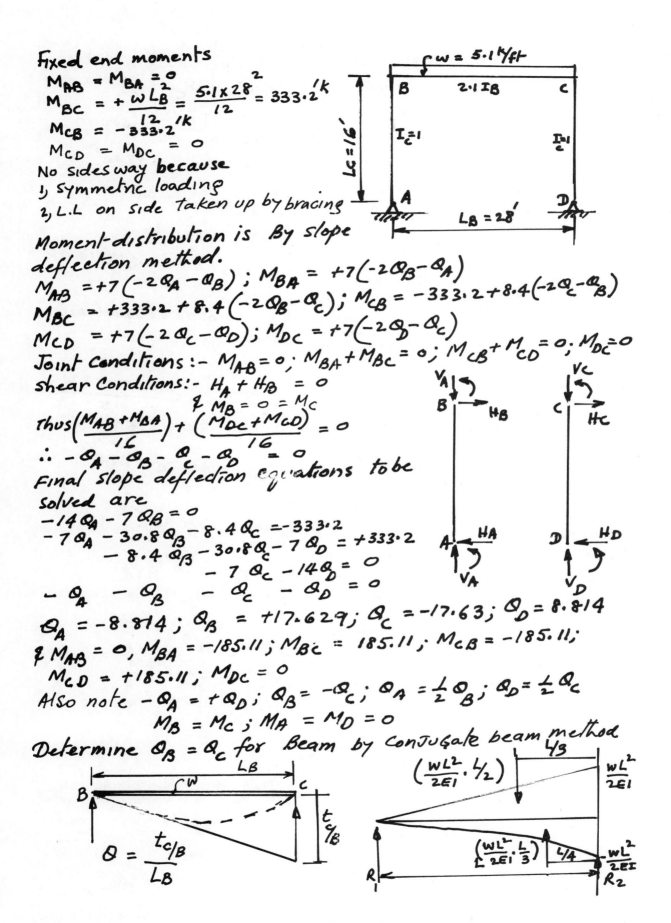

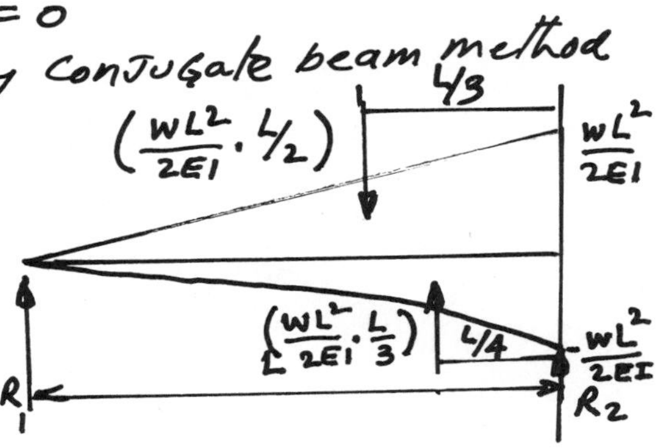

$$\Sigma M_B = 0 \;\therefore\; R_1 L = \left(\frac{wL^2}{2EI}\cdot\frac{L}{2}\right)\frac{L}{3} - \left(\frac{wL^2}{2EI}\cdot\frac{L}{3}\right)\frac{L}{4}$$

$$R_1 = \frac{wL^3}{24EI} = R_2 = \theta_B = \theta_C$$

$$S_o = \frac{M}{F_b} = \frac{wL^2}{8F_b} = \frac{5.1\times 28^2\times 12}{8\times 20} = 300 \text{ in}^3$$

$$S_n = 0.79\times S_o = 0.79\times 300 = 237 \text{ in}^3$$

Try W 21 X 112 & r for WT 10x56 = 3.01

$$F_b = 22000 - 0.679\left(\frac{336}{3.01}\right)^2 = 13{,}550 \text{ psi}$$

Also

$$F_b = 12000000/336\times 1.87 = 19{,}110 \text{ psi} \leftarrow$$

$$f_b = \frac{M}{S} = \frac{5.1\times 28^2\times 12}{8\times 249.6}\times 0.79 = 18{,}950 \text{ psi} < 19{,}110 \text{ ok}$$

$$\therefore I_{xB} = 2620.6 \text{ in}^4$$

$$\theta_B = \theta_C = \frac{wL_B^3}{24EI_B} = \frac{5.1\times 28^3\times 144}{24\times 29000\times 2620.6} = 0.00883 \text{ radians}$$

$$\frac{I_B}{L_B} = k_B = \frac{2620.6}{336} = 7.82$$

$$w = p = \frac{1}{1+2k/J} = \frac{J}{J+2K} \text{ or } J = \frac{2pk}{1-p} = \frac{2\times 0.5\times 7.82}{1-0.5} = 15.64$$

$$J.E = \frac{15.64\times 29000}{12} = 378000\,'^{\#} = 378\,'^{K}$$

For $M\theta$ curve of connection, when $\theta = 0.01$ & $M = JE = 378'^K$

$M_c = 118\,'^K$ & $\theta_c = 0.00328$ radians.

Moment in Beam $= \frac{5.1\times 28^2}{8} - 118 = 381.8$ Say $382\,'^K$

Moment in Column $= 118\,'^K$

$\because \Sigma M_A = 0 \;\therefore\; 5.1\times 28\times 14 - V_D\times 28 = 0,\quad V_D = 71.4^K = V_A$

$\because \Sigma M_B = 0 \;\therefore\; H_A\times 16 = 118,\quad H_A = 7.375^K = H_D$

Final Moment Diagram & Free body.

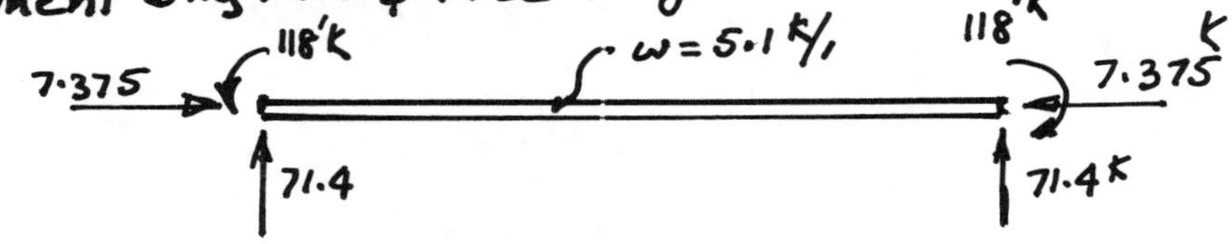

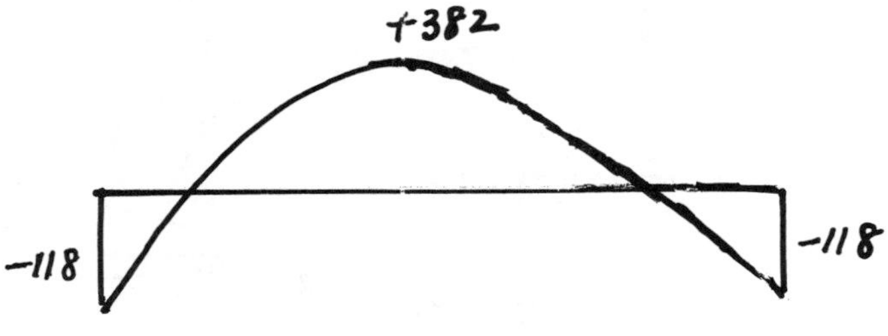

Beam Design $M_{max} = 382'^{K} = 4584000$ lb in

Axial load $= 7.375^{K}$

$S_{req'd} = \frac{4584000}{22000} = 209 \text{ in}^3$

Try W 21x112 Properties

$w = 112$ #/ft	$I_x = 2620.6 \text{ in}^4$
$A = 32.93 \text{ in}^2$	$S_x = 249.6 \text{ in}^3$
$d = 21.00$ in	$r_x = 8.92$ in
$b_f = 13''$	$I_y = 289.7 \text{ in}^4$
$t_f = 0.865''$	$S_y = 44.6 \text{ in}^3$
$t_w = 0.527''$	$r_y = 2.96$ in
$\frac{d}{A_f} = 1.87''$	$I_f = I_y/2$

$r = \sqrt{\frac{I_f}{A_f + A_w/6}} = 3.35''$

Check $l/r < 40$ so $\frac{336}{3.35} = 100 > 40$ N.G

$l_b \le 13 b_f$; $13 \times 13 = 169$, $336 > 169$ NG

$\le 545 \frac{A_f}{d}$; $\frac{545}{1.87} = 292$ $336 > 292$ N.G

∴ Use formula (4) or (5) for F_b & $C_b = 1.0$

4) $F_b = 22000 - 0.679 \left(\frac{336}{3.35}\right)^2 = 15210$ psi

5) $F_b = \frac{12 \times 10^6}{336 \times 1.87} = 19100$ psi ←

$f_a = \frac{P}{A} = \frac{7.375}{32.93} = 0.239$ ksi

From chart (a) Fig 10.7 Page 331 steel structure by beedle

$G = \frac{I_B L_c}{I_c L_B} = 1.2$ & 10, $K_B = 0.87$ ∴ $\frac{Kl}{r_y} = \frac{0.87 \times 336}{2.96} = 99$

$F_a = 13100$ psi

then $\frac{f_a}{F_a} + \frac{f_b}{F_b} \le 1$ So $\frac{0.239}{13.10} + \frac{\frac{4584}{249.6}}{22} = 0.971 < 1.0$ ok

Use W21x112 For Beam.

Column Design $I_c = \frac{I_B}{2.1} = 0.476 I_B = 1250 \text{ in}^4$

Try W18x77 Properties

$d = 18.16''$	$I_x = 1286.8 \text{ in}^4$
$b_f = 8.787$	$I_y = 88.6 \text{ in}^4$
$t_f = 0.831$	$S_x = 141.7 \text{ in}^3$
$t_w = 0.475$	$r_x = 7.54''$
$\frac{d}{A_f} = 2.49$	$r_y = 1.98''$

$r = \sqrt{\frac{I_y/2}{A_f + A_w/6}} = 2.26''$

since $l_b < 13 \times 8.79$ use non compact value of F_b from ④ & ⑤ formula of AISC

$F_b = 22000 - \frac{0.679}{1.75}\left(\frac{192}{2.26}\right)^2 = 19208$ psi

Also $F_b = \dfrac{12 \times 10^6}{192 \times 2.49} = 25100$ Psi Use $F_b = 22000$ Psi

$f_a = \dfrac{71.4}{22.63} = 3.15$ ksi

$\dfrac{KL}{r_y} = \dfrac{0.85 \times 192}{1.98} = 82$

k is obtained from Page 331 of Beedle $G = \dfrac{I_c L_B}{I_B L_c} = 0.833$ & $G = 10$

$F_a = 15130$ Psi.

$\because C_m = 0.85$ & $f_b = \dfrac{1416}{141.7} = 10$ ksi

Formula 7(a) of A.I.S.C

$$\frac{f_a}{F_a} + \frac{C_m f_b}{\left(1 + \frac{f_a}{F_e'}\right) F_b} \leq 1$$

& $F_e' = \dfrac{149000}{\left(\frac{0.85 \times 192}{2.54}\right)^2} = 31800$

$\dfrac{f_a}{F_e'} \simeq 0$

$\therefore 0.208 + \dfrac{0.85 \times 10}{22} = 0.594 < 1.0$ ok.

New value of F for check $= \dfrac{249.6}{273.6} = 91.3\%$

Design Connection

Top Plate is designed to yield @ an end moment equal to 25% of allowable resisting moment of Beam. This classifies as a relative flexible connection

$\therefore M = \frac{1}{4} S_x F_b = \frac{1}{4} \times 249.6 \times 22 = 1373''$k

But actual M from Plot $= 118'$k $= 1416''$k ←

$T = \dfrac{M}{d} = \dfrac{1416}{21.0} = 67^k$

$A_{PL} = \dfrac{T}{F_y} = \dfrac{67}{36} = 1.86$ IN^2

Use $6 \times \frac{5}{8}$ PL cut as shown, As supplied $= 2.5$ IN^2

Weld design:- Length of ½" Fillet weld $= \dfrac{67}{4.8} = 13.95$ Say 14"

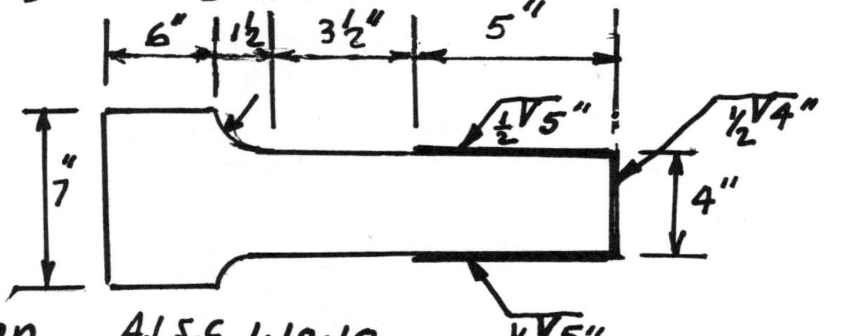

Seat Design A.I.S.C 1.10.10

$F_p = 27$ k/□" $= \dfrac{R}{t_{wB}(N+K)}$

$\therefore N = \dfrac{R}{27 t_{wB}} - K = \dfrac{71.4}{27(0.527)} - 1.625 = 3.40''$

$\therefore$ Seat length $= 3.4 + 0.5 = 3.9$ Say $4\frac{1}{2}''$

$M = 71.4(4.5 - 1.7) = 200''$K

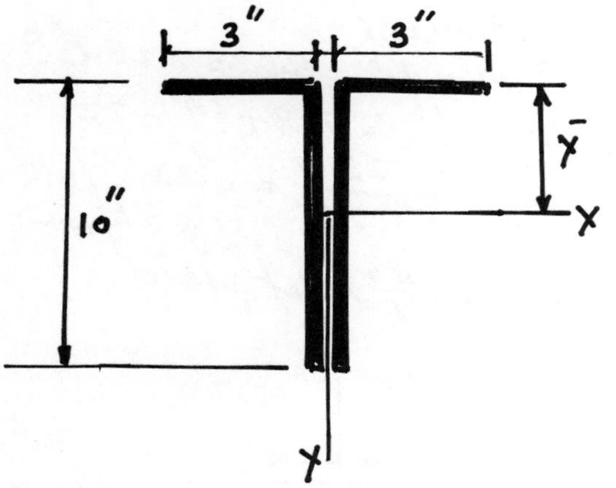

Try Vert. Leg = 10"
Hor. Leg = 3"

$$\bar{y} = \frac{2 \times 10 \times 5}{20 + 6} = 3.85''$$

$$I_x = 2\left[\frac{3.85^3 + 6.15^3}{3} + 2(3.85)^2\right]$$

$= 253 \text{ IN}^4$

$$q_z = \frac{200 \times 3.85}{253} = 3.02^{k}/''$$

$$q_y = \frac{71.4}{22} = 3.24^{k}/''$$

$$q = \sqrt{3.02^2 + 3.24^2} = 4.43^{k}/''$$

Use 1/2" Weld, which gives $q_{allowable} = 4.8^{k}/''$

Use ST W 10×31, Properties $d = 10.50''$ $t_f = 0.615$
$b_f = 8.24''$ $t_w = 0.400$

Check if stiffeners are required $L = 5''$

in col – comp. flg $t_{wc} < \frac{A_p}{t_B + 5K} = \frac{1.86}{0.5 + 0.5 \times 1.375} = 0.475$

∴ $0.24 < 0.475$ No stiffener Req'd

col – Ten. flg $t_f < 0.4\sqrt{A_p} = 0.4\sqrt{1.86} = 0.548 < 0.831$

No Stiffener Req'd. ok

Bracing Design

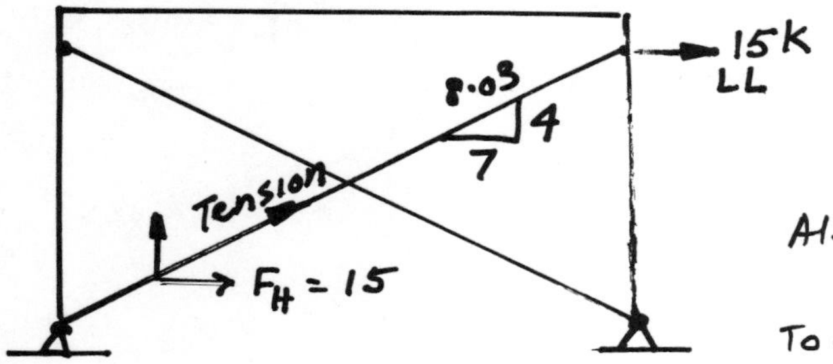

$$\frac{F}{8.03} = \frac{15}{7}, \quad F = 17.2^k$$

$$\frac{F_V}{4} = \frac{15}{7}, \quad F_V = 8.6^k$$

AISC Try clevis #4, Safe load $= 21^k$

To find size of rod

$$F_t = 22^{ksi} = \frac{P}{A}$$

$$A = \frac{P}{F_t} = \frac{17.2}{22} = 0.788 \text{ IN}^2$$

Use $1\frac{3}{4}''\phi$ clevis Rod, $A = 1.75 \square''$

check stress $F_t = \frac{17.2}{1.75} = 9.83^{ksi} < 22^{ksi}$ ok

Use CLEVIS #4, $1\frac{3}{4}''\phi$ Rod & use 8ST20 Bracing member

Properties of 8ST20, $d = 8.00''$, $b_f = 7.00''$, $t_f = 0.503''$, $t_w = 0.307''$

Check welding stress in ST $F = \frac{P}{2L} = \frac{74.1}{16} = 4.73^{k}/'' < 4.8^{k}/''$ ok

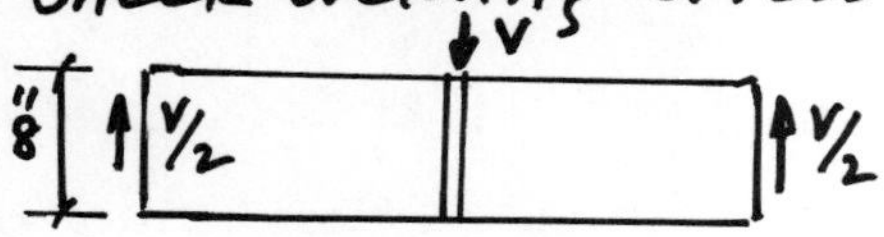

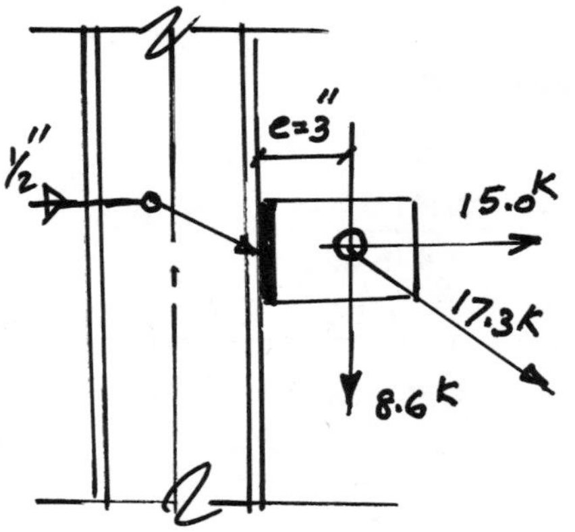

Check Moment

$e = 3''$, $M = Pe = 8.6 \times 3 = 25.8\ ''k$

$Z = bd + \frac{d^2}{3} = 7 \times 8 + \frac{64}{3} = 77$

$F = \frac{M}{Z} = \frac{25.8}{77} = 0.335\ k/in^2 < 4.8\ k/in^2$

Hence use 1/2" Fillet weld.

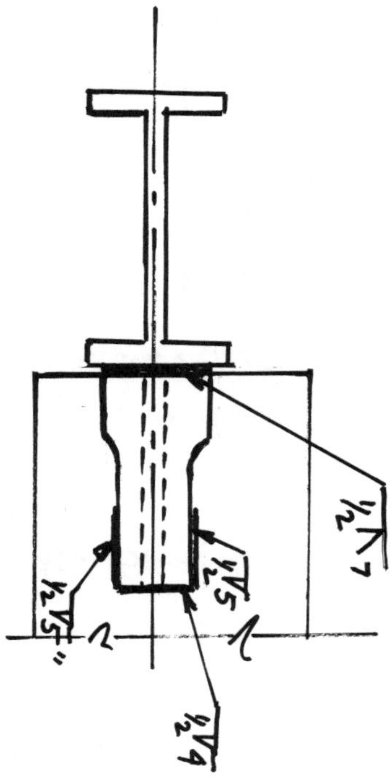

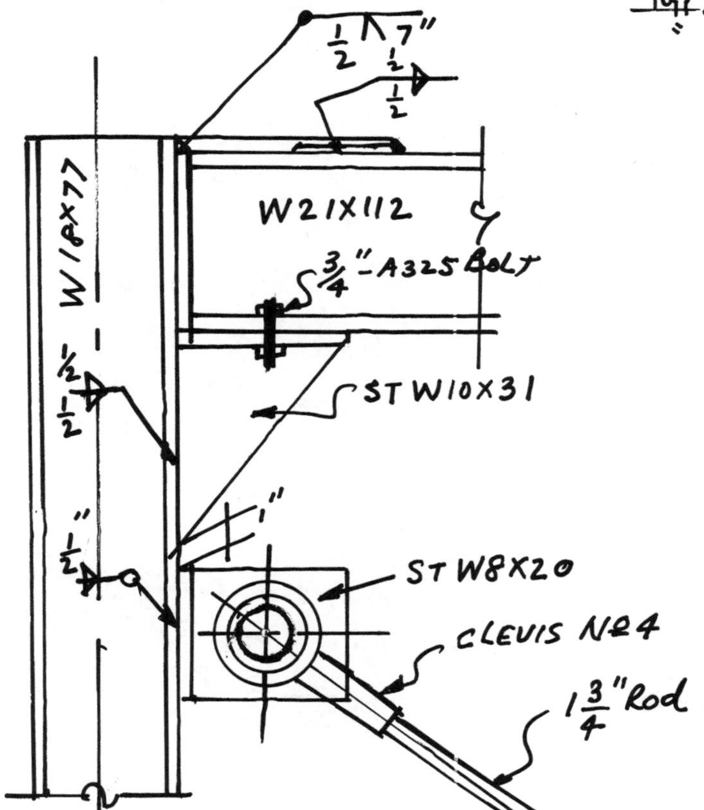

TENSION MEMBER

EXAMPLE 2-13

Given:- Design a pair of A-36 Angles to support a tensile force of 60 kips. The member is 12 ft. long between joint centers and is connected to a 3/8 in. gusset plate with 7/8 in. rivets.

Maximum stress on net section = $0.60F_y$ - AISC 1.5.1.1

Allowable stress for A_{36} steel = 22 ksi

Net cross sectional area for 2 ∟s $= \frac{60}{22} = 2.73$ sq.in

for 1 ∟ = 1.37 □"

Assume angle thickness $= \frac{1}{4}$"

& also only one hole will be deducted from each angle ie 0.25 □" cross sectional area would be deducted from each angle.

then gross Area of angle = 1.37 + 0.25 = 1.62 □"

Agr of ∟ $4 \times 3 \times \frac{1}{4}$ = 1.69 > 1.62 ok.

As per AISC 1.14.3, net section ≤ 0.85 × 1.69 × 2

≤ 2.87 > 2.73 ok

Double shear of 7/8" rivet & Bearing in one direction on two $\frac{1}{4}$" thick ∟s = 15.91 ksi

No of rivets req'd $= \frac{60}{15.91} = 3.77$ use 4.

spacing of rivet 3"

use c/c distance between Joints as length of member for computing L/r. Also r_z of 2 ∟s $4 \times 3 \times \frac{1}{4}$ with 3/8" apart $= 0.65$ in, $\therefore \frac{L}{r_z} = \frac{12 \times 12}{0.65} = 221 < 240$ ok

Hence two angles are placed with long legs back to back with 3/8" spacing.

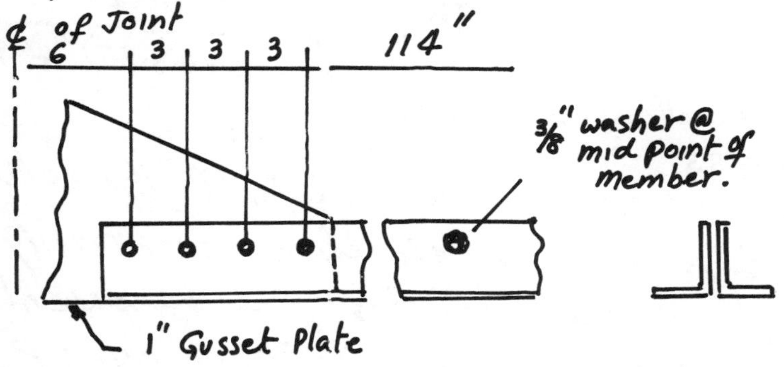

CONNECTIONS

EXAMPLE 3-14

Given:- Design an eccentricity loaded connection moment parallel to the plane of the fastener group as well as weld group.

fastener group

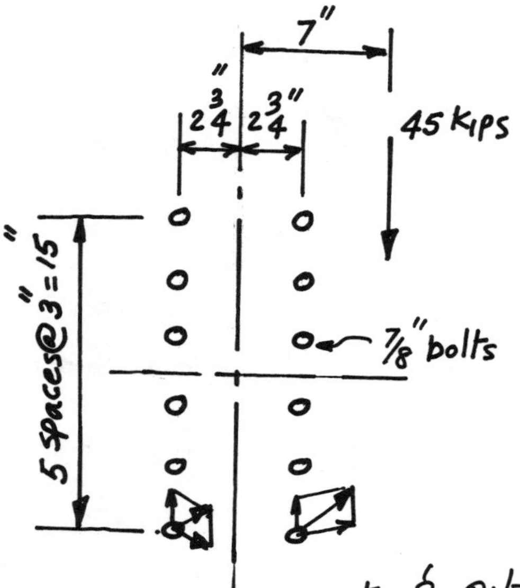

A 7/8" bolt - A325 S.S = 9.02k & pitch = 3" c/c

$$J = 0.601\left[12\times2.75^2+4\times1.5^2+4\times4.5^2+4\times7.5^2\right] = 244\ in^4$$

$$f_v = \frac{Pe}{A} = \frac{45}{12\times0.601} = 6.24\ ksi$$

Most highly stressed bolts are top & bottom bolt near load.

In the four bolts @ corner,

Horizontal moment component of stress $= \frac{Pe}{J} r$

$$= \frac{45\times7}{244}\times7.5 = 9.68\ ksi$$

Vertical moment component of stress $= \frac{45\times7}{244}\times2.75 = 3.55\ ksi$

∴ Shear in most highly stressed bolt

$$= \sqrt{(6.24+3.55)^2+9.68^2} = 13.76\ ksi$$

& max. allowable shear stress $= 15\ ksi$

Check by A.I.S.C Manual Table XII, the actual eccentricity of 7" is reduced to an effective eccentricity & for 6 fasteners per vertical row, this effective eccentricity is 3.5" & corresponding coefficient of 7.99, gives $P = 7.99\times9.02 = 72.1^k > 45$ Hence ok.

Weld group.

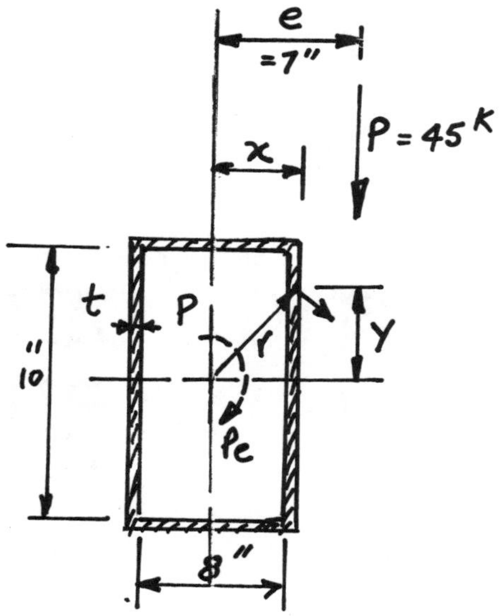

$J = I_x + I_y$

& for the line $J = 2\left[8 \times 5^2 + 10^3/12\right] + 2\left[10 \times 4^2 + 8^2/12\right] = 972 \text{ IN}^3$

The most highly stressed points are the upper and lower corners on the side of the load.

At corners, the horizontal component of stress $= \left(\frac{45 \times 7}{972}\right)5 = 1.62\text{ K}/''$

the vertical component of stress $= \left(\frac{45 \times 7}{972}\right)4 = 1.29\text{ K}/''$

Direct vertical stress $= \frac{45}{36} = 1.25\text{ K}/''$

$\therefore f_v = \sqrt{1.62^2 + (1.29 + 1.25)^2} = 3.01\text{ K}/''$

So that $\frac{3.01}{21.0}\sqrt{2} = 0.20$ in E70 fillet weld is required

& $\frac{1}{4}$" weld be used.

Check by A.I.S.C Table XVIII, K = 0.8 and a = 0.7

Coefficient C = 1.38 for E70 fillet.

req'd number of sixteenth of an inch in the fillet weld

$= \frac{45}{1.38 \times 10} = 3.2$

ie 1/4" fillet weld be used.

3

PLASTIC DESIGN OF STEEL STRUCTURES

The method of structural design that is based upon valuation of the load that will induce failure of a structure is termed as Plastic Design (Limit Design) when applied to steel structures. Plastic Design is concerned with an allowable load which equals the ultimate load divided by an appropriate factor called Load Factor.

In fact Plastic Design recognizes that a structure may be loaded beyond the initial yielding. If the load is increased gradually with incremental load on the structure, it will collapse at the ultimate load.

EXAMPLE 3-01

Given:- (A) Compute the minimum area of cover plates required, area and theoretical length, to be used with a W 10X 21 Member of ASTM A-36 Steel. No other cover plates and no other cross-section is to be used in this part of the problem. Consider the entire length of the W and plates. Neglect the weight of the and the plates. This is a plastic design and the loads given are ultimate loads already. Load Factor is 1.70.

(B) The dead load is now to be included. Design plastically according to Part II AISC Specifications using ASTM A-36 Steel. Any cross-section(s) and cover plate systems may be employed now. Restrict the length of any given member to no more than 48 feet; thus, a connection will be required and is to be of high-strength bolts. Do not design the connection at D in

Let right span CD Governs:- Effect of U.D.L is taken just to add numerical value of M_s due to ultimate load of Dead wt of beam as main loading effecting the design are point loads.

$M_p = M_{SK}/2 = \frac{146.86}{2} = 73.43'^k$

$Z = \frac{73.43 \times 12}{36} = 24.48 \ in^3$

SELECT B 12 x 19 ; $Z = 24.8 \ in^3$, $M_p = 74.4'^k$, $d = 12.16''$

Span BC

$M_{SG} = M_{SH} = 117.9'^k$; $M_s/2 = \frac{117.9}{2} = 58.95'^k < M_p = 74.4$ ok

Span AB $M_{SE} = 104.78'^k = M_p + KM_p$

$= M_p + \frac{5}{20} M_p = \frac{5}{4} M_p$

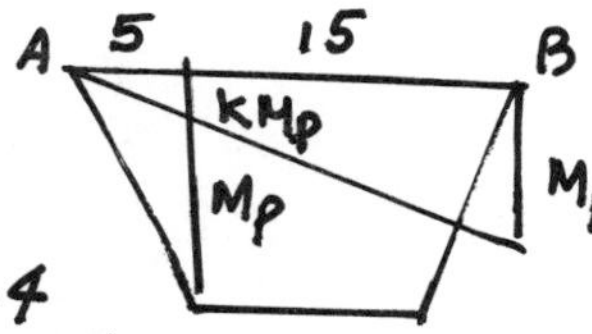

$\therefore M_p = 104.78 \times 4/5$

$= 83.82'^k > M_p$ selected ie 74.4

Hence Cover Plate is req'd in section AB only.

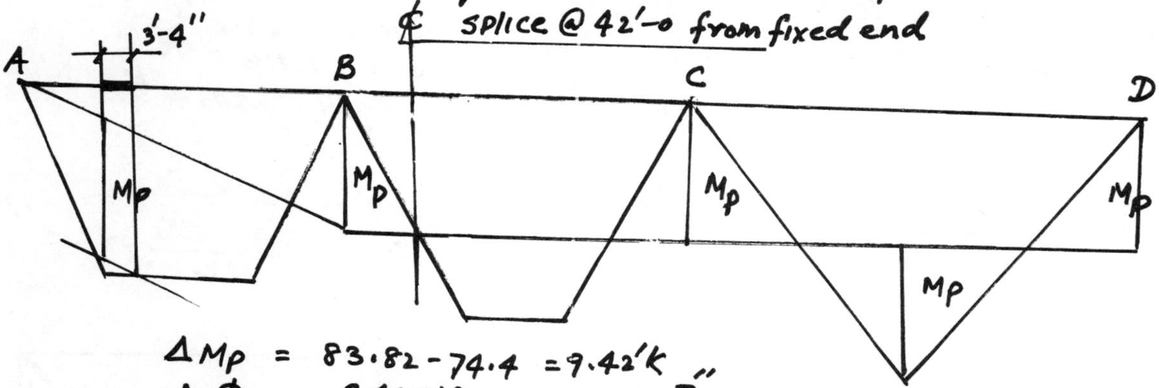

$\Delta M_p = 83.82 - 74.4 = 9.42'^k$

$A\ PL = \frac{9.42 \times 12}{36 \times 12.19} = 0.258 \ \square''$

Provide $3\frac{1}{2}'' \times \frac{3}{16}'' = 0.656 \ \square'' > 0.258 \ \square''$ ok

ΔM_p Provided $= \frac{0.656 \times 36 \times 12.19}{12} = 24'^k$

Length Cover PL $= 3'-4''$

3) Mechanism 2 Beam Mechanism.

4) Reactions Computed Statically

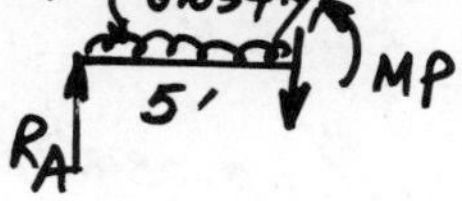

$R_A \times 5 - \frac{0.034 \times 5^2}{2} = 74.4 + 24$

$R_A = 19.76^K$

$R_B = (41.4 + 0.68 - 19.76) + 14.5 + 0.38 = 37.20^K$

$R_D \times 12 - \frac{0.034 \times 12^2}{2} = 74.4$

$R_D = 6.40^K$

$R_C = [29 + 0.73 - 14.86] + [24.07 + 0.82 - 6.40]$

$= 33.36^K$

$R_{Total} = 19.76 + 37.20 + 6.40 + 33.36 = 96.72^K$

this problem. Details are required.

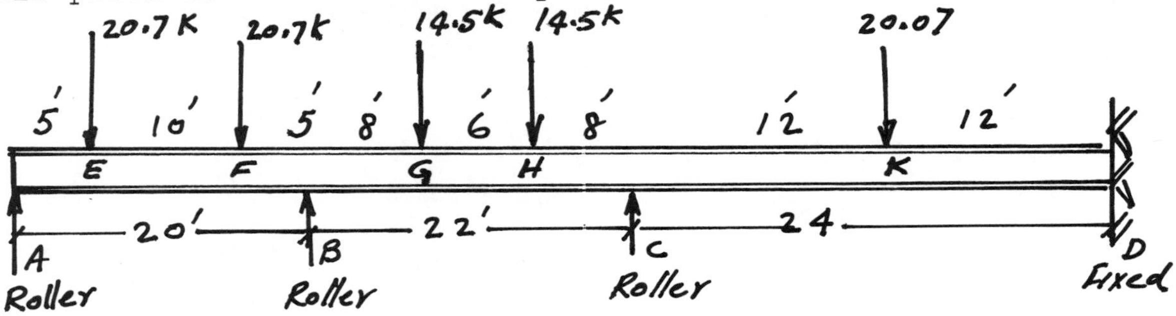

(C) Consider the support at A: What type of support will be required if the structure is erected at 65 F and the temperature range of the structure in use is -25 F to 120 F? Give a detail of it in your submittal.

Solution:- All loads are ultimate

A)

1) Moment diagram:- $M_{SE} = M_{SF} = 5 \times 20.7 = 103.5'^{K}$

$M_{SG} = M_{SH} = 8 \times 14.5 = 116.0'^{K}$

$M_K = \frac{PL}{4} = \frac{24.07 \times 24}{4} = 144.4'^{K}$

2) Section to be used W10x21

Properties

$Z = 24.11 in^3$; $F_y = 36$ ksi

$d = 9.9$ in ; $M_p = \frac{24.1 \times 36}{12} = 72.3'^{K}$

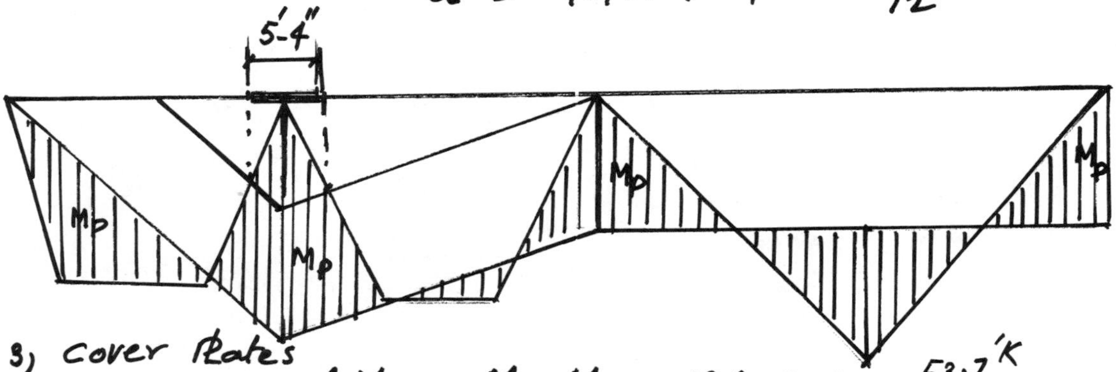

3) Cover Plates

$\Delta M_p = M_s - M_p = 126 - 72.3 = 53.7'^{K}$

$A\,PL = \frac{\Delta M_p}{F_y d} = \frac{53.7 \times 12}{36 \times 9.9} = 1.82 \square''$

$\therefore$ Use $5\frac{1}{4}'' \times \frac{3}{8}'' \times 5'-6''$

ΔM_p provided $= \frac{1.97 \times 36 \times 9.9}{12} = 58.5'^{K}$

B) 1) Assume Dead weight beam $= 20^{\#}/' = 20 \times 1.7 = 34^{\#}/' = 0.034^{K}/'$

2) Moment Diagram

	Due to Pt load	Due to U.DL	Total $'^{K}$
$M_{SE} = M_{SF} = 5 \times 20.7$	$= 103.5'^{K}$	$+\left(\frac{0.034 \times 5}{2}(20-5)\right) = 1.28$	104.78
$M_{SG} = M_{SH} = 8 \times 14.5$	$= 116.0'^{K}$	$+\left(\frac{0.034 \times 8}{2}(22-8)\right) = 1.90$	$117.9'^{K}$
$M_{SK} = \frac{24.07 \times 24}{4}$	$= 144.42'^{K}$	$+\left(\frac{0.034 \times 12}{2}(24-12)\right) = 2.44$	$146.8'^{K}$

5, Shear force $V_{max} = 22.32K$

$V_{allowable}$ (AISC Sec 2-4) = $20 \times 0.26 \times 12.16 = 63.2$

$\therefore 22.32 < 63.2$ ok

6, Cross Section

$\frac{b}{t} = \frac{4.01}{0.349} = 11.5 < 17$ ok

$d/w = \frac{12.16}{0.240} = 50.7 < 55$ ok

7, Splice:- splice for shear at inflection point. It is to be done with the elastic analysis.

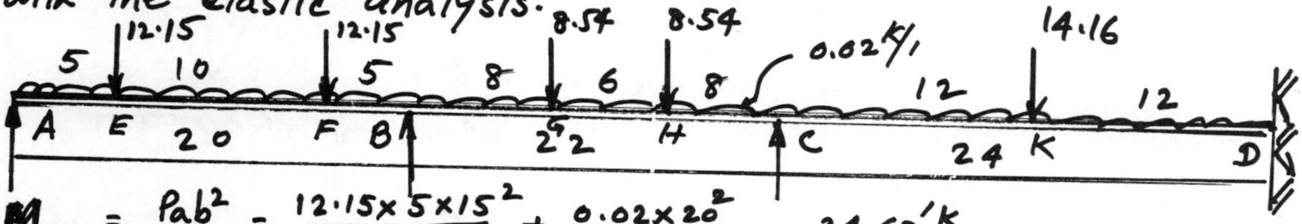

$M_{AB} = \frac{Pab^2}{L^2} = \frac{12.15 \times 5 \times 15^2}{20^2} + \frac{0.02 \times 20^2}{12} = -34.68'K$

$M_{BA} = +34.68'K$

$M_{BC} = -28.51'K = -M_{CB}$

$M_{CD} = \frac{PL}{8} + \frac{wL^2}{12} = \frac{14.16 \times 24}{8} + \frac{0.02 \times 24^2}{12} = -43.44'K = -M_{DC}$

Since the length of cover plate is very small. For analysis of moment distribution, consider beam of constant EI.

$M_{SE} = M_{SF} = 5 \times 12.15 = 60.75'K$

$M_{SG} = M_{SH} = 8.54 \times 8 = 68.32'K$

$M_K = \frac{14.16 \times 24}{4} = 84.96$

$K_{AB} = K_{BA} = 3/20$; $K_{BC} = K_{CB} = 4/22$; $K_{CD} = K_{DC} = 4/24$

$D.F_{BA} = \frac{3/20}{3/20 + 4/22} = 0.46$; $DF_{BC} = \frac{4/22}{3/20 + 4/22} = 0.54$

$DF_{CB} = \frac{4/22}{4/22 + 4/24} = 0.52$; $D.F_{CD} = \frac{4/24}{4/22 + 4/24} = 0.48$

By Moment distribution $M_B = 38.72'K$; $M_C = 32.49'K$; $M_D = 48.90'K$

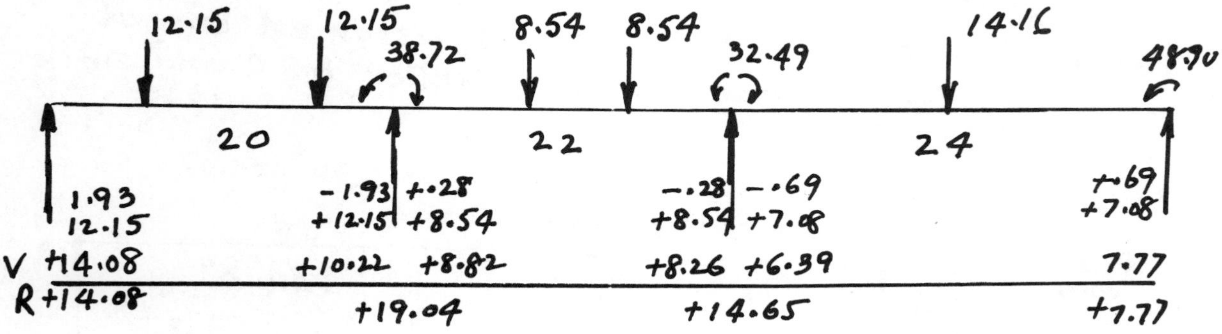

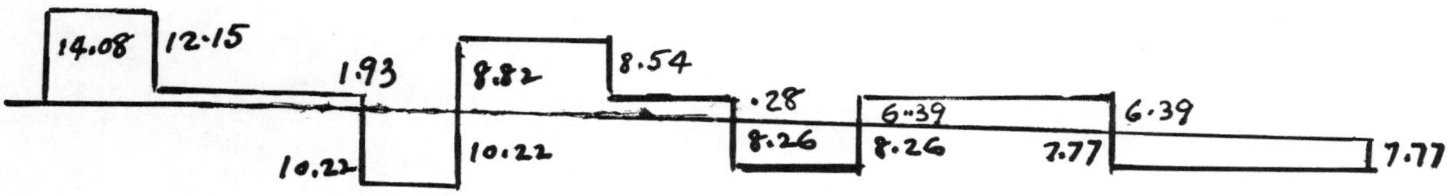

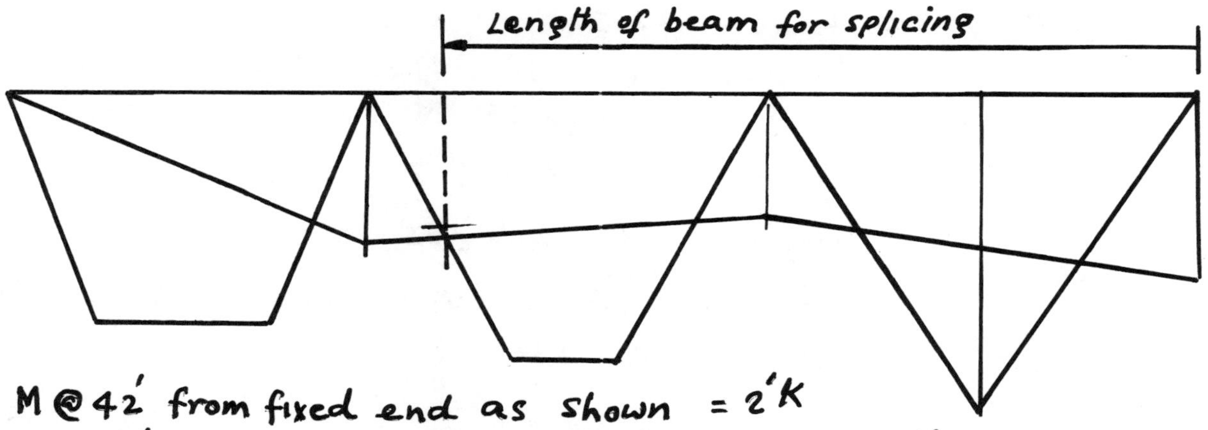

M @ 42′ from fixed end as shown $= 2'^{K}$

℄ location of splice from plastic Moment diagram

use $5/8''$ H.S. Bolt D.S $= 9.20^{K}$

Shear found elastically $= 8.82^{K}$

No of Bolts $= \frac{8.82}{9.20} \simeq 0.96$ say 1

Since 1 No bolt is not practical atleast 4 No are req'd. Also the moment is negligible and ℘ is designed to resist shear. Let there be $2 - \frac{1}{4}'' \times 10'' \times 10''$ splice plate.

$\Sigma y^2 = 3^2 = 9$

$R_y = \frac{8.82}{4} = 2.21$

$R_x = \frac{M y}{\Sigma y^2}$ -

$\therefore R = \sqrt{R_y^2 + R_x^2}$

$9.20^2 = R_y^2 + R_x^2$

$84.4 = 4.9 + R_x^2 \quad \therefore R_x = 8.8$

$\therefore 8.8 = \frac{M \cdot 3}{9} = \frac{M}{3}$

$\therefore M = 8.8 \times 3 = 26.4''^{K} = 2.2'^{K} > 2'^{K}$ ok

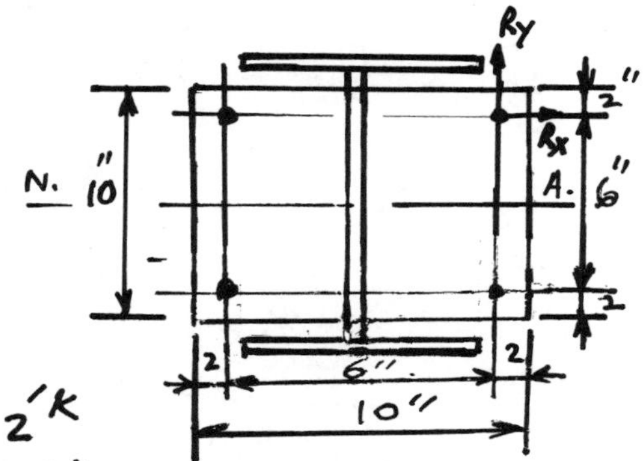

Use $2 - \frac{1}{4}''$ ℘ $10'' \times 10''$ splice ℘ with $4 - 5/8''$ H.S. Bolt.

8) BRACING:- Entire length of beam is assumed braced, Provide welded vertical Plates @ section B & C and similar @ section E, F & K.

9) Elastic deflection:-

$$\Delta_{max} = \frac{W l^3}{48 E I} = \frac{24.07 \times 24^3 \times 1728}{48 \times 30 \times 10^6 \times 130}$$

$$= 1.04'' > \frac{24 \times 12}{360}$$

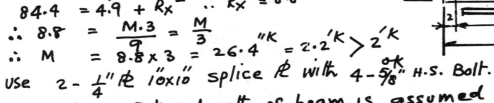

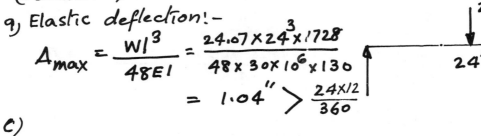

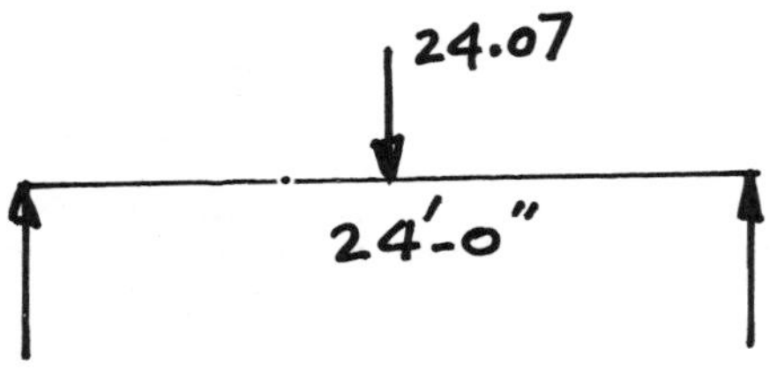

c)

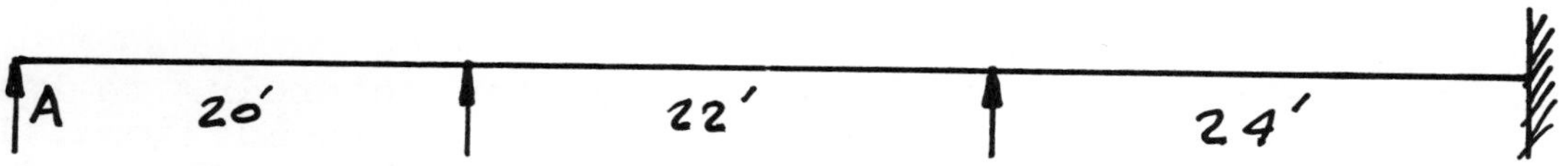

Given:- Erection temperature 65 F; temperature range of structure -25 F to 120 F.
Required:- Type of support at A?
Use AISC $\mathcal{E}$, average coefficient of expansion = 0.0000065t where t is the difference of temperature from room temperature and to 200 F. The expansion bearings are required 1. to allow free thermal expansion, 2. to reduce the redundancy of the structure and 3. to reduce the foundation settlement.

1. Sliding Joint:- (a) Used for short spsn and small loads. (b) It is a satisfactory device for distributing end reaction over a sufficient area.

Example:- A base plate bolted to masonary foundation and a sole plate riveted to the bottom of a flange of girder or lower chord of truss.
Although the two plates are generally planed and supposed to slide freely one on the other, the coefficient of friction may be high enough to develop a considerable amount of horizontal resistance, especially if dirt and rust accumulateed between plates, thus a uniform pressure is unattainable.
Secondly, although the slotted hole at the one end allows adjustment for expansion due to temperature change.
According to AASHO Specifications (spans of less than 50') may be arranged to slide upon metal plates with a smooth surface and no provision for deflection of span need be made.

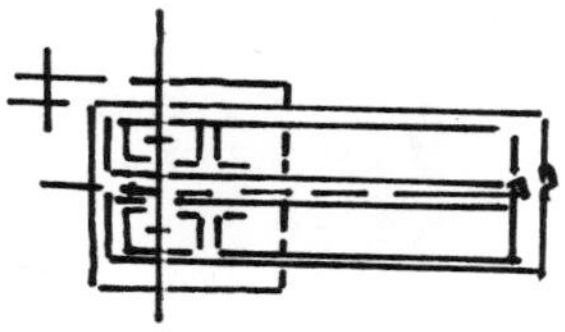

2. Roller Joint:- It is to ensure free expansion preferred to a round roller, because for a given diameter they occupy less space than the round ones. Since the motion of the rollers is quite small relative to their radius, the arcs that are actually used are also small and segmental roller is generally sufficient. Segmental rollers should be connected by two rods, which prevent the roller from moving independently of one another.

$$f = \sqrt{\frac{PE}{2\pi R(1-\mu^2)}}$$

where f - max. bearing stress #/□" between roller and flat surface
P - load #/" of roller
R - radius of roller, inches
E - modulus of elasticity
μ - poision ratio of steel

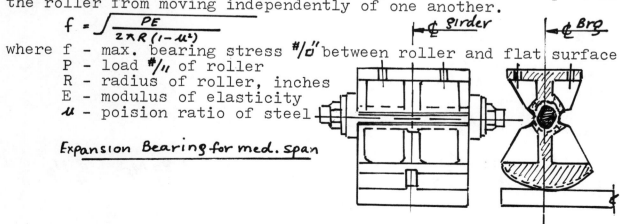

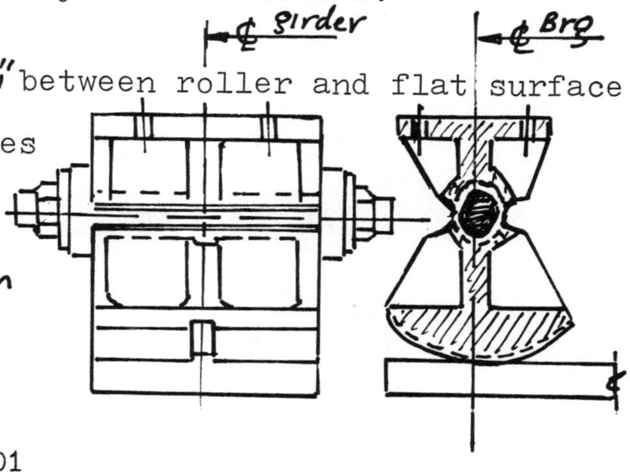

Expansion Bearing for med. span

EXAMPLE 3-02

Given:- Design the following continuous beam according to Part II (Plastic Design) of the AISC Specifications th Edition. Use varying cross-section and/or cover plates to achieve the most economical weighted structure. Design by pre-selection of the moment diagram.

Use ASTM A-36 Steel. It is not necessary to check all details such as deflection, web crippling, etc. The DL of the members themselves may be neglected.

These loads are working loads.

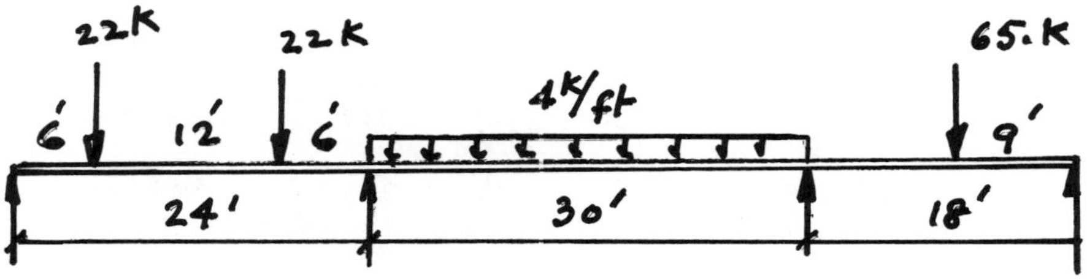

OPTION

A moment distribution solution of this problem would be of interest to see the difference between the working load moments, which are essentially elastic, and the plastic design moments, which are the ultimate loading.

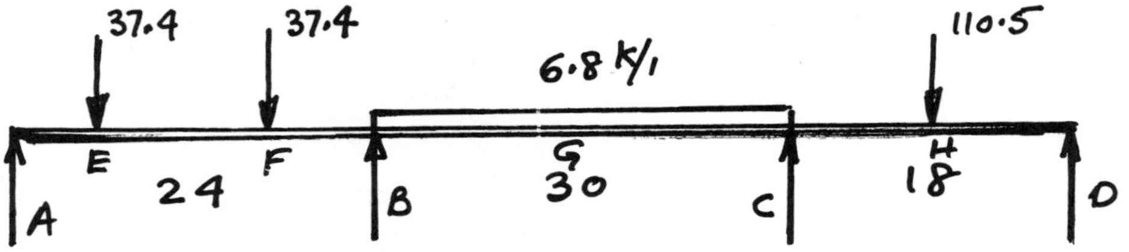

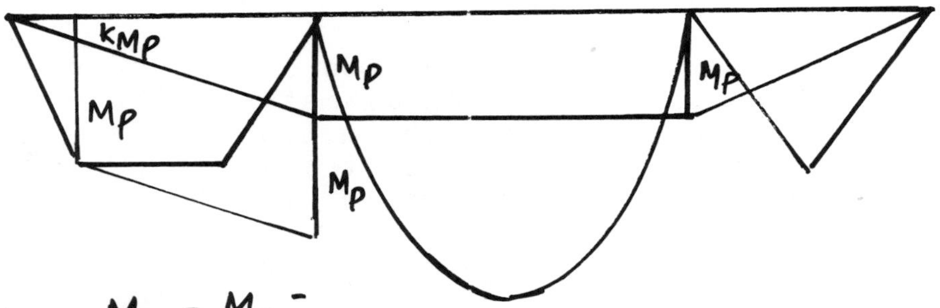

Span AB $= M_E = M_F$

$= 37.4 \times 6 = 224.4'^K$

Span BC $= M_G = \dfrac{6.8 \times 30 \times 30}{8} = 765'^K$

Span CD $= M_H = \dfrac{110.5 \times 9}{4} = 498'^K$

$\therefore M_S = M_p + KM_p$

for span AB, $224.4 = M_p + KM_p = M_p + \frac{6}{24} M_p = \frac{5}{4} M_p$

$\therefore M_p = \dfrac{224.4 \times 4}{5} = 180'^K$

$Z = \dfrac{180 \times 12}{36} = 60 \text{ IN}^3$

Choose W12x45 $Z = 64.9 \text{ IN}^3$

Span CD

$M_s = M_p + K M_p = M_p + \dfrac{M_p}{2} = \tfrac{3}{2} M_p$

$498 = \tfrac{3}{2} M_p \quad \therefore M_p = \dfrac{498 \times 2}{3} = 332'^K$

$Z = \dfrac{332 \times 12}{36} = 110.67 \text{ IN}^3$

Choose W12x79 $Z = 119.3 > 110.67$ ok

Span BC :- We will use W12x79, $M_p = \dfrac{119.3 \times 36}{12} = 358'^K$

$\therefore$ Add'l moment to be provided $= 765 - 2 \times 358$
$= 49'^K$

$Z = \dfrac{49 \times 12}{36} = 16.33 \text{ IN}^3$

$A = \dfrac{16.33}{12} = 1.36 \square''$

use $6 \times \frac{1}{4}''$ PL, $A = 1.5 > 1.36$ ok.

Length of flange plate to reinforce section

$$l = L\sqrt{1 - \frac{2M_p}{M_s}} = 30\sqrt{1 - \frac{716}{765}} = 7.59'$$

Provide 7'-9" on the central portion of 30' span.

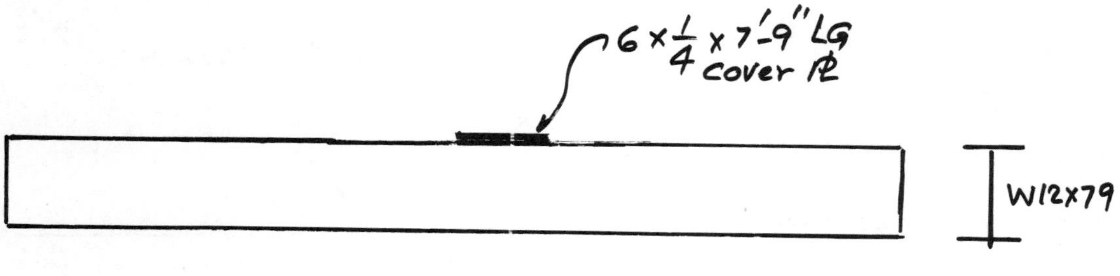

EXAMPLE 3-03

Given:- Solve by plastic design for the required M_p to resist the loads shown. They are already ultimate loads. Use simple plastic theory and conclude with the final resultant moment diagram and the free-body diagram of the entire structure. Knee joints are rigid. Use ASTM A-36 Steel. Bases are fixed.

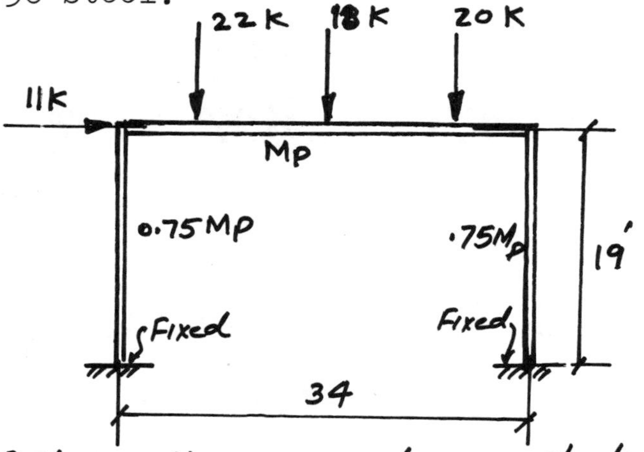

Solutions:- Frame is redundant of 3°, its collapse involves 4 plastic hinges. There are 7 possible plastic hinges hence 7 mechanism.

1) Beam mechanism @ 22^k

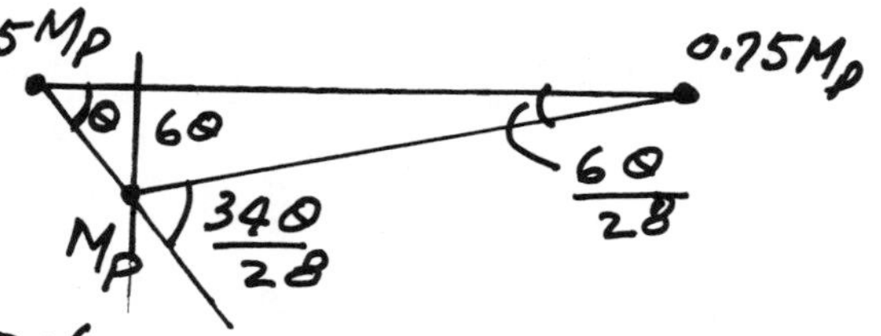

$W_I = 0.75M_p\theta + M_p\frac{34}{28}\theta + 0.75M_p\frac{6\theta}{28}$

$= M_p(0.75 + 1.22 + 0.16)\theta$

$= 2.13\,M_p\theta$

$W_E = 22\times6\theta + 18\times6\theta\times\frac{18}{28} + 20\times6\theta\times\frac{6}{28}$

$= \theta(132 + 69.43 + 25.71)$

$= 227.14\,\theta$

$\because W_I = W_E \;\therefore\; 2.13M_p\theta = 227.14\theta;\; M_p = 107'^k$

2) Beam mechanism @ 18^k

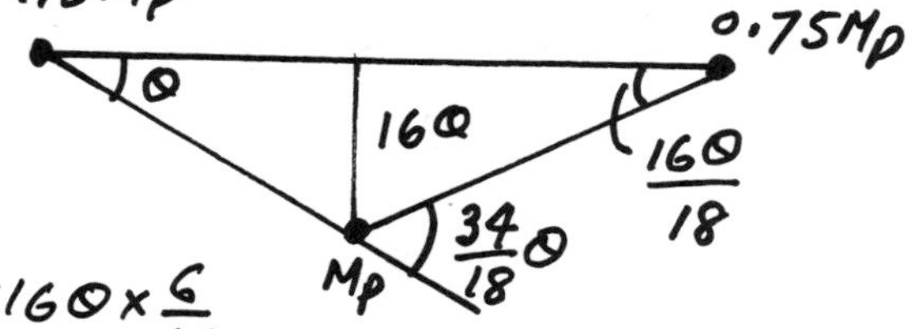

$W_I = 0.75M_p\theta + M_p\frac{34}{18}\theta + 0.75M_p\frac{16}{18}\theta$

$= M_p(0.75 + 1.89 + 0.67)\theta$

$= 3.31\,M_p\theta$

$W_E = 22\times16\theta\times\frac{6}{16} + 18\times16\theta + 20\times16\theta\times\frac{6}{18}$

$= \theta(132 + 288 + 106.7) = 526.7\theta$

$\because W_I = W_E \;\therefore\; 3.31M_p\theta = 526.7\theta;\; M_p = 159'^k$

3) Beam mechanism @ 20K

$W_I = 0.75 M_p \theta + M_p \frac{34}{6}\theta + 0.75 M_p \frac{28}{6}\theta$

$= M_p (0.75 + 5.67 + 3.5)\theta$

$= 9.92 M_p \theta$

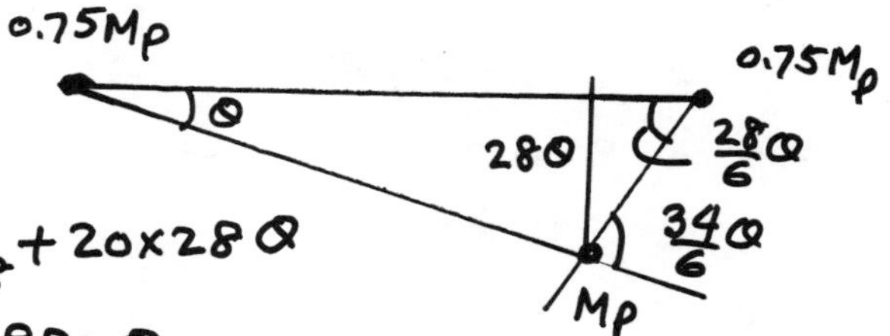

$W_E = 22 \times 28\theta \times \frac{6}{28} + 18 \times 28\theta \times \frac{16}{28} + 20 \times 28\theta$

$= \theta(132 + 288 + 560) = 980\theta$

$\because W_I = W_E \therefore 9.92 M_p \theta = 980\theta;\ M_p = 98.6'K$

4) Portal mechanism.

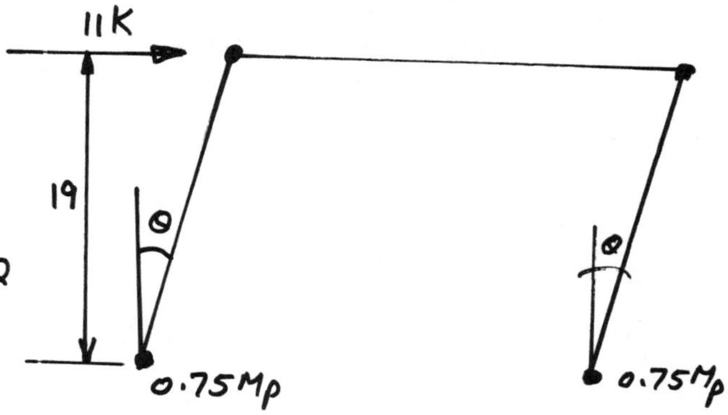

$W_I = 0.75 M_p \theta + 0.75 M_p \theta$

$= 1.5 M_p \theta$

$W_E = 11 \times 19\theta = 209\theta$

$W_I = W_E \therefore 1.5 M_p \theta = 209\theta$

$\therefore M_p = 139.3'K$

5) Combined mechanism 4th + 1st

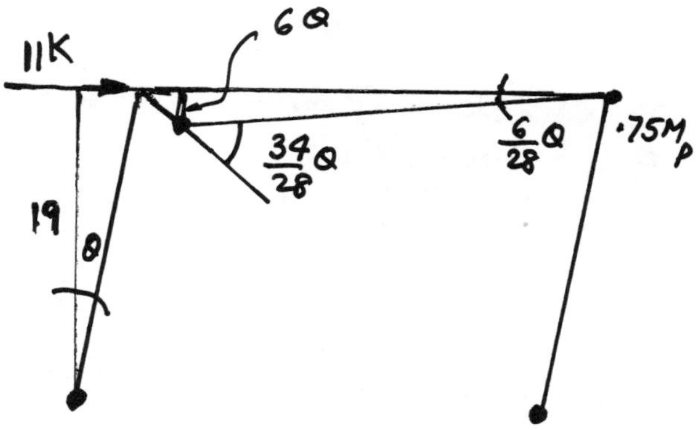

$W_I = 1.5 M_p \theta + 2.13 M_p \theta$

$= 3.63 M_p \theta$

$W_E = 227.14\theta + 209\theta$

$= 436.14\theta$

$\because W_I = W_E$

$\therefore 3.63 M_p \theta = 436.14\theta$

$M_p = 120'K$

6) Combined mechanism 4th + 2nd.

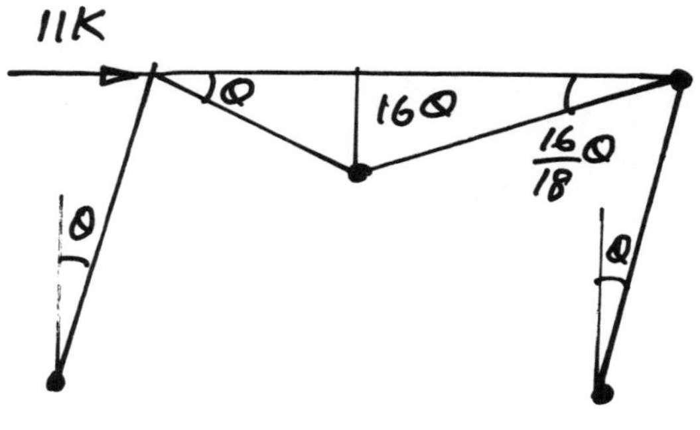

$W_I = 1.5 M_p \theta + 3.31 M_p \theta$

$= 4.81 M_p \theta$

$W_E = 526.7\theta + 209\theta$

$= 735.7\theta$

7, combined mechanism
4th + 3rd

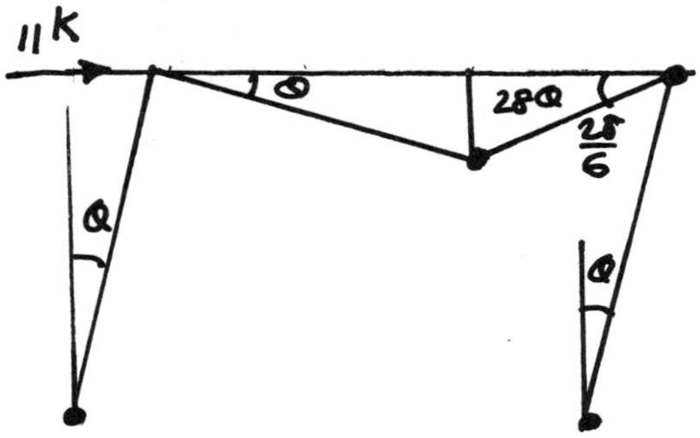

$W_I = 1.5 M_p Q + 9.92 M_p Q$

$= 11.42 M_p Q$

$W_E = 980Q + 209Q$

$= 1189Q$

$\because W_I = W_E$

$\therefore 11.42 M_p Q = 1189 Q$

$M_p = 103.6'^k$

$\because$ Max M_p governs of mechanism # 2 & = $159'^k$

$\therefore$ M_p on Column $= \frac{3}{4} \times 159 = 119.3'^k$

Moment Diagram.

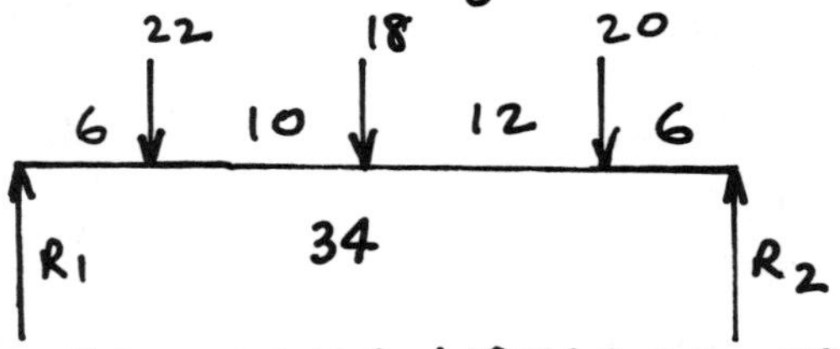

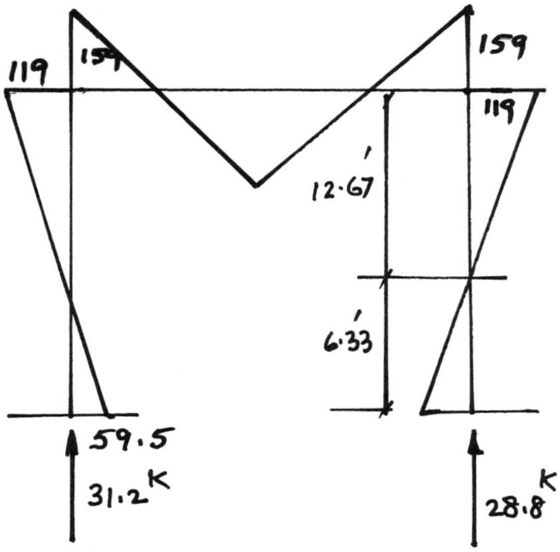

$R_2 \times 34 = 22 \times 6 + 18 \times 16 + 20 \times 28$

$R_2 = 28.8^k$

$R_1 = 60 - 28.8 = 31.2^k$

To check columns:-

Right hand col.

$\frac{119.3 + 119.3}{19} = 12.56$

Left hand col.

$119.3 - 1.56 \times 19$

$= 84.66 < 119$ ok.

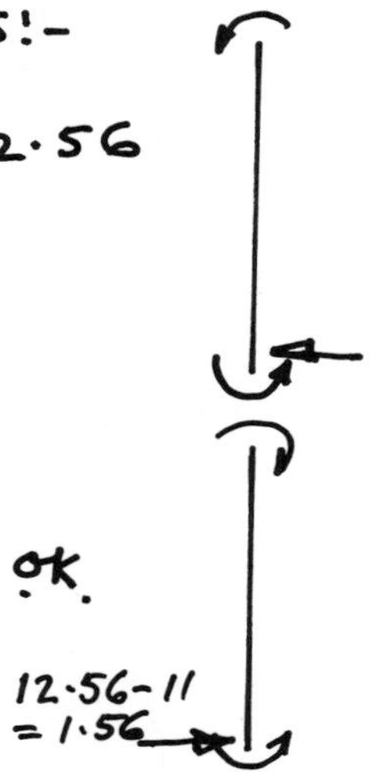

Free body diagram →

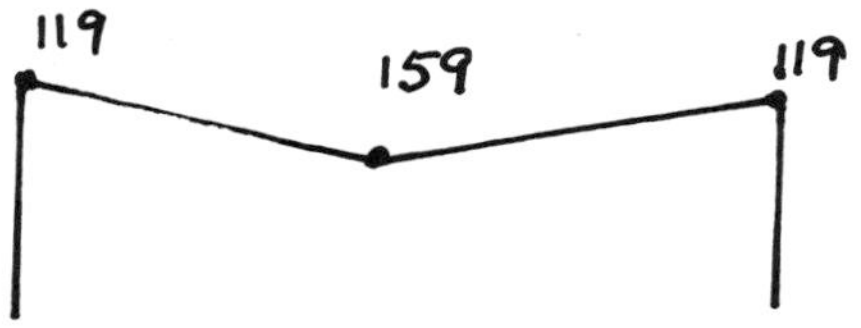

EXAMPLE 3-04

Given:- (A) Find the ultimate load.
(B) Plot the Load Deflection Curve for the rigid bar.

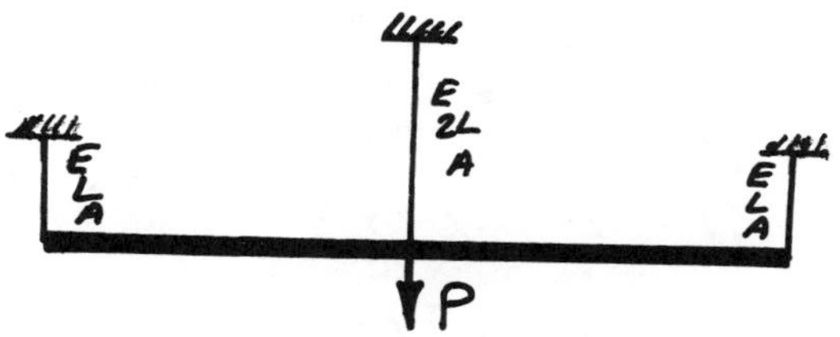

A)

Elastic case

Remove supports & replace by reactions

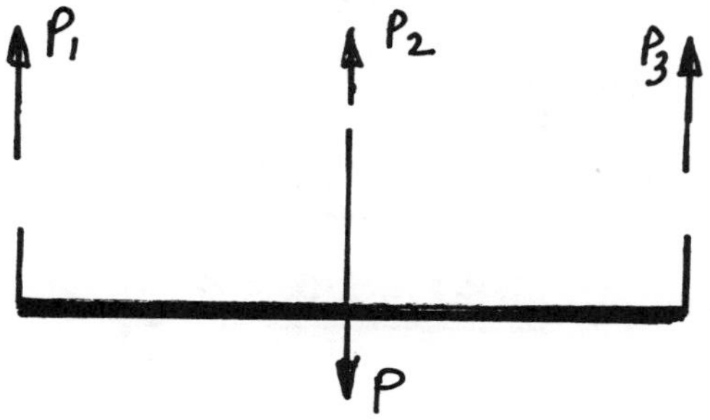

$\Sigma F_v = 0$

$P_1 + P_2 + P_3 - P = 0$

$\Sigma M = 0$

$\because P_1 = P_3$

Bar being rigid $\delta_1 = \delta_2$

$$\frac{P_1 L}{AE} = \frac{P_2\, 2L}{AE}$$

$$P_1 = 2P_2 = P_3$$

$$P_2 = \frac{P_1}{2} = \frac{P_3}{2}$$

$$P_1 + \frac{P_1}{2} + \frac{P_1}{2} - P = 0$$

$$P_1 = \frac{2}{5}P \text{ or } P = \frac{5}{2}P_1$$

$\because$ Small length of wire is most severely loaded & will fail when reaches σ_y

$P_1 = \sigma_y A \quad \therefore \quad P_{El} = \frac{5}{2}\sigma_y A$

$\delta_{El} = \frac{5}{2}\sigma_y \frac{A.L}{A.E} = \frac{5}{2}\sigma_y \frac{L}{E}$

$\Sigma F_v = 0 \quad ; \quad P_{UL} = 3\sigma_y A$

Ultimate load $= 3\sigma_y A$ & $\delta_{UL} = \frac{3\sigma_y AL}{A.E} = \frac{3\sigma_y L}{E}$

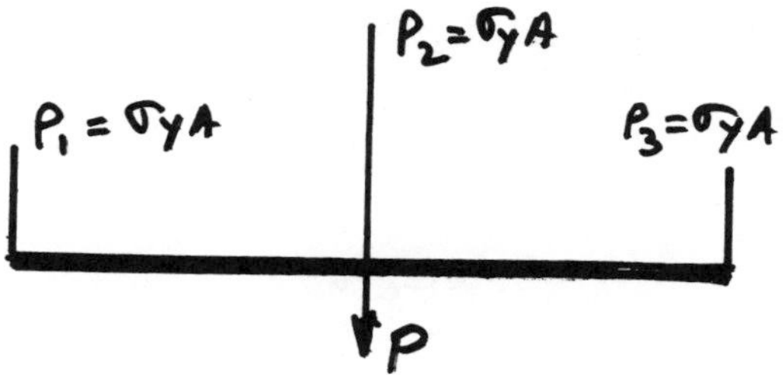

B) Plot of load Deflection curve

Assume $A = 1\,\square''$, $L = 100''$, $E = 30\times10^3$, $\sigma_y = 36\,ksi$

$$\delta_{el} = \frac{5}{2}\frac{\sigma_y L}{E} = 0.3''$$

$$\delta_{ul} = 3\frac{\sigma_y L}{E} = 0.36''$$

$$P_{el} = \frac{5}{2}\sigma_y A = 90^K$$

$$P_{ul} = 3\sigma_y A = 108^K$$

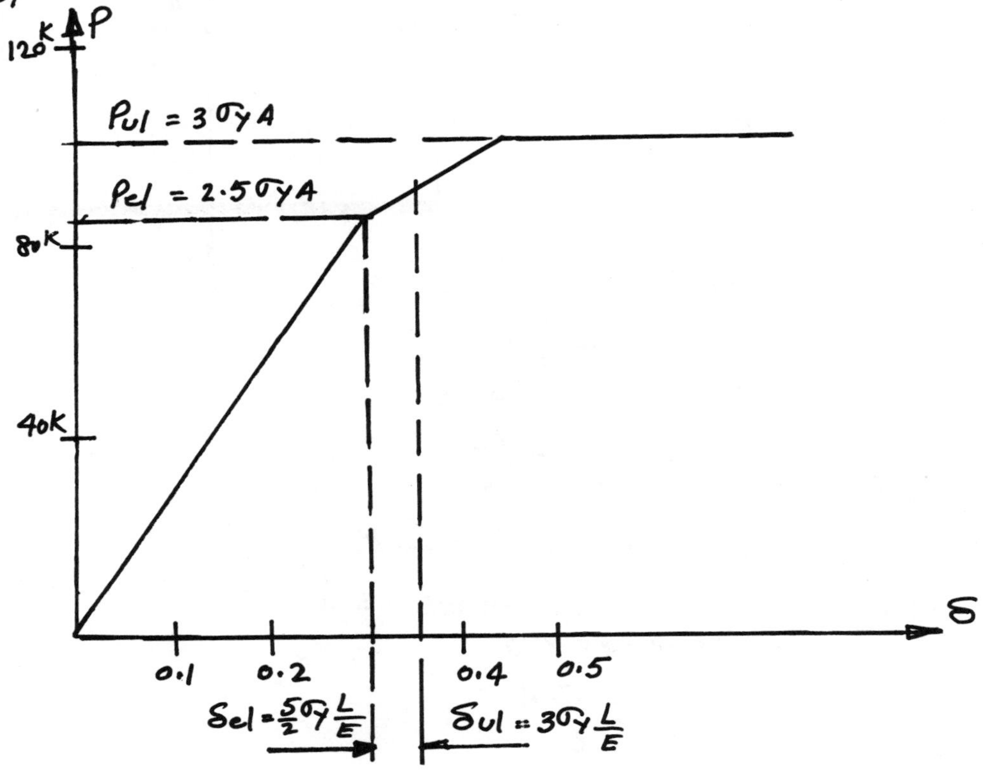

EXAMPLE 3-05

Given:- Find the Section Modulus and the Plastic Modulus. Also locate the N.A. for the following section.

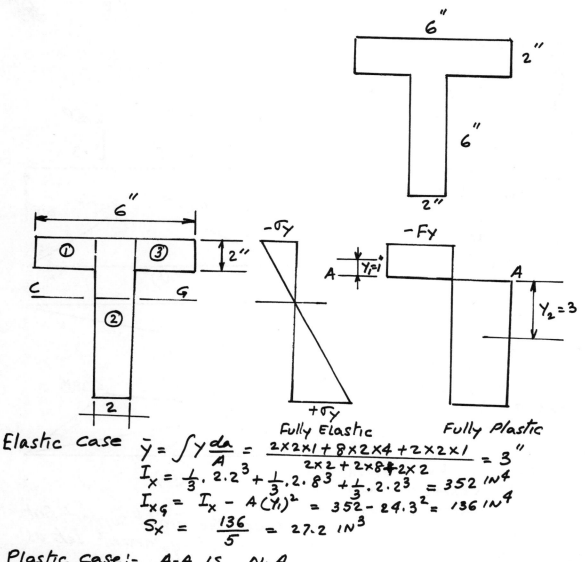

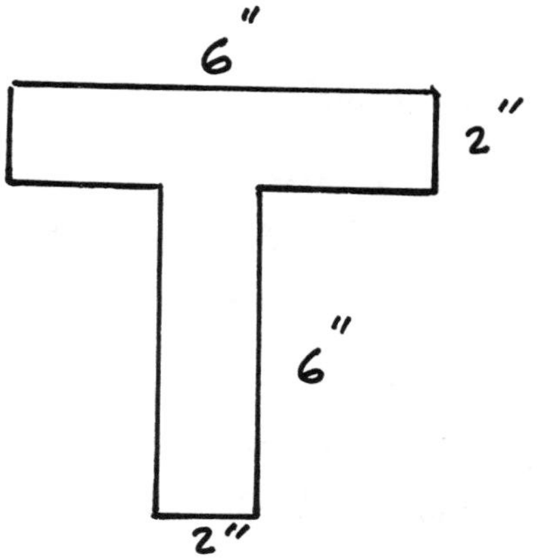

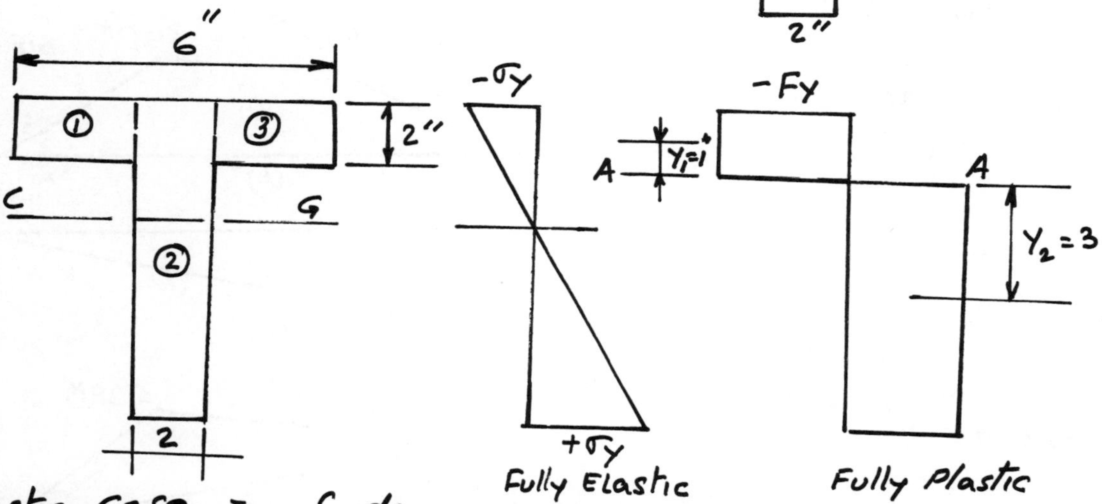

Elastic case $\bar{y} = \int y \frac{da}{A} = \frac{2\times2\times1 + 8\times2\times4 + 2\times2\times1}{2\times2 + 2\times8 + 2\times2} = 3''$

$I_x = \frac{1}{3}\cdot 2\cdot 2^3 + \frac{1}{3}\cdot 2\cdot 8^3 + \frac{1}{3}\cdot 2\cdot 2^3 = 352\ IN^4$

$I_{xG} = I_x - A(Y_1)^2 = 352 - 24\cdot 3^2 = 136\ IN^4$

$S_x = \frac{136}{5} = 27.2\ IN^3$

Plastic case:- A-A is N.A

$Z_x = \frac{A}{2}(Y_1 + Y_2) = \frac{24}{2}(1+3) = 48\ IN^3$

Neutral Axis:- Elastic case:- Passes through the centroid 3" from top fiber

Plastic case:- lies below Elastic N.A from the same axis AA 2" from Top Fiber.

EXAMPLE 3-06

Given:- Find P if η = 1.85 and the member is W 10 x 45. Use A-36 Steel.

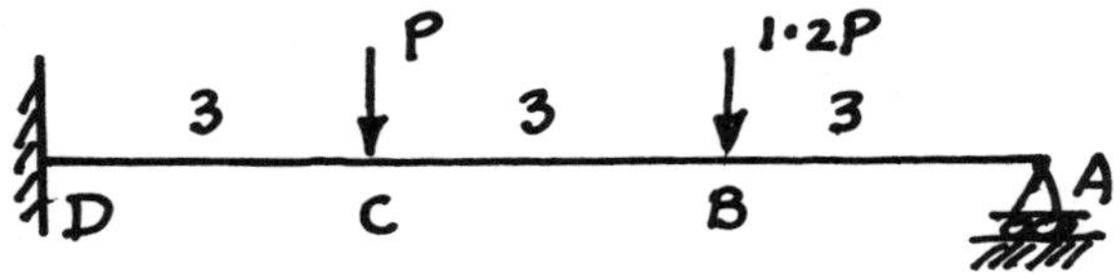

$\eta = 1.85$

$Z_{W10\times45} = 55 \text{ in}^3$

$M_p = 55\times36 = 1980''K$

$= 165'K$

a, Use redundant Mp

b, Moment diagram for elastically determinant beam

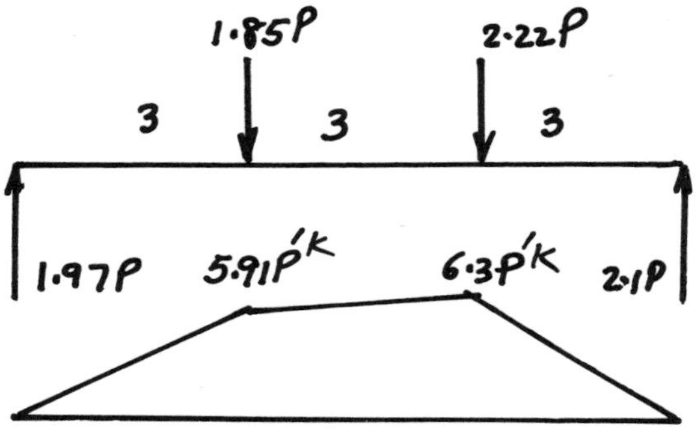

(b)

c, Moment diagram due to redundant.

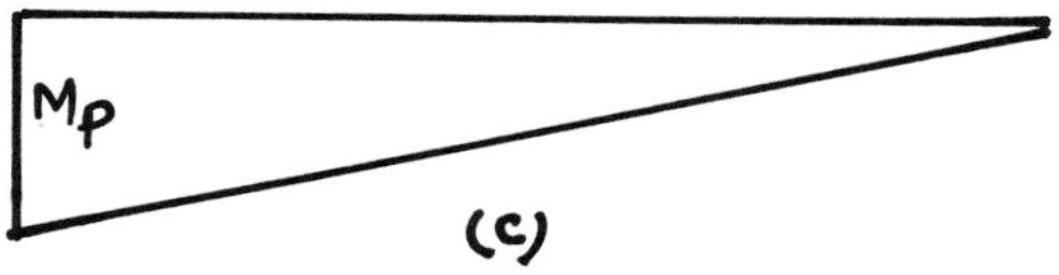

(c)

d, combination of b, c to form mechanism for unknown plastic hinge at D

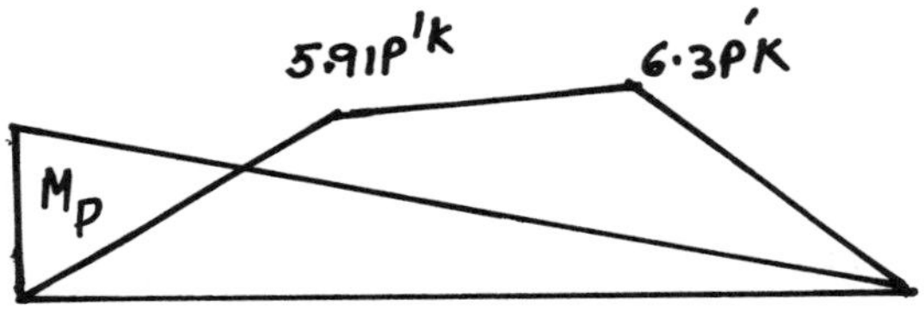

(d)

Since the beam has real hinge at D, it will become mechanism upon the formation of two plastic hinges. One of these hinges, develop at the right support. But whether other hinge forms at B, C is not apparant. Let us try both possibilities.

Assume hinge at B:- $6.3P - \frac{M_p}{3} = M_p$

$\therefore M_p = \frac{18.9P}{4}\ 'K$

Now Assume hinge at C:- $5.91P - \frac{2M_p}{3} = M_p$

$M_p = \frac{17.73}{5} P'K$

Hence beam is designed for $M_p = \frac{18.9P}{4}$

$\therefore \frac{18.9P}{4} = 165$ & $P = 34.9K$ & $P_U = 1.85\times34.9 = 64.57^K$

e) Check if $M \leq M_p = 165'K$

$P = 34.9^K$

$1.2P = 1.2 \times 34.9 = 41.9^K$

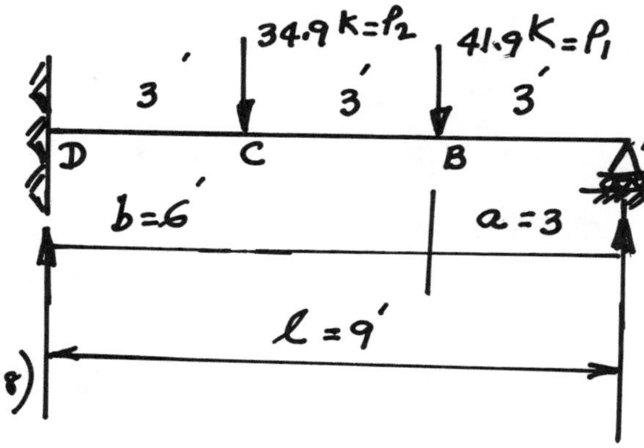

$$R_B = \frac{P_1 b^2}{2l^3}(a + 2l) + \frac{P_2 b^2}{2l^3}(a + 2l)$$

$$= \frac{41.9 \times 36}{2 \times 729}(3 + 18) + \frac{34.9 \times 9}{2 \times 729}(6 + 18)$$

$$= 26.76^K$$

$$R_A = (41.9 + 34.9) - 26.76 = 50.04^K$$

$M_D = 115.17'^K$, $M_C = 56.92'^K$, $M_B = 80.3'^K$

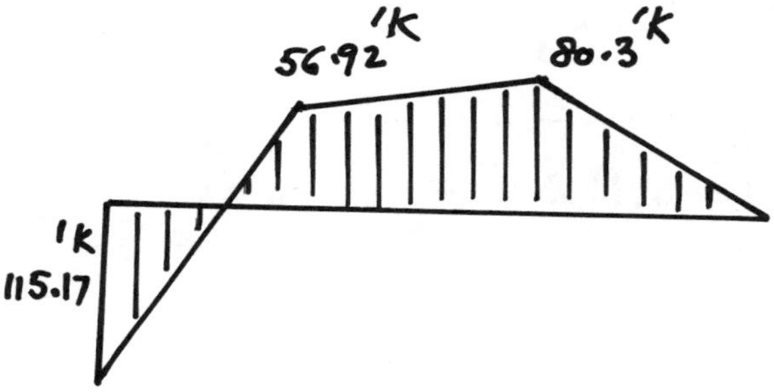

Hence $M < M_p$

EXAMPLE 3-07

Given:- Find P for the following beam.

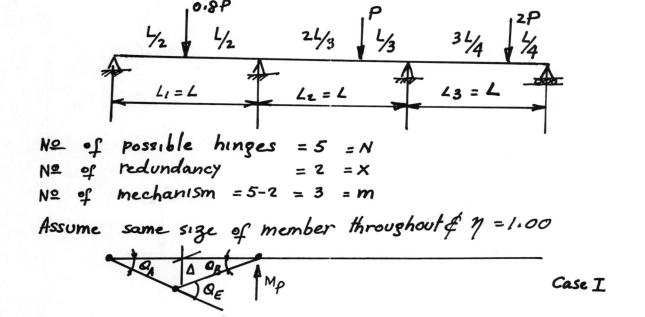

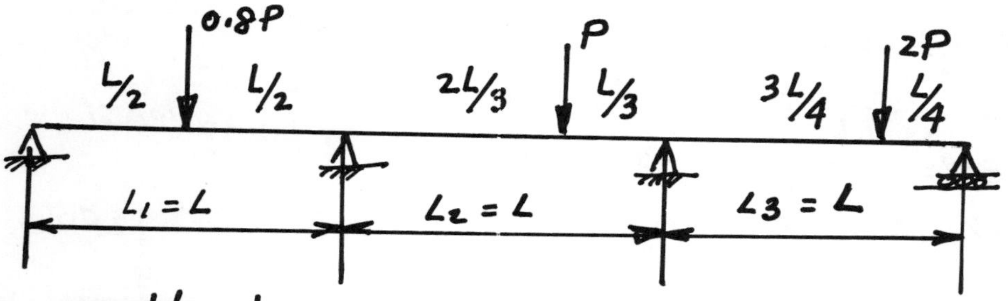

No of possible hinges = 5 = N

No of redundancy = 2 = X

No of mechanism = 5-2 = 3 = m

Assume same size of member throughout & $\eta = 1.00$

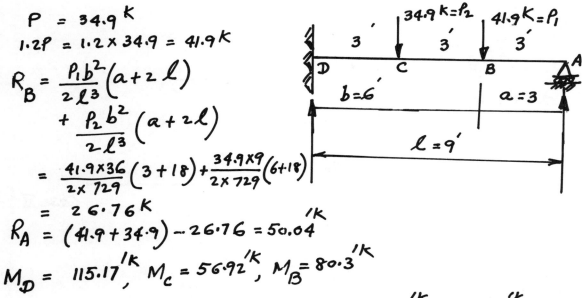

Case I

$$\theta_A = \frac{\Delta}{L/2} = \frac{2\Delta}{L} = \theta_B$$

$$\theta_E = \frac{4\Delta}{L}$$

$$\therefore \; 0.8P \times \Delta = M_p \cdot \frac{2\Delta}{L} + M_p \cdot \frac{4\Delta}{L} = M_p \times \frac{6\Delta}{L}$$

$$P = M_p \frac{6}{0.8L} = \frac{7.5 M_p}{L}$$

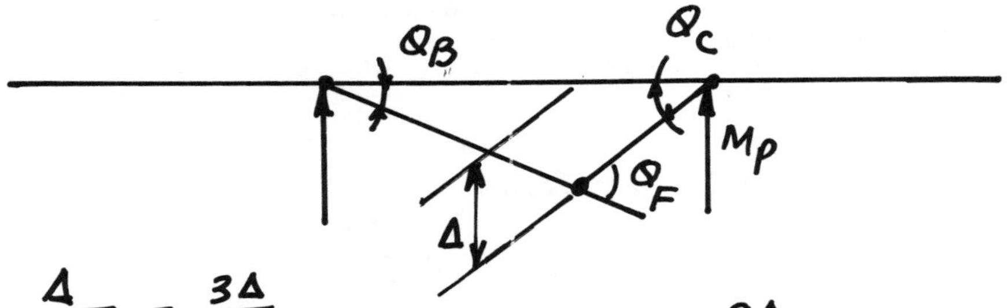

Case II

$$\theta_B = \frac{\Delta}{2L/3} = \frac{3\Delta}{2L}$$

$$\theta_C = \frac{3\Delta}{L} \qquad \therefore \; \theta_F = \frac{3\Delta}{2L} + \frac{3\Delta}{L} = \frac{9\Delta}{2L}$$

$$\therefore \; 1.85P\Delta = M_p\left(\frac{3\Delta}{2L} + \frac{3\Delta}{L} + \frac{9\Delta}{2L}\right) = 9M_p\frac{\Delta}{L}$$

$$P = \frac{9.0}{1.85}\frac{M_p}{L} = 4.86\frac{M_p}{L}$$

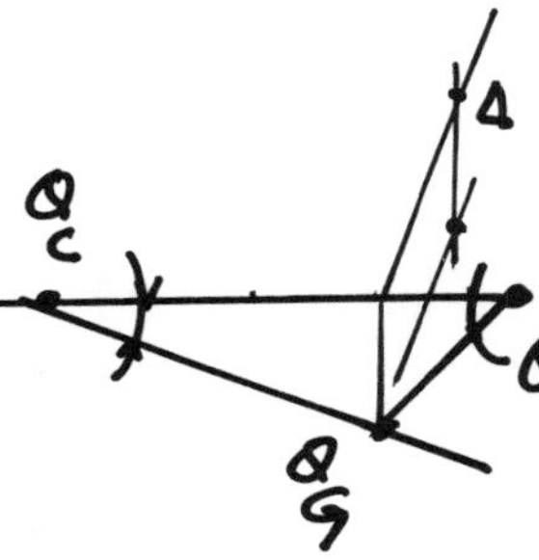

Case III

$$\theta_C = \frac{\Delta}{3L/4} = \frac{4\Delta}{3L}$$

$$\theta_D = \frac{\Delta}{L/4} = \frac{4\Delta}{L}$$

$$\theta_G = \frac{4\Delta}{3L} + \frac{4\Delta}{L} = \frac{16\Delta}{3L} \quad \therefore \; 2P\Delta = M_p\frac{4\Delta}{3L} + M_p\frac{16\Delta}{3L} = M_p\frac{20\Delta}{3L}$$

$$\therefore \; P = \frac{20}{3 \times 2L} M_p = \frac{3.33 M_p}{L}$$

Hence governing load is $P = \frac{3.33}{L} M_p$ being least.

To check $M \leq M_p$

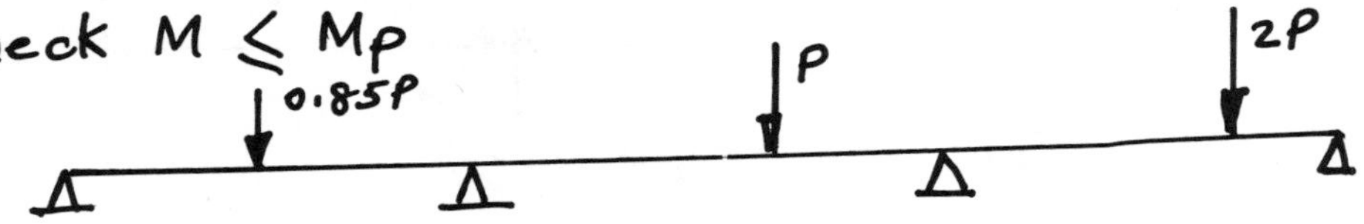

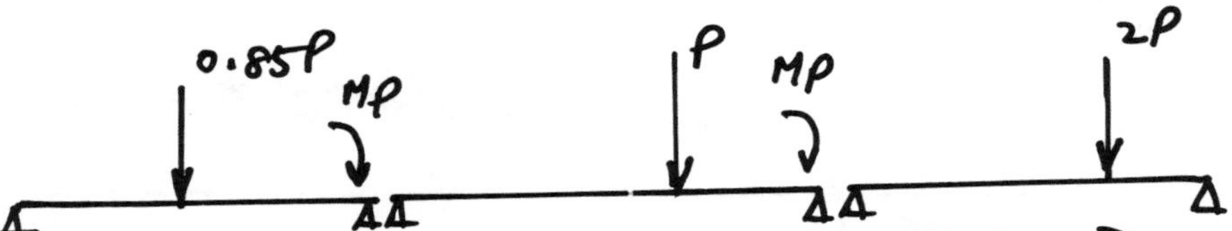

$\frac{1}{L}\left(\frac{PL}{2} - M_p\right)$ $\quad \frac{1}{L}\left[\frac{2}{3}L(P) - M_p\right]$ $\quad \frac{1}{L}\left[\frac{3}{4}L(2P) - M_p\right]$

Case I ; $M = \frac{1}{L}\left(\frac{PL}{2} - M_p\right)\frac{L}{2} = 0.25\,PL - 0.5M_p$

Case II ; $M = \frac{1}{L}\left(\frac{2}{3}LP - M_p\right)\frac{2L}{3} = 0.44PL - 0.67M_p$

Case III ; $M = \frac{1}{L}\left[\frac{3}{4}L.2P - M_p\right]\frac{3L}{4} = 1.12PL - 0.75M_p$

Hence $M < M_p$ in all cases.

EXAMPLE 3-08

Given:- Design of continuous beam on three supports.

(A) Use the same W in both spans. Find the minimum size.
F 36; 1.85

(B) Explain how you would determine what W beam to use in a 20' span to make a design more economical and where would you splice the two.

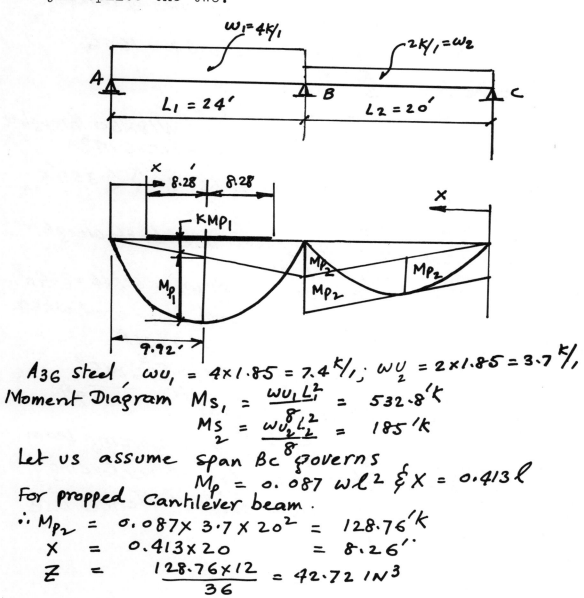

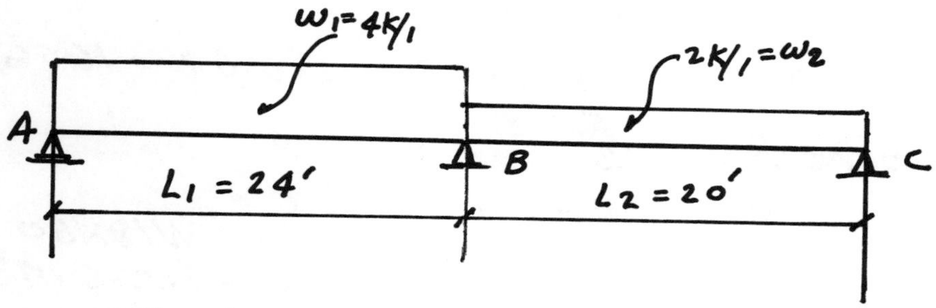

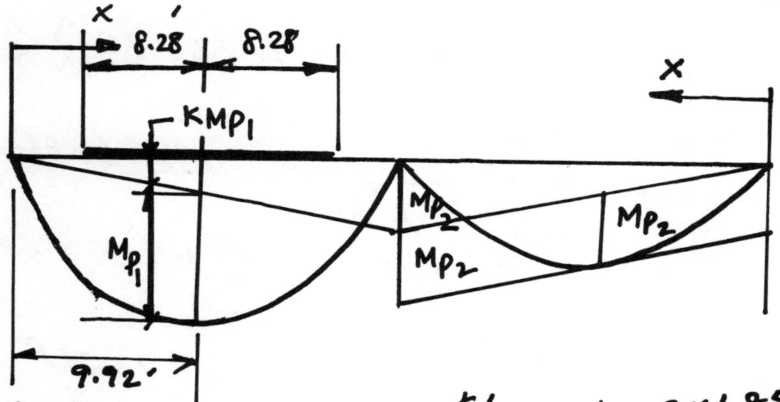

A36 Steel, $w_{u_1} = 4 \times 1.85 = 7.4^K/_1$; $w_{u_2} = 2 \times 1.85 = 3.7^K/_1$

Moment Diagram $M_{s_1} = \frac{w_{u_1} L_1^2}{8} = 532.8'^K$

$M_{s_2} = \frac{w_{u_2} L_2^2}{8} = 185'^K$

Let us assume span BC governs

$M_p = 0.087\,wl^2$ & $X = 0.413l$

For propped cantilever beam.

$\therefore M_{p_2} = 0.087 \times 3.7 \times 20^2 = 128.76'^K$

$X = 0.413 \times 20 = 8.26'$

$Z = \frac{128.76 \times 12}{36} = 42.72\ IN^3$

use W12 X 31 $Z = 44\ IN^3$ throughout.

for span AB $X = 0.413\,l = 0.413 \times 24 = 9.92'$

$M_{p_1} + K M_{p_1} = M_{s_1}$

$(1+K) M_{p_1} = 532.8$ or $\left(1 + \frac{9.92}{24}\right) M_{p_1} = 532.8$

$\therefore M_{p_1} = 380'^{K} > M_{p_2} = 128.76'^{K}$

cover Pl on section AB

$\Delta M_p = M_{p_1} - M_{p_2} = 251.24'^{K}$

$A_{Pl} = \frac{251.24 \times 12}{36 \times 12.09} = 6.95\ \square''$ use $6 \times \frac{1}{4}''$ Pl

Length of cover plate

$l = L_1 \sqrt{\frac{M_{p_1} - M_{p_2}}{M_S}}$ By properties of Parabola

$= 24 \sqrt{\frac{251.24}{532.8}} = 24 \times 0.69 = 16.56'$

for comparison let AB span governs

$M_{p_1} = 0.087 \times 7.4 \times 24' = 359'^{K}$

$Z = \frac{359 \times 12}{36} = 119.67$ use W18X60 throughout $Z = 122.6\ in^3$

For span BC

$M_p = 0.087 \times 3.75 \times 20^2 = 128.76'^{K} < 359'^{K}$ ok

No cover plate use W18X60

Hence for economical purposes use least weight W12X31, but.

If W18X60 is used, weight of Beam = 60X44 = 2640#

if W12X31 is used & Reinforcing plate is used where needed, then weight is 31 X 44 = 1364#

$2 \times 6 \times 1\frac{1}{4} \times 16.56 \times \frac{25.50\#}{ft} = 845\#$

2209#

net saving in weight = 2640-2209

= 431#

This saving in weight in favour of reinforcing beam plus the cost of rivetting or welding of reinforcing plate will not be economical overall. Hence use W18X60 throughout.

EXAMPLE 3-09

Given:- Find the value of P and the diameter of the cable for simultaneous failure of the beam and cable.

σ_Y of cable = 40000 psi

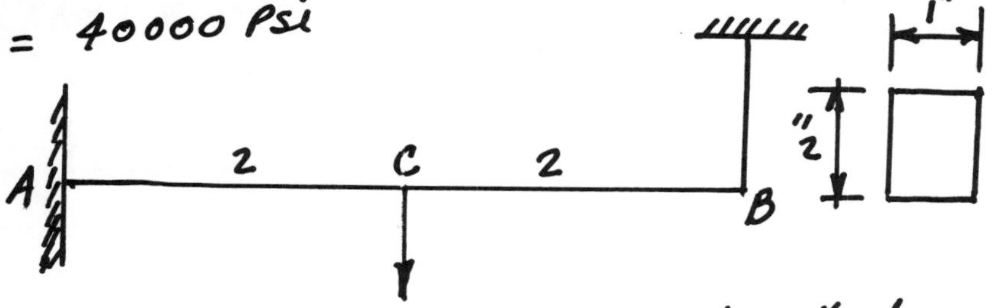

Since cable is just acting as tension member, the beam can be treated as proped cantilever

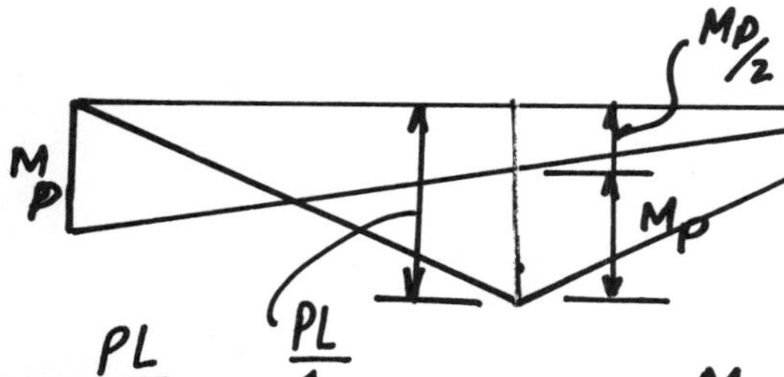

$$\left(M_p + \frac{M_p}{2}\right) = \frac{PL}{4}$$

$$\frac{3}{2} M_p = \frac{P \times L \times 12}{4} \quad ; \quad \therefore P_U = \frac{M_p}{8}$$

$$M_p \text{ of Beam} = 40000\left(\frac{bh^2}{4}\right) = 40000 \times \frac{1 \times 2^2}{4} = 40000''\#$$

$$P_U = \frac{40000}{8} = 5000\#$$

For simultaneous failure of cable, let plastic hinge be formed at C under load P for yielding

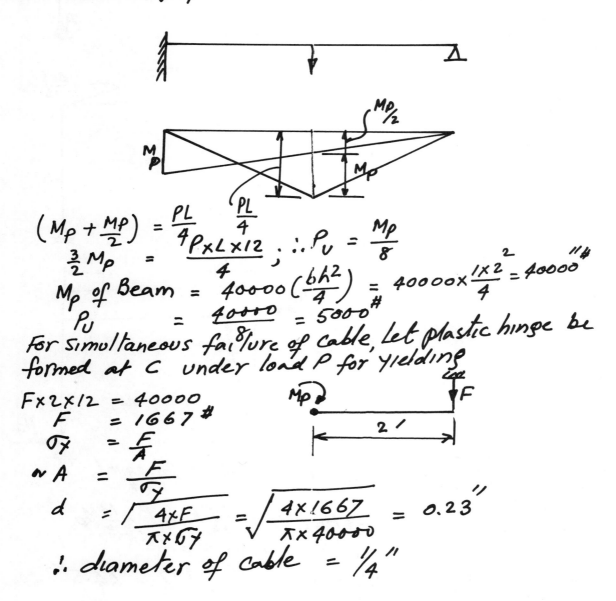

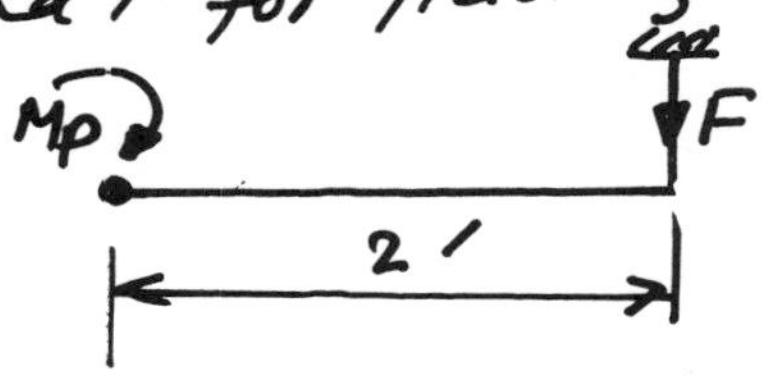

$$F \times 2 \times 12 = 40000$$

$$F = 1667\#$$

$$\sigma_Y = \frac{F}{A}$$

$$A = \frac{F}{\sigma_Y}$$

$$d = \sqrt{\frac{4 \times F}{\pi \times \sigma_Y}} = \sqrt{\frac{4 \times 1667}{\pi \times 40000}} = 0.23''$$

$\therefore$ diameter of cable = 1/4"

EXAMPLE 3-10

Given:- (A) Find the ultimate load if all members are W 10x45 for A-36 Steel.

(B) What is different if AB is W 10x54 and (BC, CD) are W 10x45.

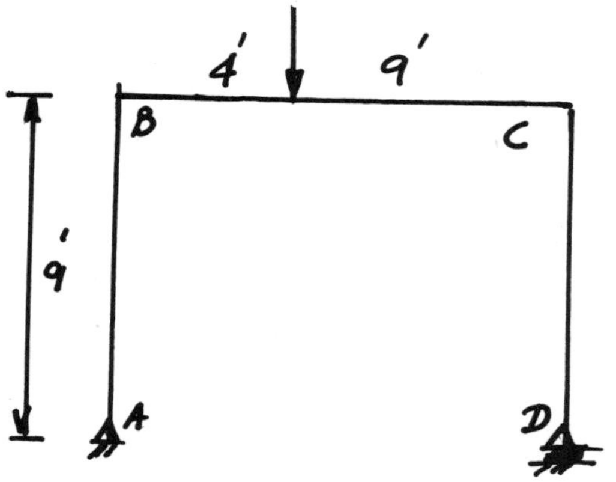

a) Use redundant at D

$$\frac{Pab}{L} = \frac{4\times9\times P}{13} = \frac{36P}{13}$$

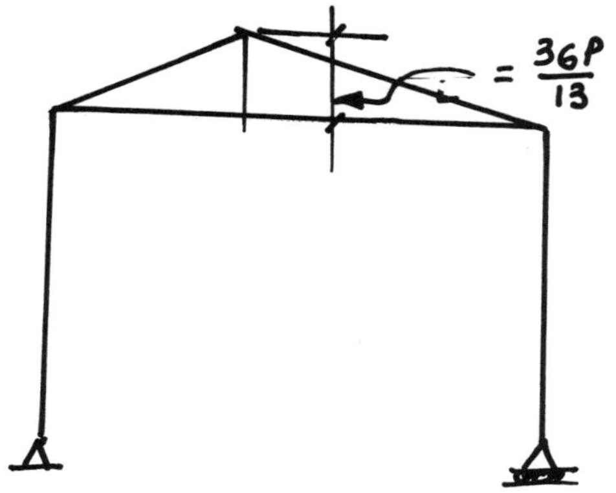

b)

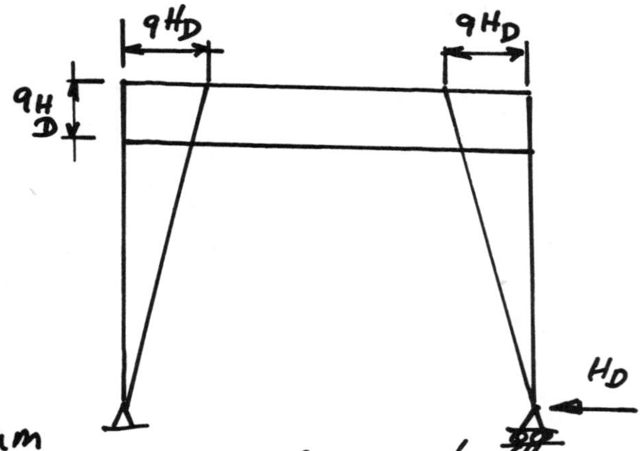

c) Composite Moment Diagram

The hinges will form at B, C & under P for equal members

$\therefore M_p = 9H_D = \frac{36P}{13} - 9H_D$; $M_p = \frac{18}{13}P$ or $P = \frac{13}{18}M_p$

$\because M_p$ of W10x45 $= 36\times55 = 1980''^K = 165'^K$

$P_u = \frac{13}{18}\times165 = 119.17^K$ & $P_W = \frac{119.17}{1.85} = 64.5^K$

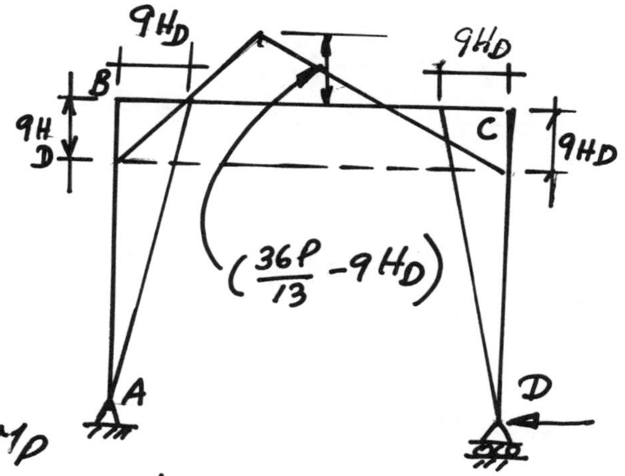

M_p in Col. AB = $9H_D = M_p$

But if W10x54 is used for Col. AB

then $M_p = \frac{36 \times 67}{12} = 201'^{k}$

M_p for Col. CD & Beam BC is $165'^{k}$

There is no difference except it is not economical to use higher member.

If AB is made lighter than $M_p = 165'^{k}$, then AB would have yielded.

EXAMPLE 3-11

Given:-

FIND P_U if $P = \frac{wL}{2}$ & $F = \alpha wL$; $\sigma_y = 36$ Ksi; $\alpha = 1/4''$

$Z = 55$ in^3, $M_p = \frac{55 \times 36}{12} = 165'^{k}$

Possible hinges = 4

Redundancies = 1

No. of independant mechanism = 3

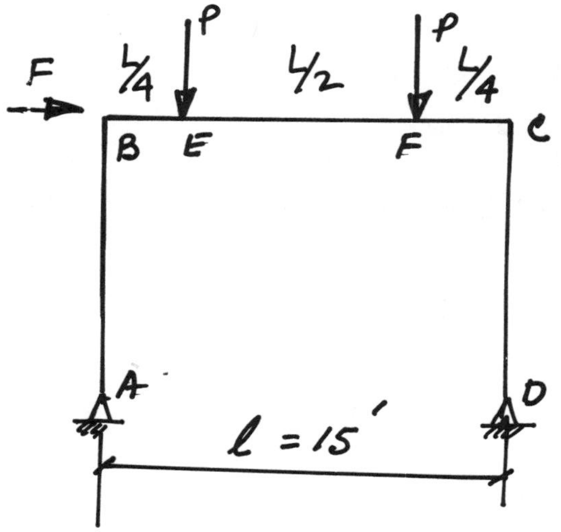

Beam mechanism

1, hinges @ B, E & C

$W_e = P\Delta + P\Delta/3 = 1.33 P\Delta$

$W_I = M_p(\phi_c + \phi_p + \phi_c)$

where $\phi_B = \frac{\Delta}{\ell/4} = \frac{4\Delta}{L}$

$\phi_C = \frac{\Delta}{3L/4} = \frac{4\Delta}{3L}$

$\phi_p = \phi_B + \phi_C = \frac{16\Delta}{3L}$

$$W_I = M_p\left(\frac{4\Delta}{L} + \frac{16\Delta}{3L} + \frac{4\Delta}{3L}\right) = \frac{32}{3L} M_p \Delta$$

$\because W_E = W_I$

$$1.33 P_U = \frac{32}{3L} M_p \Delta$$

$$P_U = \frac{8 M_p}{L}$$

$$= \frac{8 \times 165}{15} = 88^{'K}$$

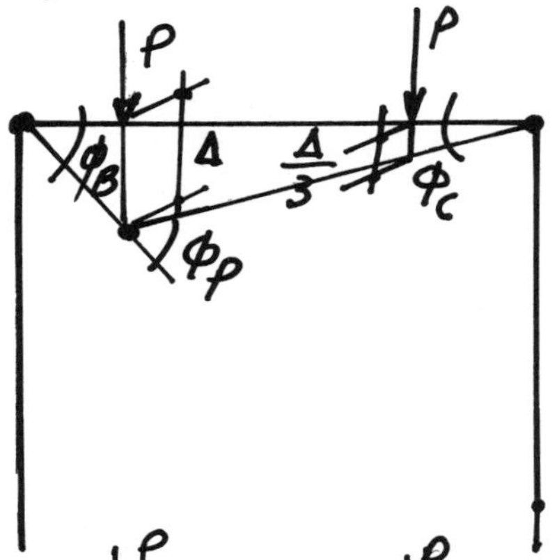

2. Beam Mechanism

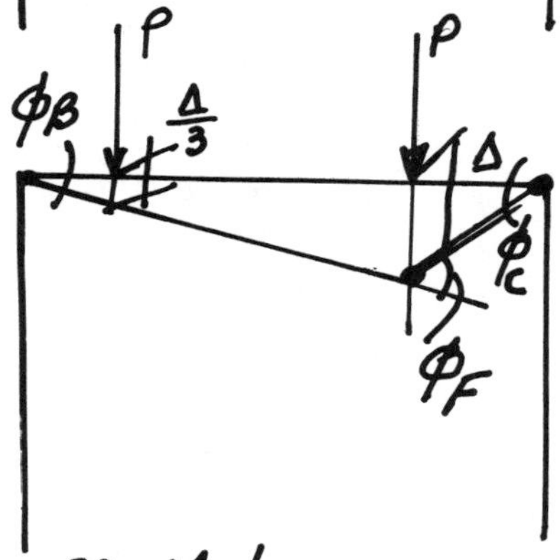

$$\phi_B = \frac{\Delta}{\frac{3L}{4}} = \frac{4\Delta}{3L}$$

$$\phi_C = \frac{\Delta}{\frac{L}{4}} = \frac{4\Delta}{L}$$

$$\phi_F = \frac{4\Delta}{3L} + \frac{4\Delta}{L} = \frac{16\Delta}{3L}$$

$\because W_I = W_E$

$$\frac{P\Delta}{3} + P\Delta = M_p(\phi_B + \phi_C + \phi_F) = \frac{32}{3L} M_p L$$

$$P_U = \frac{32}{3L} M_p = \frac{32 \times 165}{3 \times 15 \times 1.33} = 88^K$$

3. Panel mechanism

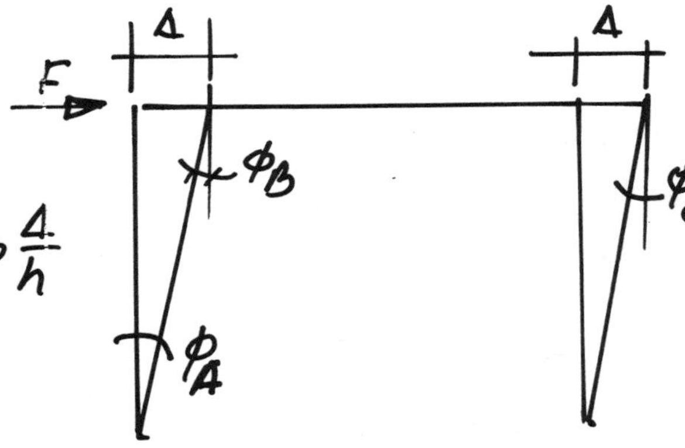

$$\phi_A = \phi_B = \frac{\Delta}{h} = \phi_C$$

$$W_E = W_I$$

$$F\Delta = M_p\left(\frac{\Delta}{h} + \frac{\Delta}{h}\right) = 2M_p \frac{\Delta}{h}$$

$$F = \frac{2}{h} M_p$$

or $2\alpha P = \frac{2}{h} M_p$ & $\alpha = \frac{L}{4}$

$$P_U = \frac{4}{h} M_p = 4 \times 165 = 66^K$$

4, Combined mechanism

$$\theta_A = \frac{\Delta_1}{h} \; ; \; \phi_B = \frac{\Delta_2}{L/4} = \frac{4\Delta_2}{L}$$

$$\because \theta_A = \phi_B = \frac{\Delta_1}{h} = \frac{4\Delta_2}{L}$$

$$\phi_{C_1} = \frac{\Delta_2}{\frac{3L}{4}} = \frac{4\Delta_2}{3L}$$

$$\phi_{C_2} = \frac{\Delta}{h}$$

$$\phi_C = \phi_{C_1} + \phi_{C_2} = \frac{4\Delta_2}{3L_1} + \frac{\Delta_1}{h}$$

$$= \frac{4\Delta_2}{3L_1} + \frac{4\Delta_2}{L} = \frac{16\Delta_2}{3L}$$

$$\phi_E = \phi_B + \phi_{C_1} = \frac{4\Delta_2}{L} + \frac{4\Delta_2}{3L}$$

$$= \frac{16\Delta_2}{3L}$$

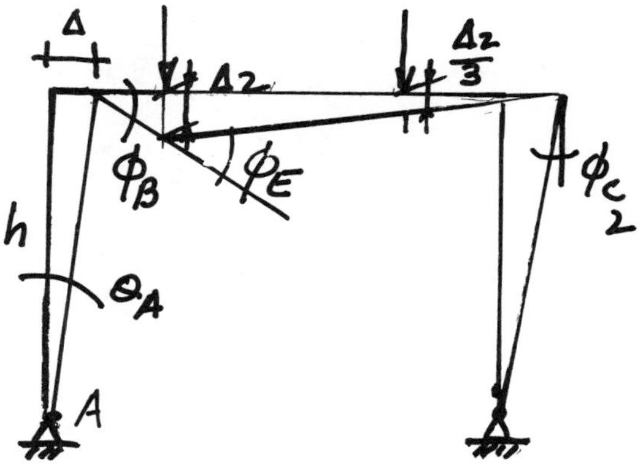

$$W_E = W_I$$

$$F\Delta_1 + P\Delta_2 + \frac{P\Delta_2}{3} = M_P(\phi_E + \phi_C)$$

$$F \cdot \frac{4h\Delta_2}{L} + P\Delta_2 + \frac{P\Delta_2}{3} = M_P\left(\frac{16\Delta_2}{3L} + \frac{16\Delta_2}{3L}\right)$$

$$\frac{2\alpha P \times 4 \times h}{l} + P + \frac{P}{3} = M_P \frac{32}{3L}$$

$$\left(2 \times \frac{1}{4} \times \frac{4 \times 16}{15} + 1 + 0.33\right)P = 165 \times \frac{32}{3 \times 15} = \frac{352}{3}$$

$$2.66 P_U = \frac{352}{3}$$

$$P_U = 44.1^k$$

5, Combined mechanism when hinge will form under 2nd load.

$$\theta_A = \frac{\Delta_1}{h} = \phi_{C_1}$$

$$\phi_B = \frac{\Delta_2}{\frac{3L}{4}} = \frac{4\Delta_2}{3L} = \phi_A$$

$$\phi_{C_2} = \frac{\Delta_2}{L/4} = \frac{4\Delta_2}{L}$$

$$\phi_F = \phi_B + \phi_{C_2} = \frac{16\Delta_2}{3L}$$

$$\phi_C = \phi_{C_1} + \phi_{C_2} = \frac{\Delta_1}{h} + \frac{4\Delta_2}{L}..$$

$$= \frac{16\Delta_2}{3L}$$

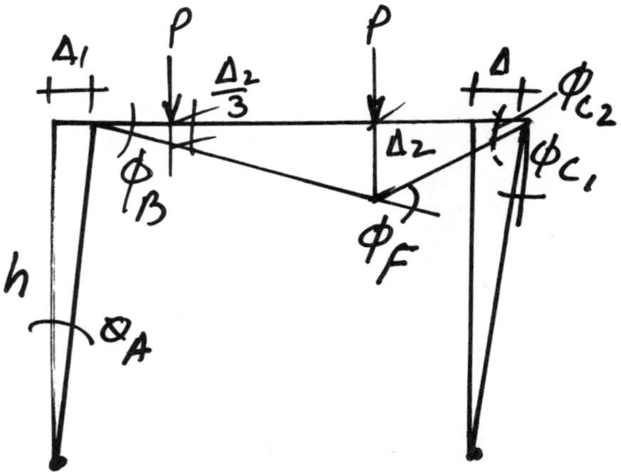

$$\therefore W_{Ext} = W_{INT}$$

$$\left(P\Delta_2 + \frac{P\Delta_2}{3} + F\Delta_1\right) = M_P(\phi_F + \phi_C)$$

$$\therefore P\left(1+0.33+\frac{2\times\frac{L}{4}\times4\times10}{3\times15}\right)=M_p\left(\frac{32}{3L}\right)$$

$$1.77P_U = \frac{352}{3}$$

$$P_U = 66.3^K$$

Hence structure will fail under combined mechanism when hinges will form at E&C.

$$P_U = 44.1K$$

$$\frac{wl}{2} = 44.1$$

$$w = \frac{44.1\times2}{15} = 5.88^{K}/_{1}$$

EXAMPLE 3-12

Given:- Check the adequacy for shear and modify the design for the following loaded beam. Use A-36 Steel.

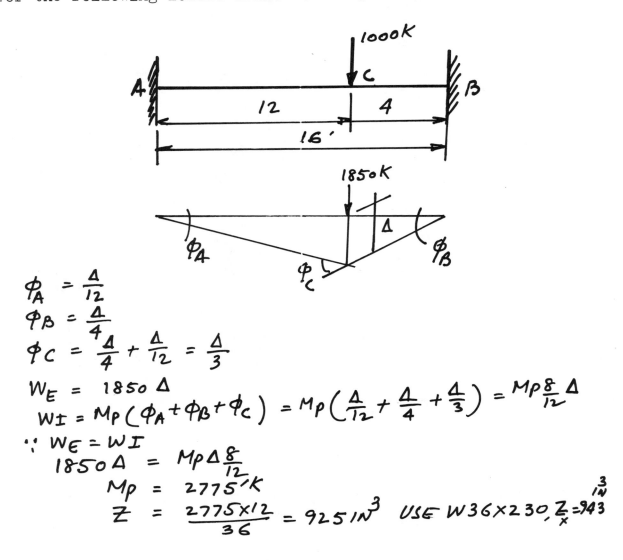

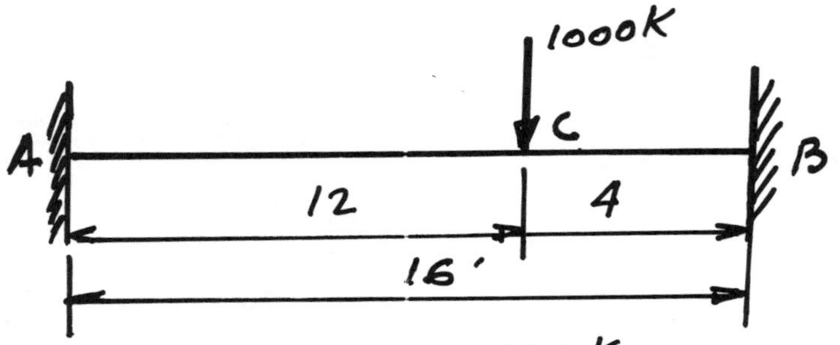

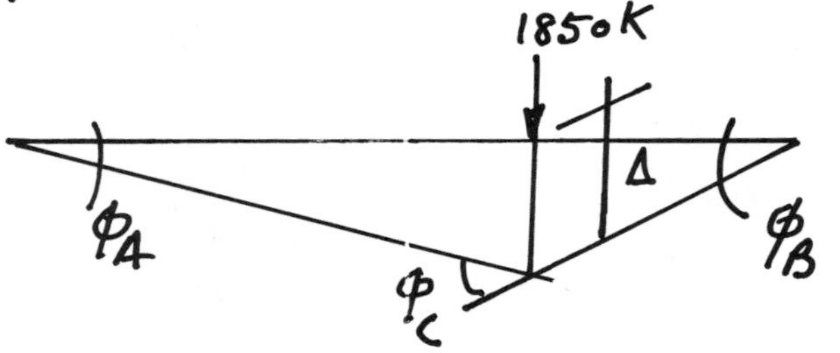

$$\phi_A = \frac{\Delta}{12}$$

$$\phi_B = \frac{\Delta}{4}$$

$$\phi_C = \frac{\Delta}{4}+\frac{\Delta}{12} = \frac{\Delta}{3}$$

$$W_E = 1850\,\Delta$$

$$W_I = M_p(\phi_A+\phi_B+\phi_C) = M_p\left(\frac{\Delta}{12}+\frac{\Delta}{4}+\frac{\Delta}{3}\right) = M_p\frac{8}{12}\Delta$$

$$\because W_E = W_I$$

$$1850\Delta = M_p\Delta\frac{8}{12}$$

$$M_p = 2775'K$$

$$Z = \frac{2775\times12}{36} = 925\,IN^3 \quad \text{USE } W36\times230,\ Z_x = 943\,IN^3$$

Properties of W36X230, $t_w = 0.765$, $d = 35.88''$

check shear under point of loading C

$V = \frac{2M_p}{4} = \frac{2775}{2} = 1387.5^k$

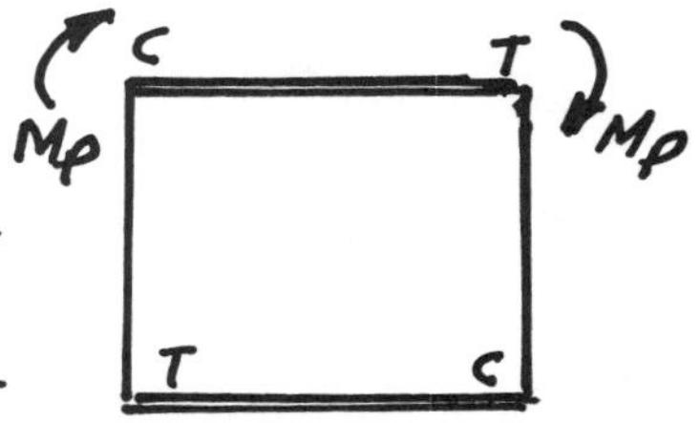

Vallowable A.I.S.C 5.76 $= 20 t_w d$

$= 20 \times 0.765 \times 35.88$

$= 550^k$

∵ Vallowable < Vactual ie $550 < 1387.5$

∴ There are three possibilities of modifying design

1, use heavier beam W36X300

Vall. $= 20 \times 0.945 \times 36.72 = 697 < 1387.5$ NG

2, Provide doubler plate to increase thickness of web

$t_{w\,req'd} = \frac{1387.5}{20 \times 35.88} = 1.94''$

Check web thickness $\frac{d_w}{t_w} \leq 70 - 100\frac{P}{P_y}$ — A.I.SC 25

$d_w = 35.88 - 1.26 = 34.62''$ ∴ $\frac{d_w}{t_w} = \frac{34.62}{2.765} = 12.5 < 70$ ok

$t_w = 2 + 0.765 = 2.765$

Use $34.62 \times 2''$ PL

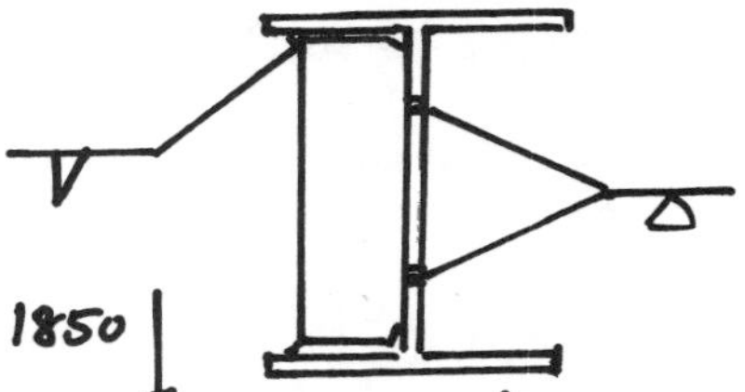

3, Provide stiffener

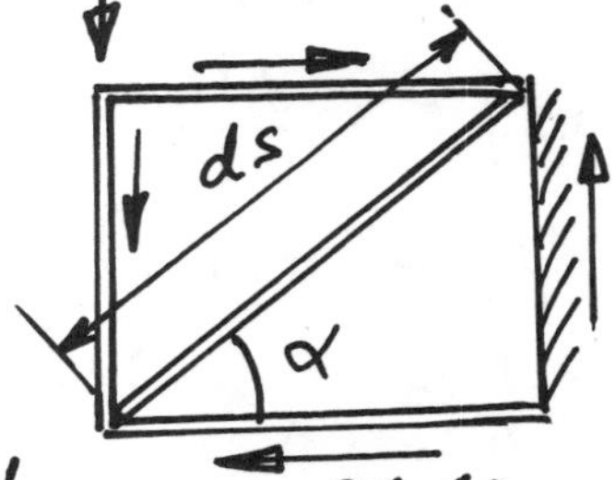

$A_{stiff} = \frac{F_s}{F_y} = \frac{\Delta V/\sin\alpha}{F_y}$

ΔV = Excess shear

$= 1387 - 550 = 837^k$

$A_{stiff_s} = \frac{837/0.584}{36} = 40\ in^2$

$d_s = \sqrt{34.62^2 + 48^2} = 59.2''$ ∴ $\tan\alpha = \frac{34.62}{48.0} = 0.72$

$A_{1\,stiff} = \frac{40}{2} = 20$, ∴ $b_s = 15$, $t_s = 1\frac{3}{8}$ $\sin\alpha = 0.584$

if $\frac{b_s}{t_s} \leq 17$ then $\frac{15}{1.375} = 10.9 < 17$ ok

Hence W36X230 WITH pair of diagonal $7\frac{1}{2}'' \times 1\frac{3}{8}''$ stiffener from the point of loading to fixed end.

EXAMPLE 3-13

Given:- Find the ultimate load in terms of M_p if all the members are equal.

$$F = \alpha wL, \quad h = L/3; \quad h_1 = L/4$$

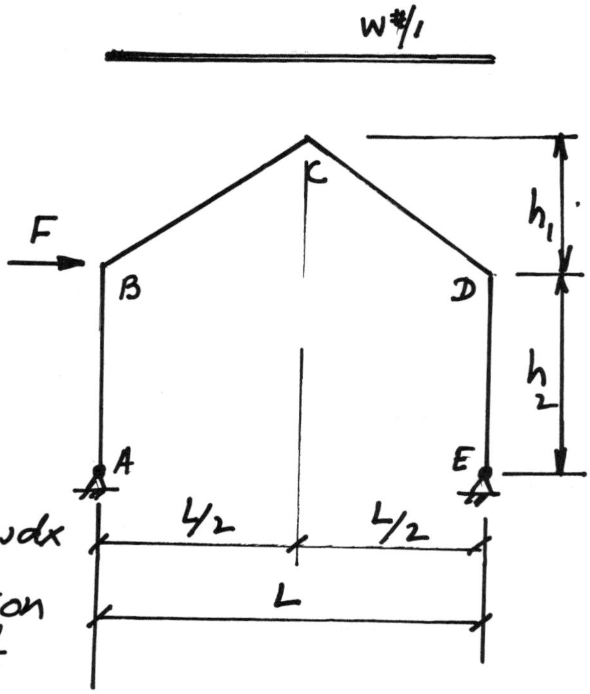

$$\theta_A L = \phi_F (L-a)$$

$$\phi_F = \frac{L}{L-a}\theta_A$$

$$\phi_D h = \phi_F (y+h)$$

$$\phi_D = \frac{y+h}{h}\phi_F$$

$$= \frac{y+h}{h}\frac{L}{L-a}\theta_A$$

$$W_E = F\Delta_B + \int_0^a (\theta_A x) w\,dx + \int_a^L [(\theta_A x) - \phi_F (x-a)] w\,dx$$

where $\Delta_B \rightarrow$ arbitrary motion

$$W_E = F\Delta B + \theta_A w \frac{x^2}{2}\Big|_0^a + \theta_A \frac{wx^2}{2}\Big|_a^L - \phi_F \left(\frac{x-a}{2}\right)^2 w\Big|_a^L$$

$$= F\Delta B + \frac{wLa}{2h}\Delta_B$$

$$= \Delta_B \left[F + \frac{wLa}{2h}\right]$$

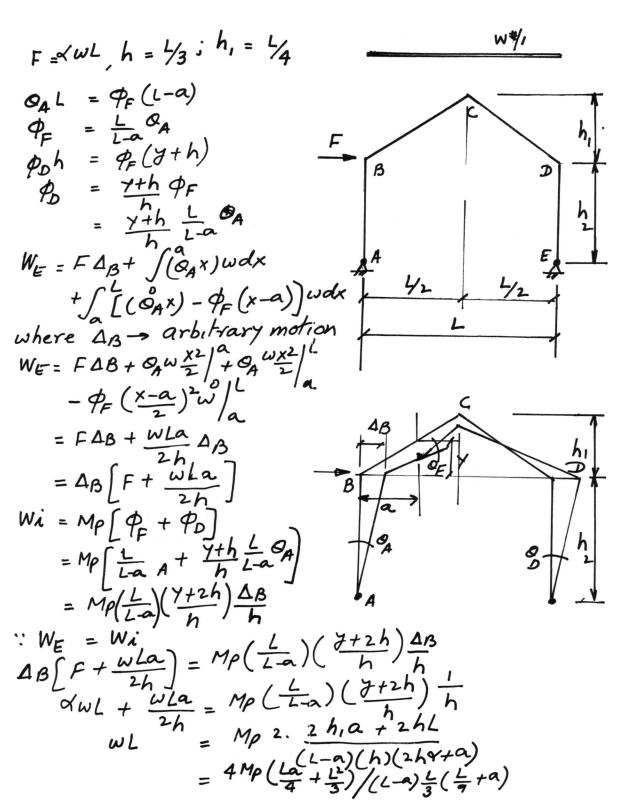

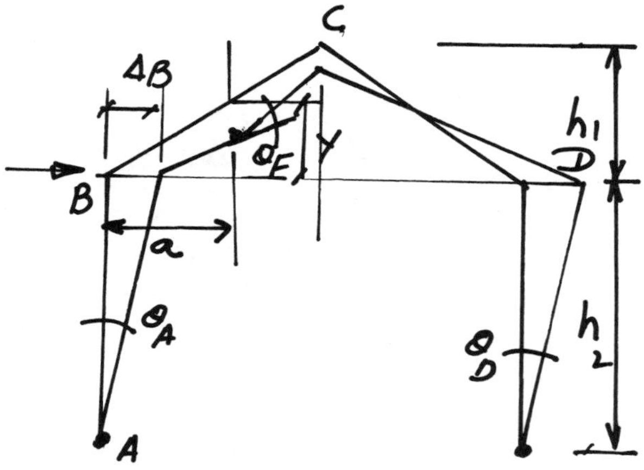

$$W_i = M_p [\phi_F + \phi_D]$$

$$= M_p \left[\frac{L}{L-a} A + \frac{y+h}{h}\frac{L}{L-a}\theta_A\right]$$

$$= M_p \left(\frac{L}{L-a}\right)\left(\frac{y+2h}{h}\right)\frac{\Delta B}{h}$$

$$\because W_E = W_i$$

$$\Delta B\left[F + \frac{wLa}{2h}\right] = M_p\left(\frac{L}{L-a}\right)\left(\frac{y+2h}{h}\right)\frac{\Delta B}{h}$$

$$\alpha wL + \frac{wLa}{2h} = M_p\left(\frac{L}{L-a}\right)\left(\frac{y+2h}{h}\right)\frac{1}{h}$$

$$wL = M_p\, 2.\, \frac{2h_1 a + 2hL}{(L-a)(h)(2h\alpha + a)}$$

$$= 4M_p\left(\frac{La}{4} + \frac{L^2}{3}\right) \Big/ (L-a)\frac{L}{3}\left(\frac{L}{9} + a\right)$$

$$\therefore \quad wL = \frac{12M_p\left[\frac{3a+4L}{12}\right]}{(L-a)(L/9+a)}$$

$$= \frac{9M_p[3a+4L]}{(L-a)(L+9a)}$$

$$= 9 \cdot M_p\left[\frac{3a+4L}{L^2+8aL-9a^2}\right]$$

$$\frac{d(wL)}{da} = 9M_p\left[\frac{(L^2+8aL-9a^2)3-[3a+4L][8L-18a]}{(L^2+8aL-9a^2)^2}\right]$$

$$\text{Let} \quad \frac{d(wL)}{da} = 0$$

$$\therefore \quad 0 = 9M_p\left[\frac{(L^2+8aL-9a^2)3-[3a+4L][8L-18a]}{(L^2+8aL-9a^2)^2}\right]$$

$$\because M_p \neq 0$$

$$\therefore (L^2+8aL-9a^2)3-[24aL-54a^2+32L^2-72aL] = 0$$

$$\text{or} \quad 27a^2+72aL-29L^2 = 0$$

$$a = \frac{-72L \pm \sqrt{5184L^2+3130L^2}}{54} = 0.359L$$

$$\therefore \quad WL = \frac{9M_p[3a+4L]}{(L-a)(L+9a)} = \frac{9M_p \times 5.077L}{0.641L \times 4.231L} = \frac{16.8M_p}{L}$$

EXAMPLE 3-14

Given:- Find P of the following vierendial truss.

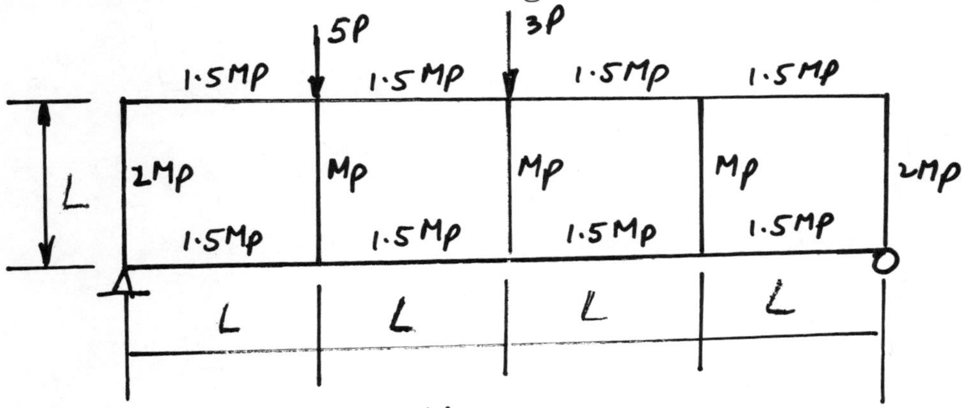

There are 22 possible hinges

No of redundancy $= 3m + R - 3J$

$= 3 \times 13 + 3 - 3 \times 10 = 12$

No of independant mechanism $= 22 - 12 = 10$

ie 6 Joint mechanism, 4 Panel mechanism

Since all loads are applied at the Joints, no Beam mechanism exist.

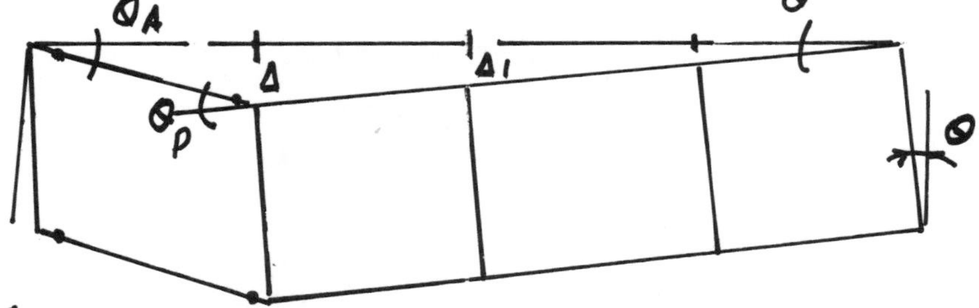

1.

$$\theta = \frac{\Delta}{3L}$$

$$\Delta_1 = \frac{\Delta}{3L} 2L = \frac{2\Delta}{3}$$

$$\theta_p = \frac{\Delta}{3L} + \frac{\Delta}{L} = \frac{4\Delta}{3L}$$

$$5P\Delta + 3P\frac{2\Delta}{3} = 1.5M_p\left[\left(\frac{\Delta}{2} + \frac{4\Delta}{3L}\right)4 + \left(\frac{4\Delta}{3L}\right)^2\right]$$

$$21P\Delta = 18\frac{M_p}{L}\Delta$$

$$\therefore P = \frac{18}{21}\frac{M_p}{L} = 0.86\frac{M_p}{L}$$

11.

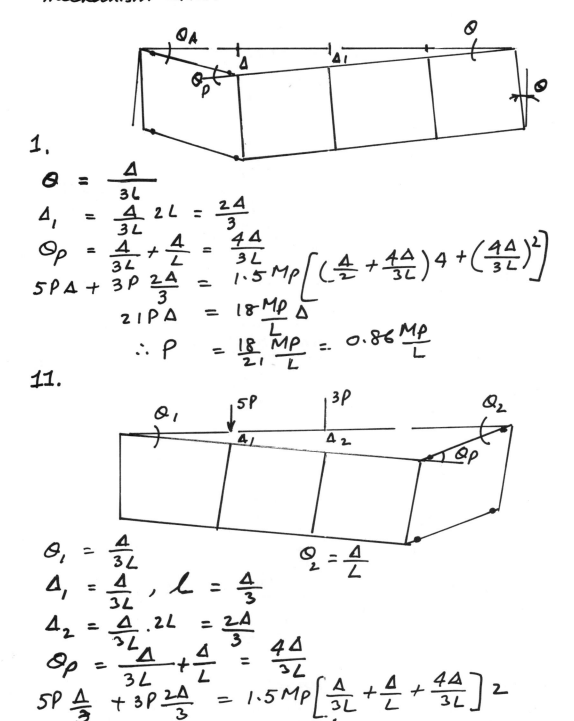

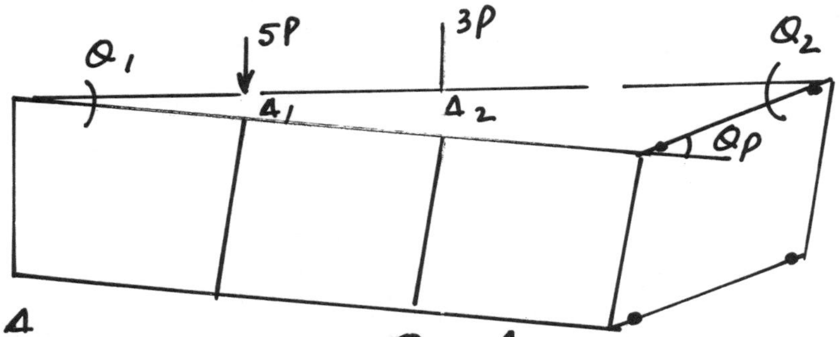

$$\theta_1 = \frac{\Delta}{3L} \qquad \theta_2 = \frac{\Delta}{L}$$

$$\Delta_1 = \frac{\Delta}{3L}, \ l = \frac{\Delta}{3}$$

$$\Delta_2 = \frac{\Delta}{3L} . 2L = \frac{2\Delta}{3}$$

$$\theta_p = \frac{\Delta}{3L} + \frac{\Delta}{L} = \frac{4\Delta}{3L}$$

$$5P\frac{\Delta}{3} + 3P\frac{2\Delta}{3} = 1.5M_p\left[\frac{\Delta}{3L} + \frac{\Delta}{L} + \frac{4\Delta}{3L}\right]2$$

$$11P\Delta = 24M_p\frac{\Delta}{L}$$

$$P = 2.18\,M_p/L$$

III

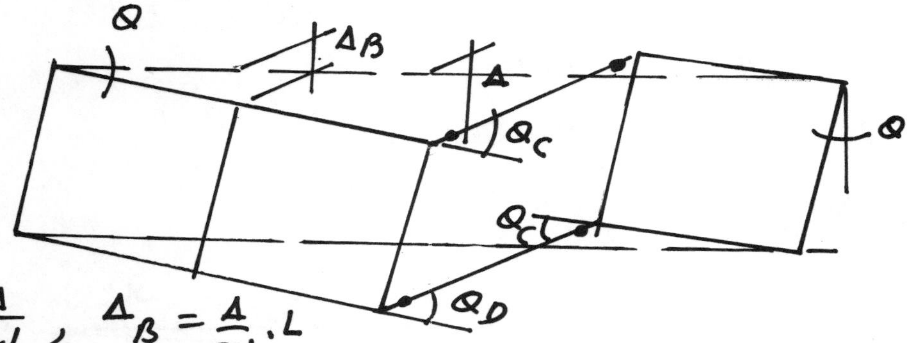

$$\theta = \frac{\Delta}{2L}, \quad \Delta_B = \frac{\Delta}{2L} \cdot L = \frac{\Delta}{2}$$

$$\theta_C = \frac{\Delta}{2L} + \left(\frac{\Delta}{2L} + \frac{\Delta}{L}\right) = \frac{2\Delta}{L} \quad \& \quad \theta_D = \frac{2\Delta}{L}$$

$$5P\frac{\Delta}{2} + 3P\Delta = 1.5M_p\left(\frac{2\Delta}{L} + \frac{2\Delta}{L}\right)2$$

$$P = 2.18\frac{M_p}{L}$$

IV.

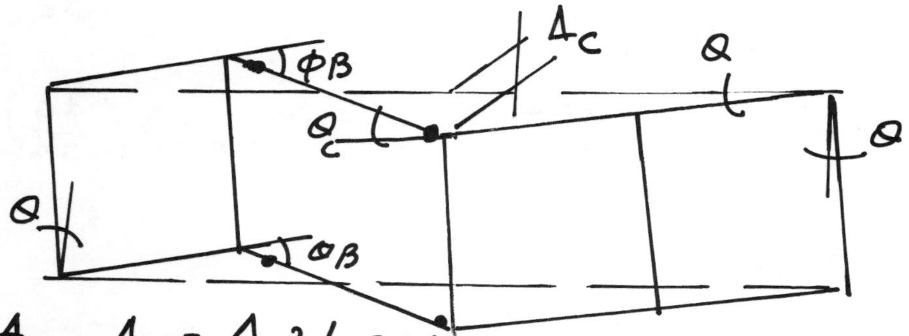

$$\theta = \frac{\Delta}{L}, \quad \Delta_C = \frac{\Delta}{L}2L = 2\Delta$$

$$\theta_B = \left(\frac{\Delta}{L}2L + 2\Delta\right)\frac{1}{L} = \frac{4\Delta}{L} = \theta_C$$

$$5P\Delta + 3P(-2\Delta) = 1.5M_p\left(\frac{4\Delta}{L} + \frac{4\Delta}{L}\right)2$$

$$P = -24M_p/L$$

COMPOSITE MECHANISM. (1)

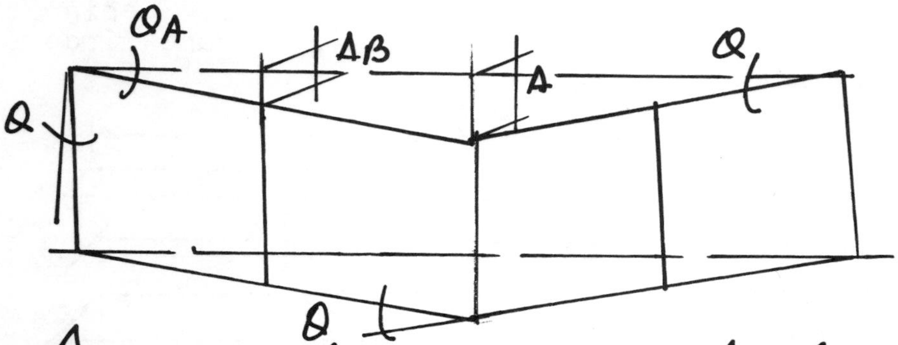

$$\theta_A = \frac{\Delta}{L}, \quad \Delta_B = \frac{\Delta}{2L}L = \frac{\Delta}{2}, \quad \theta_C = \frac{\Delta}{2L} + \frac{\Delta}{2L} = \frac{\Delta}{L} = \theta_A$$

$$5P\frac{\Delta}{2} + 3P\Delta = 2M_p\frac{\Delta}{2L} + 1.5M_p\left(\frac{\Delta}{L} + \frac{\Delta}{L}\right)2$$

$$11P = 14M_p/L$$

$$P = 1.273M_p/L$$

Composite mechanism (2)

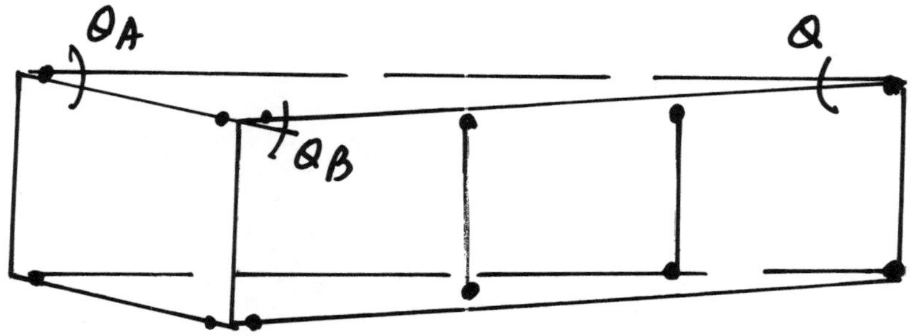

$$\theta = \frac{\Delta}{3L}$$

$$\theta_A = \frac{\Delta}{L}, \quad \theta_B = \theta_A + \theta = \frac{\Delta}{L} + \frac{\Delta}{3L} = \frac{4\Delta}{3L}$$

$$\Delta_c = \frac{\Delta}{3L} \cdot 2L = \frac{2\Delta}{3}$$

$$5P\Delta + 3P\frac{2\Delta}{3} = 1.5M_p\left(\frac{\Delta}{L}\right)4 + 1.5M_p\left(\frac{4\Delta}{3L}\right) + 2M_p\left(\frac{\Delta}{3L}\right)$$

$$21P\Delta = 26\frac{M_p\Delta}{L}$$

$$P = 1.24\frac{M_p}{L}$$

Hence (1) Panel mechanism Governs

$$P = 0.86M_p/L.$$

EXAMPLE 3-15

Given:- In a floor system, the girders are spaced at 15' C/C and are 40 ft. long. Using A-36 Steel and a working load 2.5 kips per ft. per girder, select a girder size. Design the necessary lateral bracing and stiffness. Assume girders are clamped at both ends.

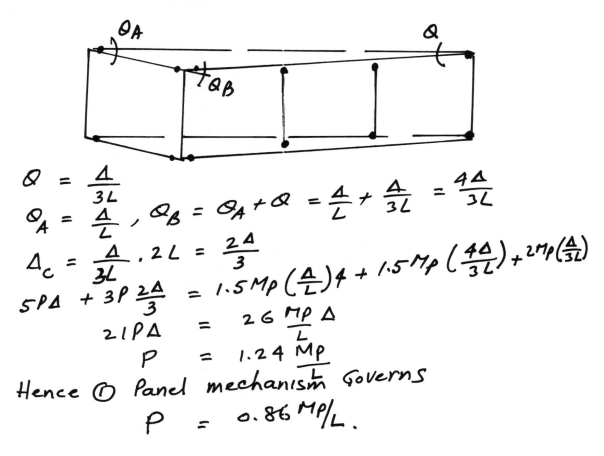

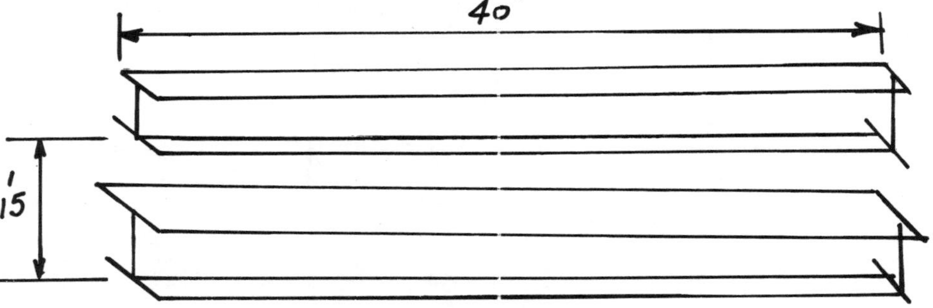

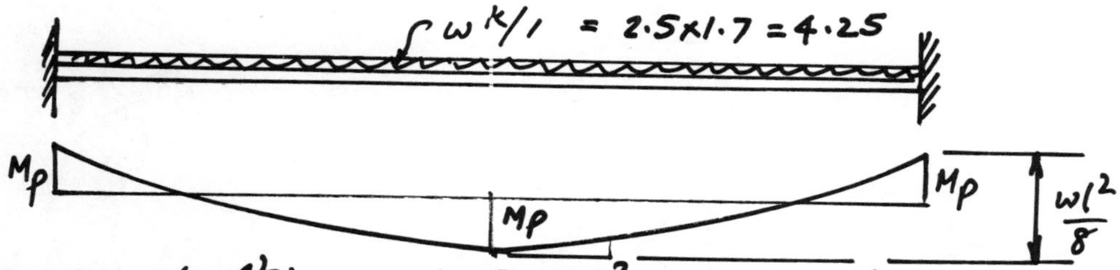

$$M_p \text{ req'd} = \frac{1}{2}\left(\frac{wl^2}{8}\right) = \frac{4.25\times40^2}{16} = 425'^k = 5100''^k$$

$$Z = \frac{M_p}{\sigma_y} = \frac{5100}{36} = 141.7\ \text{IN}^3$$

TRY W 18×70, $Z = 144.7\ \text{IN}^3$

check Local buckling

$$\frac{d}{w} = \frac{18.0}{0.438} = 41.2 < 70 \quad \text{ok}$$

$$\frac{b}{t} = \frac{8.75}{0.751} = 11.65 < 17 \quad \text{ok}$$

$$V_{max} = \frac{wl}{2} = 85 \text{ kips}$$

$$V_{allow} = 19.5\times0.438\times18 = 154^k > 85 \quad \text{ok}$$

USE W 18×70 Girder.

Spacing for Lateral bracing

In region of near uniform moment @ center

$$L_{cr} = 38\,r_y = 38\times1.95 = 74.3\ \text{in}$$

In region of moment gradient @ ends.

$$L_{cr} = 65\,r_y = 65\times1.95 = 126.5\ \text{in}$$

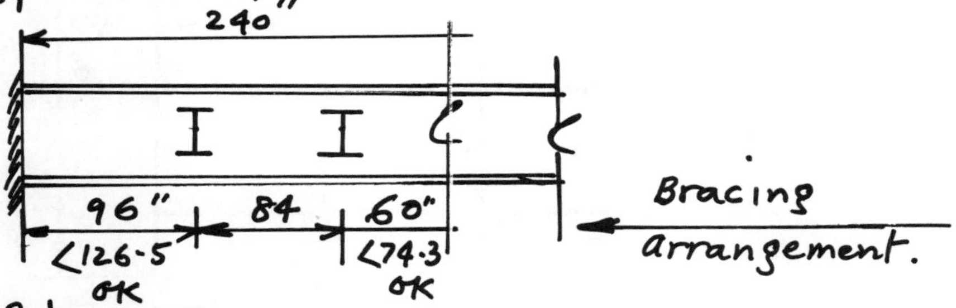

Design of bracing

$$L_b = 180'', \quad d_b = \frac{3\,\epsilon_y L_b A d}{b^2 t}$$

for W18×70, $b = 8.75''$; $t = 0.751''$

$d = 18.0''$; $A = 20.56\,\square''$

$$\epsilon_y = \frac{36}{29000} = 0.00124$$

$$d_b = \frac{3\times0.00124\times180\times20.56\times18.0}{(8.75)^2(0.751)} = 4.31''$$

Try 6 B 12 Bracing Members.

$$A_{br} = \frac{0.22\, b^2 t}{L_1 + L_2}$$

$$= \frac{0.22 \times 8.75^2 \times 0.751}{2 \times 60} = 0.106\,\square'' \leq 3.53\ \text{IN}^2\ \text{ok}$$

$$\frac{L_{br}}{L_a} = 0.19\left[\frac{L_a}{b}\right]\left[\frac{A_b}{A_{br}}\right]$$

$$= 0.19 \times \frac{60}{8.75} \times \frac{3.53}{0.106} = 43.5 > \frac{180}{60} = 3\ \text{ok}$$

Use B 6×12 Bracing Member

EXAMPLE 3-16

Given:- Design girder, column and bracing in 3rd story from, top in 10 story frame 3 bay. Story height 12.5' bay width 25'. Wind load 5 k at roof, 10 k at the other girders. Distributed load at the girder 1.4 k/ft. typical.

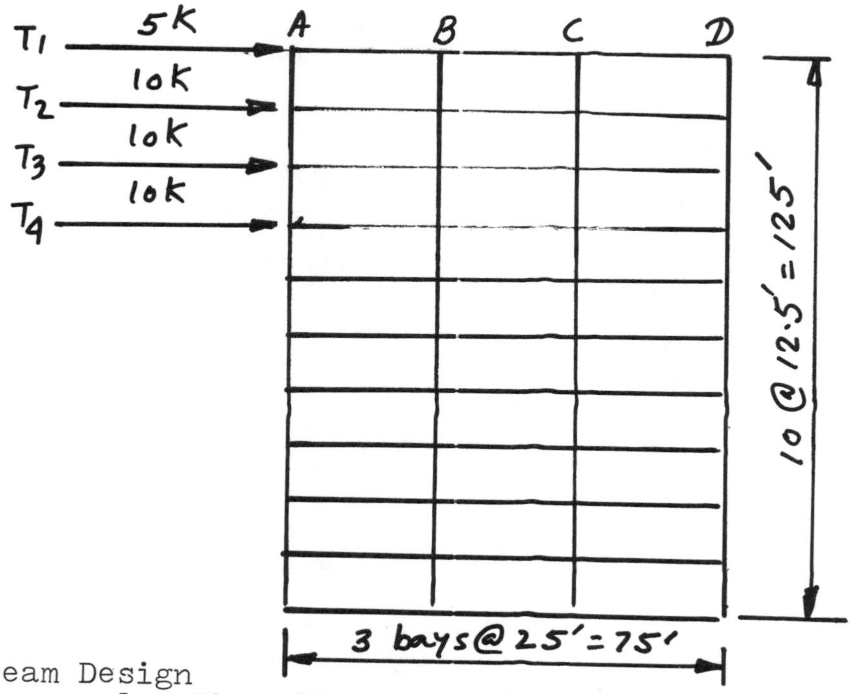

Girder-Beam Design

Assumptions: 1. The effect of axial load on M is neglegible.

2. The shearing stress does not affect the yield stress of any fiber.

3. Local and lateral torsional buckling does not occur.

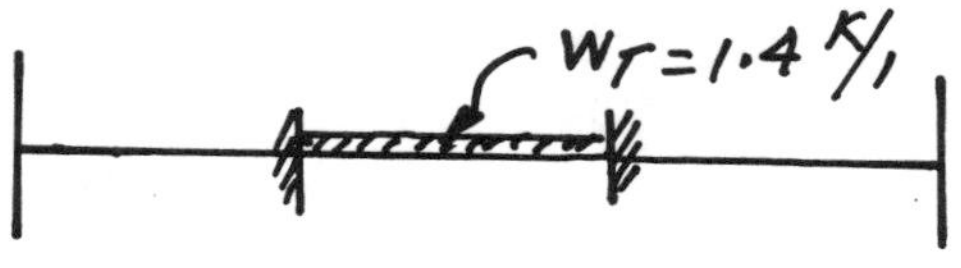

$$M_p = \frac{1.85\, W_T L^2}{16} = 101'^{K}$$

$$Z = \frac{101 \times 12}{36} = 33.67\ \text{IN}^3$$

Use W10×29, $Z = 34.7\ \text{IN}^3$ & $M_p = 104.1'^{K} = 1249.2''^{K}$

Column design:-
gravity load in 3 top storeys

storey	P_{tA}	P_{tB}	P_{tC}	P_{tD}	$\Sigma H/1.4$
T	17.5	35.0	35.0	17.5	3.6
T-1	35.0	70.0	70.0	35.0	10.7
T-2	52.5	105.0	105.0	52.5	17.9
T-3	70.0	140.0	140.0	70.0	25.0

Exterior Col.

Axial force $= 52.5 \times 1.85 = 97.1$

$70.0 \times 1.85 = 129.5$

$M_{PA} = M_{Pg} + V\frac{d_c}{2}$ where $V = \frac{(1.4)(1.85)}{2}\left[25 - \frac{2\times10}{12}\right] = 30.2^K$

$= 1249.2 + 30.2 \times \frac{10}{2} = 1400.2''K$

$M_{PC_2} + M_{PC_3} \geqslant M_{PA}$

& assuming $M_{PC_2} = M_{PC_3}$

$\therefore M_{PC_2} = \frac{1400}{2} = 700''K$

$Z = \frac{700}{36} = 19.5\ in^3$, Try W10X25, $Z = 29.5\ in^3$, $r_x = 4.26\ in$ & $A = 7.35\ in^2$

$\frac{P_2}{P_y} = \frac{97.1}{7.35\times36} = 0.368$

$\frac{P_3}{P_y} = \frac{129.5}{7.35\times36} = 0.49$

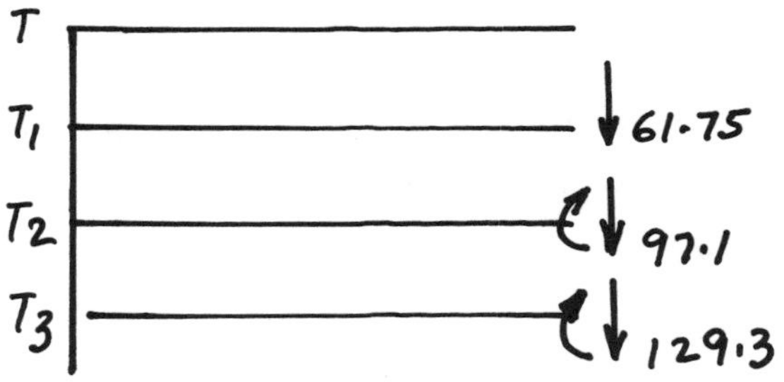

$M_{PC_2} = 1.18(1-0.368)(36)(29.5)$

$= 823''K$

$M_{PC_3} = 1.18(1-0.49)(36)(29.5)$

$= 640''K$

$M_T = M_{PC_2} + M_{PC_3} = 823 + 640 = 1463''K > 1400$ ok.

$\because \frac{P_2}{P_y}$ or $\frac{P_3}{P_y} < 0.6$ $\therefore$ No increase in col. size

Use W10X25.

Interior Col. B_{2-3} & C_{2-3}

Assume Col braced in YY axis & design governs by Axial

force. $T_{2-3} = 140^k$

Try W10×39, $A = 11.48 \, in^2$; $P_y = 413.3^k$, $r_x = 4.27''$, $Z = 47 \, in^3$

$$\frac{L_V}{r_x} = \frac{(12.5-1.2)\times 12}{4.27} = 32, \quad \sigma = 34.83 \text{ ksi}$$

$$A_{reqd} = \frac{140}{34.83} = 4.04 < 11.48 \text{ ok} \quad \text{Use W10×39}$$

Assume Check board loading for Col.

$$W_L = 0.75 W_T = 0.75 \times 1.85 \times 1.4 = 1.94 \, ^K/_{Ft}$$

$$W_D = 0.25 W_T = 0.65 \, ^K/_{Ft}$$

$$W_T = 1.94 + 0.65 = 2.59 \, ^K/_{ft}.$$

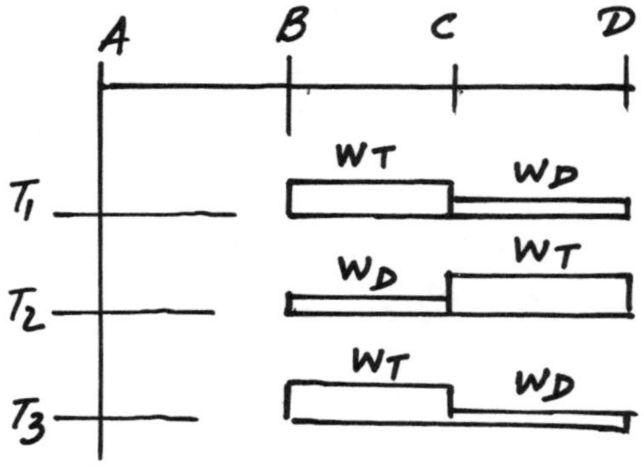

M_{max} @ JT C_2

$$M_{C_1} = M_{C_2} = M_{C_3} = 1.15 M_p + W_T \frac{L_G}{2} \frac{d_c}{2}$$

$$= 1.15 \times \frac{36}{12} \times 34.7 + 2.59 \times \frac{24.17}{2} \times \frac{10}{2\times 12}$$

$$= 132.5'^K$$

The above moment will be resisted by Col. C_{1-2}, C_{2-3} & g_{CD}

$$M_{CD} = M_p + \frac{W_D^2 L_G}{2} \times \frac{d_c}{2} = 104 + \frac{0.65 \times 24.17}{2} \times \frac{10}{2} \times \frac{L}{12}$$

$$= 120'^K$$

θ_{ph} (Rotation at which Max. moment is reached)

$$= f \frac{\sigma_Y}{E}\left(1 - \frac{4}{3}\frac{W_D}{W_T}\right)\frac{L_G}{d_G} = 1.33\times 10^{-3}\left(1 - \frac{4}{3}\times\frac{0.69}{2.59}\right)\frac{24.17}{0.83}$$

$$= 0.0184$$

Col C_{1-2}, $q = 0$, Col C_{2-3} & $q = -1$

Check W10×39

$$C_{1-2}: \frac{h}{r_x} = 32, \quad \frac{P_{1-2}}{P_y} = \frac{105}{413.3} = 0.255$$

$$\frac{M}{M_{PC}} = 1 \quad \therefore M_{T_2} = 141.0$$

$$C_{2-3} \quad \frac{h}{r_x} = 32; \quad \frac{P_{2-3}}{P_y} = \frac{140}{413.3} = 0.338$$

$\frac{M}{M_{pc}} = 0.81 \quad \therefore M_{T3} = 141 \times 0.81 = 114$

$M_{Total} = 120 + 141 + 114 = 375 > 132.5$ ok

Bracing design:-

Interior bay

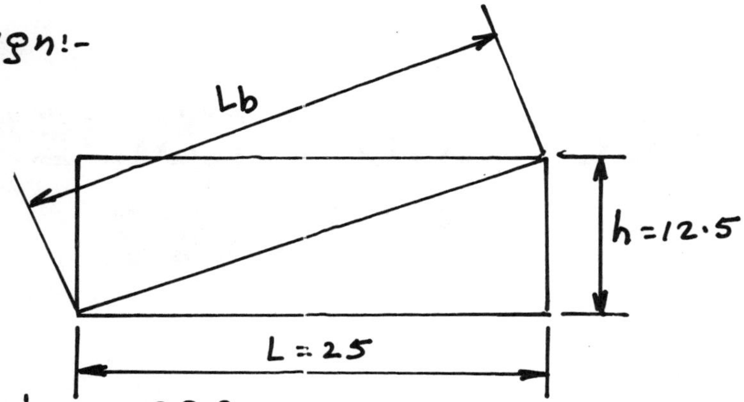

$L_b = 28.3, \quad \frac{L_b}{h} = \frac{28.3}{12.5} = 2.26$

$\left(\frac{L_b}{h}\right)\left(\frac{L_b}{L}\right)^2 = 11.56$ & $\frac{L_b^3}{hL^2} \times \frac{1}{E} = 3.85 \times 10^{-4}$

$A_b = \frac{1}{E} \frac{L_b^3}{hL^2} \Sigma F_{PW}$ where $\Sigma F_{PW} = 4 \times 245 = 980$

$= 3.85 \times 10^{-4} \times 980 \times 1.85 = 0.70 \text{ in}^2$

By Equation 22.10 of structural steel design by Ronald press ie $A_b = \frac{1}{E} \frac{L_b^3}{L^2 h} \Sigma F P_W + \frac{L_b}{h} \frac{\Sigma H}{F_y}$

$= 0.70 + 2.26 \times \frac{25 \times 1.4}{36} = 2.89 \square''$

Check Deflection

$$\Delta = \frac{\Sigma H}{1.4E \frac{L^2 h}{L_b^3} A_b - \Sigma 1.4 P_W} = \frac{35 \times 10^{-4}}{0.259 \times 2.89 - 0.70}$$

$= 0.7 \times 10^{3} = 0.0007 < 0.002$ ok

Use 2 Ls $4 \times 3 \times \frac{1}{4}$, $A = 3.38 \square''$

$A_{net} = 3.38 - 0.22 = 3.16$

$\frac{A_{req'd}}{A_g} = \frac{2.89}{3.38} = 0.85 < 0.85$ ok

$\frac{L_b}{r} = \frac{28.5 \times 12}{1.16} = 298 < 300$ ok

4

OFFICE AND RESIDENTIAL BUILDINGS

This chapter presents a practical approach to the design of Office and Residential Buildings of Reinforced Concrete and Structural Steel, based on the American Concrete Institute Standard Building Codes 318-71, 77 and AISC 7th Edition. The full design example along with the procedure is presented.

Analysis and Design:- Required loadings are as a rule, prescribed in applicable local codes and ordinances. The supporting structure must resist any and all of the prescribed loads. Lateral loads (wind, earthquake) should be assessed according to the latest information which may be more conservative than existing codes. For the structures which are to resist seismic forces and buildings of great heights, dynamic response analysis are recommended.
Buildings usually consist of multistoreyed and multipanelled network of beams and columns which are built monolithically and rigidly with each other at their junctions. All members of such a frame are continuous at their ends, thus moments are reduced due to continuity. Loads are distributed uniformly thus localised excessive loadings are eliminated. The effects of horizontal loads such as wind and earthquake are spread over the whole structure in steel or concrete frame or hi-rise building frame is very much lighter as compared to one in brick/stone building. Thus reducing the load on foundation. Also, the earthquake stresses which are proportional to the weight of the structure, also becomes small.

Method of Analysis for Horizontal Forces Due to Winds and Earthquake

1. Portal Method

Assumptions:- a. The points of contraflexure of all members lie at their midpoints.

b. The interior columns take horizontal shear equal to double of that taken by an exterior column.

Both assumptions imply:

a. Both ends of the column have equal fixity.

b. The interior column is connected to the beam on either side thus making the structure statically determinate.

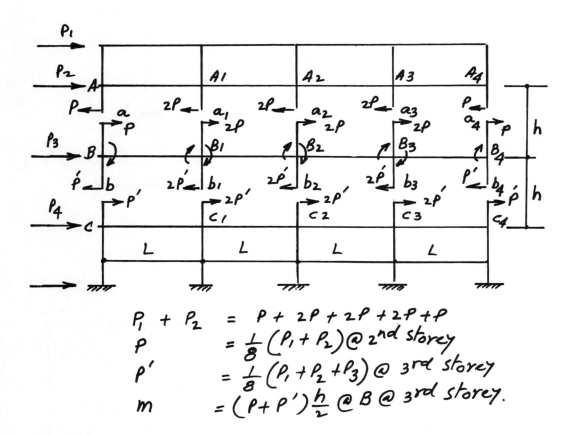

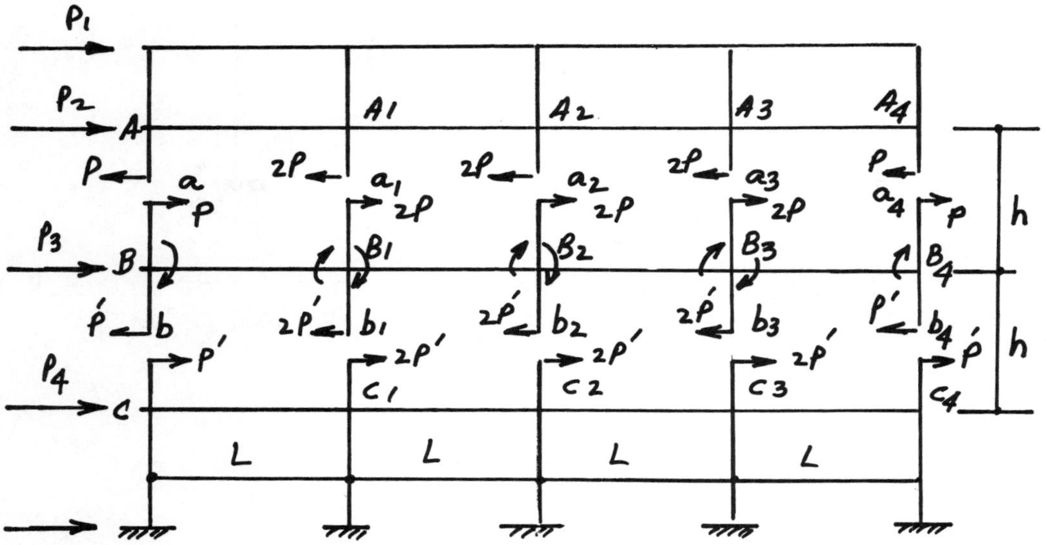

$$P_1 + P_2 = P + 2P + 2P + 2P + P$$

$$P = \frac{1}{8}(P_1 + P_2) \text{ @ } 2^{nd} \text{ storey}$$

$$P' = \frac{1}{8}(P_1 + P_2 + P_3) \text{ @ } 3^{rd} \text{ storey}$$

$$m = (P + P')\frac{h}{2} \text{ @ } B \text{ @ } 3^{rd} \text{ storey.}$$

2. Cantilever Method

Assumptions:- a. Inflection points at the middle at all columns and girders.

b. The columns are usually assumed equal in area.

c. Direct column stresses are proportional to the distances from the neutral axis.

$$2(V_1 X_1 + V_2 X_2) = F_1 \frac{h}{2}$$

Also

$$H_1 = \frac{V_1 L_1}{h} \text{ — shear force in } AA.$$

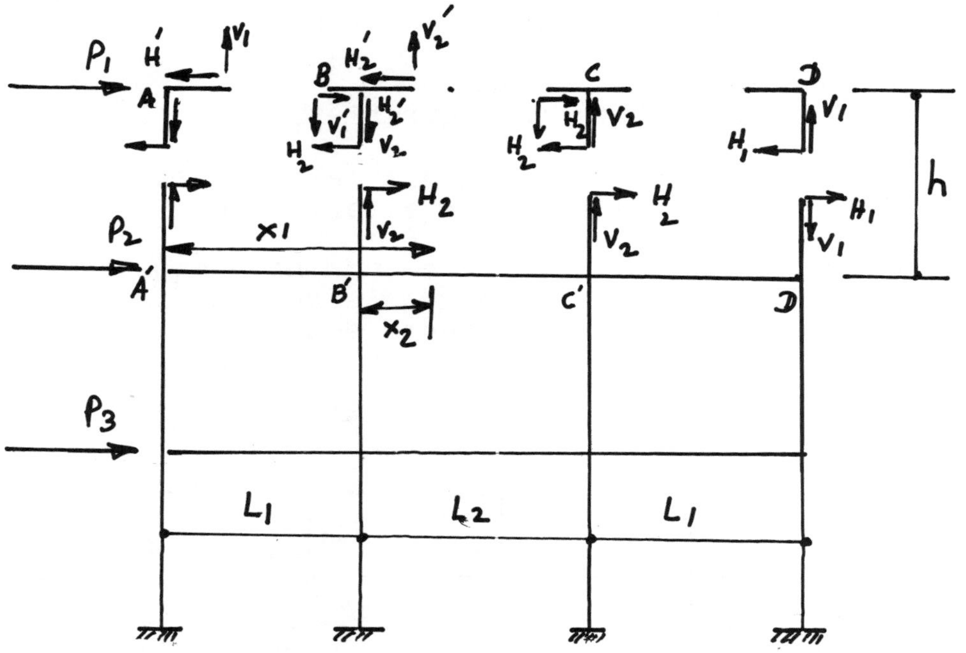

EXAMPLE 4-01

Given:- Make a wind analysis (Shear and Moment) of the H.V.A.C. storey below the roof of the frame by the Portal Method.

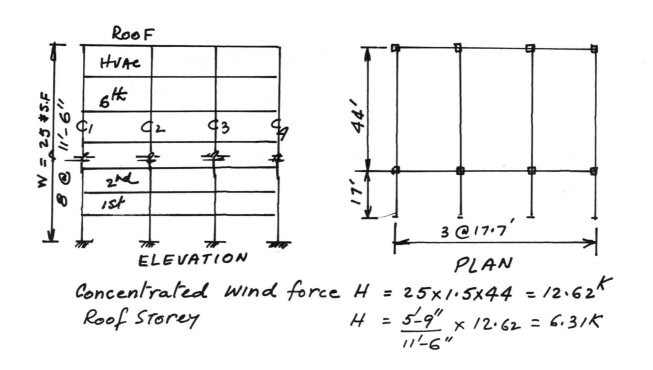

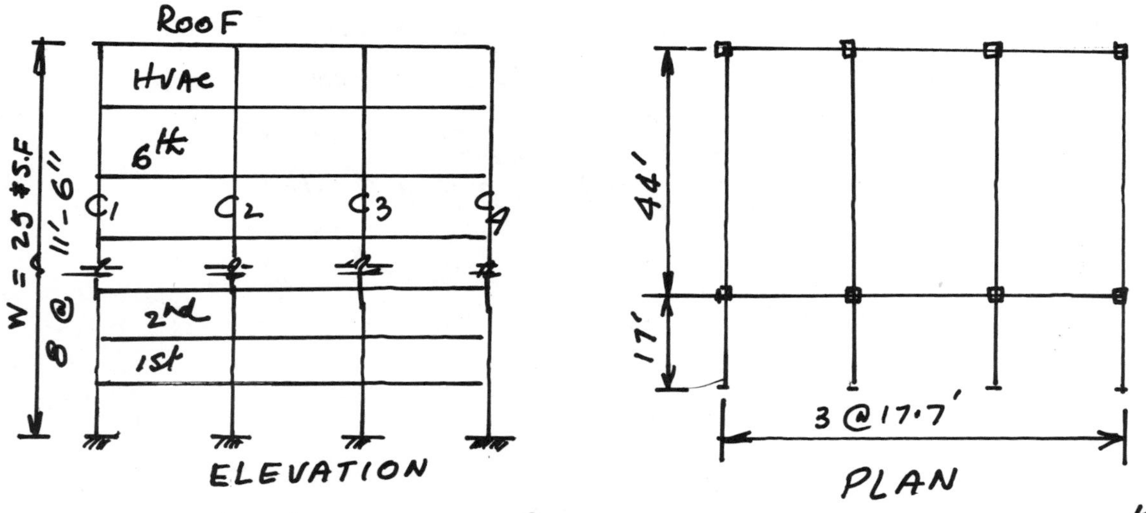

Concentrated wind force $H = 25 \times 1.5 \times 44 = 12.62^K$

Roof Storey $H = \frac{5'-9''}{11'-6''} \times 12.62 = 6.31K$

Portion of storey shear taken by each column.

Col. No	C_1	C_2	C_3	C_4
Aisle width	8.85	17.7	17.7	17.7
% of Total Shear	6.25	12.5	12.5	12.5

Shear above H.V.A.C storey Floor

$$H = 6.31 + 12.62 = 18.93^k$$

shear below H.V.AC storey Floor

$$H = 18.93 + 12.62 = 31.55^k$$

Distribution of Shears.

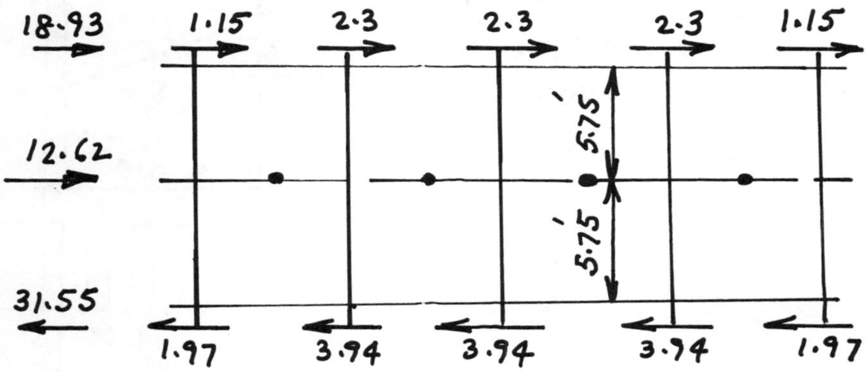

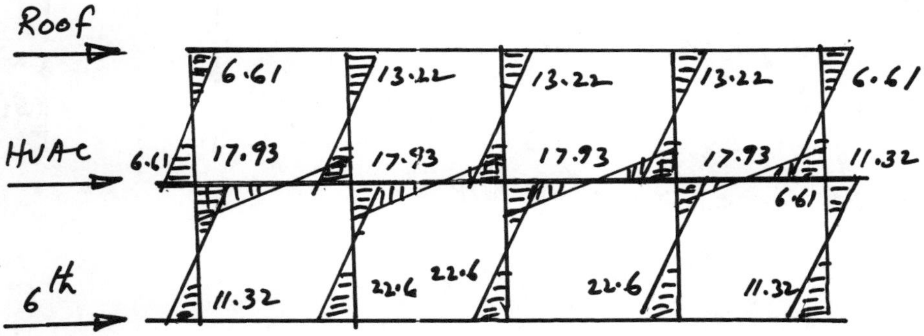

EXAMPLE 4-02

Given:- Determine the capacity of a 20 in. square reinforced concrete column shown in the figure. The column is reinforced with 4-#18 bars with f 60 ksi and lateral ties. Concrete strength is fc 3 ksi. Assume the factored load P to have a minimum eccentricity of 2 in. and that the slenderness can be ignored.

Assume $c = 24''$

Then $\beta = 0.75$ for $f_c' = 3000$ psi

$a = \beta c = 0.75 \times 24 = 18''$

$e = 12\,M_U/P_U$

$\varepsilon_{yield} = \dfrac{60}{29000} = 0.00207$

Stress in steel = 60 ksi

∴ strain diagram is linear and the maxi. compression strain is 0.003 in/in.

Strain in reinforcing steel is 0.00258 & 0.00092"/".

∴ ε_{yield} < strain in reinf. st.

∴ stress in steel = 0.00092×29000
= 26.7k

$a = 0.75 \times c = 0.75 \times 24 = 18''$

$f_c = 0.85 \times 6 = 5.1$ ksi

Compression force on concrete
$= 5.1 \times 20 \times 18 = 1836^k$

$e = \dfrac{20}{2} - \dfrac{18}{2} = 1''$ from centroid of col.

Compressive force on pair of reinforcing steel
$= 8 \times 60 - 8 \times 5.1 = 439k$

Compressive force on other pair of reinforcing steel = 8(26.7−5.1)
= 173k

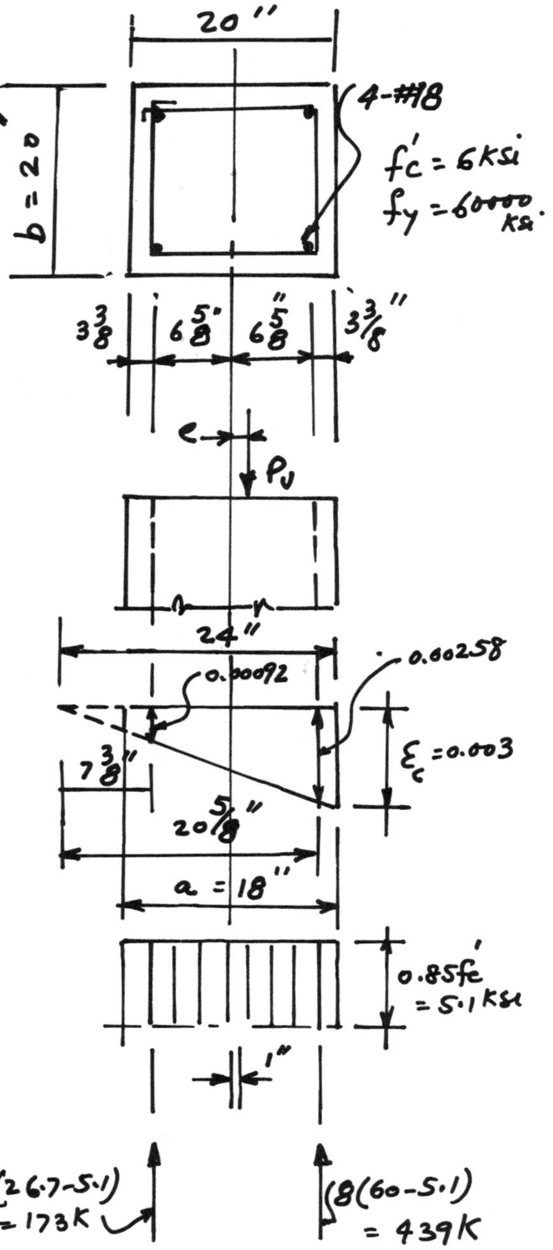

$P_U = 0.70(1836 + 173 + 439) = 1714^k$

$M_U = 0.70\left[1836 \times \frac{1}{12} + (439 - 173)\,\dfrac{20\frac{5}{8}}{3} \times \frac{1}{12}\right]$

$= 209^k$

$e = \dfrac{209 \times 12}{1714} = 1.46 < 2^{in}$ ok.

EXAMPLE 4-03

Given:- Design an interior panel of office tower with storey height 11.5 ft., column size 30" x 30", as a ribbed floor using steel pan forms. The columns are placed 23'-4" on center. Live Load 50 psf, partition load 15 psf and ceiling 15 psf.

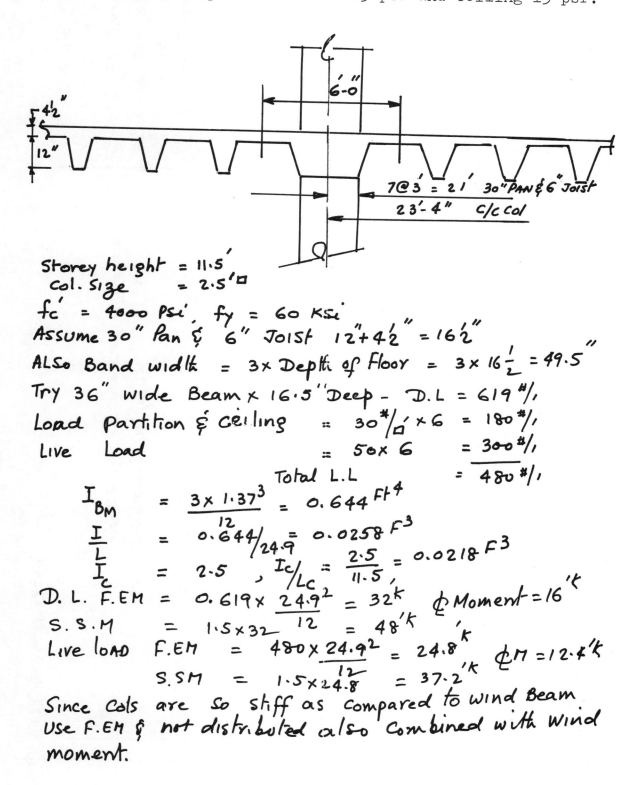

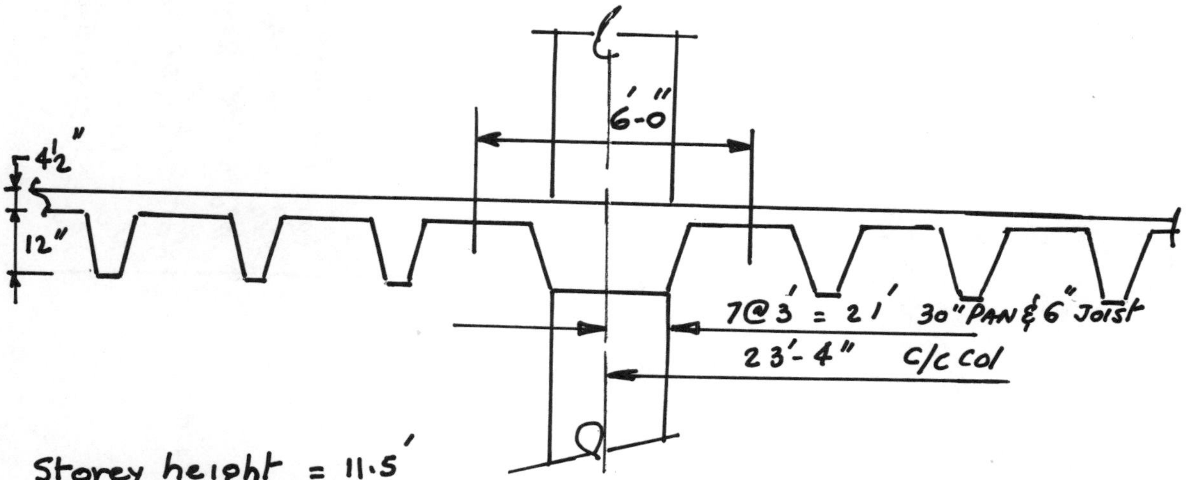

Storey height = 11.5'

Col. size = 2.5'□

$f_c' = 4000$ psi, $f_y = 60$ ksi

Assume 30" Pan & 6" Joist 12" + 4½" = 16½"

Also Band width = 3 × Depth of Floor = 3 × 16½ = 49.5"

Try 36" wide Beam × 16.5" Deep - D.L = 619 #/'

Load Partition & ceiling = 30 #/□' × 6 = 180 #/'

Live Load = 50 × 6 = 300 #/'

Total L.L = 480 #/'

$$I_{BM} = \frac{3 \times 1.37^3}{12} = 0.644 \text{ Ft}^4$$

$$\frac{I}{L} = 0.644/24.9 = 0.0258 \text{ F}^3$$

$$I_c = 2.5, \quad I_c/L_c = \frac{2.5}{11.5} = 0.0218 \text{ F}^3$$

$$\text{D. L. F.EM} = 0.619 \times \frac{24.9^2}{12} = 32^k \qquad ℄ \text{ Moment} = 16'^k$$

$$\text{S.S.M} = 1.5 \times 32 = 48'^k$$

$$\text{Live load F.EM} = 480 \times \frac{24.9^2}{12} = 24.8'^k \qquad ℄ M = 12.4'^k$$

$$\text{S.SM} = 1.5 \times 24.8 = 37.2'^k$$

Since Cols are so stiff as compared to wind Beam Use F.EM & not distributed also combined with wind moment.

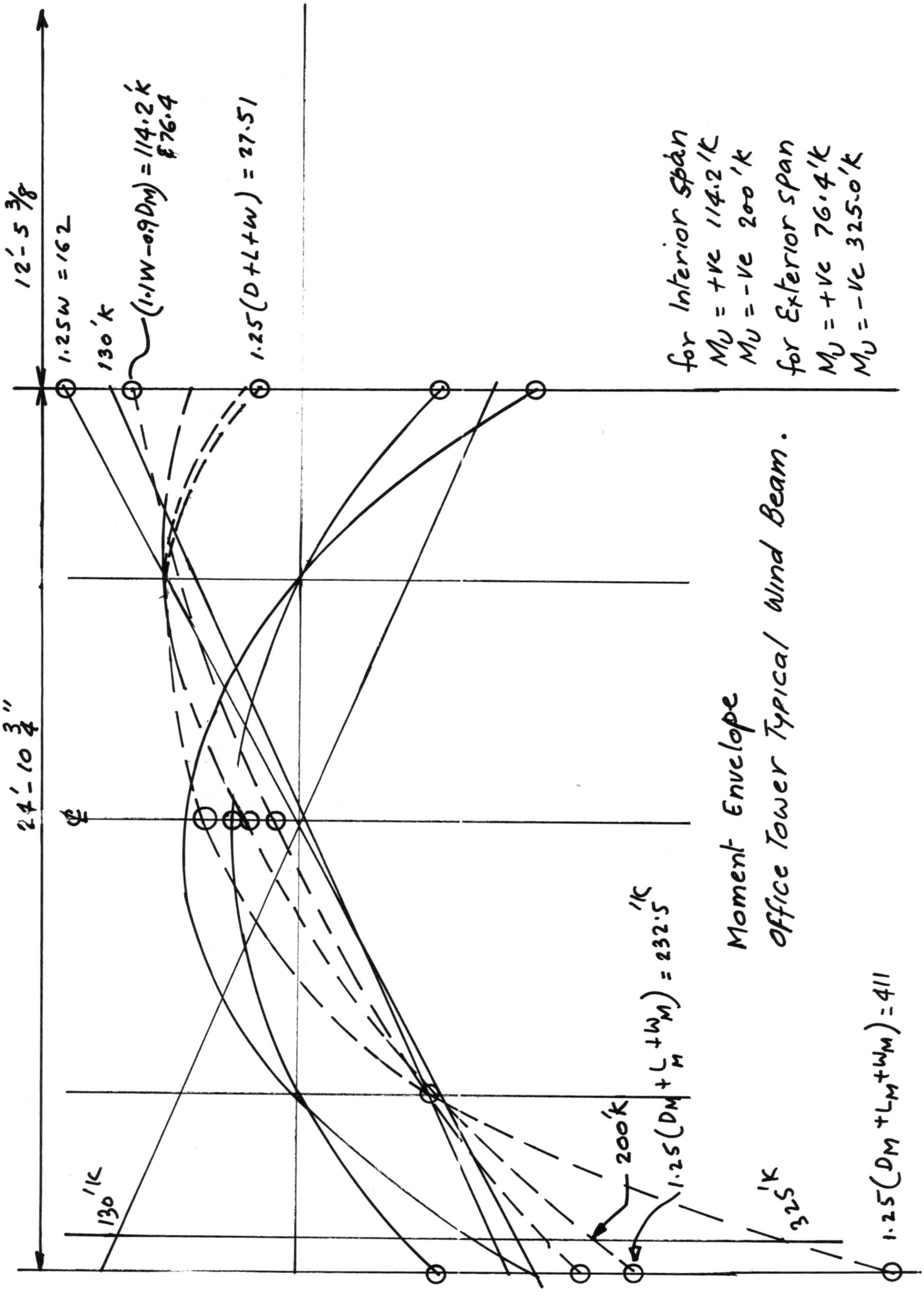
24'-10 3/4"
12'-5 3/8
℄
1.25W = 162
130'K
(1.1W-0.9DM) = 114.2'K
& 76.4
1.25(D+L+W) = 27.51
for Interior span
MU = +ve 114.2'K
MU = -ve 200'K
for Exterior span
MU = +ve 76.4'K
MU = -ve 325.0'K
Moment Envelope
Office Tower Typical Wind Beam.
130'K
200'K
1.25(DM + LM + WM) = 232.5'K
325'K
1.25(DM + LM + WM) = 411

V Wind $= 10.47^k$, D.L $= 619 \times \frac{21}{2} = 6.5^k$

L.L $= 480 \times \frac{21}{2} = 5.04K$

$1.25(D + L + W) = 27.51$; $(1.5L + 1.8D) = 19.45^k$

$(1.5 D_M + 1.8 L_M) = 92.6$; $(0.9D + 1.1W) = 171.8^k$

$$v = \frac{27510}{15.25 \times 36} = 50 \text{ psi} < 2\phi\sqrt{4000} = 108 \text{ ok}$$

From the graph of moment envelope (next sheet)

−ve moment $= 200'^K$

$$\frac{M_U}{\phi b d^2} = \frac{200000 \times 12}{0.9 \times 15.25^2 \times 36} = 318$$

$$p = 0.005$$

$$A_s = \rho b d = 0.005 \times 36 \times 15.25 = 2.745 \square''$$

+ve Moment $= 114.2'^K$

$$\frac{M_U}{\phi b d^2} = \frac{114.2 \times 12000}{0.9 \times 15.25^2 \times 36} = 182$$

use $p_{min} = 0.003$

$$\therefore A_s = 0.003 \times 36 \times 15.25 = 1.647 \square''$$

EXAMPLE 4-04

Given:- Design K-Brace bent design.

Floor Beam:-

Analysed as two span Beam continuous over simple supports.

$-M = \frac{1}{8} \times 1.6 \times 12.75^2 = 32.5'^K$

$S = \frac{32.5 \times 12}{4} = 16.25 \text{ in}^3$

use W10x21

$R_{col} = \frac{3}{8} \times 1.6 \times 12.75 = 7.7^k$

$R_{center\ column} = 2 \times \frac{5}{8} \times 1.6 \times 12.75$

$= 25.5^k$

Neglect Direct wind stresses & Consider increase in allowable

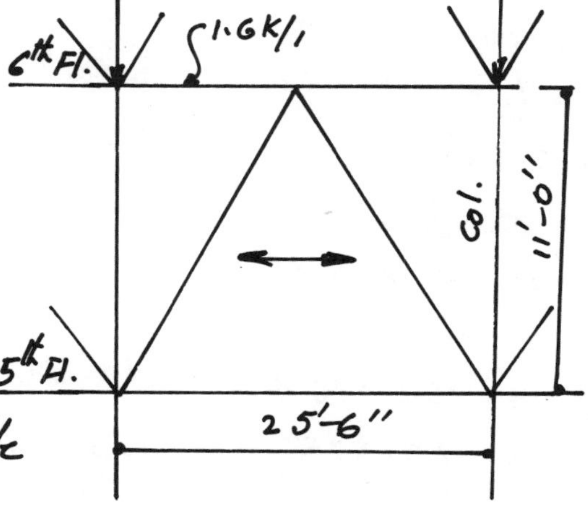

Stresses for combined loading

Bracing c/c Length of Bracing $= \sqrt{11^2 + 12.75^2} = 16.84'$

Wind force in ea: Brace $= \frac{50}{2} \times \frac{16.84}{12.75} = 33^K$

Compression in Brace for gravity load $= \frac{25.5}{2} \times \frac{16.84}{12.75} = 16.84^K$

Total Compression $= 33.0 + 16.84 = 49.84^K$

Unsupported length $= 16.84 - 1.0 = 15.84'$

For $\frac{L}{r} = 200$, $r_{req'd} = \frac{15.84 \times 12}{200} = 0.95$

Use $\angle\ 8 \times 6 \times \frac{7}{16}$" $f_a = \frac{49.84}{5.93} = 8.4^{KSI}$

$F_a = 7.34 \times 1.33 = 9.7^{KSI}$

EXAMPLE 4-05

<u>Given</u>:- Design full storey Knee Brace bent design.

c/c Brace length

$= \sqrt{7.75^2 + 12^2}$

$= 14.29'$

Wind in ea. Brace

$= \frac{50}{2} \times \frac{14.29}{7.75} = \pm 46.1^K$

Vert. force in Ea. Brace.

$= \frac{50}{2} \times \frac{11}{7.75} = \pm 35.48^K$

Floor Beam For wind forces

$R_L = R_R = \frac{35.8 \times 10}{25.5}$

$= 14.0^K$

For gravity load

$R_L = R_R = 0.1 \times 1.6 \times 25.5 = 4.1^K$

$R_1 = 0.4 \times 1.6 \times 25.5 = 16.4$

For Combined Forces

$R_L = 14.0 - 4.1 = 9.9^K$

$R_2 = 35.5 - 16.4 = 19.1^K$

$R_1 = 35.5 + 16.4 = 51.9^K$

$-M_1 = \begin{matrix} 9.9 \times 7.75 = 69.75 \\ 1.6 \times 7.75^2/2 = 48.05 \end{matrix} \Big] = 117.80'^K$

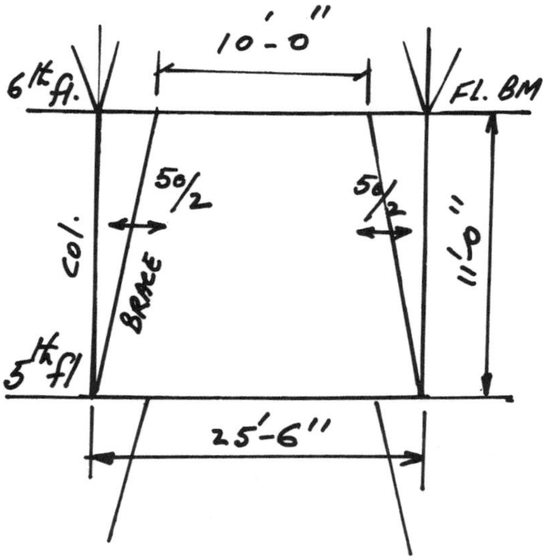

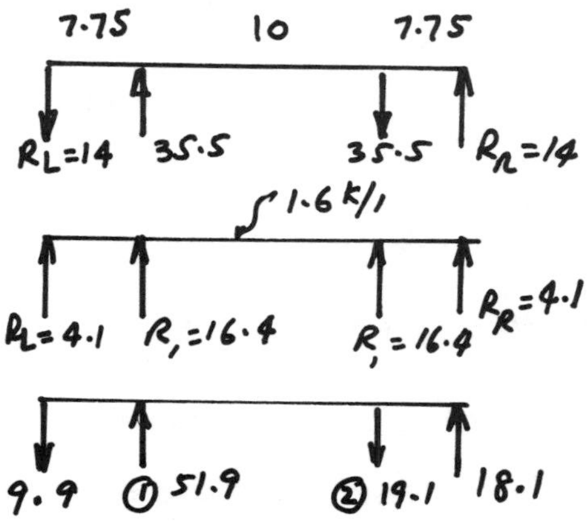

$$-M_2 = 18.1 \times 7.75 = 140.28$$
$$-1.6 \times \frac{7.75^2}{2} = \underline{-48.05}$$
$$92.23'^{K}$$

$$S = \frac{117.8 \times 12}{24 \times 1.33} = 44.3 \text{ IN}^3 \quad \text{USE W16} \times 36$$

Brace

Compression $= 50 \times \frac{14.29}{12} = 59.54^K$

$l_u = (14.29 - 1.5) \times 12 = 165''$

For $\frac{L}{r} = 200$, $r_{reqd} = \frac{165}{200} = 0.82$

Use $\angle 6 \times 6 \times \frac{1}{2}$ $\quad f_a = 59.54/5.75 = 10.35$ ksi

$F_a = 8.7 \times 1.33 = 11.6$ ksi

EXAMPLE 4-06

Given:- Design X-bent bracing.

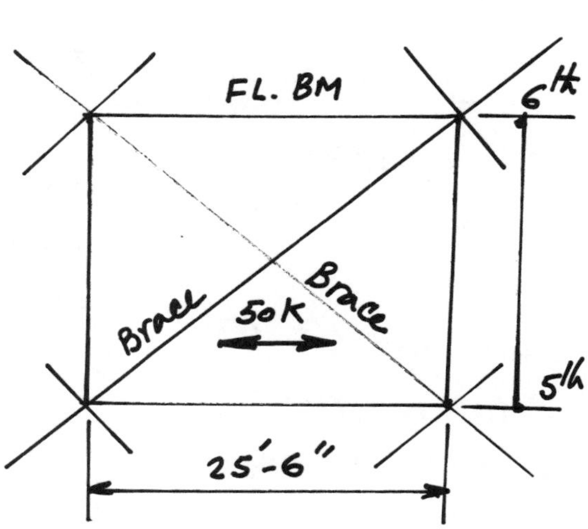

c/c Brace Length $= \sqrt{11^2 + 25.5^2}$
$= 27.8'$

For tension MBRS
$L/r \leq 300$

Wind force $= 50 \times \frac{27.8}{25.5} = 54.5^K$

Lu of Bracing
$= (27.8 - 2)/2 = 12.9'$

Providing 2' for connections

$r_{reqd} = \frac{12.9 \times 12}{300} = 0.52$

use $\angle$ $4 \times 3\frac{1}{2} \times \frac{5}{16}''$

$f_a = 54.5/(2.25 - 0.35) = 28.7$

$0.35\square'' \rightarrow$ Area of one rivet hole

$F_a = 22 \times 1.33 = 29.2$

Floor Beam $M = \frac{1.6 \times 25.5^2}{8} = 130.05'^K$

$S = 130.05 \times 12/24 = 65.02$

use W12×45

EXAMPLE 4-07

Given:- Design of rigid frame bent.

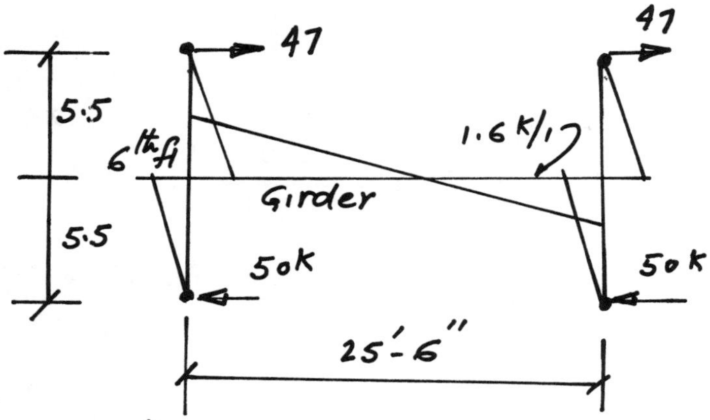

$M = (50+47)5.5 = 534'^k$

M @ Col. face $= 534 \times \frac{4.5}{5.5} = 437'^k$

M@ BM $= 534 \times \frac{11.95}{12.75} = 500'^k$

Girder

$-M_g = \frac{1.5 \times 25.5^2}{12} = 81'^k$

$-M_w = 500'^k$

$S = \frac{581 \times 12}{24 \times 1.33} = 218\ IN^3$ use W27×94

Col. design:-

a) No direct wind on Int Cols.

b) Girder wind shears at Connections are equal and opposite in directions.

Column gravity loads $= 2300^k$

Column moment $= 437 + 81 = 518'^k$

WITH WIND use W 14.42

$L_U = 11'0 - 2'-3" = 8'-9" = 111"$

$r_x = 7.26$, $S_{xx} = 707\ IN^3$

$\frac{L_U}{r_x} = \frac{111}{7.26} = 15.3$, $F_A = 20.87$

$F_B = 24$, $f_a = \frac{2300}{125.25} = 18.36$

$f_b = \frac{518 \times 12}{707} = 8.79$

$$\frac{f_a}{0.6F_y} + \frac{f_b}{F_b} = \frac{18.36}{0.6 \times 36} + \frac{8.79}{24} = 1.21 < 1.33$$

DYNAMIC ANALYSIS

Most recently, dynamic response analysis has been introduced which furnishes forces, moments, deformation to a substantial degree, the real conditions and stresses that occur under complex earthquake motion.

For the calculation of lateral forces by static approach as per recommendations of the Structural Engineers Association of California (SEAL), the following approach is being used by the Los Angeles Building Code. In accordance with the L.A. Building Code, the structural systems must comply with the following requirements:-

1. All buildings designed with a horizontal force K 0.67 or 0.80 shall have a space frame ductile moment resisting.
2. Buildings more than 160 ft. in height shall have space frames ductile moment resisting capable of resisting not less than 25 percent of the required seismic forces for the structure as a whole.

The major portion of the requirements concerning the earthquake resistant design of the structure by a dynamic method of analysis.

Seismic Base Shear by Static Analysis

V = Minimum design base shear = ZKCW

Z = Seismic coefficient dependent on the seismic probability zone.

W = The total dead load, including permanent installations, kips

K = (horizontal force factor) = 0.67 for ductile frame buildings without shear walls.
= 0.80 for ductile frame buildings with shear walls.
= 1.33 for buildings with a box system as defined by SEAL.

T = (fundamental period of vibration of the building, in seconds in the direction under consideration.) $= 0.05 h_n / D^{\frac{1}{2}} = 0.10N$

C = $0.05/T^{1/3} = 0.10$ (for main frame)

D = The dimension of the building in feet in a direction parallel to the applied forces.

N = The total number of stories above the exterior grade to level n.

h_n = The total height of the building above the base in feet.

Distribution of Lateral Forces by Static Analysis

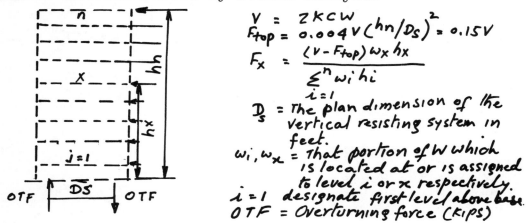

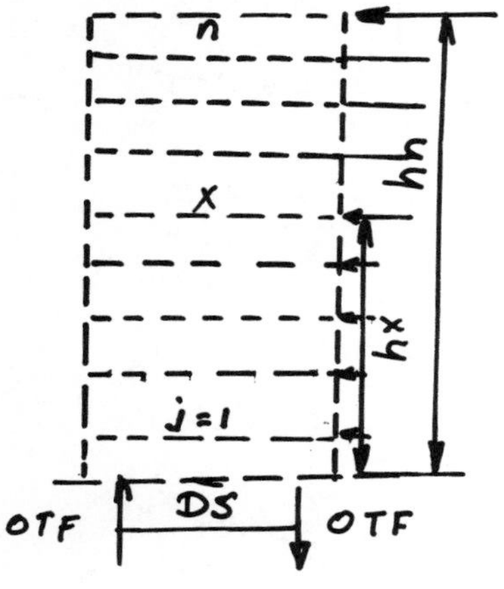

$$V = ZKCW$$

$$F_{top} = 0.004V(h_n/D_s)^2 = 0.15V$$

$$F_x = \frac{(V - F_{top}) w_x h_x}{\sum_{i=1}^{n} w_i h_i}$$

D_s = The plan dimension of the vertical resisting system in feet.

w_i, w_x = That portion of W which is located at or is assigned to level i or x respectively.

i = 1 designate first level above base.

OTF = Overturning force (KIPS)

Seismic Torsion:- During earthquakes, buildings will be subjected to horizontal torsion if centers of mass and rigidity do not coincide. These torques are resisted by shears in the lateral force resisting system. Hence the design of the buildings must consider the increase due to torsion over the shear determined above.
Interior frames such as elevator shafts should not be used as even the lateral force resisting element. As an example, the elevator shaft shown in the plan has four resisting frames located along the perimeter.

Torsional shear on frame A

$$F_1 = k K_1 a$$

Torsional shear on frame B

$$F_2 = k K_2 b$$

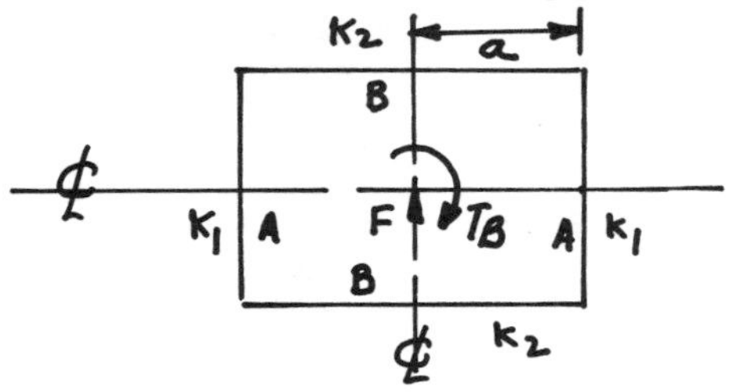

The sum of resisting moments due to these shears must equal the torque T.

$$T = 2F_1 a + 2F_2 b = 2kK_1 a^2 + 2kK_2 b^2$$

$$k = \frac{T}{2(K_1 a^2 + K_2 b^2)}$$

$$F_1 = \frac{T K_1 a}{2(K_1 a^2 + K_2 b^2)} \qquad \text{where } K_1, K_2 \text{ — stiffness of frame A, B.}$$

$$F_2 = \frac{T K_2 b}{2(K_1 a^2 + K_2 b^2)}$$

EXAMPLE 4-08
Given:- Design of a seven storey steel building.
Data:- Building located in Seismic Zone 4 and characteristic site period T_s = 1.0 sec. braced N/s direction on column lines 1 and 5. Ductile moment frame in E/W directions. Floors and roof 3 in metal deck with $3\frac{1}{4}$" light weight (110 pcf) concrete fill.
Storey height 11'6" and 8' clear ceiling height. Steel A-36, h.s bolt A 325 F, welding electrode E70.
Loads:-

Roof Loading

Roofing and Insulation	= 7.0	
Metal Deck	= 3.0	
Concrete Fill	= 44.0	= 67 PSF
Ceiling and Mechanical	= 5.0	
Steel Framing/Fire Proof	= 8.0	
Live Load		= 20 PSF
		87 PSF

Floor Loading

Metal Deck	= 3.0	
Concrete Fill	= 44.0	
Ceiling and Mechanical	= 5.0	
Partition	= 20.0	= 85 PSF
Steel Framing/Beams/Girders		
Columns/Fire Proof	= 13.0	
Live Load	= 50.0	= 50 PSF
		135 PSF

Curtain wall Av. WT = 15 P.S.F

1. East West Seismic Forces.

Total Lateral force $V = ZIKCSW$ U.B.C (1)

$Z = 1.0$ FOR ZONE 4

$I = 1.0$ (U.B.C table 23I)

$K = 0.67$ (U.B.C table 23-I)

$V = 1 \times 1 \times 0.67\, CSW = 0.67\, CSW$

To find C, $T = 0.5\, N^{2/3} = 0.5 \times 7^{2/3} = 1.83$ sec

$C = \frac{1}{15\sqrt{T}} = \frac{1}{15\sqrt{1.83}} = 0.050$

$S = 1.2 + 0.6\left(\frac{T}{T_S}\right) - 0.3\left(\frac{T}{T_S}\right)^2$

$= 1.2 + 0.6\left(\frac{1.8}{1.0}\right) - 0.3\left(\frac{1.8}{1.0}\right)^2 = 1.31$

$V = 1.0 \times 1.0 \times 0.67 \times 0.05 \times 1.31 W = 0.044 W$

$W_{fL} = (122.5 \times 77.5)(0.085) + (400 \times 11.5)(0.015)$

$= 874^k$

$W_{ff} = (122.5 \times 77.5)(0.067) + (400 \times 8.75)(0.015)$

$= 687^k$

$W_{Total\,DL} = 6 \times 874 + 687 = 5930^k$

$V = 0.044 \times 5930 = 2630^k$

$V = F_t + \sum_{i=1}^{n} F_i$

$F_x = \frac{(V - F_t)\, w_x h_x}{\sum_{i=1}^{n} w_i h_i}$

$= \frac{227\, w_x h_x}{\sum_{i=1}^{n} w_i h_i}$

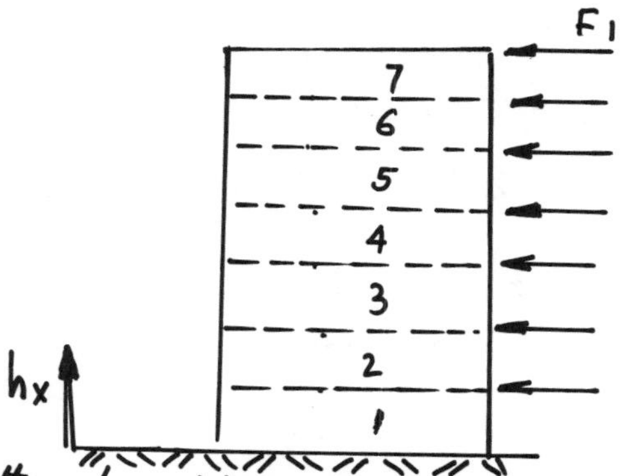

Distribution of lateral forces over the height of Building
Fi is the Earthwork force at each Level.

FL. LVL	h_x	W_x	$w_x h_x \times 10^{-2}$	$\frac{w_x h_x}{\sum w_i h_i}$	F_x^a K	V_x^a K	F_x^b K	V_x^b K
R	83	687	570	0.203	79	-	119	
7	71.5	874	625	0.222	50	79	75	119
6	60.0	874	524	0.187	43	129	64	194
5	48.5	874	424	0.151	34	172	51	258
4	37.0	874	324	0.115	26	206	39	309
3	25.5	874	222	0.079	18	232	27	348
2	14.0	874	122	0.043	10	250	15	375
1						260		390
			Σ 2811	1.00	250		390	

$e = 0.050 \times 120 = 6$

$R_A = R_D = 1.0; \quad R_1 = R_5 = 4$

V_A (Shear Dist. NEW Direction)

$$= R_A\left[\frac{V_x}{\Sigma R_{EW}} + \frac{(V_x e)d}{\Sigma R_y (d)^2}\right] \doteq V_{Dx}$$

$$= 1.0\left[\frac{V_x}{2\times 1.0} \pm \frac{(V_x\, 6)\, 37.5}{2\times 1.0\times(37.5)^2 + 2\times 4\times 60^2}\right]$$

$$= 0.51\, V_x = V_{Dx}$$

Portal method Design Analysis

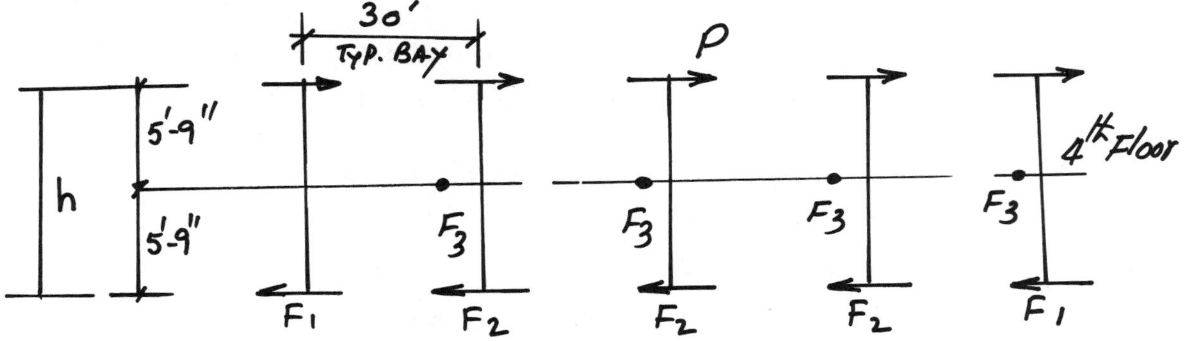

$2F_1 + 3F_2 = V_{A,3} = V_{D,3}$

$V_{A,3} = V_{D,3} = 0.51 V_3 = 0.51 \times 348 = 177^K$

$2F_1 + 3F_2 = 177 \quad \& \quad F_1 = F_2/2$

$\therefore 4F_2 = 177, \quad F_2 = 44.3^K$

$\Sigma M_P \quad 30F_3 = 11.5F_2 = 510$

$F_3 = 17^K$

$\Delta_s = \Delta_c + \Delta_g$ where $\Delta_c = \dfrac{Fh_3}{2EI_c}$

$\& \quad \Delta_g = \dfrac{F_L h^2}{2EI_g}$

Allowable drift/storey $= 0.005h = 0.69$ in

$$\therefore \quad 0.69 = \frac{Fh^3}{2EI_c} + \frac{F_L h^2}{2EI_g}$$

$\& \quad P_T = P_E + P_V$ = Int. Col. axial force + Roof + 4 FL + Cur. wall

$= 0 + (30\times 13.75)(0.67)$

$+ (30\times 13.75)\, 4\, (0.085 + 0.020)$

$= 228$ kips @ 3rd storey.

$M_T = M_E + M_V$

where $M_E = K\left[\frac{h}{2} \times F_V\right] = 0.67\left(\frac{11.5}{2} \times 44.3\right) = 171^{K'}$

$M_V = 0$

$\therefore M_T = 171^{'K}$

$P_{EQUIV.} = P + M_x Q_x + M_y B_y$

$= \frac{228 + (171 \times 12)\,0.185}{1.33} = 456^K$

SELECT W14X127 $P_{all.} = 721^K$

To find girder size

$0.69 = \frac{44.3 \times (11.5 \times 12)^3}{12 \times 29000 \times 1480} + \frac{44.3 \times 30 \times 12\,(11.5 \times 12)^2}{12 \times 29000 \times I_g}$

$= 0.23 + 872/I_g$

$I_g = 1790\ in^4$

use W 24x68 of $I_g = 1820\ in^4$

Stress check of frame members

W24X68 $M_T = kF_3\, L/2 = 0.67 \times 17 \times \frac{30}{2} = 171^{'K}$

$M_V = \frac{wL^2}{12} = (0.96 + 0.17)\frac{30^2}{12} = 85^{'K}$

$M_T = 171 + 85 = 256^{'K}$

$S_{req'd} = \frac{M_T}{1.33 F_b} = \frac{256 \times 12}{1.33 \times 24} = 96.2 < 153$ ok

W14X127 Col. $P_T = 228K$ $M_T = 171^{'K}$

$M_{TF} = M_T \frac{h_c}{h} = 171 \times \frac{11.5 - 2}{11.5} = 141^{'K}$

$G_A = G_B = \frac{\Sigma I_c/L_c}{\Sigma I_g/L_g}$

$= \frac{2 \times 1480}{2 \times \frac{1820}{3}} = 2.12$

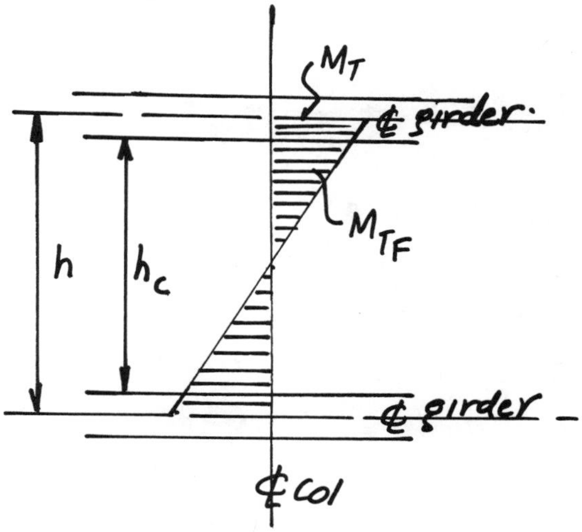

$K_x = 1.62$

$\left(\frac{Kl}{r}\right)_y = \frac{1 \times 11.5 \times 12}{3.76} = 37$

$\therefore F_a = 19.4\ ksi$

$\left(\frac{Kl}{r}\right)_x = \frac{1.62 \times 11.5 \times 12}{6.29} = 36$

$\therefore F_a = 19.5$

$F_{ex}' = 11.5$; $C_{mx} = 0.85$; $f_a = \frac{228}{37.3} = 6.1\ ksi$

$f_{bx} = \frac{141 \times 12}{202} = 8.4$ ksi, $F_{bx} = 0.66 F_y = 24$ ksi

$$\frac{f_a}{F_a} + \frac{C_{mx} f_{bx}}{\left(1 - \frac{f_e'}{F_{ex}'}\right) F_{bx}} + \frac{C_{my} f_{by}}{\left(1 - \frac{f_a}{F_{ey}'}\right) F_{by}} \leq 1.33$$

$$\frac{6.1}{19.4} + \frac{0.85 \times 8.4}{\left(1 - \frac{6.1}{11.5 \times 1.33}\right) 24} + 0 = 0.62 \leq 1.33 \text{ ok}$$

use W 14×127 Col.

Plastic hinge check of Frame Members.

Strong col, weak beam concept

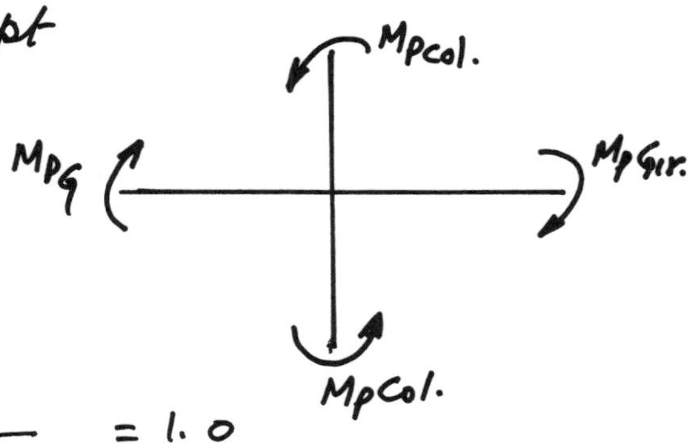

$$\Sigma M_p Col > M_p Gir$$

$$\frac{P}{P_{cr}} + \frac{C_m M}{\left(1 - \frac{P}{P_e}\right) M_m} \leq 1.0$$

For W14×127 Col.

$$\frac{1.3 \times 228}{1.7 \times 37.3 \times 19.4} + \frac{0.85 M}{\left(1 - \frac{1.3 \times 228}{\frac{23}{12} \times 37.3 \times 115}\right) M_p} = 1.0$$

$\therefore M = 0.92 M_p$

$\therefore M_{pcol} = 0.86 M_p = 0.86 \times 36 \times 226 = 7000''^k$

$$\frac{P}{P_y} + \frac{M}{1.18 M_p} \leq 1.0$$

$$\frac{1.3 \times 228}{37.3 \times 36} + \frac{M}{1.18 M_p} = 1.0 \quad \therefore M = 0.92 M_p$$

Hence $M_p Col. = 7000''^k$

For W 24×68 girder

$M_p = 36 \times 176 = 6340''^k$

$\Sigma M_p Col = 2 \times 7000 = 14000''^k$

$\Sigma M_p girder = 2 \times 6340 = 12680''^k$

$14000 > 12680 \quad \therefore$ W14×127 Col. ok

Buckling check of frame member

W 24×68 girder

$b/2t_f = 8.5 > 7.7$

$$\frac{d}{t_w} = \frac{412}{\sqrt{F_y}}\left(1 - \frac{1.4P}{F_y}\right) = 68.7 > 57$$

Bracing l = 28'-10" clear

Assume $1 > \frac{M}{M_p} > 0.5$

$$\frac{l_{cr}}{r_y} = \frac{1375}{F_y} + 25 = 63.2$$

l_{cr} = 63.2 × 1.87 = 118" or 9'-10" < 28'-10" ok

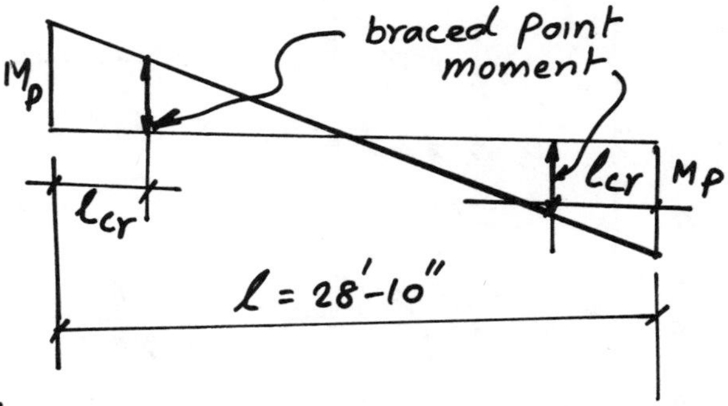

$\frac{M}{M_p}$ = 0.33 > 0.5 ok

∴ Brace girder @ 1/3 Point.

W 14×127 Column.

$\frac{b}{2t_f}$ = 8.5 > 7.36 ok

$$\frac{d}{t_w} = \frac{257}{\sqrt{F_y}} = 42.8 > 24 \text{ ok}$$

Bracing l = 10'-0, ∴ $1 > \frac{M}{M_p} > 0.5$

$$\frac{l_{cr}}{r_y} = \frac{1375}{F_y} + 25 = 63.2$$

l_{cr} = 63.2 × 3.76 = 237" = 19'-9" > 10'

Assume no Intermediate Bracing

$\frac{M}{M_p}$ = ± 10 ok ∴ NO Bracing.

Check on building period & C.S. Factor

(CS) design ≥ (CS) actual

$$\Sigma W_x \delta_x^2 = 687(4.25)^2 + 874(3.85)^2 + 874(3.34)^2 + 874(2.67)^2 + 874(2.10^2 + 1.43^2 + 0.82^2) = 47580$$

$$\Sigma F_x \delta_x = 119(4.25) + 75(3.85) + 64(3.34) + 51(2.67) + 39(2.10) + 27(1.43) + 0.84(0.82) = 1278$$

$$T_{act} = 2\pi\sqrt{\Sigma w_1 \delta_1^2 \div g[\Sigma F_1 \delta_1 + (f_t + f_c)\delta x}$$

$$= 2\pi\sqrt{47580 \div (32.2 \times 12)1278} = 1.95$$

$$C_{act} = \frac{1}{15\sqrt{1.95}} = 0.048$$

$$S_{act} = 1.20 + 0.6 \times \frac{1.95}{1.0} - 0.3\left(\frac{1.95}{1.0}\right)^2 = 1.23$$

C_s act. $= 0.048 \times 1.23 = 0.059$

C_s des. $= 0.05 \times 1.31 = 0.65 > 0.059$ ok

Connection design.

Girder moment connection.

Full penetration welding for connecting girder flange to column along with a single shear plate connection at web.

$V_T = V_E + V_V = 0.67 \times 17 + (0.96 + 0.17)\frac{28.8}{2} = 27.7^k$

Use 7/8"ϕ A 325 F H.S. Bolts.

$n = \frac{27.7}{9.02 \times 1.33} = 2.3$

$V_E = \frac{2M_p}{l} = \frac{2 \times 36 \times 176}{12 \times 28.8} = 36.7$

$V_v = (0.96 + 0.17)\frac{28.8}{2} = 16.3^k$

$V_T = 36.7 + 16.3 = 53^k$

Use 7/8"ϕ H.S. Bolts.

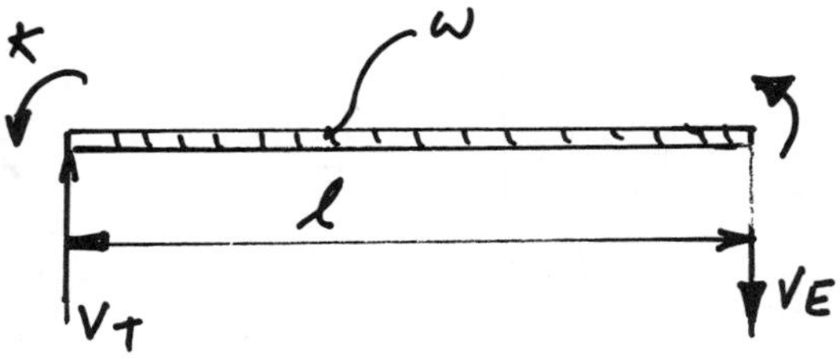

$\tau_U = 0.45\sigma_U = 0.45 \times 120 = 54$ ksi

$P_U = \tau A = 54 \times 0.419 = 22.6^k$/Bolt

$n = \frac{V_T}{P_U} = \frac{53}{22.6} = 2.4$ Bolts

Hence plastic capacity of Bolt governs.

Use 4- 7/8"ϕ.

Shear Plates

$M_T = V_T \times 3 = 53 \times 3 = 159''^k$

Using 3/8" shear plates & 1'-0" long

$f_V = \frac{1.5 \times 53}{12 \times 0.375} = 17.7 < 0.55F_y = 19.8$ ok

$f_b = \frac{M_T}{Z} = \frac{159}{0.375 \times \frac{12^2}{4}} = 11.8$ ksi $< F_y = 36$ ok

Using two sided fillet weld to col.

$f_V = \frac{53}{2 \times 12} = 2.21^k/''$; $f_H = \frac{159}{2 \times \frac{12^2}{4}} = 2.21^k/''$

$f_R = \sqrt{f_V^2 + f_H^2} = 3.12^k/''$

Use E70 electrodes.

$\tau_U = 0.5\sigma_U = 35$ ksi, for 1/16" × 1" Fillet $\sigma_U = \tau_U A = 35 \times 1 \times \frac{1}{16} \times 0.707$
$= 1.55$ ksi

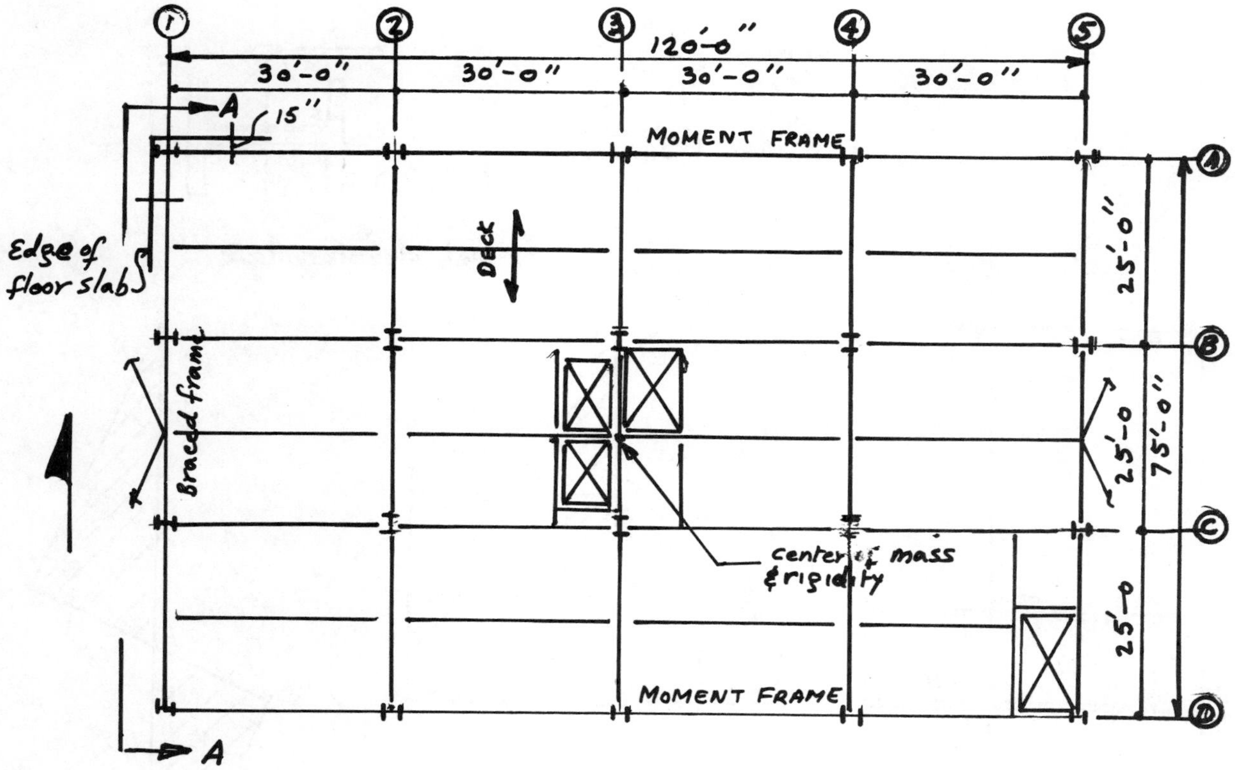

Typical floor framing Plan

Typical Sec. @ Deck.

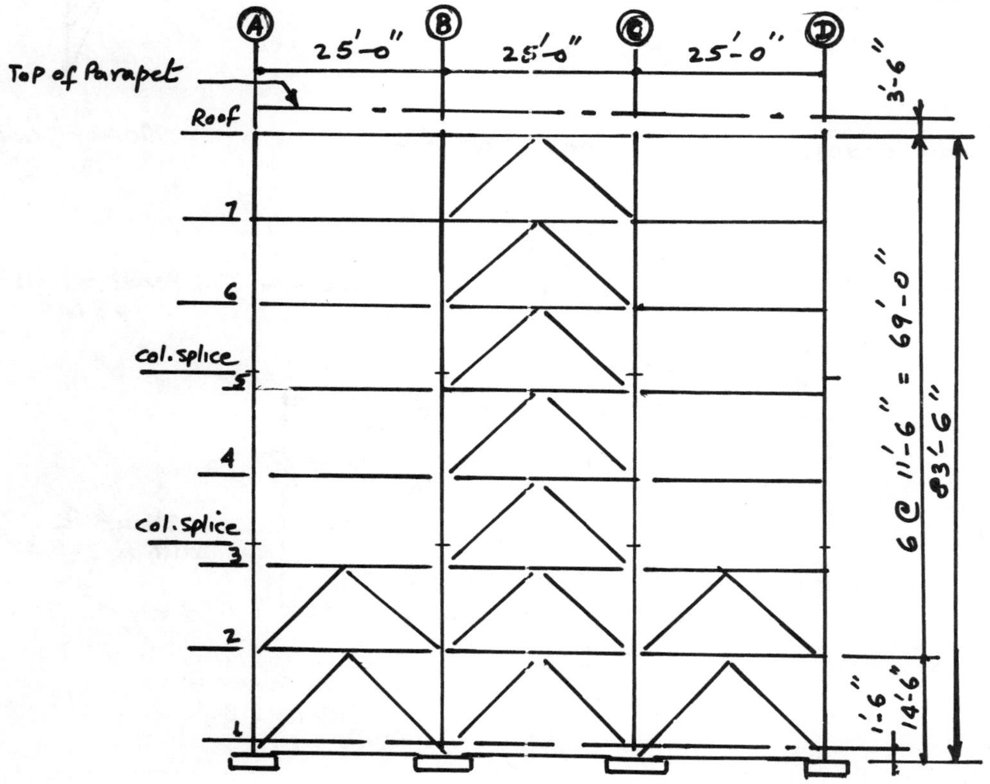

Braced frame elevation A-A

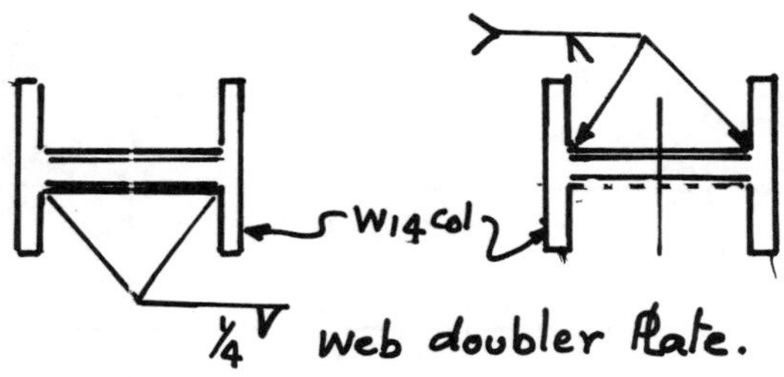

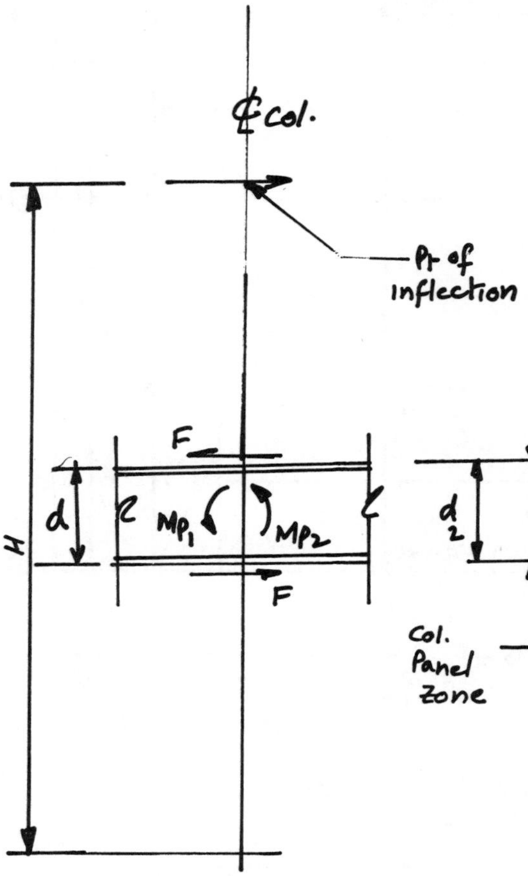

Free body diagram

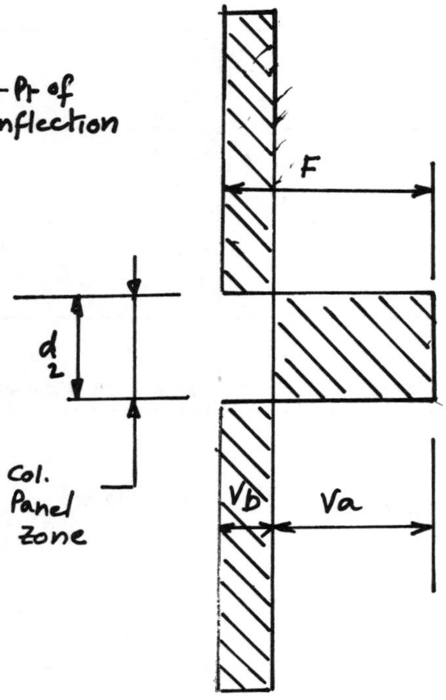

Shear diagram

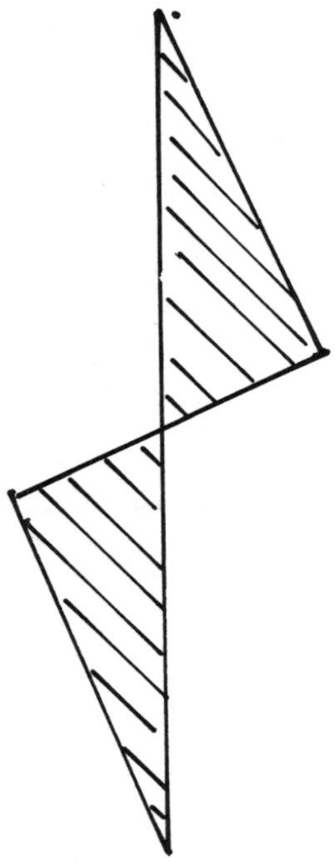

Moment diagram

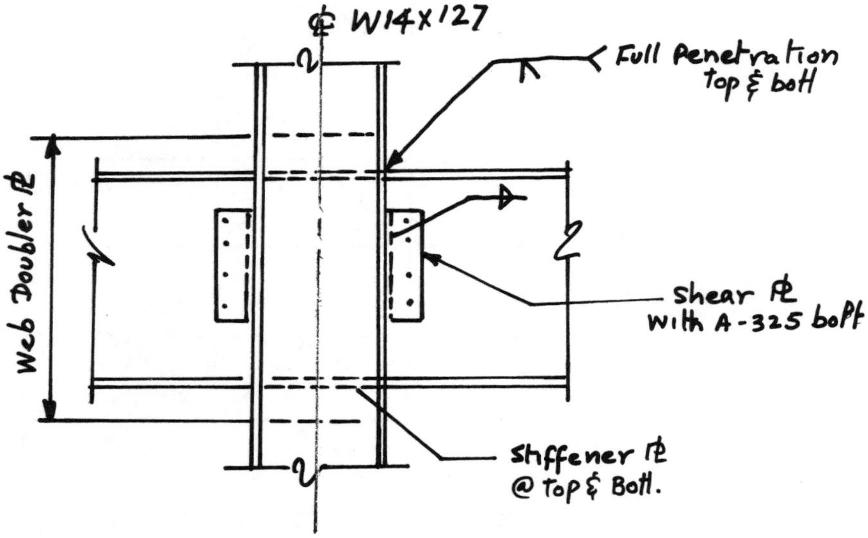

$$\eta = \frac{f_R}{\sigma_U} = \frac{3.12}{1.55} = 2 \quad \text{ie } 1/8\text{" fillet needed.}$$

use $\frac{5}{16}$" fillet weld.

check if stiffener needed.

$$t < \frac{C_1 A_f}{t_b + 5K} \text{ or } t \leq \frac{d_c\sqrt{F_y}}{180}$$

$$t = 0.61 > \frac{1 \times 8.96 \times 0.58}{0.58 + 5 \times 1.69} = 0.57 > \frac{11.25 \times \sqrt{36}}{180} = 0.37$$

$$t_f < 0.4\sqrt{C_1 A_f} = 0.4\sqrt{1 \times 8.9 \times 0.58} = 0.91 < 1.0 \text{ ok}$$

Resulting shear for Col. Panel zone for W24x68 girder & W14x127 col.

$$V_a = \frac{M_{P1}}{0.95 d_1} + \frac{M_{P2}}{1.95 d_2} - \left(\frac{M_{P1} + M_{P2}}{H}\right)$$

$$= \frac{2 \times 36 \times 176}{0.95 \times 23.71} - \frac{2 \times 36 \times 176}{12 \times 11.5} = 471^K$$

$$F_v = 0.55 F_y = 19.8 \text{ ksi}$$

$$t_{req'd} = \frac{V_a}{F_v d} = \frac{471}{19.8 \times 14.62} = 1.62$$

$$t_{pl} = t_{req'd} - t_w = 1.62 - 0.61 = 1.01''$$

use 1" web doubler Plate.

EXAMPLE 4-09

Given:- Design a typical residential dwelling according to the local building code, including a typical two-car garage.

Two long walls transmit the earthquake forces if the motion is in the EAST-WEST direction, while the short walls share the work if the motion is north and south.

Typical Calculations for dwelling wall height 10'-6".

Building is divided up by many interior walls which resists lateral loads.

Exterior walls 8" Conc. Masonry, d = 5.3"

Interior walls 6" Conc. Masonry

Live load on roof = 20 #/□'

Horizontal load to building wind = 15 #/□'

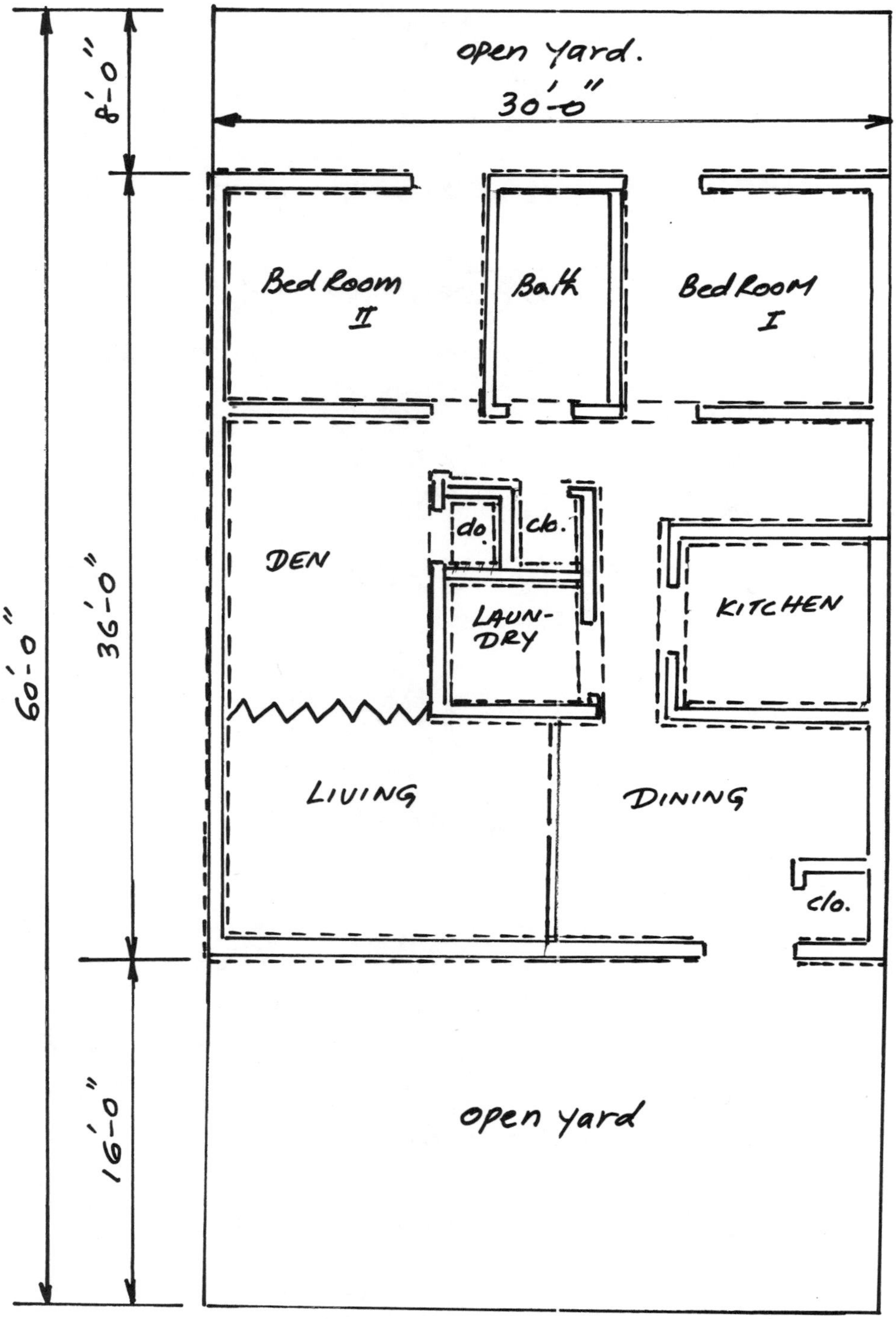

Residence
Lot area = 60x30 = 1800□'
Built up area = 60% lot = 1080□'

$$\text{Unit Shear } V = \frac{1260}{2 \times 44 \times 0.87 \times 7.62} = 2.14 \text{ Psi}$$

$$\text{Overturning Moment} = 630 \times 8 = 5040'\#$$

$$\text{Resisting Moment} = \left[(4 \times 61 \times 7) + (200 \times 5)\right] 2.5 = 6750'\#$$

Garage

6" conc. Masonry wall

$$\text{wind Moment} = 15 \times \frac{8^2}{8} = 120'\#$$

use #4 @ 48" o/c

use f_m = 300 Psi

Flex. Coefficient

$p = 0.002$, $pn = 0.088$

$k = 0.34$, $J = 0.887$

$b = 36"$, $d = 2.8"$

$$f_m = \frac{120 \times 4 \times 12 \times 2}{0.341 \times 0.887 \times 36 \times (2.8)^2} = 146 \text{ Psi}$$

$$f_s = \frac{120 \times 4 \times 12}{0.887 \times 0.2 \times 2.8} = 11900 \text{ Psi}$$

Assume Front rigid frame

$$\text{Wind} = 105 \times 10.69 = 1130\#$$

Being two equal piers

$$M = \frac{1130 \times 8}{2} = 4520'\#$$

2-#4 @ Ea end of ea. pier

$$p = \frac{2 \times 0.2}{5.62 \times 18} = 0.00395$$

$pn = 0.174$, $k = 0.44$, $J = 0.85$

$2/kJ = 5.3$

$$f_m = \frac{4520 \times 12 \times 5.3}{5.62 \times (18)^2} = 160 \text{ Psi}$$

$$f_s = \frac{4520 \times 12}{0.4 \times 0.85 \times 20} = 8630 \text{ Psi}$$

$$P_{min} = 300 \times 10 + (43 \times 1.83 \times 8) = 3630$$

$$f_a = \frac{3630}{5.62 \times 22} = 30 \text{ Psi}; \quad \frac{h}{t} = \frac{96}{6} = 16 \text{ \& Reduction factor} = 0.9$$

$$F_{a\,comb.} = 135 \times 0.9 \times 1.33 = 164 \text{ Psi} \;\&\; F_{b\,allow.} = 225 \times 1.33 = 300 \text{ Psi}$$

∴ Pier ok. Hence Concrete grade beam gives Fixity to Pier @ base.

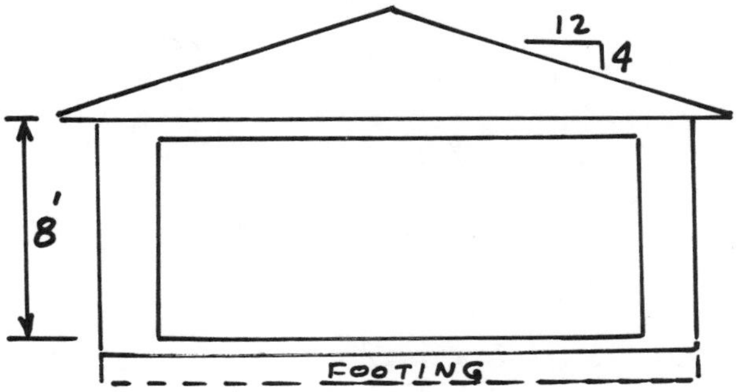

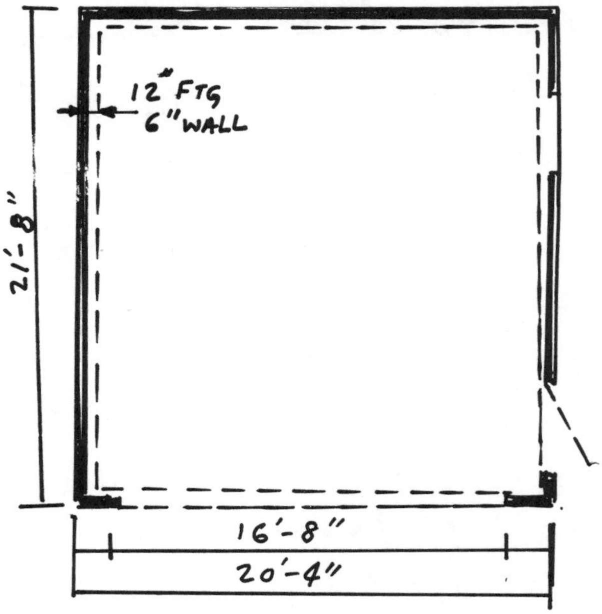

Siesmic load = 0.133 gravity

Assume vert. reinforcing bars in 8" wall may be Minimum #4 @ 48".

wall between Dining room window & Kitchendoor as most critical.

P = Roof Dead Load + Liveload + (Lintel load x Length supported)

$= (360+12)(2.33+2.0+2.83) = 2670^{\#}$

$\frac{P}{A} = \frac{2670}{24 \times 5.2} = 21.4$ Psi where 5.2 is solid equ. thickness of wall.

M = wind x width to center of opening ea. side x $\frac{(height)^2}{8}$

$= 15 \times 7.62 \times 8^2/8 = 915'^{\#}$

with 2-#4 vert. bars ea. side of opening as min. steel & assuming low stress uninspected construction

$p_n = \frac{2 \times 0.2 \times 44}{5.3 \times 24} = 0.138$

for f_s = 20000 Psi, values of $K = 0.41$, $J = 0.86$, $2/KJ = 5.71$

$f_m = \frac{915 \times 12 \times 5.60}{24 \times (5.3)^2} = 91.2$ Psi

for $\frac{h}{t} = \frac{126}{8} \simeq 16$, reduction factor $= 0.94$.

Use combined formula

$$\frac{21.4}{0.94 \times 135 \times 1.33} + \frac{91.2}{225 \times 1.33} = 0.43 < 1.0$$

Hence 8" wall is ok, use 2-#4 @ top of wall, 2-#4 @ sill & 2-#4 in footing.

Lintels:- Max size 3'-4" & Load/ft = 372#

Depth of $12\frac{1}{2}$" is adaquete. Check return wall at the front of the house

Wind load = $15 \times 7 \times 7.5 = 787^{\#}$

Siesmic Load = $0.133(10 \times 10 \times 39) + (61 \times 3.5 \times 26) = 1260$

Since the piers each side of the building are equal. Hence divide the force equally between them.

EXAMPLE 4-10

Given:- Design of Pierced Shear-Wall on rigid foundation.

Concrete walls 9" thick

Height of Building = 25 story @ 10' = 250'

wind pressure = 25 lb/□'

wind load on each wall p = 25×75 = 1875 #/'

Unit-weight of Floors & Roof

D.L = 150 #/□'

Imposed = 50 #/□'

200 #/□'

Unit weight of cladding (including roof Parapet) = 400 lbs/ft per storey.

Total Vertical load/wall

Cladding = 2×25×17.5×400 = 350,000

Self wt./including plaster both sides = 25×40×10×125 = 1250,000

Floor and roof D.L = 25×50×17.5×150 = 3281,250

Imposed load = 25×50×17.5×50 = 1093,750

Max. Total load = 5975,000 #

Min total load = 4881250 #

On A

Min total load = $4881250 \times \frac{22.5}{40}$ = 2745703 #

Max total load = $5975000 \times \frac{22.5}{40}$ = 3360938 #

on B

Min total load = $4881250 \times \frac{17.5}{40}$ = 2135547 #

Max total load = $597500 \times \frac{22.5}{40}$ = 3 938 #

Computation

$I_L = \frac{1}{12} \times \frac{9}{12} \times 3^3 = 1.69\ Ft^4, \quad E_\alpha = \frac{10^3}{12 \times 1.69} = 49.3/'$

$I_A = \frac{1}{12} \times \frac{9}{12} \times 22.5^3 = 712\ Ft^4, \quad I_B = \frac{1}{12} \times \frac{9}{12} \times 17.5 = 335\ ft^4$

$A_A = \frac{9}{12} \times 22.5 = 16.9\ Ft^2, \quad A_B = \frac{9}{12} \times 17.5 = 13.1\ □'$

$X = 10 + \frac{1}{2}(22.5 + 17.5) = 300\ ft$

1. The storey-height is constant throughout the height of the building.
2. Due to the connection afforded by the floor slabs, the deflected central axes of the two wall elements form parallel curves.
3. The cross-sectional areas and stiffnesses of each wall element are constant throughout the height of the building, but the two elements may be dissipated dimensionally within the limits imposed by the validity of assumptions. There is a point of contraflexure at mid-span of each lintel.
4. Each lintel is fully fixed in direction relative to the extreme inner faces of wall elements at each end; e.g. the effective span is equal to the clear dimension.
5. There are a large number of storeys. (This assumption is necessary in such that the change in vertical strain in the wall elements can be treated mathematically as a differential.)
6. The material of which the wall is constructed is homogeneous and isolated and all stresses are within the elastic range.

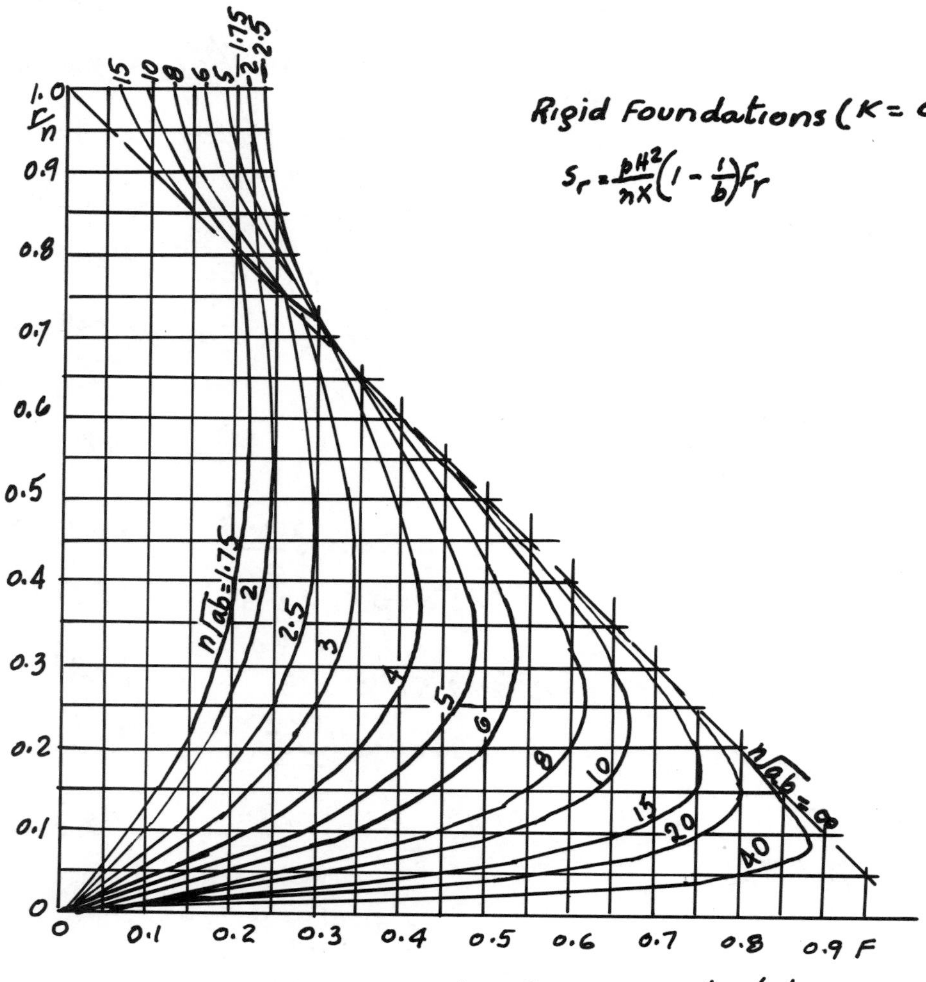

CHART II Shearing Forces on Lintels.

Reproduced from the pamphlet of Pierced Shear Wall Design by D. Magnus, courtesy of Cement and Concrete Association, London, England.

RIGID FOUNDATIONS ($K=0$)

M = Total applied moment

M_L' = Bending moment due to lintel action $= pH^2\left(1-\frac{1}{b}\right)\frac{r}{m}$

$M_{\omega}r$ = Sum of net bending moments in both wall elements $= M - M_L r$

AM_r = Net bending moment in wall element A $= M_{\omega}r\,\frac{I_A}{I_A+I_B}$

Net bending moment in wall element B $= M_{\omega}r\,\frac{I_B}{I_A+I_B}$

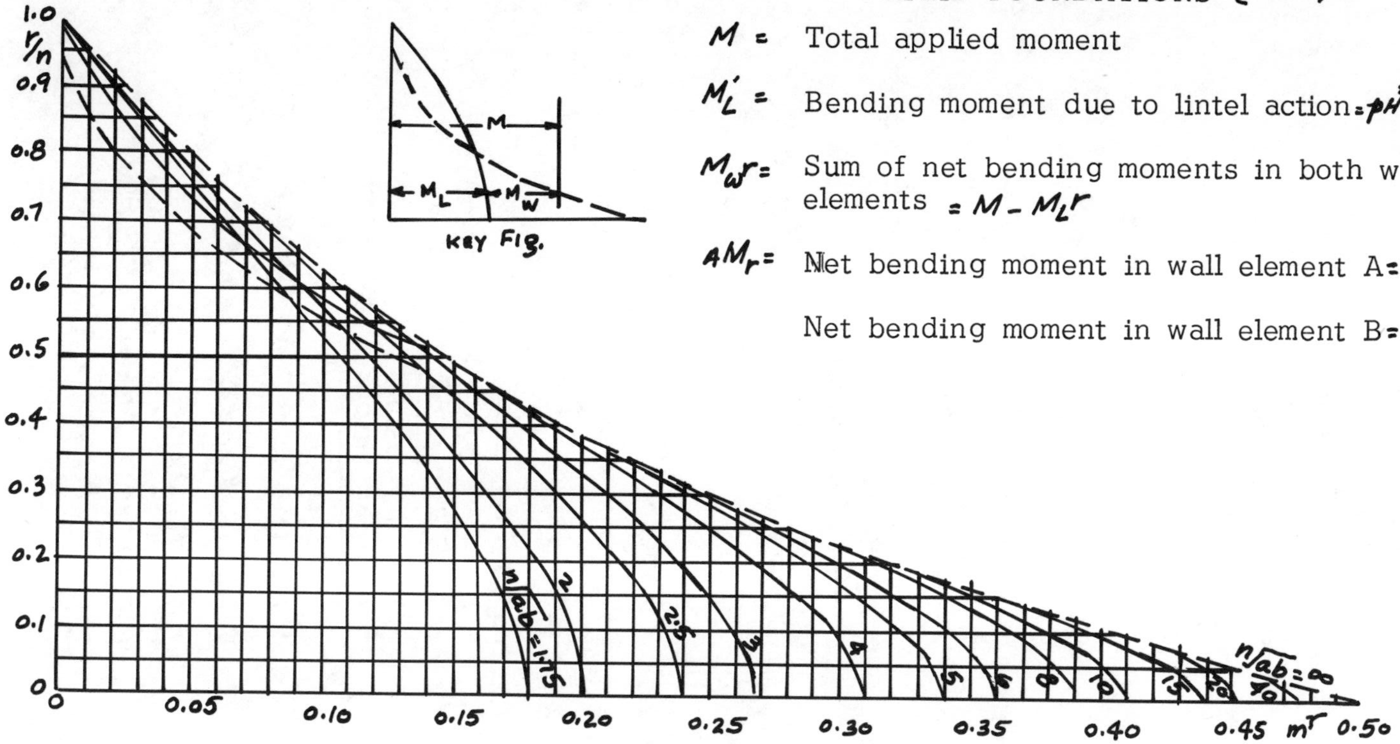

CHART III Bending Moments in walls.

Reproduced from the pamphlet of Pierced Shear Wall Design by D. Magnus, courtesy of Cement and Concrete Association, London, England.

$$I_{NA} = \frac{(712+335)(16.9+13.1) + (16.9 \times 13.1 \times 30^2)}{16.9 + 13.1} = 7680\ Ft^4$$

$$a = \frac{250}{25 \times 49.3} \times \frac{16.9+13.1}{16.9 \times 13.1} = 0.0275$$

$$b = \frac{7680}{712+335} = 7.35$$

$$ab = 0.0275 \times 7.35 = 0.202$$

$$\sqrt{ab} = 0.449\ ;\ n\sqrt{ab} = 20 \times 0.449 = 8.98$$

Max. shearing force in Lintel occure @ 0.23 H above G.L. Say 6th floor

$$pH^2 = 1275 \times 250^2 = 79687500\ \#' \text{ (Chart II)}$$

$$1 - \frac{1}{b} = 1 - \frac{1}{7.35} = 0.864$$

$$\text{Max shearing Force} = \frac{79687500}{25 \times 30} \times 0.864 \times 0.65 = 59670$$

From chart III

$$M_L = 79687500 \times 0.864 \times 0.40 = 27540000\ '\#$$

$$M = 79687500 \times 0.50 = 39843750\ '\#$$

$$M_W = 39843750 - 27540000 = 12303750\ '\#$$

$$M_A = 12303750 \times \frac{712}{712+335} = 8367020\ '\#$$

$$M_B = 12303750 \times \frac{335}{712+335} = 3636730\ '\#$$

$$\Sigma S_{r\,wind} = \frac{27540000}{30} = 918000\ \#$$

Max vert. stress in wall At Ground Floor

ELEMENT A

Due to Direct load $= \frac{3361}{16.9} \times \frac{1000}{144} = 1381\ \#/\square''$

Due to wind (Shearing force on lintel) $= \frac{918}{16.9} \times \frac{1000}{144} = 377\ \#/\square''$

Due to Bending (wind) $= \frac{8367 \times 11.25}{712} \times \frac{1000}{144} = 918$

Hence Compressive stress. Total $2676\ \#/\square''$

Min. vert stress in wall @ Ground floor.

Due to direct load $= \frac{2746}{16.9} \times \frac{1000}{144} = 1128$

Due to shearing force on lintel $= 918/16.9 \times \frac{1000}{144} = 377$

Due to Bending (wind) = $\frac{8367 \times 11.25}{712} \times \frac{1000}{144}$ = −918

Total Compressive stress = 687 #/□"   +687

Now if we neglect Lintel action

The moment = 39843750 #/ft @ G.L

max stress in Element A :-

due to Direct load = 1381 #/□"

due to Bending (wind)

$= \frac{39843 \times 11.25}{712 + 335} \times \frac{1000}{144} =$ 2973 #/□"

Total Compressive force   4354 #/□"

Min. Stress

Due to Direct load   1128 #/□"

Due to Bending (wind)   −2973 #/□"

−1845 #/□"

Thus the use of Pierced shear wall design would permit a weaker concrete to be used and also avoid the necessity for providing vertical tension reinforcement; but an amount of shear reinforcement required in the Lintel.

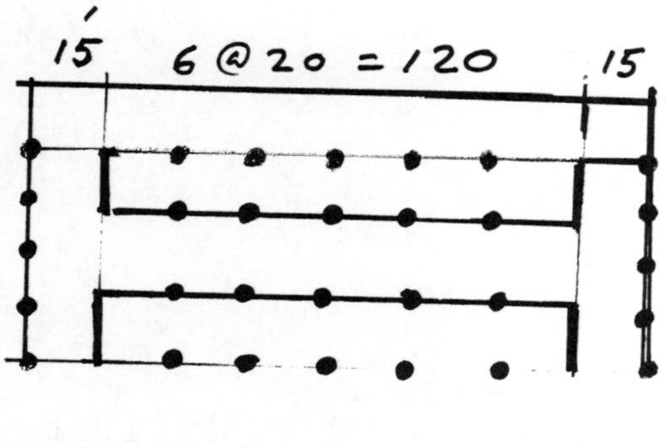

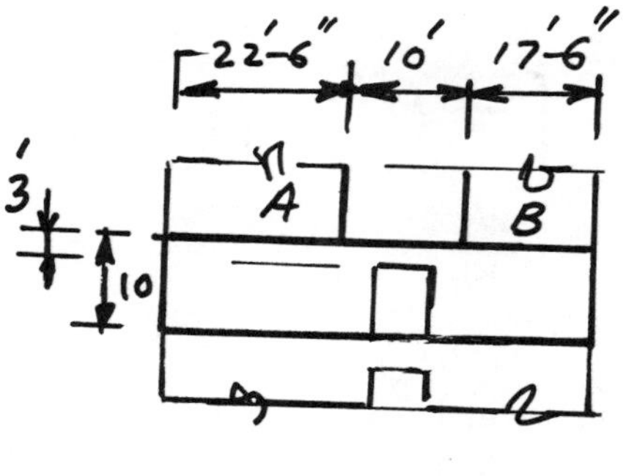

BASEMENT WALLS

Reinforced concrete basement wall, designed as beams loaded by earth pressure are of two types:
1. Supported at the top and bottom, reinforced vertically.
2. Supported by columns, reinforced horizontally.
Assumptions:-
1. A fluid pressure of 30 pcf is ample safe.
2. When walls are parallel and adjacent to a street alley, railroad, there is an additional surcharge of 3 ft. for alleys and streets and 6-10 ft. for railroads depending on the distance to the track.
3. Without a surcharge, the earth pressure is zero at ground level and maximum Wh at basement floor level.
4. With the surcharge, the pressure at ground level is $W_1 = Wh_x$ and at the basement level $W_2 = W(h + h_x)$
5. The minimum thickness of the basement wall is 8" to prevent ground water leakage.
Nomenclature
W = Earth pressure psf.
W_1 = Earth pressure on top surcharged wall.
W_2 = Earth pressure on bottom surcharged wall.
h = Height of wall in feet.
h_x = Height of surcharge in feet.
R_1 = Reaction at top.
R_2 = Reaction at bottom.
M = Maximum bending moment.
x_1 = Distance from to point of maximum moment.
Formulae
No surcharge

$$R_1 = \frac{1}{3}\frac{Wh}{2} \; ; \; M = 0.064Wh^2 \text{ ft lbs}$$

$$R_2 = \frac{2}{3}\frac{Wh}{2} \; ; \; M = 0.77\,Wh^2 \text{ ''}$$

$$x_1 = \frac{1}{\sqrt{3}}(h) = 0.58h$$

with surcharge

$$R_1 = \frac{2W_1 + W_2(h)}{6} \; ; \; M = \frac{1}{8}\frac{W_1 + W_2}{2}(h)^2 \text{ ft-lbs}$$

$$R_2 = \frac{W_1 + 2W_2(h)}{6} \; ; \; M = 0.75(W_1 + W_2)h^2$$

$$x_1 = \frac{1}{2(C-1)}\left[-1 \pm \sqrt{\left[\frac{2}{3}(2+C)(C-1)+1\right]}\,h\right.$$

$$\text{where } C = \frac{W_2}{W_1}$$

EXAMPLE 4-11
Given:- Basement Walls supported top and bottom.
Distance finished floor to floor 12', ground level with first floor. Column 30" square spaced 18' centers. One wall no surcharge, the other adjacent to alley. Height of wall from center of 4" first floor slab to point 6" below basement floor level (allows 12" embedment).

Height of wall = 12'-0" - 0-2" + 0'-6" = 12'-4"

$f'_c = 3000^{psi}, \; f_y = 60000 \, psi$

a) No surcharge

$W = 12.33 \times 30 = 370^{\#}$

$M = 0.77 \times 370 \times 12.33^2 = 43300''^{\#}, \; a = \dfrac{A_s f_y}{0.85 f'_c b} = 2.0$

Assume 12" wall $d = 10.5''$, $M_u = 1.7 \times 43.3 = 73.61$

$$A_s = \frac{M_u}{\phi f_y (d - a/2)} = \frac{73.61}{0.9 \times 60 \times (10.5 - 1)} = 0.14 \, in^2$$

use #4 @ 9" o/c

$$p = \frac{0.14}{12 \times 10.5} = 0.001 \text{ or } 1\%.$$

b) with surcharge

$W_1 = 3 \times 30 = 90, \quad W_2 = (3 + 12.33)30 = 460$

$M = 0.75 \times (90 + 460) 12.33^2 = 62700$

$$A_s = \frac{62.7 \times 1.7}{0.9 \times 60 \times (10.5 - 1)} = 0.207 \, IN^2$$

use #4 @ 9" o/c.

Case II Supported at Columns

net span = 18'-0 - 2'-6" = 15'-6"

Ht. of wall 1st Fl. to Bott. Basement slab = 12'-0" + 0'-4" = 12'-4"

No surcharge

$W = 12.33 \times 30 = 370, \; M = 370 \times 15.5^2 = 89000$

$$A_s = \frac{89 \times 1.7}{0.9 \times 60 (10.5 - 1)} = 0.29''^2 \text{ use } \tfrac{1}{2}''\phi \text{ @ } 9'' \text{ o/c}$$

with surcharge

$W_1 = 3 \times 30 = 90, \quad W_2 (3 + 12.33) 30 = 460$

At Top $M = 90 \times 15.5^2 = 21600$

At Bott. $M = 460 \times 15.5^2 = 110600 \; ''^{\#}/ft$

$$A_{s\,Top} = \frac{21.6 \times 1.7}{0.9 \times 60 \times (10.5 - 1)} = 0.07 \text{ use \#5 @ 24'' o/c}$$

$$A_{s\,Bott} = \frac{110.6 \times 1.7}{0.9 \times 60 \times (10.5 - 1)} = 0.37 \text{ use \#5 @ 9'' o/c.}$$

EXAMPLE 4-12

Given:- Design a one way slab system for a flat roof. All spans are 15' from center to center of 12" wide supports, clear spans are 14'. Superimposed load consists of 40 psf Live and 20 psf Dead. Use grade 60 reinforcing bars and a concrete strength f'_c = 3000 psi.

Assume thickness for $l_n = 14'\text{-}0''$

for end span $h_{min} = 7''$ and for interior span

$h_{min} = 6''$

∵ Super imposed loads are very nominal

∴ max Deflection allowed $= \dfrac{l}{180} = 0.93''$

$w_d = 1.4(75+20) = 133$ psf

$w_l = 1.7(40) = 68$ psf

$w_u = w_d + w_l = 201$ psf

V_u @ 1st interior support $= \frac{1}{2}(14)(0.201)(1.15) = 1.62^k$

V_u @ other supports $= \frac{1}{2}(14)(0.201) = 1.41^k$

$w_u l_n^2 = (0.201)(14)^2 = 39.40^{kft}$ per 1' width of slab.

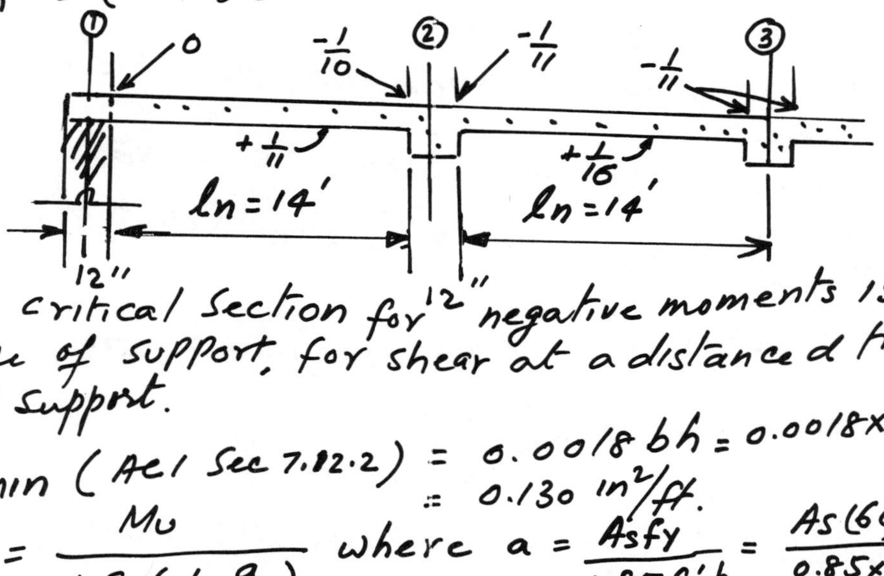

Since critical section for negative moments is at the face of support, for shear at a distance d from the face of support.

$A_{s\,min}$ (ACI Sec 7.12.2) $= 0.0018\,bh = 0.0018 \times 6 \times 12$

$= 0.130\ in^2/ft.$

also $A_s = \dfrac{M_u}{\phi f_y (d - \frac{a}{2})}$ where $a = \dfrac{A_s f_y}{0.85 f'_c b} = \dfrac{A_s(60)}{0.85 \times 3 \times 12} = 1.96 A_s$

assume $A_s = 0.2\ in^2$ ∴ $a = 0.39$

By moment Coeff $+M_u = 3.58^{kft}$; $-M_u = 3.94^{kft}$

∴ $A_s = \dfrac{3.58 \times 12}{0.9 \times 60 (5 - 0.19)} = 0.17\ in^2/ft$ Use #4 @ 14 for 1st interior support, top Bar, $A_s = \frac{3.94}{3.58} \times 0.17 = 0.19\ in^2/ft$

use #4 @ 12

Bottom bar $A_s = \frac{2.47}{3.58} \times (0.17) = 0.12\ in^2/ft < 0.13$

max spacing of bars $= 3t = 18''$

So use #4 @ 18''.

Developement length of #4 φ bar

$$l_a = 12 - 2 = 10^{in}$$

$$\frac{-M_u}{V_u} = \frac{3.58 \times 12}{1.41} = 30.5^{in}$$

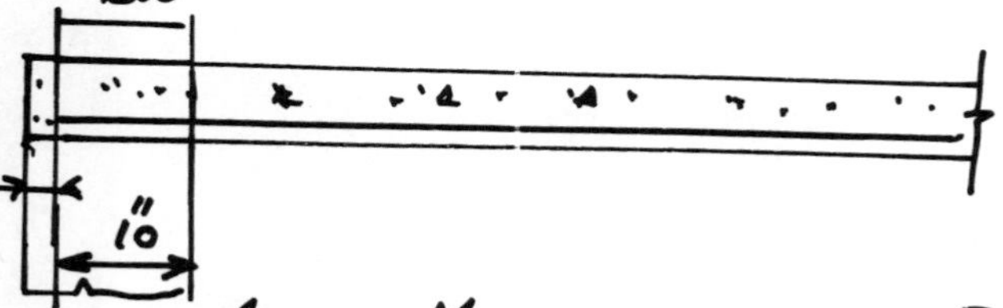

$$l_d = l_a + \frac{-M_u}{V_u} = 10 + 30.5 = 40.5'' \text{ say } 41''$$

$$l_{d_{reqd}} = 0.0004\, d_b f_b = 0.0004 \times 5 \times 60 = 12^{in}$$

$$V_c = \phi 2 \sqrt{f_c'}\, b_w d = 0.85 \times 2\sqrt{3000} \times 12 \times 5/1000 = 5.59^k$$

$$V_u = 1.62 - (0.201)\frac{5}{12} = 1.54 < 5.59 \text{ ok}$$

$$\Delta_{end\ span} = \frac{3.25}{384} \frac{w l_n^4}{E I_g} \quad \text{critical}$$

$$\text{where } I_g = \frac{12 \times (6)^3}{12} = 216$$

$$\therefore \Delta = \frac{3.25 \times (40)(14)^4 \times 1728}{384 \times 3.6 \times 10^6 \times 216} = 0.029^{in} < 1.0 \text{ ok}$$

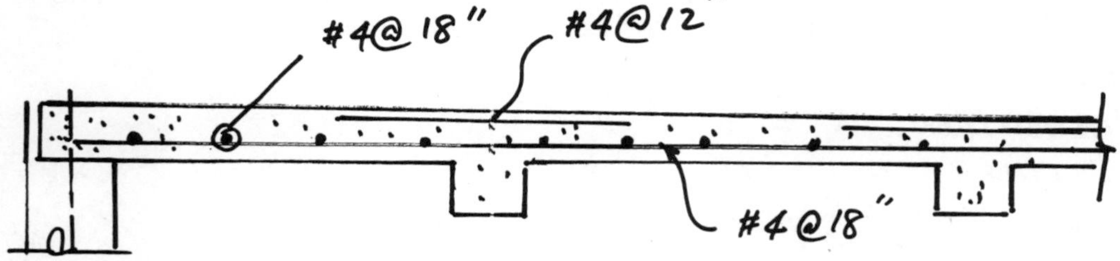

5

INDUSTRIAL BUILDINGS

Industrial buildings are defined as buildings designed and constructed to support and house a manufacturing factory or to store the raw materials or products of a factory. The degree of sophistication of an industrial building depends upon its function and use, and will be dictated by process requirements. The industrial building is to be designed from an economic point of view to achieve the function with the least spending. In industrial buildings, column spacing is determined by the requirement of material handling equipment for the most economical storage area. The design requires a long span heavily loaded floor system when greater column spacing from 20-25 ft. is required.

EXAMPLE 5-01
Given:- Design a main fabrication shop of ammunition factory of SAAD-3 Project, Bagdad, Iraq with Indian Standard Institute Building Code. (STRUCTURAL STEEL FRAME)

Dead load = 15 kg/M2
Insulation = 2 "
purlin = 16 "
Misc. (Bus Ducts framing) = 17 "
50 kg/m²

D.L of Portal frame per ft. length = $50 \times \frac{9.69}{9.0} \times 6.0 = 323$ kg/m
D.L of frame = 60 "
383 kg/m
Say = 0.4 T/m.

Wind load @ 70 kg/M² = 70×6 = 420 kg/M Say 0.42 T/M

Live load @ 75 kg/M²

Reduction Allowance due to pitch = 2k /Ea. deg of inclination above 10°

$\tan\theta = \dfrac{3.6}{9.0} = 0.4$

$\theta = 21°50'$ Say 22°

∴ Live load = 75 − 2×12 = 51 kg/M²

Live load = 51×6 = 306 kg/M Say 0.32 T/M.

Hence Dead Load = 0.40 T/M

Live Load = 0.32 T/M

Wind load = 0.42 T/M

$\dfrac{h}{L} = \dfrac{5.05}{18} = 0.28$

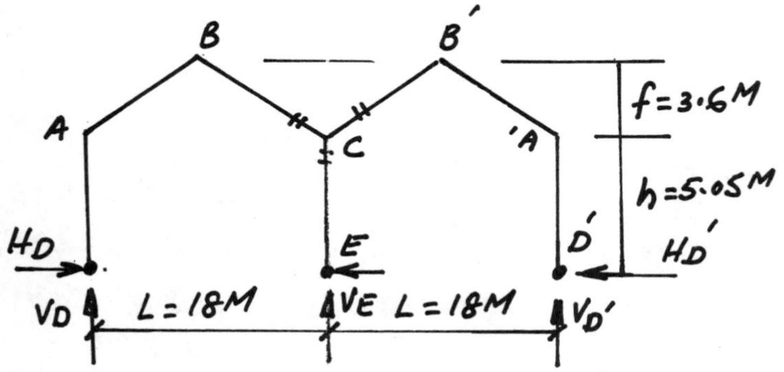

Analysis of portal frame shall be done on the following load combinations:-

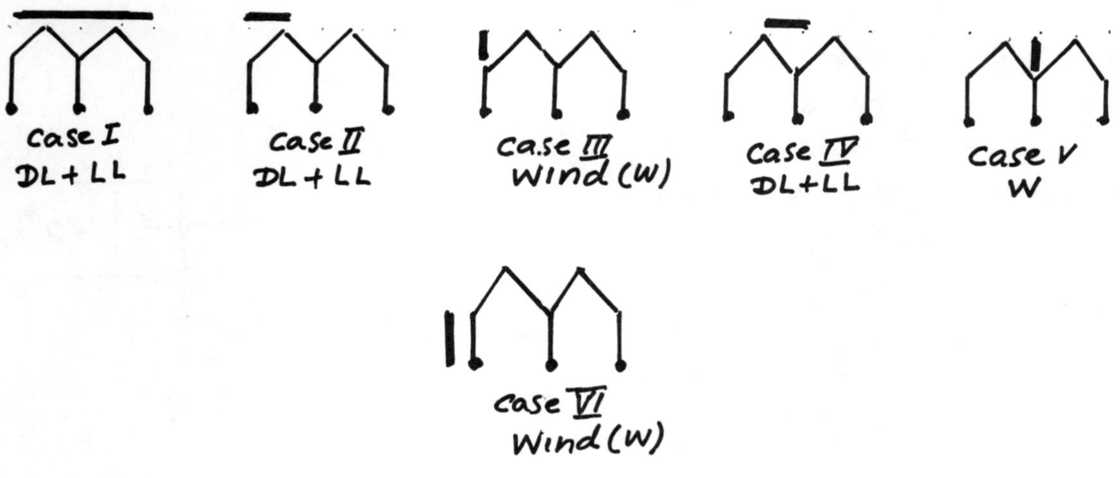

Case		Total load		
I (DL+LL)	Total load	$W = 0.72 \times 36$	=	26.0 T
II (DL+LL)	"	$W = 0.72 \times 9$	=	6.5 T
III (WIND)	"	$W = 0.42 \times 36$	=	1.51 T
IV (DL+LL)	"	$W = 0.72 \times 9$	=	6.50 T
V (WIND)	"	$W = 0.42 \times 36$	=	1.51 T
VI (WIND)	"	$W = 0.42 \times 5.05$	=	2.12 T

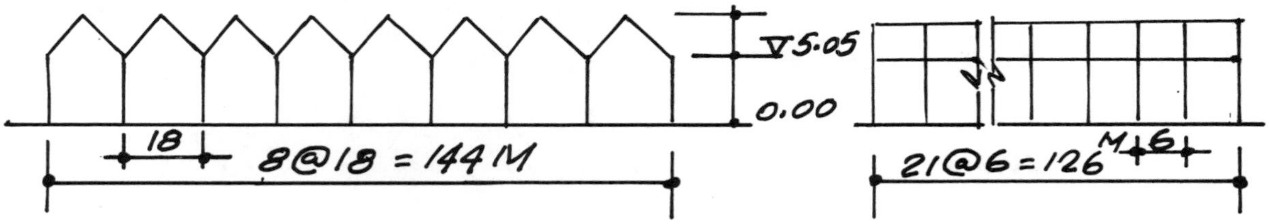

Moments in load combination (B)

$$= 14.99 \times (1 - 0.33) = 10.04\ TM$$

where 0.33 is reduction for wind effect.

Hence governing moments in load combination (A)

$$= 12.4\ TM.$$

Design of Columns:-

Exterior Design moments $= -12.04 \times 0.9 = 11.16\ TM$

Vertical reaction Max. $= +6.69\ T$

reaction Min. $= -3.12\ T$

Try IS MB 400.

Min. yield stress

$F_y = 2600\ kg/cm^2$ (Pg 41 of I.S code)

Properties of ISMB 400

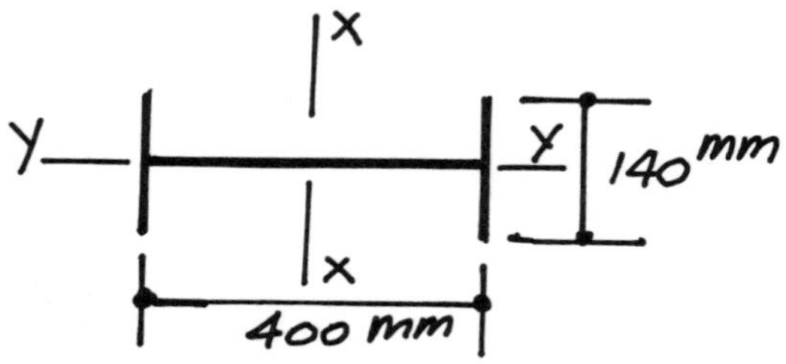

$A = 78.46\ cm^2$, $I_{xx} = 20458.4\ cm^4$

$I_{yy} = 622.10\ cm^4$, $r_{xx} = 16.15\ cm$

$r_{yy} = 2.82\ cm$, $S_{xx} = 1022.9\ cm^3$

$S_{yy} = 88.9\ cm^3$, $L_{xx} = 505\ cm$

$L_{yy} = 505\ cm$, $K = 0.85$

	Moments T.M							Hor. Reaction. T			Vert. Reaction. T		
Loading	M_A	M_A'	M_B	M_B'	M_{C_1}	M_{C_2}	$M_{C\,II}$	H_D	H_D'	H_E	V_D	V_D'	V_E
Case 1	0.03× 26×18 =−12.4	0.03× 468 =−12.4	0.01 ×468 =+4.68	0.01 ×4 68 =+4.68	0.031 ×468 =−14.5	0.031 ×468 =−14.5	0	0.104 ×26 =−2.7	0.104 ×26 =−2.7	0	0.244 ×26 =+6.3	0.244 ×26 = 6.3	0.5 ×26 =+13.0
II	0.0675 ×6.5×18 =−7.90	0.0115 ×117 =−1.34	0.022 ×117 = 2.57	0.0063 ×117 =−0.74	0.042 ×117 =−4.9	0.014 ×117 =1.64	0.056 ×117 =6.55	0.24× 6.5 =−1.56	0.004 ×6.5 =−0.026	0.20× 6.5 =−1.3	0.78 ×6.5 =+5.1	0.0025 ×6.5 =+0.016	0.2× 6.5 =+1.3
III	0.51× 1.51×3.6 =+2.78	0.28 ×5.44 =−1.52	0.22 ×5.44 =−1.20	0.12× 5.44 =−0.66	0.26× 5.44 =−0.9	0.45 ×5.44 =2.45	0.62 ×5.44 =−3.38	0.365× 1.51 =0.55	0.20× 1.51 =−0.30	0.437× 1.51 =−0.35	0.235 ×1.51 =−0.35	0.147 ×1.51 =+0.22	0.088 ×1.51 =+0.13
IV	0.05× 6.5×18 =−5.85	0.007 ×117 =10.82	0.027 ×117 =3.16	0.002× 117 =−0.23	0.077× 117 =−9.0	0.02 ×117 =−2.34	0.056 ×117 =−6.55	0.18 ×6.5 =0.19	0.03 ×6.5 =0.19	0.23 ×6.5 =1.5	0.23× 6.5 =+1.5	0.03× 6.5 =−0.2	0.805 ×6.5 =5.23
V	0.39× 1.51×3.6 =−2.12	0.3× 5.44 =1.63	0.08× 5.44 =0.435	0.12× 5.44 =0.65	0.28× 5.44 =1.52	0.48 ×5.44 =−2.61	0.72× 5.44 =3.92	0.21 ×1.51 =0.32	0.21 ×1.51 =0.32	0.23 ×1.51 =0.35	0.23× 1.51 =+0.35	0.15× 1.51 =−0.23	0.08 ×1.51 =0.12
VI	0.22× 2.12×5.05 =+2.36	0.10× 10.71 =−1.07	0.10× 10.71 =−1.07	0.04× 10.71 =−0.43	0.02× 10.71 =−0.21	0.165× 10.71 =1.77	0.185× 10.71 =−1.98	0.10 ×2.12 =−0.21	0.10× 2.12 =−0.21	0.07 ×2.12 =−0.15	0.07× 2.12 =−0.15	0.08× 2.12 =0.17	0.01 ×2.12 =0.02
Load combination													
(A) DL+LL Case 1	−12.4	−12.4	+4.68	+4.68	−14.5	−14.5	0	−2.7	−2.7	0	+6.3	+6.3	+13.0
DL+LL +W case (B)													
Case I+II+III	−7.26	−14.99	+2.41	+3.59	−15.61	10.28	−5.36	0.62	−3.21	−1.04	+5.8	+6.69	+13.11

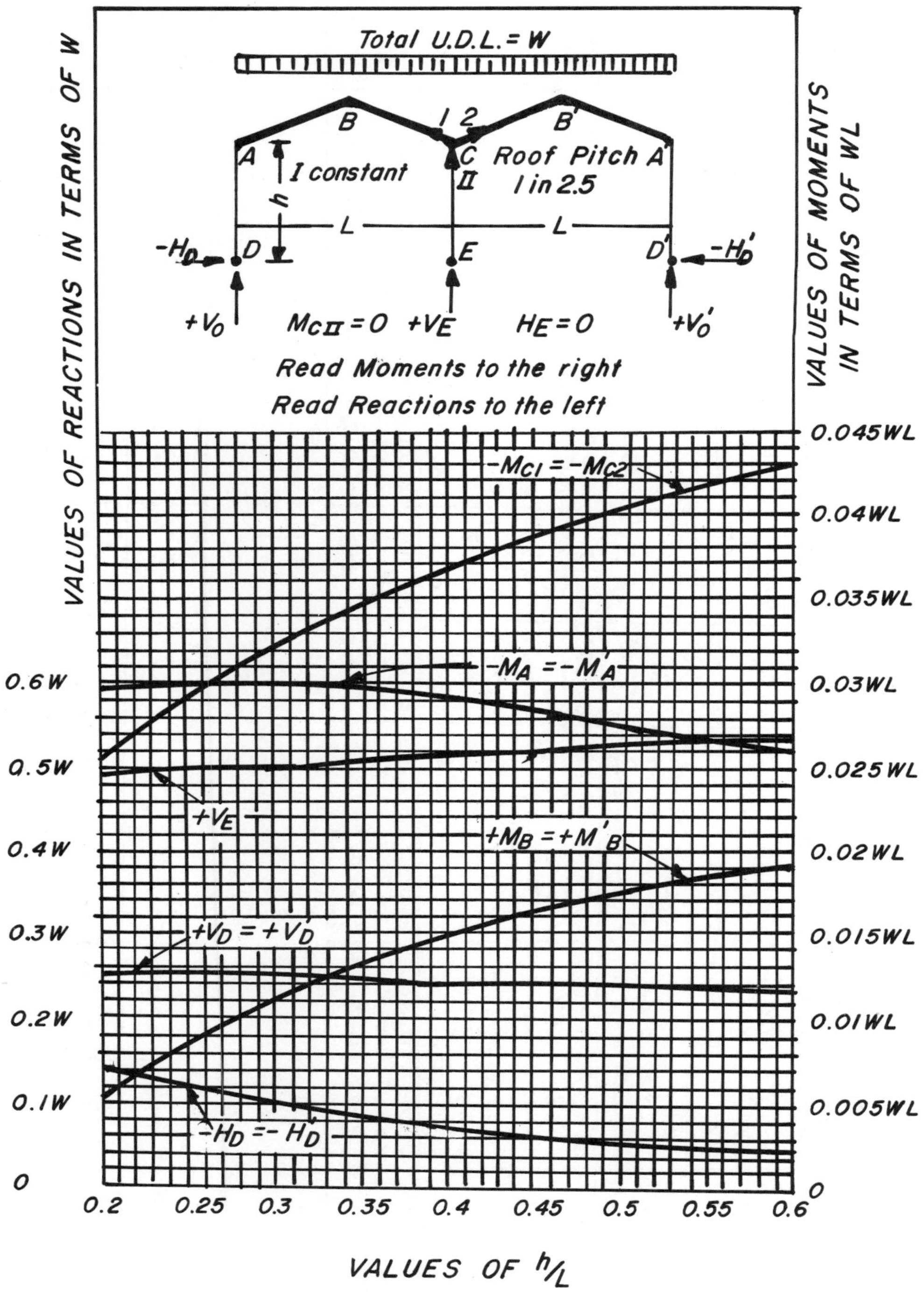

Total U.D.L. = W
A
B
1 2
C
II
B'
A'
I constant
h
Roof Pitch
1 in 2.5
L
L
D
E
D'
$-H_D$
$-H_D'$
$+V_D$
$M_{CII} = 0$
$+V_E$
$H_E = 0$
$+V_D'$
Read Moments to the right
Read Reactions to the left
VALUES OF REACTIONS IN TERMS OF W
VALUES OF MOMENTS IN TERMS OF WL
$-M_{C1} = -M_{C2}$
$-M_A = -M'_A$
$+V_E$
$+M_B = +M'_B$
$+V_D = +V'_D$
$-H_D = -H'_D$
0.6W
0.5W
0.4W
0.3W
0.2W
0.1W
0
0.045WL
0.04WL
0.035WL
0.03WL
0.025WL
0.02WL
0.015WL
0.01WL
0.005WL
0
0.2
0.25
0.3
0.35
0.4
0.45
0.5
0.55
0.6
VALUES OF h/L

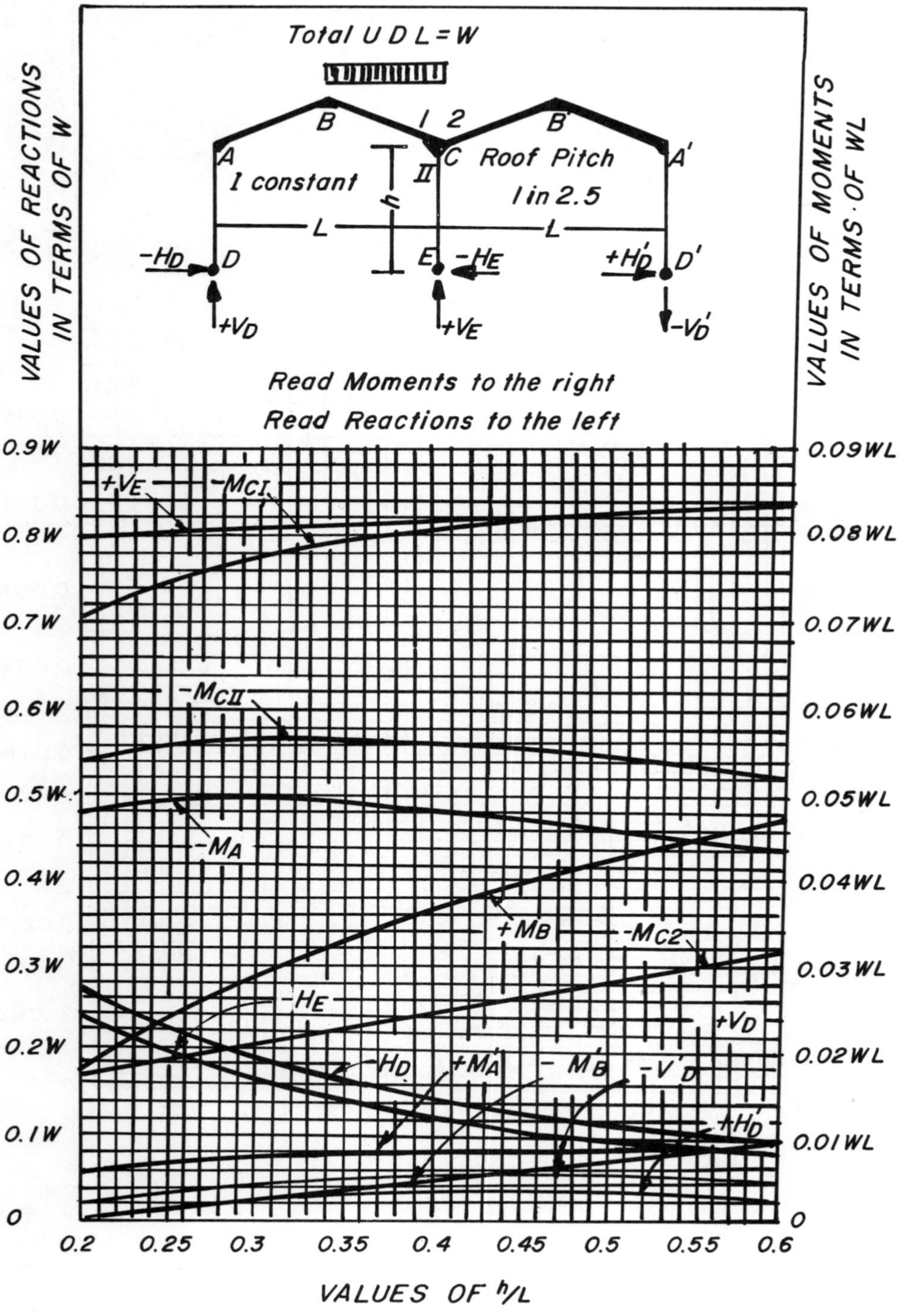

Total U D L = W
A
B
1 2
C
B'
A'
II
I constant
Roof Pitch
1 in 2.5
h
L
L
-H_D
D
E
-H_E
+H'_D
D'
+V_D
+V_E
-V'_D
Read Moments to the right
Read Reactions to the left
VALUES OF REACTIONS IN TERMS OF W
VALUES OF MOMENTS IN TERMS OF WL
0.9W
0.8W
0.7W
0.6W
0.5W
0.4W
0.3W
0.2W
0.1W
0
0.09WL
0.08WL
0.07WL
0.06WL
0.05WL
0.04WL
0.03WL
0.02WL
0.01WL
0
+V_E
-M_CI
-M_CII
-M_A
+M_B
-M_C2
-H_E
+V_D
-H_D
+M'_A
-M'_B
-V'_D
+H'_D
0.2
0.25
0.3
0.35
0.4
0.45
0.5
0.55
0.6
VALUES OF h/L

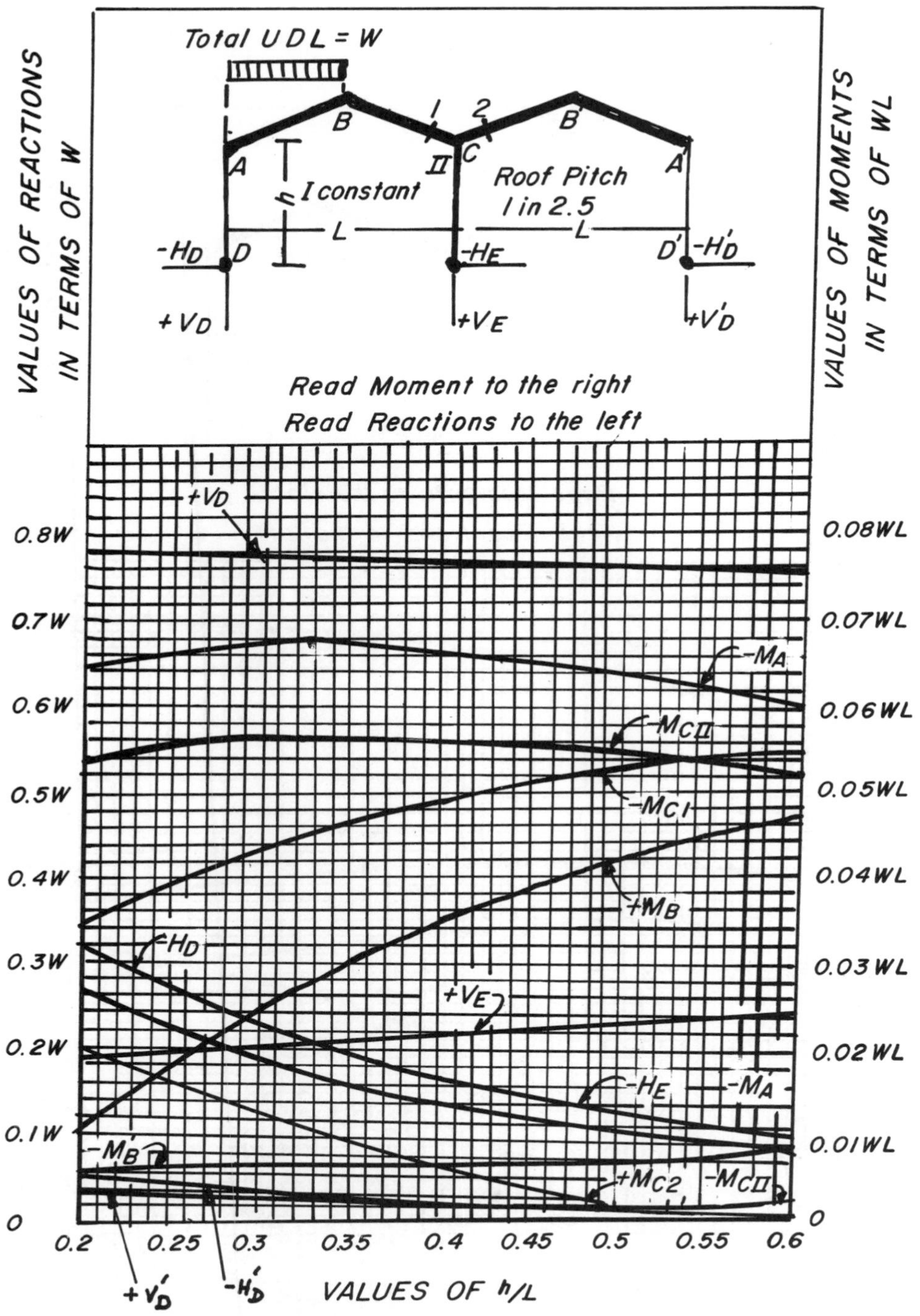
VALUES OF REACTIONS IN TERMS OF W
VALUES OF MOMENTS IN TERMS OF WL
Total UDL = W
Roof Pitch 1 in 2.5
I constant
Read Moment to the right
Read Reactions to the left
VALUES OF h/L

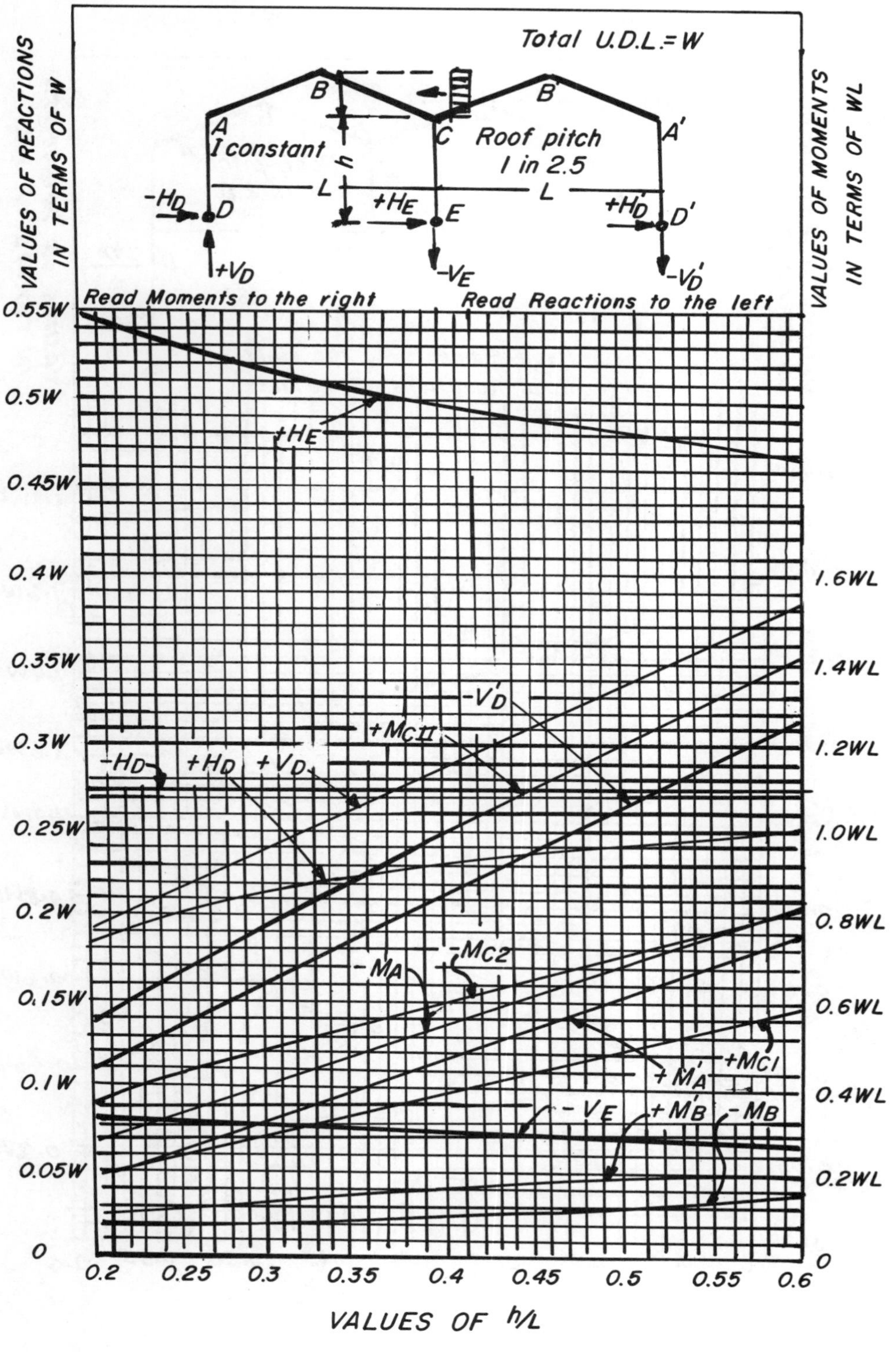

Total U.D.L. = W
B
B'
A
C
A'
I constant
h
Roof pitch
1 in 2.5
L
L
-HD
D
+HE
E
+H'D
D'
+VD
-VE
-V'D
VALUES OF REACTIONS IN TERMS OF W
VALUES OF MOMENTS IN TERMS OF WL
Read Moments to the right
Read Reactions to the left
0.55W
0.5W
0.45W
0.4W
0.35W
0.3W
0.25W
0.2W
0.15W
0.1W
0.05W
0
1.6WL
1.4WL
1.2WL
1.0WL
0.8WL
0.6WL
0.4WL
0.2WL
0
+HE
-V'D
+MCII
-HD
+HD
+VD
-MA
-MC2
+M'A
+MC1
-VE
+M'B
-MB
0.2
0.25
0.3
0.35
0.4
0.45
0.5
0.55
0.6
VALUES OF h/L

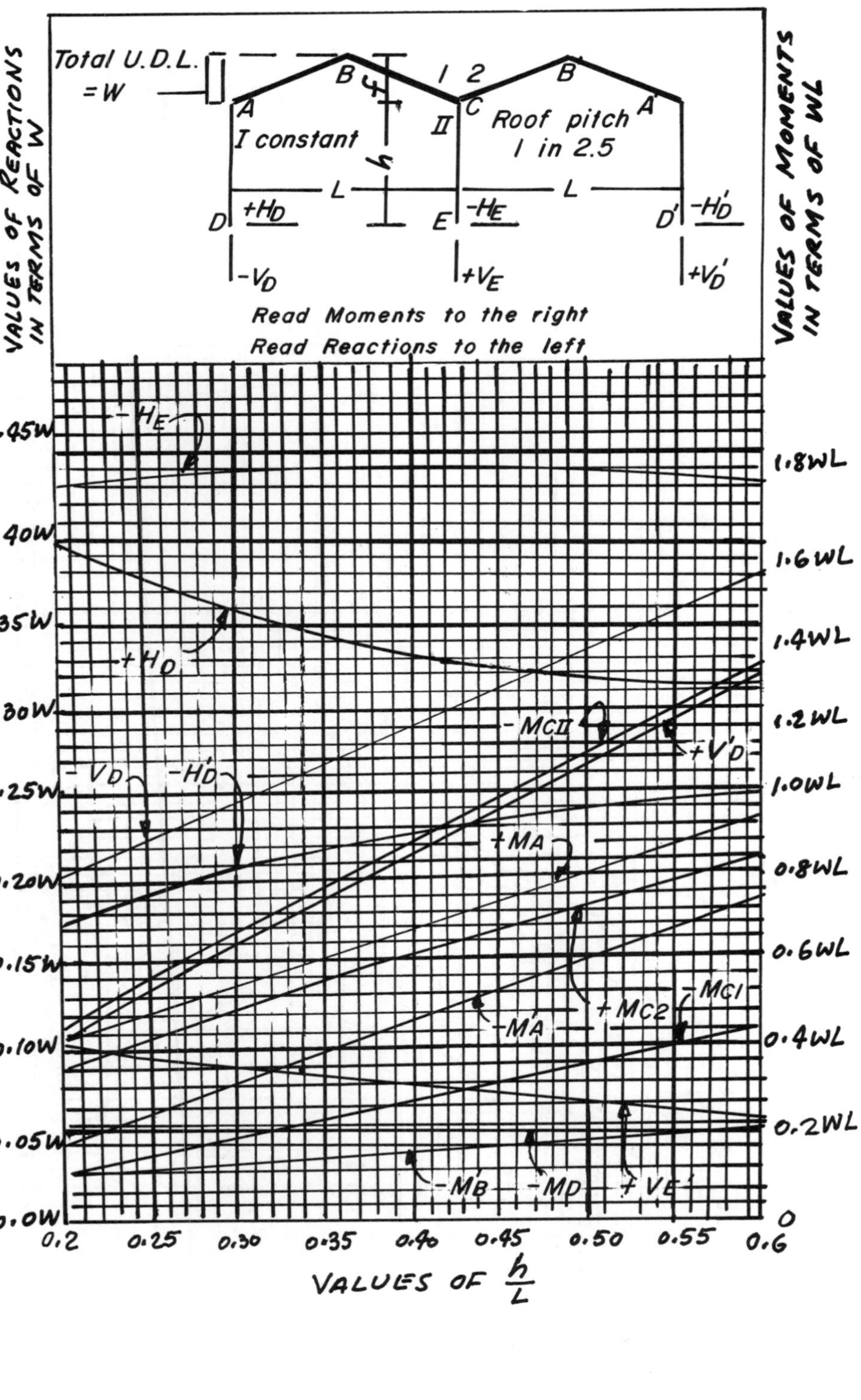
Total U.D.L. = W
A
B
1 2
B
A
C
II
I constant
Roof pitch 1 in 2.5
h
f
L
L
D
+HD
E
-HE
D'
-H'D
-VD
+VE
+V'D
Read Moments to the right
Read Reactions to the left
VALUES OF REACTIONS IN TERMS OF W
VALUES OF MOMENTS IN TERMS OF WL
-HE
+HD
-MCII
+V'D
-VD
-H'D
+MA
-M'A
+MC2
-MC1
-MB
-MD
+VE
0.45W
0.40W
0.35W
0.30W
0.25W
0.20W
0.15W
0.10W
0.05W
0.0W
1.8WL
1.6WL
1.4WL
1.2WL
1.0WL
0.8WL
0.6WL
0.4WL
0.2WL
0
0.2
0.25
0.30
0.35
0.40
0.45
0.50
0.55
0.6
VALUES OF h/L

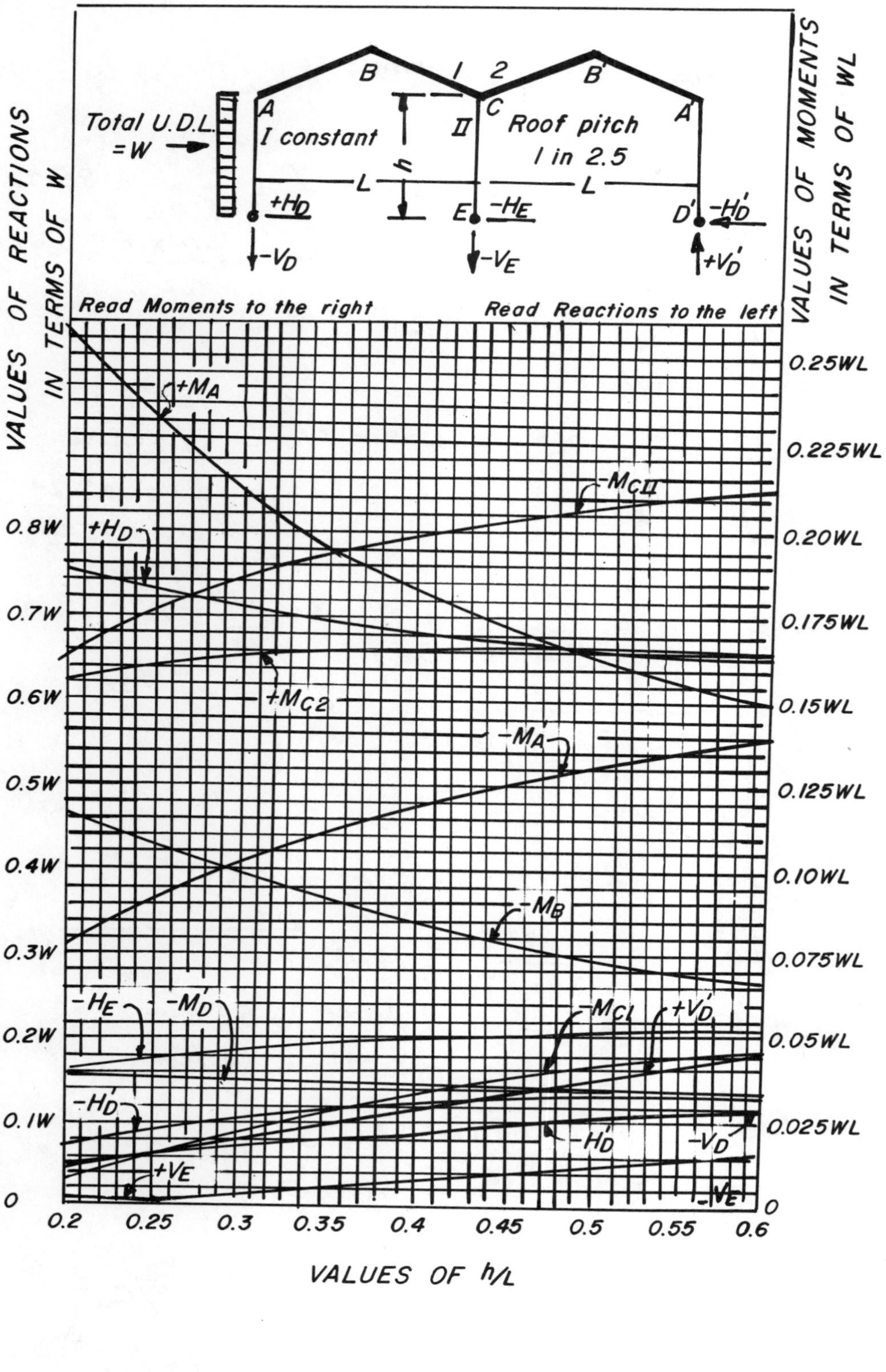

Total U.D.L. = W
I constant
Roof pitch 1 in 2.5
Read Moments to the right
Read Reactions to the left
VALUES OF REACTIONS IN TERMS OF W
VALUES OF MOMENTS IN TERMS OF WL
+M_A
-M_CII
+H_D
+M_C2
-M_A'
-M_B
-H_E
-M_D'
-M_C1
+V_D'
-H_D'
+V_E
-V_D'
-V_E
0.8W
0.7W
0.6W
0.5W
0.4W
0.3W
0.2W
0.1W
0
0.25WL
0.225WL
0.20WL
0.175WL
0.15WL
0.125WL
0.10WL
0.075WL
0.05WL
0.025WL
0
0.2
0.25
0.3
0.35
0.4
0.45
0.5
0.55
0.6
VALUES OF h/L

$$\frac{kL_y}{r_y} = \frac{l_y}{r_y} = \frac{0.85 \times 505}{2.82} = 152$$

Allowable P_c Axial stress $= 470\ kg/cm^2$ (for $L_y = 152$ & Table II of I.S.1800-62)

Cal. Avg. Axial compressive stress $f_c = \frac{6690}{78.46} = 85.27\ kg/cm^2$

Cal. Bending comp. stress $f_{bc} = \frac{11.16 \times 10^5}{1022.9} = 1091\ kg/cm^2$

Allowable $P_{be} = 1650\ kg/cm^2$

Interaction formula

$$\frac{f_c}{P_c} + \frac{C_m f_{be}}{\left(1 - \frac{f_c}{F'_{ey}}\right) P_{be}} \leq 1.0 \quad \text{where } F'_{ey} = \frac{12\pi^2 E}{23\left(\frac{KL}{r}\right)^2}$$

$$= \frac{12 \times 3.14^2 \times 2.04 \times 10^6}{23 \times (152)^2}$$

$$= 454$$

$$C_m = 0.6 - 0.4\frac{M_1}{M_2} = 0.6 \quad \text{as } \frac{M_1}{M_2} = 0$$

$$\therefore \frac{85.27}{470} + \frac{0.6 \times 1091}{\left(1 - \frac{85.27}{454}\right)1650} = 0.67 < 1 \quad \text{OK}$$

Design of rafter

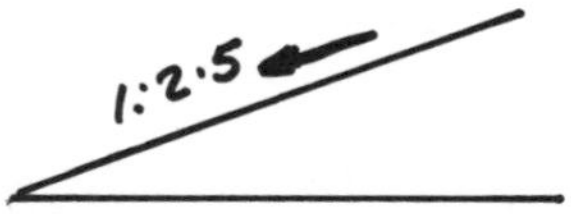

Max. $M = 12.4 + 1.2 = 13.6$ TM

Vert. reaction $= \frac{13}{2 \times 0.376} = 17.47$ T

unbraced length $= L_x = 9.69$ M $= 969$ Cm

$L_y = 1.4$ M $= 140$ Cm

Try ISM 400 $\quad \frac{KLx}{r_x} = \frac{0.85 \times 969}{16.15} = 51$

$$\therefore P_c = 1172\ kg/cm^2$$

$$f_c = \frac{17470}{78.46} = 222.66\ kg/cm^2$$

$$f_b = \frac{13.6 \times 10}{1022.9} = 1330\ kg/cm^2$$

$$\therefore \frac{222.66}{1172} + \frac{1330}{650} = 1.0 = 1.0 \quad \text{OK}$$

Design of base plate

Load on Col. $= 13T$

F_p (allowable bearing pressure on support) $= 50\ kg/cm^2$ for M_{200} Concrete

$A = \frac{13 \times 10^3}{50} = 260\ cm^2$

$B \times N = 260$

if B is 35, then $N = \frac{260}{35} = 7.43$, use $N = 50\ cm.$

$m = \frac{1}{2}(N - 0.95d)$

$= 6$

$n = \frac{1}{2}(B - 0.80b)$

$= 11.9 \leftarrow$ use.

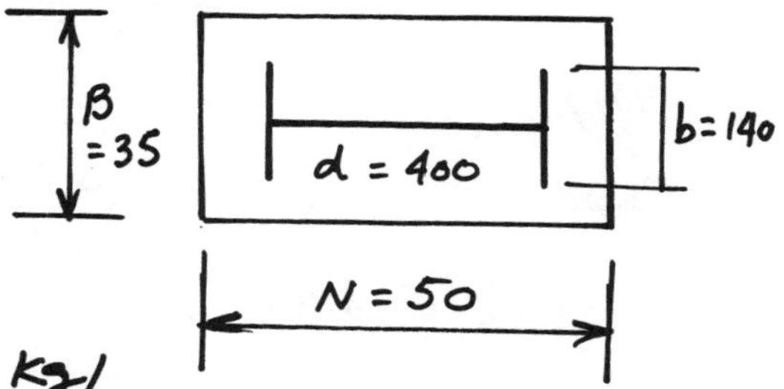

$P_{net} = \frac{13}{35 \times 50} = 7.42\ kg/cm^2$

$t = \sqrt{\frac{3 f_p n^2}{F_b}} = \sqrt{\frac{3 \times 7.42 \times 11.9^2}{1890}} = 1.29\ cm$

Use 20mm thick Plate.

Design of Purlin

$D.L = 33\ kg/m^2 \times 1.4\ M = 46\ kg/M$

$LL = 50\ kg/M^2 \times 1.4M = 70\ kg/M$

WIND LOAD	Windward	Leeward
Case (A)	$(-0.35 - 0.50)P$	$(-0.50 - 0.50)P$
Case (B)	$(+0.50 - 0.35)P$	$(+0.50 - 0.50)P$

$\therefore$ Maximum $= -1.0P$

Max. wind load/M $= -1.0 \times 1.4 \times 70 = -98\ kg/M$

Case I DL + LL & $\theta = 22^\circ$

$W = 46 + 70 = 117$ Say $125\ kg/M$

$W_x = 125 \cos 22 = 116\ kg/M$

$W_y = 125 \sin 22 = 47\ kg/M$

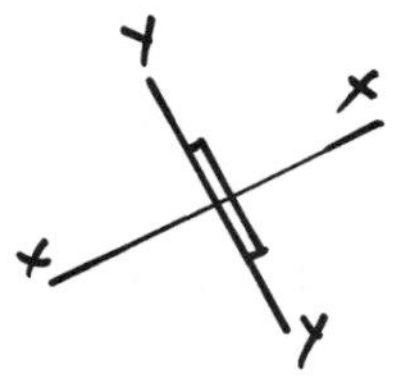

$$M_x = \frac{116 \times 6^2 \times 100}{8} = 52200 \text{ kgcm}$$

$$M_y = \frac{47 \times 6^2 \times 100}{8} = 21150 \text{ kgcm}$$

Case ② DL + WL

$$W_x = 46 \sin 22 = 17.25 \text{ kg/M}$$

$$W_y = 46 \cos 22 - 98 = 55.36 \text{ kg/M}$$

$$M_x = \frac{55.36 \times 6^2 \times 100}{8} = 24912 \text{ kgcm}$$

$$M_y = \frac{17.25 \times 6^2 \times 100}{8} = 7762.5 \text{ kg/cm.}$$

Try ISMC 150, $S_{xx} = 103.9$, $S_{yy} = 19.4 \text{ Cm}^3$

Case ① $$f_{be} = \frac{52200}{103.9} + \frac{21150}{19.4} = 1592 < 1650 \text{ ok}$$

Case ② $$f_{be} = \frac{24912}{103.9} + \frac{7762.5}{19.4} = 640 < 1650 \text{ ok}$$

$$\Delta_{act} = \frac{5}{384} \times \frac{125 \times 6 \times (6 \times 100)^3}{2.04 \times 10^6 \times 779.4} = 1.326$$

$$\Delta_{allowable} = \frac{l}{325} = \frac{600}{325} = 1.8 > 1.326 \text{ Cm ok}$$

Use ISMC 150

Design of side runner

DL a) Sheeting 2 layers + Insulation $= 18 \times 1.5 = 27$ kg/M

b) Self Wt. ISMC 150 $= 22.1$ "

49.1 kg/M

Say 50 kg/M

$$\text{Vert. Load} = 50 \text{ kg/M}$$

$$\text{Wind Load} = 70 \times 1.5 = 105 \text{ kg/M}$$

$$\text{Span} = 6\text{M}$$

$$M_{yy} = 50 \times 6^2/8 = 225 \text{ kgM}$$

$$M_{xx} = 105 \times 6^2/8 = 472.5 \text{ kgM}$$

Try ISMC 150, $S_{xx} = 103.9 \text{ Cm}^3$, $S_{yy} = 19.4 \text{ Cm}^3$

$$f_{be} = \frac{473 \times 100}{103.9} + \frac{225 \times 100}{19.4} = 1609 < 1650 \text{ ok}$$

$$\Delta = \frac{50 \times 6 \times (6 \times 100)^3}{384 \times 2.04 \times 10^6 \times 102.3} + \frac{105 \times 6 \times (600)^3}{384 \times 2.04 \times 10^6 \times 774.4}$$

$$= 0.84 < l/325 = 1.84 \text{ Cm ok.}$$

Rigid splice design

$$\frac{MB}{MB'} = 4.68TM$$

Assumed moment arm between center of Bottom bolts & center of top flange

Moment arm = 4 62 Cm

Allowable Load per bolt (20MM ϕ) = 0.8×3.14×0.945 = 2.4T

Moment capacity of 6 bolts = 2.4×0.46×6 = 6.62 TM > 4.68

Use 6 Bolts of 20ϕ.

check compression Area

$$\Delta_1 = \frac{P_1 L_1^3}{12EI_g} ; \Delta_2 = \frac{P_2 L_2^3}{12EI_g}$$

$$\because \Delta_1 = \Delta_2 \; \& \; P_T = P_1 + P_2 = 2.4T$$

Load transfer to Gusset Plate = P_2

$$\frac{P_1}{P_2} + 1 = \frac{L_2}{L_1} + 1 \text{ or } P_1 + P_2 = P_2\left(\frac{L_2 + L_1}{L_1}\right)$$

$$P_2 = \left[\frac{2.4}{1 + \frac{43}{153}}\right] = 2.35T$$

$$t = \frac{2.35}{10 \times 1.5} = 0.156 \text{ Say } 2 \text{ Cm}$$

Compression Plate $M = P_2 L = 235 \times 2 = 4.7$

$$Z = \frac{4.7}{1.65} = 2.85$$

$$t_2 = \sqrt{\frac{2.8 \times 6}{10 \times 1}} = 1.3 \text{ Cm use } 20 \text{ mm}$$

Design of Valley Joint

Moment = 15.61 Mt

25ϕ Bolt, P_t = 0.8×4.9×0.945 = 3.8T

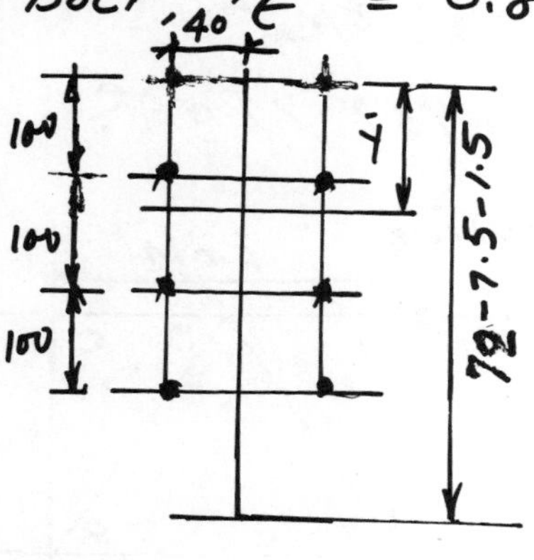

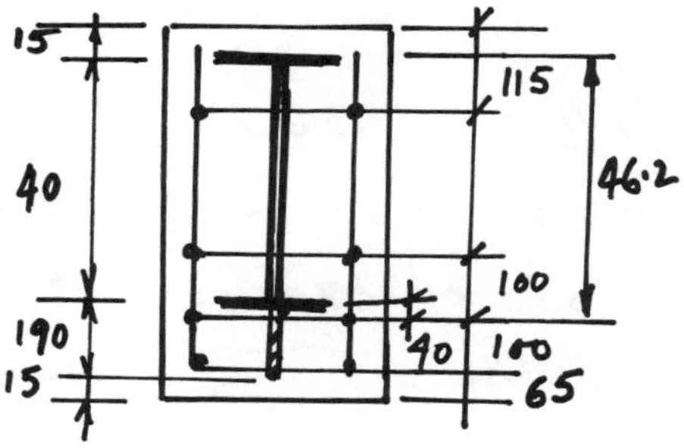

$$\frac{2 \times 4 \bar{y}^2}{2} = 8 \times 4.9 (15 - \bar{y})$$

$$4\bar{y}^2 = 59.5 - 39.2\bar{y}$$

$$\text{or } \bar{y} = 8.25$$

Lever arm $= 60 - 8.25 = 51.75$ Cm

$M_{allow.} = 8 \times 3.8 \times 0.5175 \times 1.33 = 15.73 > 15.61$ ok

Use 8 - 25 ϕ Bolts

Design of bracing at Rafter's level.

$F_1 = \left(\frac{3+5.4}{2}\right) \times 6 \times 70 = 1{,}764$ kg $= 1.8$ T

$F_2 = \left(\frac{1.8+8.0}{2}\right) \times 3 \times 70 = 504$ kg $= 0.5$ T

Strut $= 1.8 \times 1.1$ (for drag) $= 2.0$ T

tie $= 1.8 \times \frac{8.5}{6} \times 1.1 = 2.8$ T

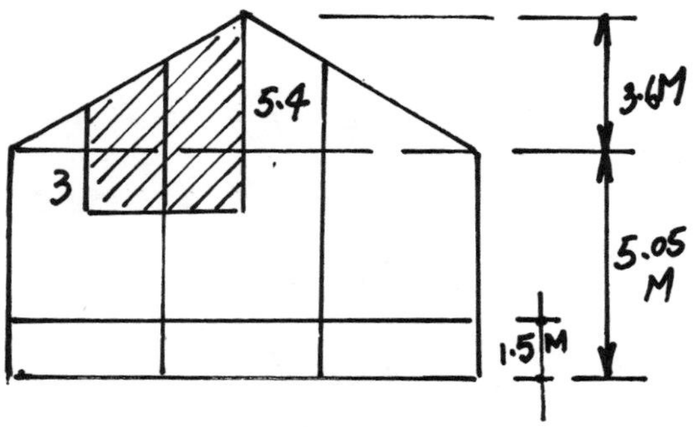

Try ISA 90×90×8

$A = 13.79$ Cm^2

$r_y = 2.75$ cm

$l_{cl.} = 8.5 - 0.6 = 8.0$ M

$\frac{l}{r} = \frac{8 \times 100}{2.75} = 290 < 350$

$F_T = 1.5 \times 13.79 = 20.68 > 2.8$ T

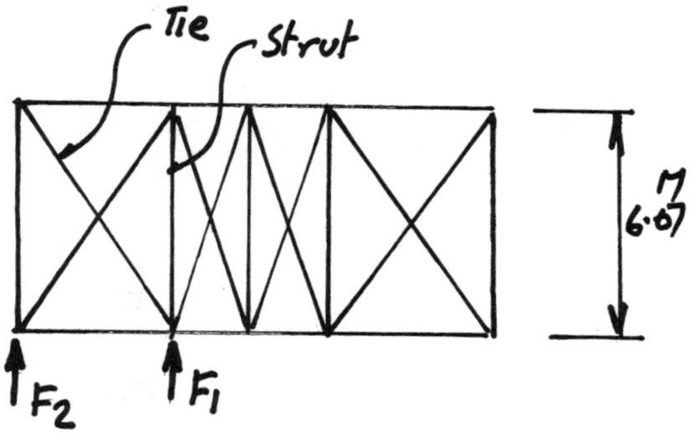

Strut T = 2.0T

try ISMC 150, $A = 20.88$ Cm^2, $r_y = 2.21$ Cm

$\frac{l}{r} = \frac{6 \times 100 \times 0.8}{2.21} = 217$; $f_a = 236$ kg/cm^2

$T_{allow.} = 236 \times 20.88 = 4928$ kg $= 4.93$ T > 2.0 ok

Bracing in longitudenal direction.

length of bracing member

$BD/BE = \sqrt{3^2 + 5.05^2} = 5.87$ M

Wind Load in Each Brace

$= \frac{2.7}{2} \times \frac{5.87}{3.0} = 2.64$ T

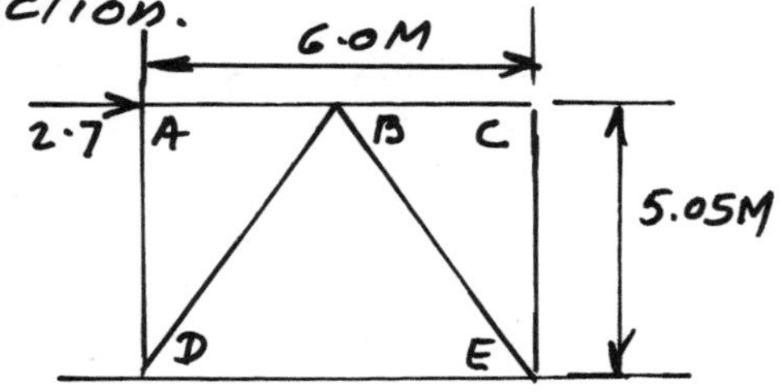

Reaction at A/D $= \frac{2.7 \times 5.05}{6} = 2.27\,T$

Tie member at top level AC.

Considering as two span Beam with support at the midspan

$B.M = 2.27 \times 3 = 6.81\,TM$

$S = \frac{6.81 \times 10^5}{1650} = 413\,Cm^3$

Try ISMC 200 double

$r_x = 8.03$

$r_y = 2.23$

$A = 28.21$

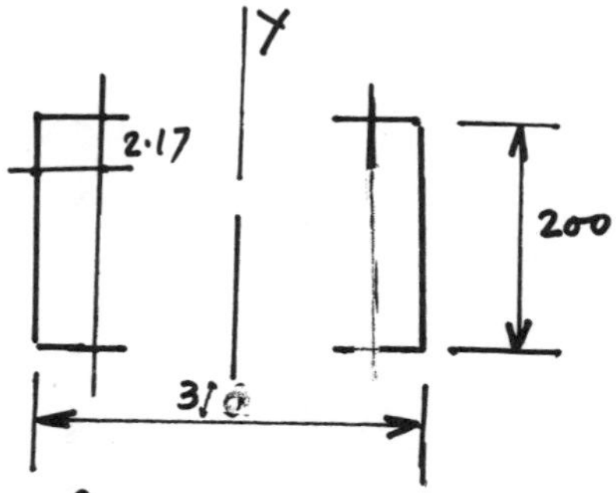

$r_{YY}(\text{Composite}) = \sqrt{\frac{140.4 + 28.21(13.3)^2}{28.21}}$

$= 13.48\,Cm$

$S = 2 \times A \times (8.03)^2$

$= 2 \times 28.12 \times (8.03)^2 = 3638\,Cm^3 > 413\,Cm^3$ ok

$\frac{l}{r} = \frac{6 \times 100}{8.03} = 74 < 180$ ok

section has been provided to suit the fitting of the bracing system.

Bracing member $F = 2.64\,T$; $L = 5.87 - 0.6 = 5.27\,M$

for $\frac{L}{r} = 200$, $r_{required} = \frac{5.27 \times 100}{200} = 2.63\,Cm$

use 2 Ls 100×100×8

$r_x = 3.07 > 2.63$ ok

also connect the members with 50×50×6 Ls on 1000 Cm c/c

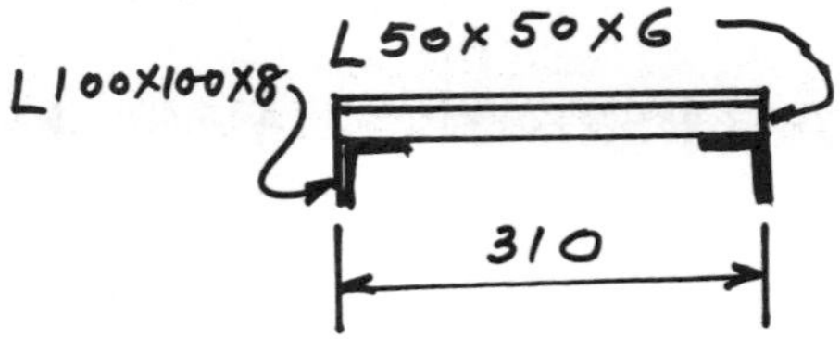

Design of foundation bolt

Shear from longitudenal side on base = 2.7T from DL+LL

Shear due to wind (Direct) $= \frac{5.05 \times 6 \times 70}{2 \times 1000} = 1.06\,T$

Shear due to drag 10% of direct wind $= 0.11\,T$

Total shear @ base $= 2.7 + 1.06 + 0.11 = 3.87\,T$

no of bolts provided = ?

Area req'd per bolt $= \dfrac{3.87 \times 1000}{1.25 \times 945 \times 2} = 1.64\ Cm^2$

use 25φ bolt

Design of Gable column.

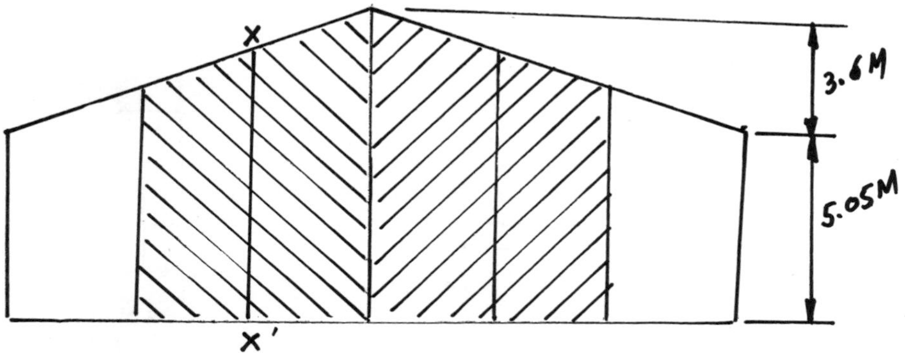

Zone of influence within XX'

Load $= 7.45 \times 6 \times 70 = 3129\ kg$

Load/M $= \dfrac{3129}{7.45} = 420\ kg/M = 0.42\ T/M$

Taking Member as simply supported

$BM = \dfrac{0.42 \times (7.45)^2}{8} = 2.91\ TM$

$S = \dfrac{2.91 \times 10^5}{1650} = 176.3\ Cm^3$

using ISMB 200

$S_x = 223.5 > 176.3$ ok

$\Delta = \dfrac{5}{384} \times \dfrac{(0.42 \times 2.45) \times (7.45 \times 100)^3 \times 1000}{(2.04 \times 10^6) \times 2235.4}$

$= 0.0066\ Cm < \dfrac{l}{325} = \dfrac{7.45 \times 100}{325} = 2.29$ ok

Foundation design (Typical)

Load

from roof $= \dfrac{6.3}{2} = 3.150\ T$

Self Wt. of Col. $= 5.05 \times 61.6 = 0.311\ T$

" " of Base Pl $= 0.3 \times 0.55 \times 15 = 0.025\ t$

" " of Bracing/Tie/strut $= 0.400\ T$

C.O $= 3.886\ T$

B.O = 3.886

Self wt of runner (4×3×22.1)×2 = 0.530 T Gable EAVE

" " " vert. cladding 13.33×22.1 = 0.295 T Gable EAVE

" " " Sheeting/insulation (1.75×3×20)×2 + ½×3×1.2×20 = 0.246 T —"—

" " " glazing (1.8×3×20) = 0.216 T —"—

5.17 T Say 5.2 T

" " " pedestal 0.6×0.35×2.0×2.4 = 1.00 T

" " " plinth Beam 0.3×0.5×3.0×2.4×2 = 2.16 T

" " " peripherial brickwall 2.0×0.24×3×2.0×2 = 5.76 T

14.10 T

Add 10% wt. of footing 1.41 T

15.51 T Say 16 T.

Add overburden due to Backfill Say 50% = 8 T

24 T.

Design of Pedestal.

Conc. Mix M200, $f_c' = 50\,kg/cm^2$ (I.S.I. 456)

Axial load = 5.2 T & evenly distributed over base plate

size of base plate = 55×30, $A = 1650\,cm^2$

Comp. stress in Concrete $= \dfrac{5.2\times10^3}{1650} = 3.15\,kg/cm^2 < 50\,kg/cm^2$ ok

Size of Pedestal 25 mm larger than base plate

350×600

load at bottom = 14.5 T

Reaction at Top $R_{XX} = 1.06\,T$

$R_{YY} = 1.65\,T$

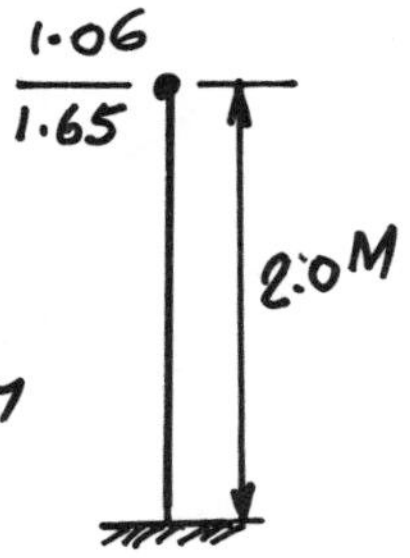

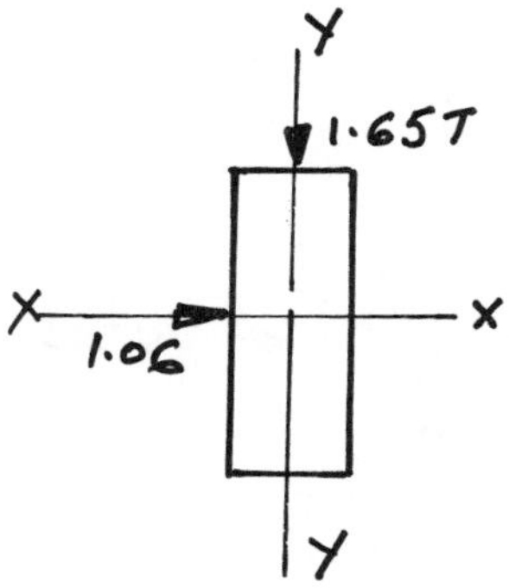

M_{XX} (base) $= 1.06\times2 = 2.12\,TM$

M_{YY} (base) $= 1.65\times2 = 3.30\,TM$

$P_U = 3.15\times1.85 + (24-3.15)\times1.5$

$= 37.10\,T$

$M_{UXX} = 2.12\times1.5 = 3.18\,T$

$M_{UYY} = 3.3\times1.85 = 4.95\,T$

$$e_{(x-x)} = \frac{3.18 \times 10^5}{37.1 \times 10^3} = 8.57\ \text{Cm} = 85.7\ \text{mm}$$

$$e_{(y-y)} = \frac{4.95 \times 10^5}{37.1 \times 10^3} = 13.3\ \text{Cm} = 133\ \text{mm}$$

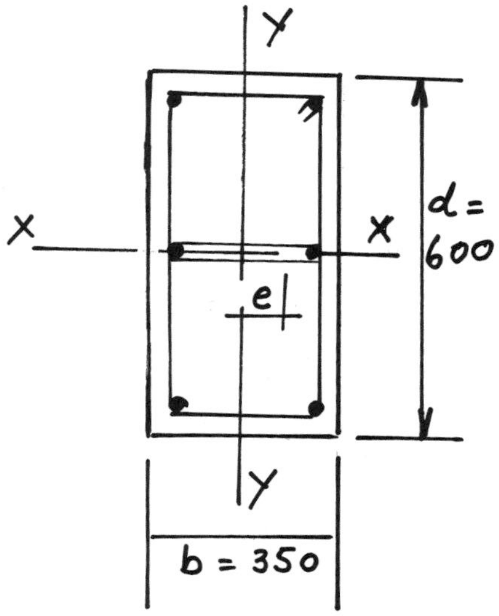

assumed $d = 600\text{mm} = 60\text{Cm}$

$b = 350\text{mm} = 35\text{Cm}$

Cover $= 50\text{mm} = 5\text{Cm}$

$$\frac{d}{b} = \frac{600}{350} = 1.71$$

$$\frac{d_1}{d} = \frac{540}{600} = 0.9$$

$$\frac{P_u}{\sigma_c bd} = \frac{37100}{200 \times 60 \times 35} = 0.88$$

$$\frac{M_u}{\sigma_c bd^2} = \frac{37100 \times 8.57 \times 1.49}{200 \times 35 \times 60 \times 60} = 0.019$$

where See θ For $N = 0$; $\phi \frac{b}{d} = 1 = \frac{\sqrt{(13.3)^2 + (1.71)^2 (8.57)^2}}{13.3} = 1.49$

from chandra's book

$$\frac{r}{\sigma_{cu}} = 0. \times 10^{-4} = 0$$

$\therefore$ Provide Nominal reinforcement ie 0.8%.

$= \frac{0.8}{100} \times 35 \times 60 = 16.8\ \text{Cm}^2$ ie 6-#20ϕ = 18.85 Cm

Lateral ties 8ϕ 200 c/c

Design of footing

$P = 24T$; $e_{xx} = \frac{2.12 \times 10^5}{24 \times 10^3} = 8.84\ \text{Cm}$

$M_{xx} = 2.12\ TM$ $\quad e_{YY} = \frac{3.3 \times 10^5}{24 \times 10^3} = 13.75\ \text{Cm}$

$M_{YY} = 3.30\ TM$

Bearing pressure of soil $= 6.6\ T/M^2$

$$\frac{M_{YY}}{M_{XX}} = 1.6$$

Area of footing required $= \frac{24}{6.6} = 3.64\ M$

use $1.75 \times 2.8 \times 0.35$ with max. eccentricity $= 13.8$ Cm.

Max. pressure on soil $= \frac{24}{1.75 \times 2.8}\left(1 \pm \frac{6 \times .138}{2.8}\right) = 6.29\ T/M^2$ $\not< 3.5\ T/M^2$

moment @ YY $= 5.2 \times 1.1 + \frac{1}{2} \times 1.1 + \frac{6.3 - 5.2}{2} \times 1.1 \times \frac{2}{3} \times 1.1$

$= 3.59\ TM$

$d_{eff.} = \sqrt{\frac{3.59 \times 10^5}{12 \times 100}} = 17.3$

Use $D = 35$ Cm, $d_{eff} = 27$ Cm.

$A_{st} = \frac{3.59 \times 10^5}{1400 \times 27 \times 0.86} = 11\ Cm^2$

Use 12 φ @ 100 c/c

Check for shear

Reaction $= \frac{16}{1.75 \times 2.8} = 3.27\ T/M^2$

Shear $= 3.27 \times 0.75 \times 1.75$

$= 4.29\ T$

$v_{xx} = \frac{4.29 \times 10^3}{105 \times 30} = 1.36\ kg/cm^2$

$< 7\ kg/cm^2$ ok

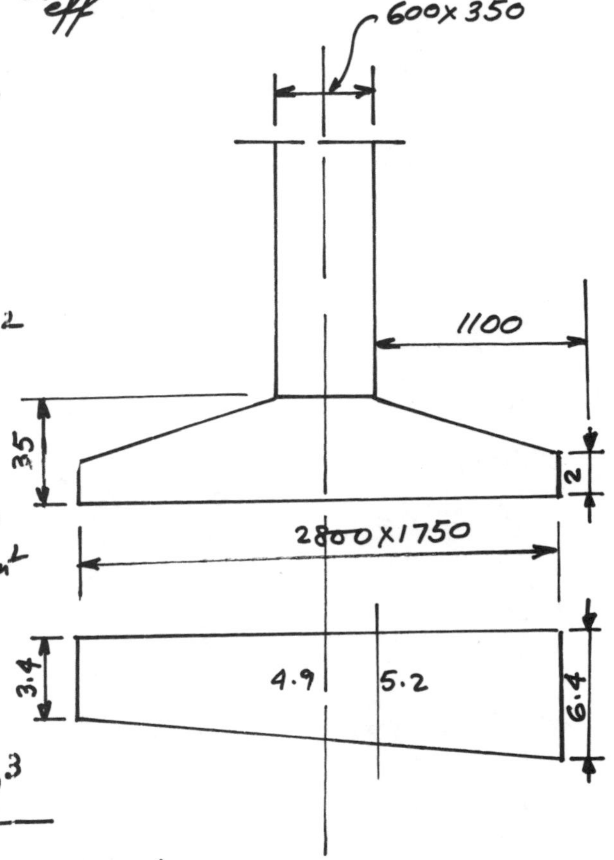

for U_{xx} σ_B

$= \frac{0.5(5.2 + 6.3) \times 1.1 \times 10^3}{0.86 \times 27 \times 38.77}$

$= 7.0\ kg/cm^2 < 8\ kg/cm^2$ where $\Sigma_0 = 38.77$ Cm

$\sigma_{max} = \frac{24}{1.75 \times 2.8}\left(1 \pm \frac{6 \times 0.09}{1.75}\right) = 6.4\ T/M^2$ & $3.4\ T/M^2$

$M_{xy} = 5.2 \times 0.7 \times \frac{0.7}{2} + \frac{1.2}{2} \times 0.7 \times \frac{2}{3} \times 0.70 = 1.5\ TM$

$A_{st} = \frac{1.5 \times 10^5}{1400 \times 27 \times 0.86} = 4.6\ Cm^2$ use 10 φ @ 150 c/c.

Design of Plinth Beam (TYPICAL)

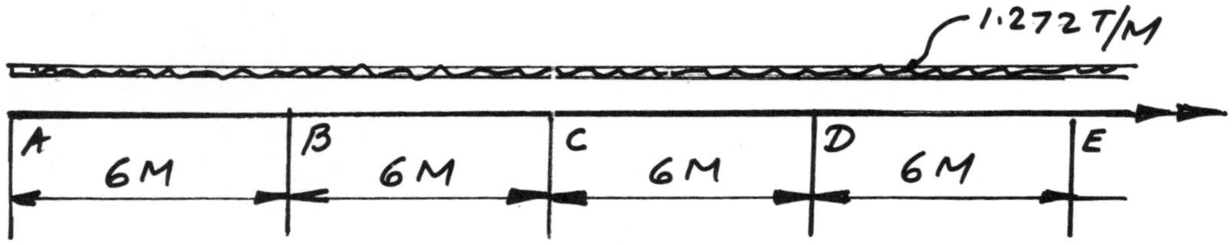

Dead load

wt of 240^{mm} th. wall, 1^M above floor = $1 \times 0.24 \times 2.0 = 0.48$ T/M

" " " " " , 1^M below floor = $0.9 \times 0.24 \times 2.0 = 0.432$

Self wt of plinth beam = $0.3 \times 0.5 \times 2.4 = 0.36$

1.27 T/M

From table 2 of R.C. design by Reynold.

$M_B = 0.105 \times 1.272 \times 6^2 = -4.81$ TM

$M_{AB} = 0.078 \times 1.272 \times 6^2 = +3.57$ TM

$M_C = 0.080 \times 1.272 \times 6^2 = -3.66$ TM

$M_{BC} = 0.046 \times 1.272 \times 6^2 = +2.11$ TM

$d_{req'd} = \sqrt{\dfrac{4.81 \times 10^5}{12 \times 30}} = 36.4$ use $D = 50^{Cm}$, $d_{eff} = 42^{Cm}$

$M_{UB} = 1.5 \times 4.81 \times 10^5 = 7.215 \times 10^5$ kgCm.

$K_B = \dfrac{7.215 \times 10^5}{30 \times 42 \times 42} = 13.64$ kg/Cm^2

p_t @ B from tables of U.S.D of R.C.C by Chandra = 0.566

p_t of AB = 0.409 when $K_{AB} = \dfrac{5.355 \times 10^5}{30 \times 42 \times 42} = 10.12$ kg/cm^2

$A_{st}\ B(-) = \dfrac{0.566}{100} \times 30 \times 42 = 7.14$ cm^2

use 4–16ϕ = 8.04 Cm^2

$A_{st}\ AB(+) = \dfrac{0.409}{100} \times 30 \times 42 = 5.16$ Cm^2

use 2–20ϕ = 6.28 Cm^2

Shear = $1.272 \times 3 = 3.82$ T

Shear Cap = $7 \times 30 \times 42 = 8.82$ T > 3.82

Provide nominal stirrup 8ϕ @ 200 c/c.

EXAMPLE 5-02

Given:- Design a combustible store of ammunition factory of SAAD-3 Project, Bagdad, Iraq with Indian Standard Institute Building Code. (R.C.C. Frame)

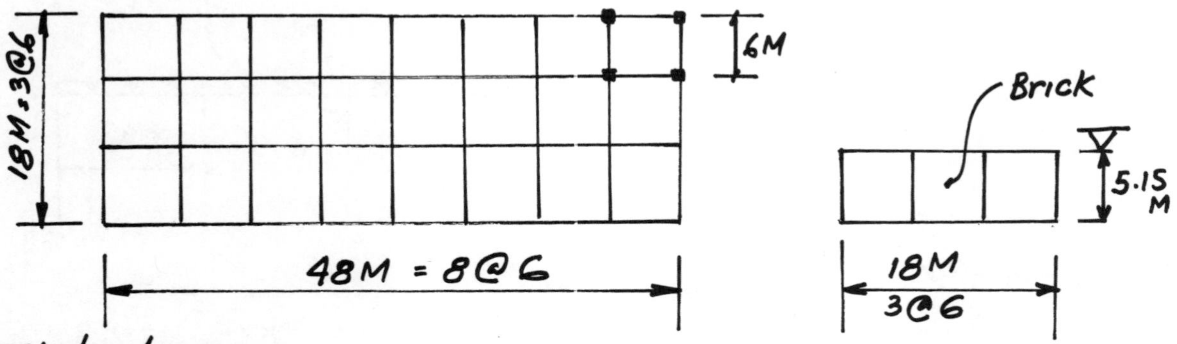

Slab design

Loading on roof

1, Tarrazo = 0.096 T/M²

2, Clay (0.15 × 1.8) = 0.270 "

3, Sand (0.05 × 1.57) = 0.079 "

4, Asphalt Board = 0.005 "

5, Styrofoam = 0.010 "

6, Sand + water proofing (0.01 × 1.51) = 0.016 "

7, Slab (0.15 × 2.4) = 0.360 "

0.836 T/M² Say 0.85 T/M²

Live Load = 0.15 T/M²

Total load = 1.00 T/M

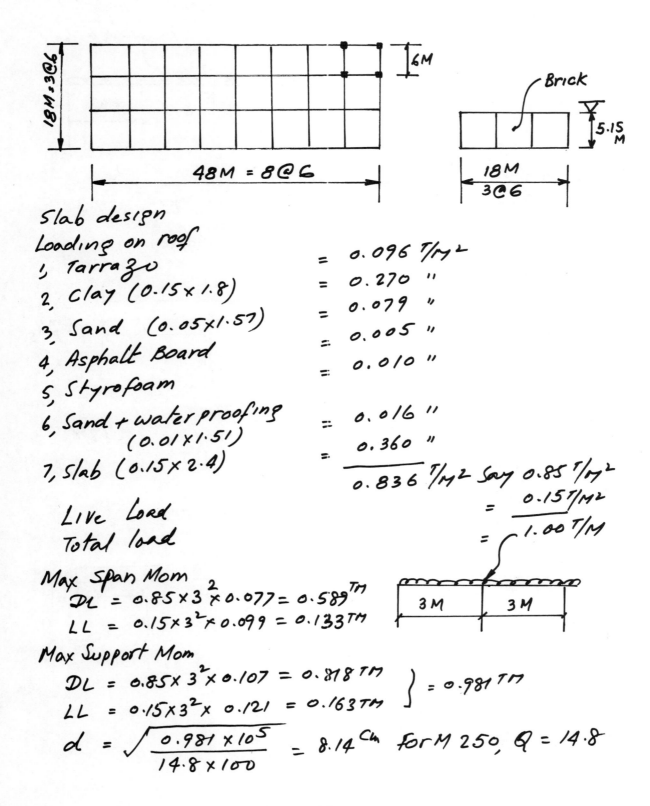

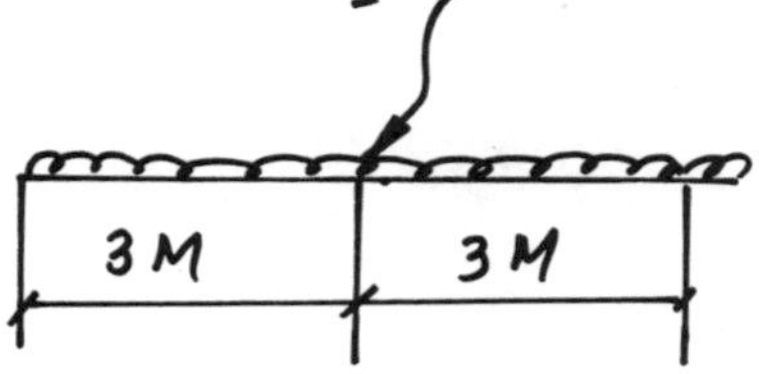

Max Span Mom

$DL = 0.85 \times 3^2 \times 0.077 = 0.589^{TM}$

$LL = 0.15 \times 3^2 \times 0.099 = 0.133^{TM}$

Max Support Mom

$DL = 0.85 \times 3^2 \times 0.107 = 0.818\ TM$

$LL = 0.15 \times 3^2 \times 0.121 = 0.163\ TM$

$\} = 0.981\ TM$

$d = \sqrt{\dfrac{0.981 \times 10^5}{14.8 \times 100}} = 8.14^{cm}$ for M 250, Q = 14.8

Projection = $0.1 \times 0.5 \times 2.4$ = 120

Water = $1 \times 0.45 \times 0.5$ = 225

585 kg/m = 0.58 T/M.

Total Load 0.90 T/M.

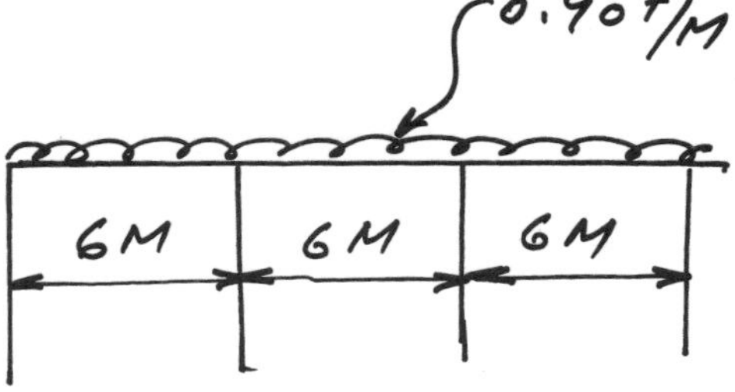

$$M_x = \frac{wl^2}{10} + \frac{Pl}{6}$$

$$= \frac{0.9 \times 6^2}{10} + \frac{10.1 \times 6}{6}$$

$$= 13.5\ TM$$

Load factor 1.85

$M_U = 1.85 \times 13.5 = 24.9\ TM$

$$A_{st} = \frac{1.81 \times 30 \times 46}{100} = 24.5^{\square''} \quad \text{for } K = \frac{24.9 \times 10^5}{30 \times 46^2} = 39.3$$

$\rho = 1.81$

use 7 - #25ϕ bars.

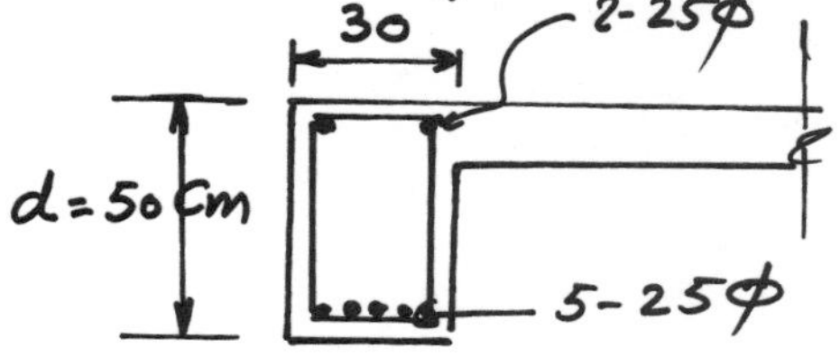

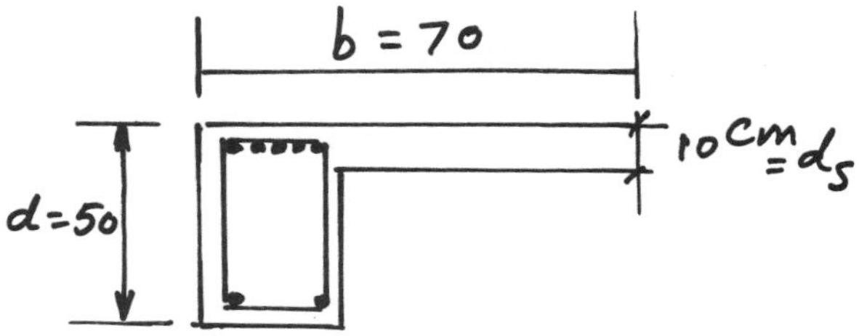

$b = 4ds + br$

$= 4 \times 10 + 30 = 70^{cm}$ $\quad f_{cb} = 85\ kg/cm^2, \ d_1 = 47^{cm}$

$$M_{rc} = \tfrac{1}{2}\left(d_1 - \tfrac{1}{3}d_s\right) f_{cb}\, b\, d_s$$

$$= \tfrac{1}{2}\left(47 - \tfrac{10}{3}\right) \times 85 \times 70 \times 10 = 13.5\ TM$$

Beam B_2 300×500

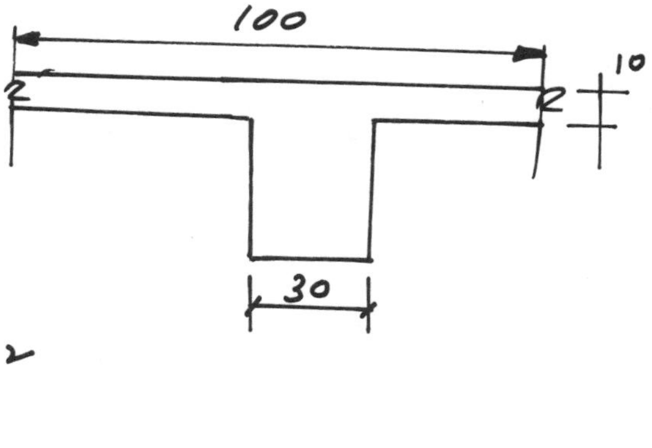

$$M_{rc} = \tfrac{1}{2}\left(47 - \tfrac{10}{3}\right) \times 85 \times 100 \times 10$$

$$= 18.5$$

$$A_t = \frac{21.5 \times 10^5}{1400 \times 0.89 \times 47} = 36.7\ cm^2$$

5 - 25ϕ = 24.54
5 - 20ϕ = 15.70 } 40.24 cm²

$$A_{st} = \frac{(21.5 - 18.5)\,10^5}{1000 \times 0.80 \times 44} = 6.7 \qquad 3\text{-}20\phi = 9.42$$

Use D = 120MM Thick.

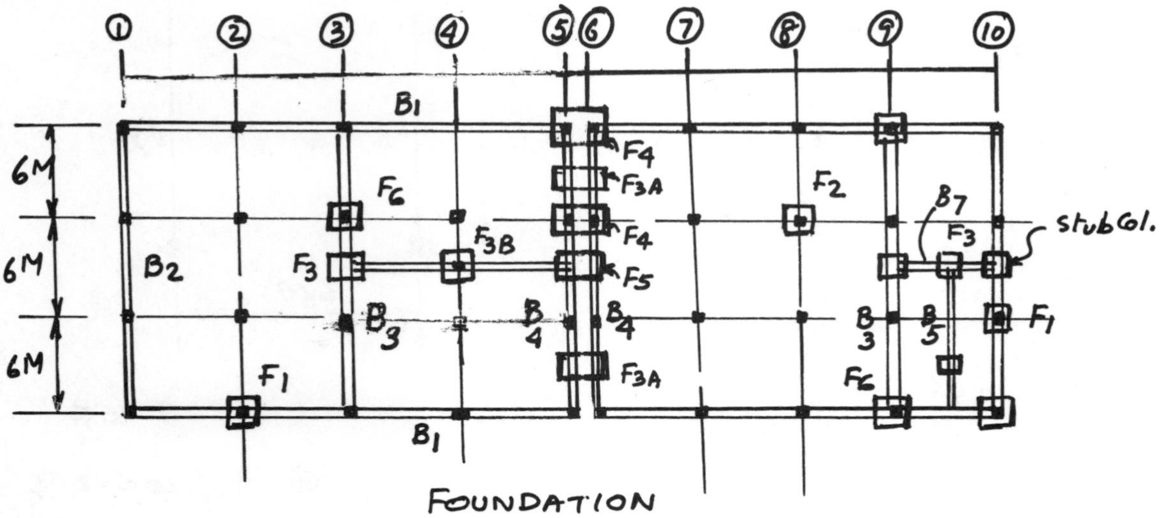

FOUNDATION

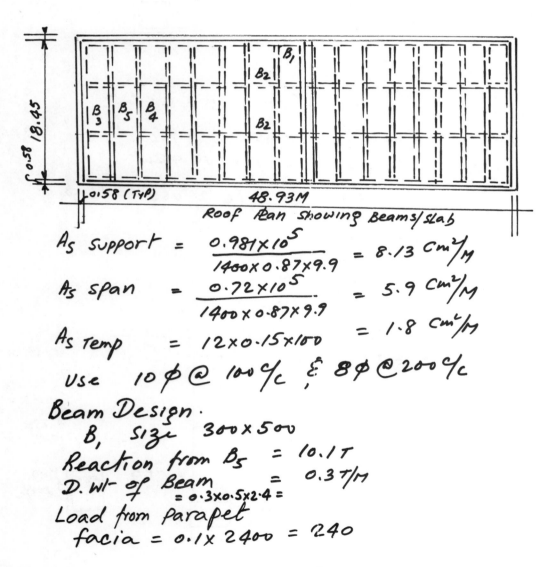

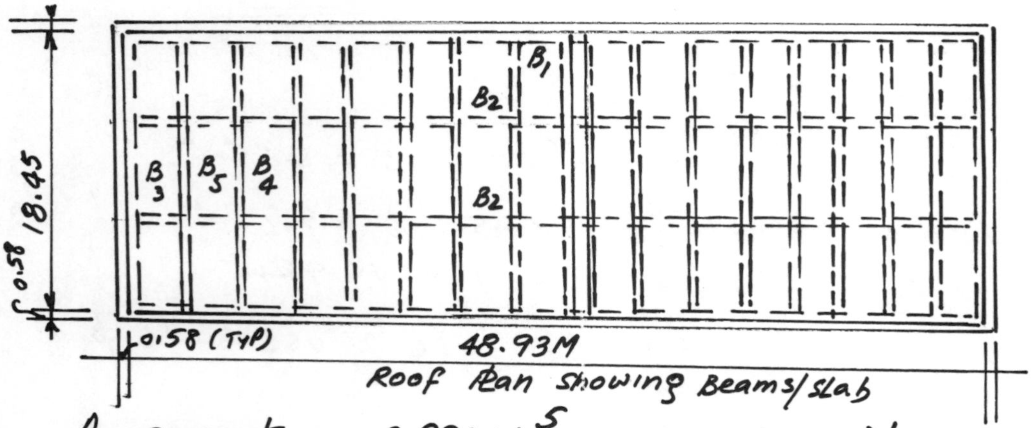

Roof Plan showing Beams/Slab

A_s support $= \dfrac{0.981 \times 10^5}{1400 \times 0.87 \times 9.9} = 8.13$ Cm²/M

A_s span $= \dfrac{0.72 \times 10^5}{1400 \times 0.87 \times 9.9} = 5.9$ Cm²/M

A_s Temp $= 12 \times 0.15 \times 100 = 1.8$ Cm²/M

Use 10 φ @ 100 c/c & 8 φ @ 200 c/c

Beam Design.

B_1 Size 300 x 500

Reaction from B_5 = 10.1 T

D. wt of Beam = 0.3 T/M
= 0.3x0.5x2.4 =

Load from parapet

facia = 0.1 x 2400 = 240

Load on col. 'P'

from beam B_2 = 11.21 t

Self wt Bm B_3

0.37×6 = 2.22 T

Gutter 0.585×6 = 3.48 T

Bk. wall 0.25×6×5.25×2 = 15.75 T

S.wt of plinth Beam

0.25×0.55×6×2.4 = 1.48 T

Swt of col

= 0.45×0.45×5.15×2.4 = 3.50 T

38.14 T Say 39 T

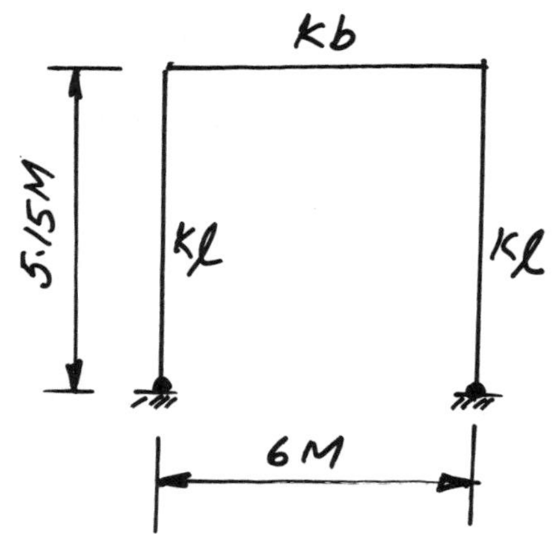

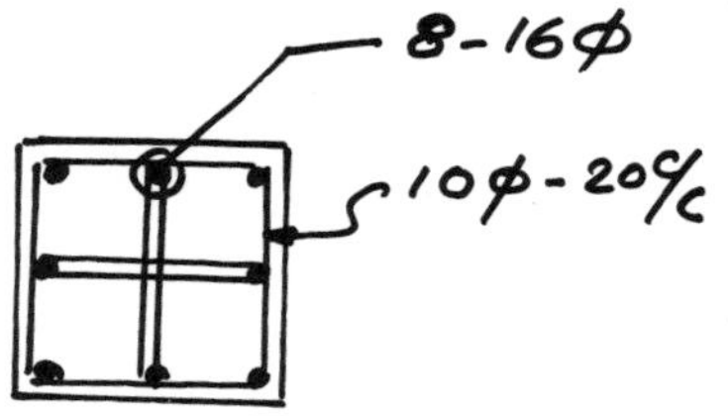

$$\frac{1.85P}{\sigma_{cu} bd} = \frac{1.85 \times 39 \times 10^3}{250 \times 45 \times 45} = 0.14$$

$$M = 250$$

$$\frac{1.85M}{\sigma_{cu} bd^2} = \frac{1.85 \times 9.6 \times 10^5}{250 \times 45 \times 45^2} = 0.07$$

$A_{sc} = A_{st} = 0.375 \times 0.3 \times 250 \times 10^{-4} \times 45 \times 45 = 5.6\ Cm^2$

$A_{s_m} = 0.25 \times 0.3 \times 250 \times 10^{-4} \times 45 \times 45 = 3.7\ Cm^2$

$A_{sc} + A_{st} + A_{sm} = 5.6 + 5.6 + 3.7 = 14.9\ Cm^2$

$A_{s_{min}} = 0.8\% = \frac{0.8 \times 45 \times 45}{100} = 16.2$ use 8-16φ

Plinth Beam for 6.0M span.

Bk wall = 0.25×4.85×2 = 2.4 T/M

Swt of BM = 0.37×0.55×2.4 = 0.5 T/M

2.9 T/M

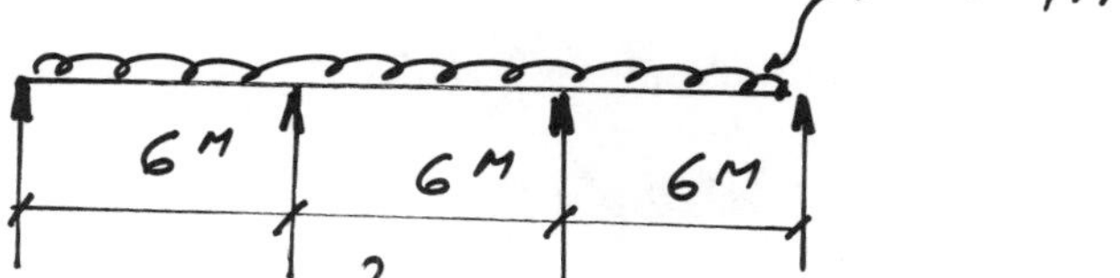

$$M_x = \frac{2.9 \times 6^2}{10} = 10.4\ TM$$

$V = 2.9 \times 3 = 8.7T$

$$A_t = \frac{10.4 \times 10^5}{1400 \times 0.89 \times 50} = 16.6$$

Use 4-25φ = 19.63 Cm^2

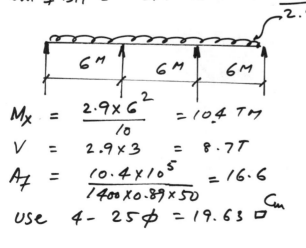

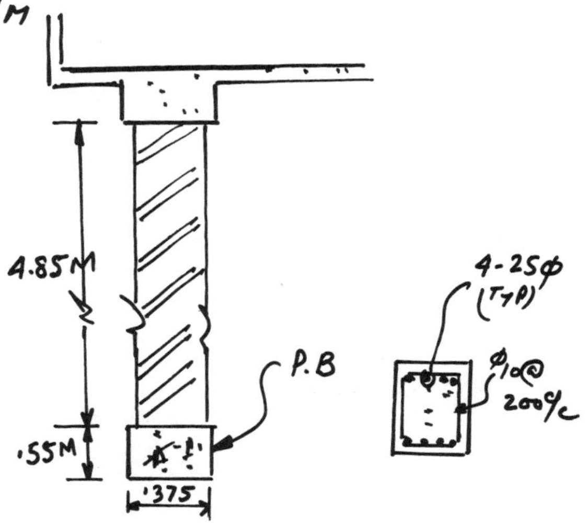

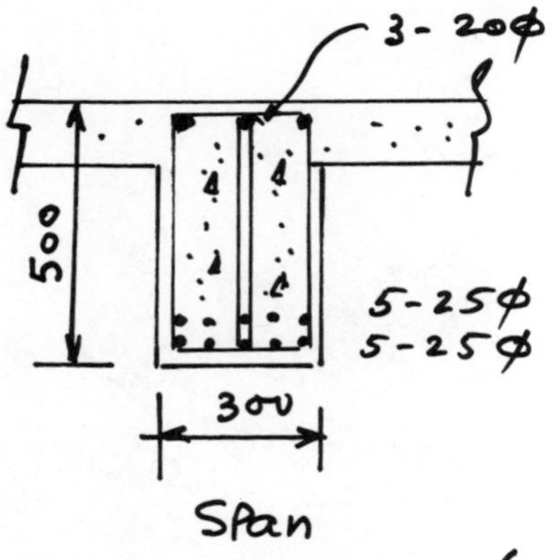

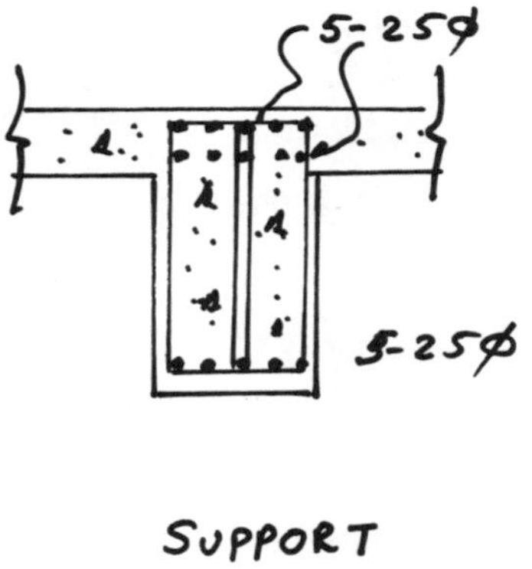

Shear stress $= \dfrac{(10.1+1.11)10^3}{30 \times 0.89 \times 47} = 8.9\ kg/cm^2 > 8\ kgm/cm^2$

Provide shear reinforcement

$$A_s = \frac{11.2 \times 10^3 \times 10}{1400 \times 0.89 \times 47} = 1.9\ cm^2$$

Use 8 φ - four legged @ 100 MM c/c

Beam B5 (300×500)

D.L 1) Load from slab $= 0.85 \times 3 = 2.55$ T/M

2) S/wt of Beam $= 0.3 \times 0.5 \times 2.4 = 0.30$ T/M

L.L 3) Load from slab $= 0.15 \times 3 = 0.45$ T/M

3.3 T/M

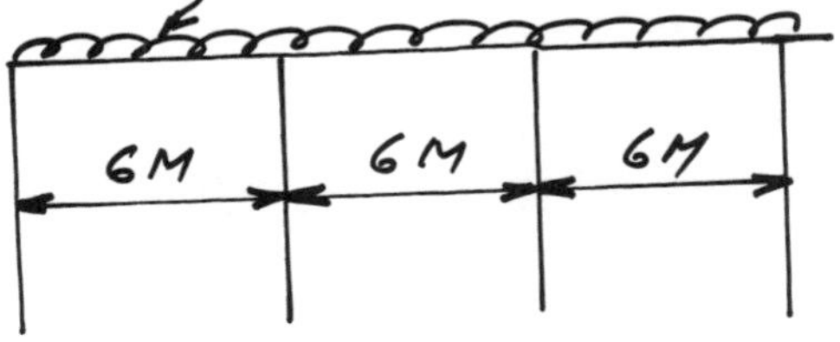

$M_x = \dfrac{wl^2}{10} = \dfrac{3.3 \times 36}{10} = 12.1$ TM

$M_U = 1.85 \times 12.1 = 22.4$ TM

$K = \dfrac{22.4 \times 10^5}{30 \times 46^2} = 35.2$

$A_{st} = \dfrac{1.6 \times 30 \times 46}{100} = 22.0$

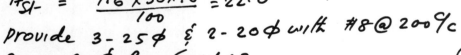

Provide 3-25φ & 2-20φ with #8@200 c/c

Beam B_3 & B_4 SIMILAR

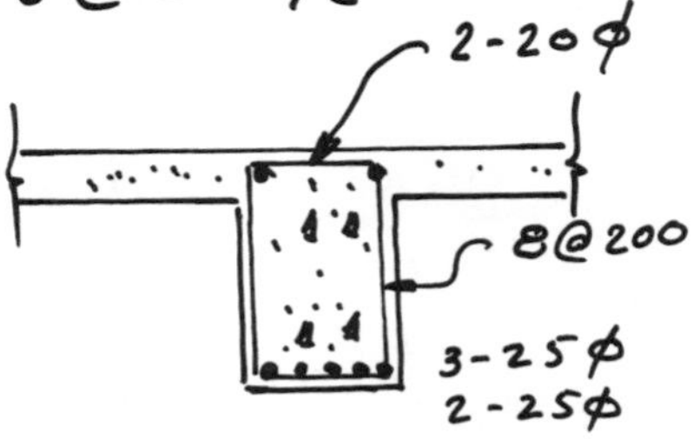

Column design "P"

$M = Me \dfrac{K_l}{K_l + K_b} = 21.5 \times \dfrac{0.00045}{0.00045 + 0.005} = 9.6$ TM

as $Me = 21.5$ TM ; $K_l = \dfrac{0.45 \times 0.45^3}{12 \times 5.15} = 0.00045$

$K_b = \dfrac{0.3 \times 0.5^3}{12 \times 6} = 0.0005$

$$u = \frac{8.19\times10^3}{37.5\times0.89\times50} = 4.9 > 7\ kg/cm^2$$

Provide nominal shear reinforcement.

stub Col. P, load $= 2.73\times6 = 16.4T$

size 25×25

$$\text{Stresses} = \frac{16.4\times10^3}{25\times25} = 26.2 < 50\ kg/cm^2 \text{ ok}$$

$$\text{Min Reinforcement } 0.8\% = \frac{0.8\times25\times25}{100} = 5.00\ cm^2$$

provide 4 - 16 φ $= 8.04\ cm^2$

Tie 10 φ @ 200 c/c

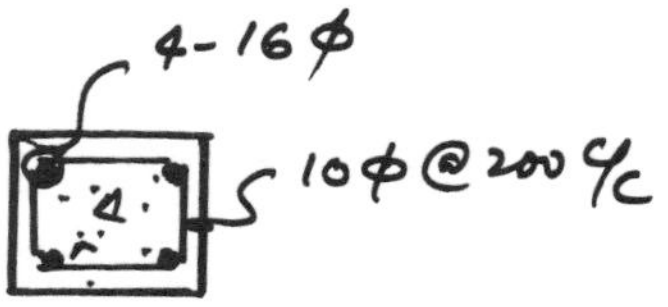

Foundation design

F3, F3A, F3B

Load transfer by Plinth Beam $= 16.4\ T$

S.wt of Column $= 0.25\times0.25\times7.25\times2.4 = 1.08$ +

$17.48T$

S wt of Foundation $1.6\times1.6\times0.2\times2.4 = 1.2T$

S.wt of Backfill $(1.8\times1.8 - 0.25\times0.25)\times1.8\times0.6 = 3.4T$

$22.1T$

Soil bearing Pressure $= 6.6\ T/M^2$

$$A = \frac{22.1}{6.6} = 3.2\ \square M$$

size Provided $= 1.8\times1.8$

$$M_x = \frac{5.4\times0.77^2}{2} = 1.6\ TM$$

$$V = 5.4\times0.77 = 4.15$$

$$d_{eff} = \sqrt{\frac{1.6\times10^5}{12\times100}} = 11.5$$

where $Q = 12\ kg/cm^2$ for M200

Use $D = 30\ cm$

$$A_{st} = \frac{1.6\times10^5}{1400\times0.89\times25} = 5.1\ cm^2$$

use 12 φ @ 14 cm c/c $= 8.08\ cm^2$

$$U = \frac{S}{Jd\,\Sigma o} = \frac{4.15\times10^3}{0.89\times25\times45.2} = 4.2 < 8\ kg/cm^2$$

ok.

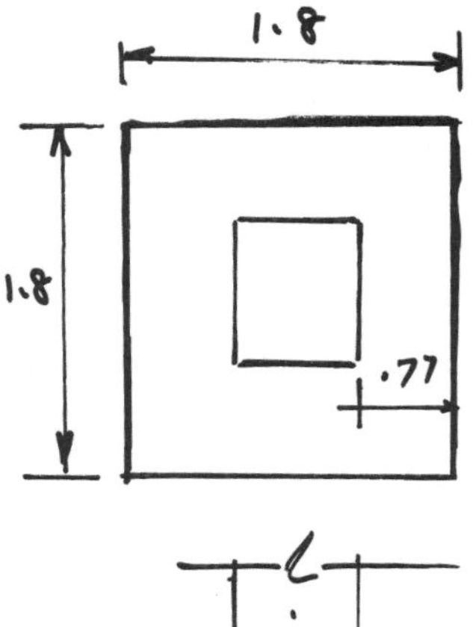

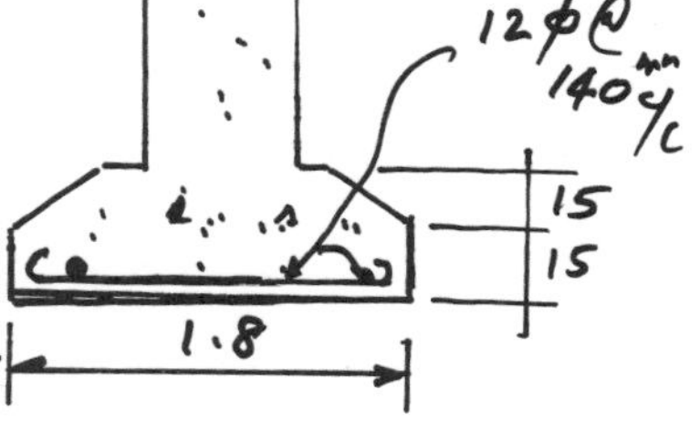

F_1 - Ext. Col

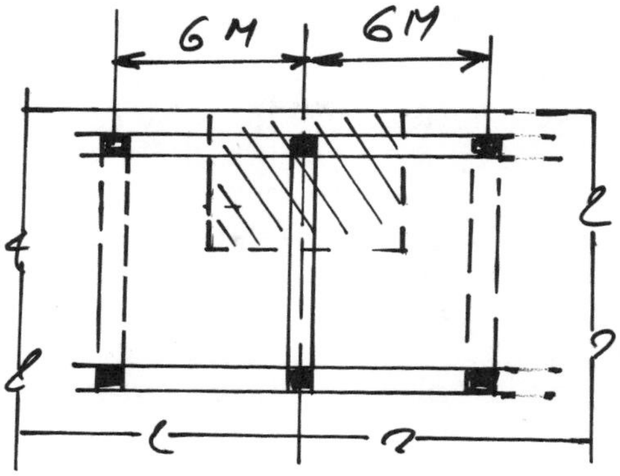

Load:- DL slab

$= 0.85 \times 3 \times 6 = 15.3T$

Beam $= 0.85 \times .45 \times 2.4 \times 9 = 3.4T$

$PPT = 0.36 \times 6 = 2.1T$

$BK = 2 \times .25 \times 6 \times 5.25 = 5.75T$

$R.Bm = 0.25 \times .55 \times 6 \times 2.4 = 1.98T$

Swt Col

$0.45 \times 0.45 \times 7.5 \times 2.4 = 3.60T$

$42.13T$

$L.L = 0.15 \times 3 \times 6 = 2.70$

$44.83T$ Say 45T

S.wt of footing $3.2 \times 3.2 \times .4 \times 2.4 = 9.8T$

Backfill $(3.2 \times 3.2 - .45 \times .45) \times 1.8 \times 0.6 = 10.8T$

66.4

$A = \dfrac{66.4}{6.6}$ say $10.0 \square^M$

size 3.2×3.2 M.

Repeat Cal. as for foundation F3. Use $D = 40^{Cm}$

& $A_{st} = 16\phi - 14$ cm c/c.

Design of Gutter.

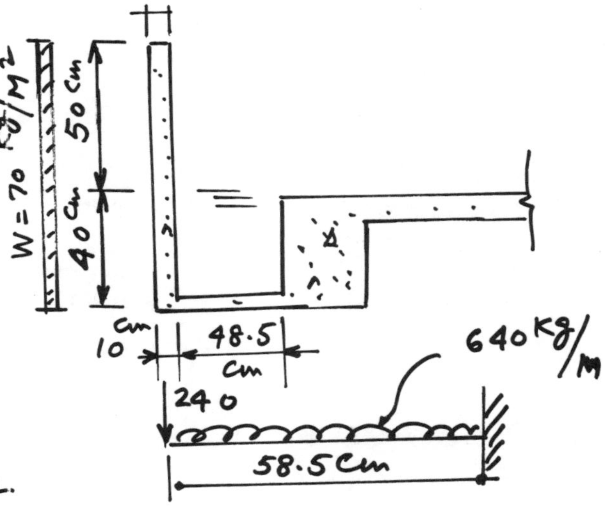

WT of water $= 1000 \times .4 = 400$

WT of Slab $= 0.1 \times 24 = 240$

$640^{kg}/M$

WT of vert. Wind

$= 0.1 \times 1 \times 2400 = 240$

$$M_x = 0.24 \times 0.58 + \frac{0.64 \times 0.58^2}{2}$$

$= 0.24 \ T/M$

$$d = \sqrt{\frac{0.24 \times 10^5}{25 \times 100}} = 3.09 \text{ Cm}$$

Use $D = 10$ Cm, $d = 8$

$$A_s = \frac{0.24 \times 10^5}{1400 \times 0.89 \times 8} = 2.4 \text{ Cm}^2.$$

Use 8ϕ @ 8 Cm c/c

$$A_{stemp} = \frac{0.15 \times 10 \times 100}{100} = 1.5$$ use 8ϕ @ 200 c/c

$A_{s\,vertical} = 8\phi$ @ 80 mm c/c for $M = \dfrac{70 \times 1^2}{2} = 35$ Kg/M.

FOUNDATION FOR INDUSTRIAL SHEDS

Foundation for large industrial sheds are normally subjected to very high moments and small direct loads. The moments may be due to wind, earthquake or crane loads. The magnitude of the moment mostly governs the size of the foundation, the design criteria being zero upthrust at the foundation edge. With this criteria even in good soils, the foundation sizes and costs are very high. Substantial reduction in cost can be achieved if an economical way is found to anchor these foundations. For foundation on rock, rock anchors can be used. More difficult problems are posed by foundations on soil. Since the direction of moments in general is reversible, ordinary soil anchors will not be suitable. A foundation which can withstand high tension/compression is an ideal solution.

EXAMPLE 5-03

Given:- Design a foundation for an industrial shed for the following data:

Vertical Load = 20T
Moment due to Wind = + 7500 TCm
Horizontal Shear = 10T
Permissible Bearing Capacity of Soil = 10T/M²
Permissible Increase in Bearing when Wind is acting = 33%.
Size of Pedestal = 75 Cm x 6 Cm.

All forces acting at top of the Pedestal.

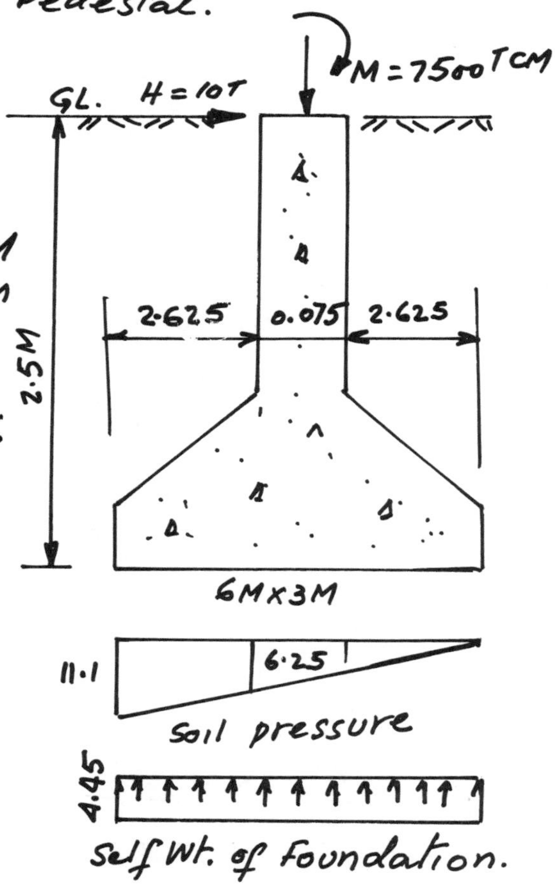

Load Vert = 20T
WT. FDN = 20T
WT. Soil $6\times3\times2\times1.65$ = 60T

Total = 100T

Mom. @ top of Pedestal = 7500 TCM
Mom. due to horiz.l F = 2500 TCM
Total moment = 10000 TCm

Intensity of Soil Pressure $= \frac{100}{6\times3} \pm \frac{10000\times6}{100\times3\times6\times6}$

$= 5.55 \pm 5.55$

$= 11.10$ or $0\ T/M^2$

B.M @ the face of Pedestal

$= 3(6.25-4.45)\frac{2.625^2}{2} + 3\left(\frac{11.1-6.25}{2}\right)\times 2.625^2\times\frac{2}{3}$

$= 52$ T.M.

$d_{eff} = \sqrt{\frac{5200000}{6\times8.7\times1.33}} = 87$ Cm

Use D = 95 Cm.

Design with under reamed pile
Let thickness of pile cap = 60 cm
depth of pile cap bott. = 70 cm below grade.

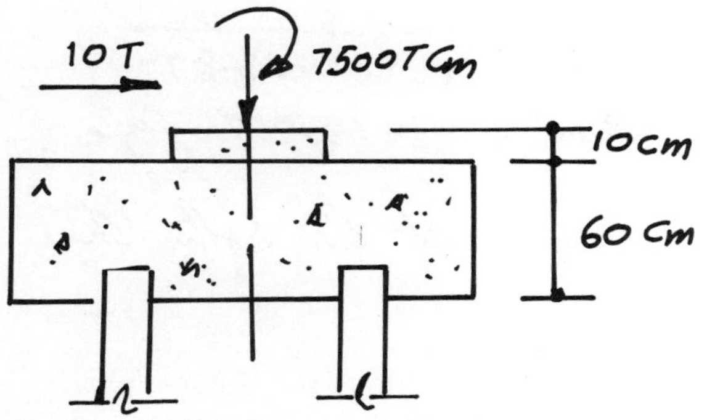

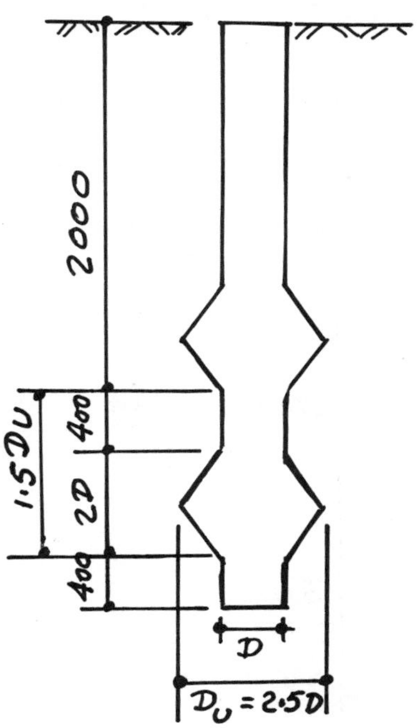

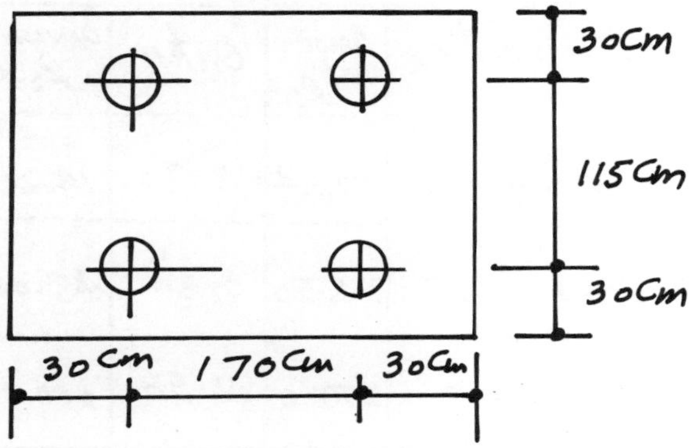

Load Vertical = 20T
Self Wt. of pile cap = 6T
Total load 26T.

Moment:-
@ top of pedestal = 7500 TCm
due to horiz. shear force = 700 TCm
Total = 8200 TCm.

Reaction on pile $= \frac{26}{4} \pm \frac{8200}{2 \times 1.70} = 30.6T;\ -17.6T.$

Provide 30 Cm ϕ × 4.5 M Long - double under reamed pile.

Capacity:- $24.0 + \frac{1}{0.3} \times 1.25 = 28.2T$

Reduction due to close spacing 10% = − 2.82

net capacity = 25.38 T

Due to wind = 25.4 × 1.33 = 33.8 T Safe

upthrust capacity = $12 + \frac{1}{0.3} \times 1.0$ = 15.3 T

close spacing reduction 10% = 1.5

∴ capacity due to wind 13.8 T

= 13.8 × 1.33 = 18.3 T Safe.

Cost Comparison:-

The consumption of materials & cost per both the scheme are give in table.

Item No	Description	Unit	Est. rate in Rs	Scheme #1		Scheme #2	
				Qtty	Amount Rs*	Qtty	amount Rs*
1	Excavation	M^3	6.0	46.4	278.4	3.20	19.20
2	Lean. Concrete	M^3	150.0	1.35	202.50	0.30	45.00
3	Conc. in foundation including shuttering	M^3	240.0	10.70	2568.0	2.50	600.00
4	Reinforced Ribbed Tor steel	Tonn's	1800.0	0.3	540.0	0.13	234.0
5	30 CM φ × 4.5 LG Double Reamed Pile	NO	300.0	-	-	4	1200.0
	Total		3586	-	-	-	2098.2

* 1 Rs = $ 0.1217

Percentage saving = $\frac{3586 - 2098.2}{3586} \times 100 = 41.45\%$.

Conclusions:-

In a factory building where overturning moments are high, under reamed piles are found to be definitely economical.

CRANE COLUMN AND GIRDER

In all structures carrying cranes over 5 tons capacity, roof truss splices and connection of truss to columns, column splices column bracing, knee braces and crane supports are needed. High strength bolts or welds may be used.

Crane Girder Connection
Crane girder supports must be capable of resisting static and dynamic horizontal and vertical forces and stress reversal. Hence a heavily loaded crane girder (for 75 ton capacity or more) is supported on columns carrying no other load, wheras less heavily loaded crane girders are supported on building columns which usually extend above the girder to carry the roof.
Since the crane moves along the girder and induces severe stress and deformation at the connections of the crane girder to column the crane girder should not be connected directly to the column, as end rotations, expansion and contraction of the girder could cause failure of connection.
Hence vertical supports should be provided by a seat and horizontal support by flexible connection.
Whether seated on building columns or seperate columns, crane girders usually are braced laterally at the supports against the building columns.

EXAMPLE 5-04
Given:- Design a crane girder and column to house overhead crane of 5 tons capacity for Ches. Elizabeth Sewage treatment plant additions in Williamsburg, Virginia.

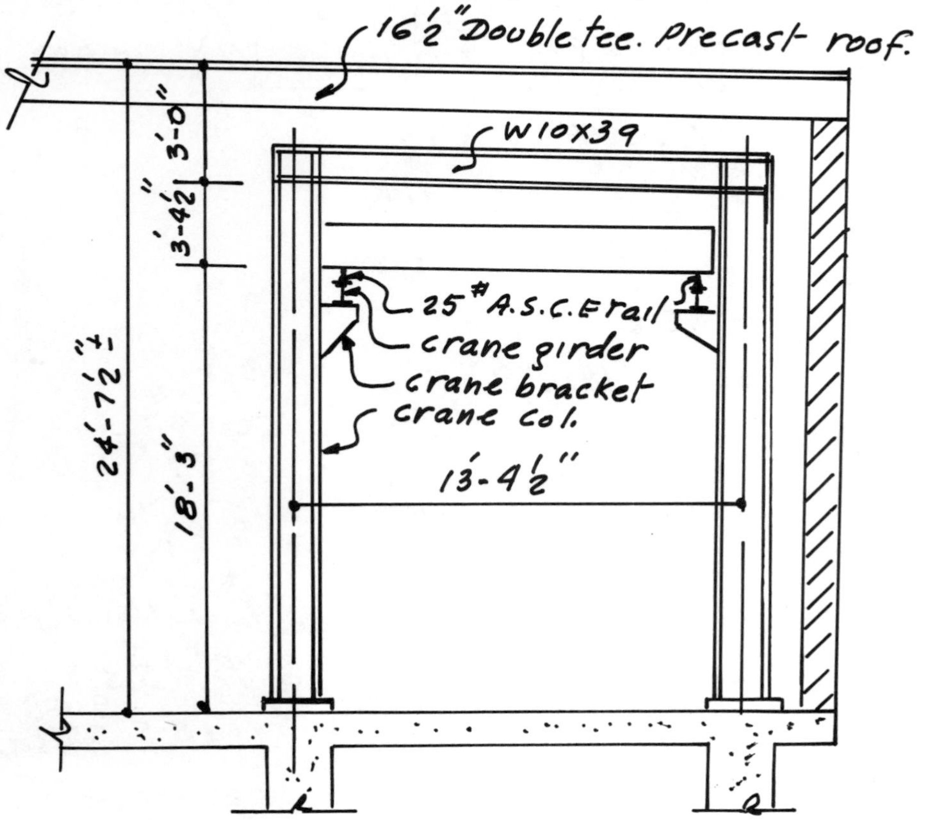

Let us assume that trolley can be no closer to runway than 1'-0". The loads are positioned for max. moment at the center of the girder than absolute.

Max. moment.

The wt. of 25# Rail to be added to the est. wt. of girder.

Distance between columns $= \frac{1}{2}(37'\text{-}0" + 1'\text{-}3") = 19.125'$

span to be considered $= 19.125 - 1.0 = 18.125'$

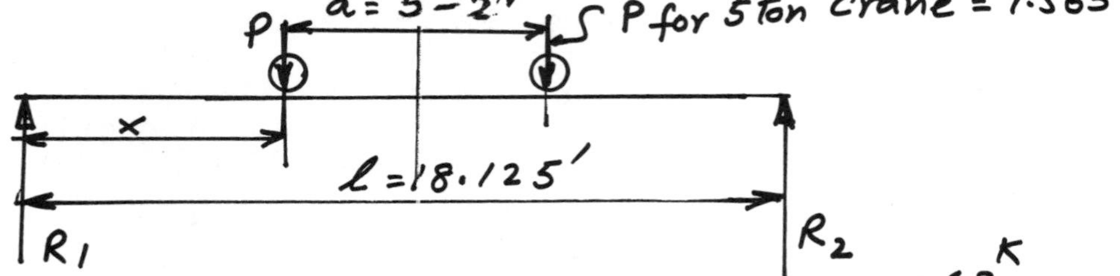

For two moving loads of 5 Ton crane $P = 7.563^K$

The location of two moving loads from structural mechanic by Ketchum.

check if $a < 0.586\,l = 10.62 > 5'\text{-}2"$

Max shear, $X = 0$ @ R_1

$$V_{max} = P + P\frac{l-a}{l}$$
$$= 7.563 + 7.563\left(\frac{18.125 - 5.167}{18.125}\right) = 12.983$$

$$\text{Max } M \text{ @ } x = \frac{1}{2}\left(l - \frac{a}{2}\right) = 7.77$$

$$\text{Max } M = \frac{P}{2l}\left(l - \frac{a}{2}\right)^2 = 50.41'^K$$

V_{max} due to own wt. of Runway beam

$$V_{max} = \frac{5}{8} \times 0.052 \times 18.125 = 0.59^K$$

$$M_{max} = 0.052 \times \frac{18.125^2}{8} = 2.13'^K$$

$$\therefore \text{Total vert. } M_{max} = 2.13 + 50.41 = 52.54'^K$$

$$V_{max} = 12.98 + 0.59 = 13.57^K$$

$$\text{Horizontal } M_{y\,max} = 2 \times 1.42 \times \frac{7.77^2}{18.125} = 9.48'^K$$

Trial section can be found out by Gaylord Handbook when $F_{bx} = F_{by} = F_b = 22$ for A_{36} & $B = 5.5$

$$S_x = \frac{M_x}{F_b}\left(1 + B\frac{M_y}{M_x}\right) = \frac{52.54}{22}\left(1 + 5.5\,\frac{9.48}{52.54}\right)$$
$$= 57.20\ IN^3$$

Try W 12X50, $r_z = 2.19$ in

$$\frac{L}{r_z} = \frac{18.125 \times 12}{2.19} = 99.10 < 119\sqrt{1.75} = 157.41$$

Formula 1.5.6(a) A.I.S.C 7th Edition

$$F_b = 24 - \frac{\left(\frac{L}{r_T}\right)^2}{1181\, C_b} = 24 - \frac{(99.10)^2}{1181 \times 1.75} = 19.24\ \text{ksi}$$

Top flange stress

$$\text{Vert. Load} = \frac{52.54 \times 12}{64.7} = 9.76\ \text{ksi}$$

$$\text{Lateral load} = \frac{9.48 \times 12}{14} = \frac{8.12\ \text{ksi}}{17.88\ \text{ksi}} < 19.24\ \text{OK}$$

Check shear

Vert. Load $F_v = 0.4 \times 36 = 14.4$ ksi

$$f_v = \frac{V}{A_w} = \frac{13.57}{10.908 \times .371} = 3.35 < 14.4\ \text{OK}$$

LAT. Load

$$V = 1.42\left(1 + \frac{12.96}{18.125}\right) = 2.43$$

$$A_w = 8.077 \times 0.641 + 6.454 \times .371 = 7.195$$

$$f_v = \frac{2.43}{7.195} = 0.382 < 14.4\ \text{OK}$$

Use W 12X50 ←

Design of Crane Column

Bent 19.125′ c/c

Wt 5 Ton Crane Trolley = 4200#

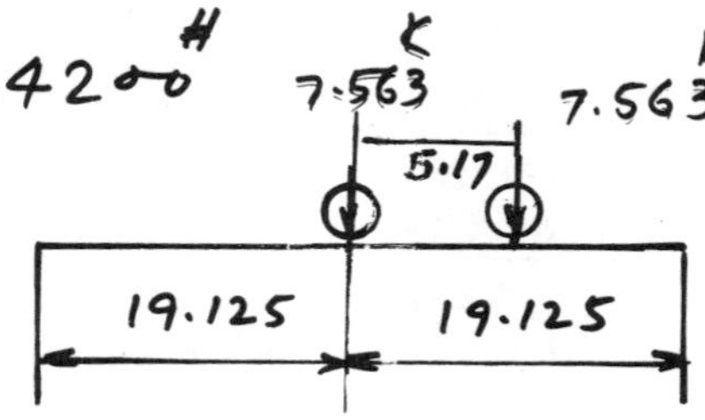

Crane load on column

$$= 7.563 + 7.563 \times \frac{13.96}{19.13}$$

$$= 13.08\text{k}$$

Girder + Rail = 0.07×19.125

$= 1.34$k

Total load on col. = $13.08 + 1.34 = 14.42^k$

Lateral force = $0.20\,(10 + 4.2) \times \frac{1}{2} = 1.5^k$

$M_o = 14.42 \times 1.0 = 14.42'^k$

$$R_1 = -\frac{6\,Pe\,a \times b}{\ell^3} = \frac{-6 \times 14.42 \times 1 \times 18.25 \times 3.38}{(21.63)^3} = -0.522$$

$$M_1 = \frac{Peb(2a-b)}{\ell^2} = \frac{14.42 \times 1 \times 3.38\,(36.5 - 3.38)}{(21.63)^2} = 3.43$$

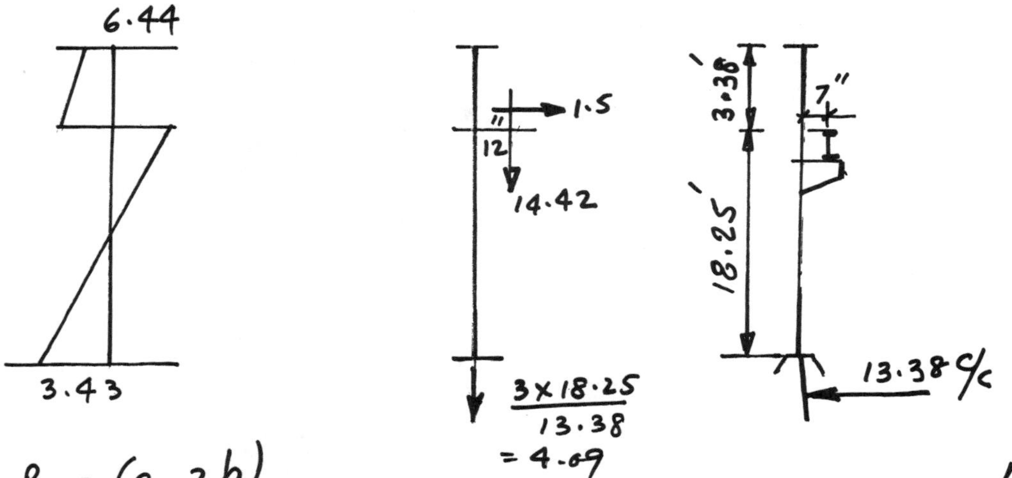

$$M_2 = \frac{Pea(a-2b)}{L^2}$$

$= 6.40'^{k}$

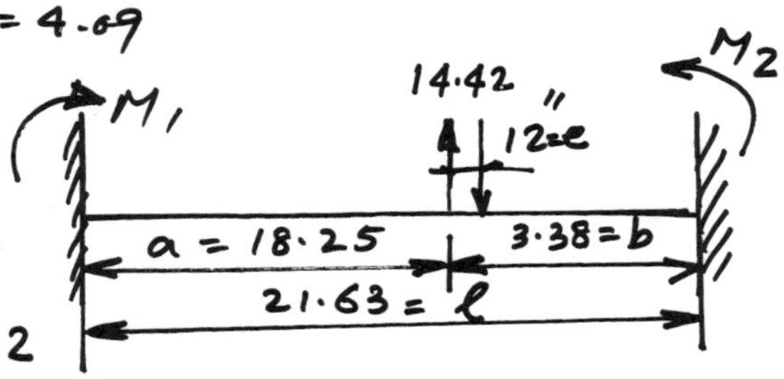

$M_+ = R_1 a + M_1 + M_0$

$= -0.522 \times 18.25 + 3.43 + 14.42$

$= +8.33'^{k}$

Since the frame is inside enclosed building, no wind is to be considered.

	Vert.	M_x	M_y
Crane	14.42	8.33'k	$0.10\ \frac{10+4.2}{15.12}\left[\frac{15.12\times 17.84^2}{38.25}\right] = 11.81$
lat. force	−4.09	–	
	10.33	8.33'k	11.81'k

Use A36 Steel. & try W10×39

$f_a = \frac{10.33}{11.5} = 0.90;\ \frac{L}{r} = \frac{18.25\times 12}{2.19} = 100 \therefore F_a = 12.98^{ksi}$

$f_{bx} = \frac{8.33\times 12}{42.2} = 2.38\ ksi;\ f_{by} = \frac{11.81\times 12}{11.2} = 12.65\ ksi$

$\frac{f_a}{F_a} + \frac{f_{bx}}{F_{bx}} + \frac{f_{by}}{F_{by}} = \frac{0.90}{12.98} + \frac{2.38}{22} + \frac{12.65}{22} = 0.752 < 1$

Hence use column W10×39

Design of top member of Rigid frame.

Since the frame is to be erected on the existing slab, hence it is safe to consider symmetrical two hinged rectangular frame with load on Bracket on one leg of col.

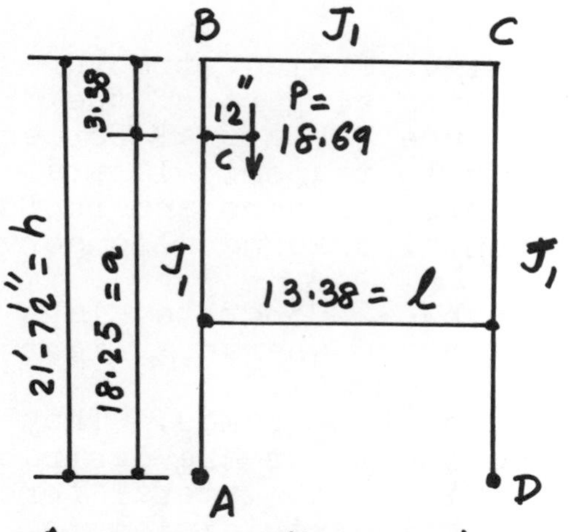

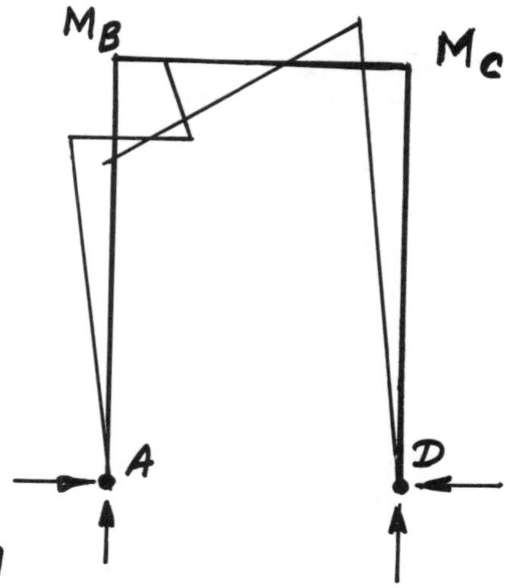

Assume all members W10x39

$\alpha = \frac{a}{h} = \frac{18.25}{21.62} = 0.844$

$k = \frac{h}{l} = \frac{21.62}{13.38} = 1.62$

$N = 2k+3 = 6.24$

$M_{B,C} = \frac{Pc}{2}\left[\frac{(3\alpha^2-1)k}{N} \pm 1\right] \therefore M_B = 19.38^{'K}$ & $M_C = -5.07^{'K}$

Use $F_b = 22$ ksi, S_x of W10x39 = 42.2 in³; $I_x = 210$ in⁴

$\therefore f_b = \frac{19.38 \times 12}{42.2} = 5.51 < 22$ ok

Use W10x39 as top member also.

Design of column Bracket.

¾"φ A 325 bolt, connection to be friction type, 2 vert. Ls 3½x3½ x 5/16"

$M_z = Pe_x = 14.42 \times 7 = 101''^K$

$T = R = F_t A = 40 \times 0.4418 = 17.67^K$

$\eta = \sqrt{\frac{6M}{pmR}} = \sqrt{\frac{6 \times 101}{2 \times 3 \times 17.67}} = 2.39$

Try 4 in each row

$\Sigma y^2 = 4(1.5^2 + 4.5^2) = 90 \text{ in}^4$

$T_m = \frac{6M}{\Sigma y^2} = \frac{6 \times 101}{90} = 6.74 < 17.67$ ok

Bolt Shear $= \frac{40}{8 \times 0.4418}$

$= 11.32 < F_v = 15$ ok.

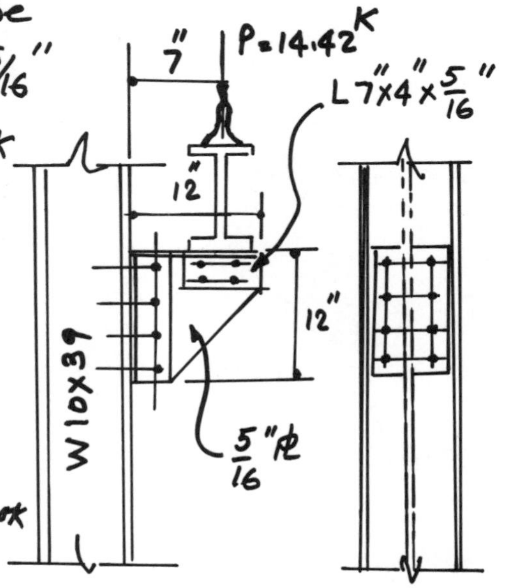

DIAPHRAGM AND BRACING

Though some sort of diaphragms used in steel framed structures are not composed of steel, they are an integral part of the building and play a basic role in resistance to lateral forces. The function of a horizontal diaphragm is to transmit lateral forces to vertical shear resisting elements. Floors and roofs usually perform this function but horizontal bracing also serves the purpose.
Two types of diaphragms - rigid and flexible: Concrete slabs with or without metal deck are rigid diaphragm wheras a light metal deck may be treated as a flexible diaphragm.
Rigid diaphragms impose equal deflection on all frames. They also distribute torsional shears. These functions are desirable in tall buildings where forces are apportioned to lateral force resisting element proportion to their relative rigidities.
In low buildings with masonary walls, the horizontal diaphragm equalizes the deflection.
The dashed line shows the shape of the exterior of the building subjected to lateral forces.

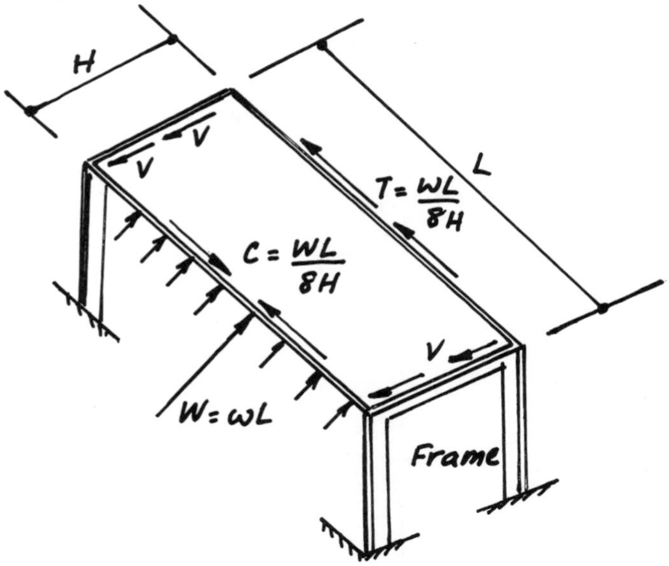

Simple diaphragm spanning between two frames.

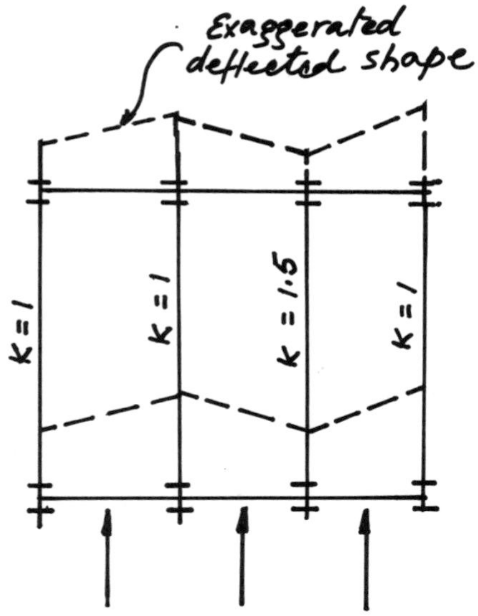

Lateral load

C = T = Chord Tension/Compression kips
W = Lateral Loads kips on diaphragm
L = Span ft. of diaphragm
H = Distance between ft. between chords

Openings in diaphragm may require special consideration depending upon their location and extent. One should evaluate all openings for their effects on diaphragm action.

6

BRIDGES

Today's bridge design is quite complex. The number of factors that influence decisions have increased and the relative importance of these factors is in a continuous state of flux. Conceptual thinking demands a great deal more ingenuity on the part of the bridge engineer in terms of conserving time and work while determining the best answer for a given bridge problem. Modern design criteria must be used with a complete awareness of the basis of determination of the need or of the criteria.

Criteria for Bridge Design
Design of bridge is controlled by the design criteria established by the agency for whom the bridges are to be contracted. These criteria are usually the same as the standard specifications published by the American Association of State Highway Officials (A.A.S.H.O.) or by the American Railway Engineering Association (A.R.E.A.).
In addition to the above, the designer should use his best engineering judgement in the selection of proper design criteria. The main requirements that a bridge must satisfy, may be classified as those of traffic service, economy, and esthetics.

RATING OF HIGHWAY AND RAILWAY BRIDGES

What is it, Why it is done, How to do it
It is a procedure of bridge inspection maintenance and rating throughout the country. It is also done to bring light to the fact that aside from the properly trained and experienced bridge engineer there are many people who do not have a clear concept

of the need and purpose of rating structures or why it differs from the design of structures.

In the process of design the criteria used are intended to produce a structure that will safely carry the specified loading for a period of years. By a judicious selection of loading and design criteria, making use of the latest technological advances in the development of material and process, the designer can safely produce a structure that will have a long useful service life. Generally speaking, there will be a little need to rate the resultant structure until such time as the designer loadings are naturally changed or the structure has been damaged or reduced by corrosion.

RATING

The term rating has been used by the bridge engineer for many years, another term, structural efficiency may be used to discuss the investigation required to determine the ability of the bridge to carry desired loadings. Thus actually the engineer is in effect testing a structure designed and built in accordance with the loading at the time of its construction to determine its performance under the heavier loading conditions which are now in effect. As the term structural efficiency implies, it is a decisive trial, a critical examination of how the material and structure react under specific conditions of given design. Highway bridges, building have high proportion of the total stress attributed to the dead load as compared to railroad bridges. Also the impact factor for highway bridges and buildings is a fixed percentage, wheras, the impact factor for railroad bridges is directly related to the speed of the locomotive passing over the structure. These loads in excess of design live loads can be carried at reduced speeds.

Under the current AREA Specifications, a new steel bridge would be designed to a Cooper E80 live load. So long as the design loads are not increased, it would not be necessary to rate the bridge. Similarly highway bridge design loads prior to World War I were H_{12}, H_{15}, and H_{20}, whereas, now design loads of trucks with trailers are $H_{12\text{-}44}$, $H_{15\text{-}44}$, HS 15-44 and HS 20-44.

Hence, it is necessary to rate the old existing bridges.

All the requirements for impact, fatigue and safety factors have to include for revision of load. In fact, if these bridges were continued in service for 60-70 years and were properly maintained, it could be fully adequate for carrying the design loading throughout their entire life.

WHY RATING IS NECESSARY

It is observed that approximately 85% of existing bridges (Highway and Railroad) have been in service over 35-40 years including many which have been in service for over 60 years. These bridges were designed using various live loads and impact requirements that were in effect at the time of their construction. Since the design live load carried from Cooper E35 to Cooper E36 for railroad bridges during the time and for H to

HS for highway bridges, it became necessary to develop a system of structural efficiency of these structures to determine their ability to carry the increased loading that the bridges and railroad were required to handle.
Rules for rating existing iron and steel bridges were revised in 1936, 1940, 1949, and 1978.

RATING STEPS

In general, the method of rating a bridge for a specific loading consists of the following procedure.

1. Determine the total load capacity of the member being investigated using the maximum allowable rating stress for the material.
2. Determine the dead load stress of the member.
3. Determine the live load and impact stress caused by the equipment on the member.
4. The difference between the load carrying value and dead load stress gives the capacity available for live load and impact. If this is greater than the live load and impact stress caused by the equipment, the member can carry the specific load.
5. If the difference between the load carrying value and dead load stress is less than the live load and impact stress caused by the equipment, check to see if the live load stress alone is greater than the available difference. If this is the case, the load is prohibited.
6. Unless critical or restricting member of bridge is known, repeat the preceding steps for all members.

As a result of investigation, the engineer will reach one of the three conclusions.

1. The proposed loading is prohibited over the bridge.
2. The proposed loading can be safely operated over the bridge
3. The proposed loading can only be operated over the bridge at restricted speed.

If the speed restriction cannot be tolerated, it then is necessary to stiffen or review the bridge.

EXAMPLE 6-01

Given:- Perform the bridge rating of the following bridge which was built in 1934 and located on 80th Street at 77th Ave. over the Long Island Railroad in Queens, New York. The bridge is to be rehabilitated for HS 20-44 Loading and to provide the minimum clearance of 18'-6" over the tracks.

Description of the existing bridge: The floor beams and girders are supported on steel columns to which brackets support- the sidewalks are attached. The deck of the roadway is supported by floor beams. The entire structure is encased in concrete against fire proofing.

Concrete Deck capacity (as built)

Deck loads		@ ℄	@ curb
concrete slab	12" @	150 Lbs	9" @ 113 Lbs

Asph W.S (added) 3"@ 36 — 222 p.s.f 3"@ 36 — 185 psf

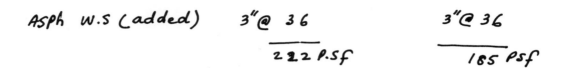

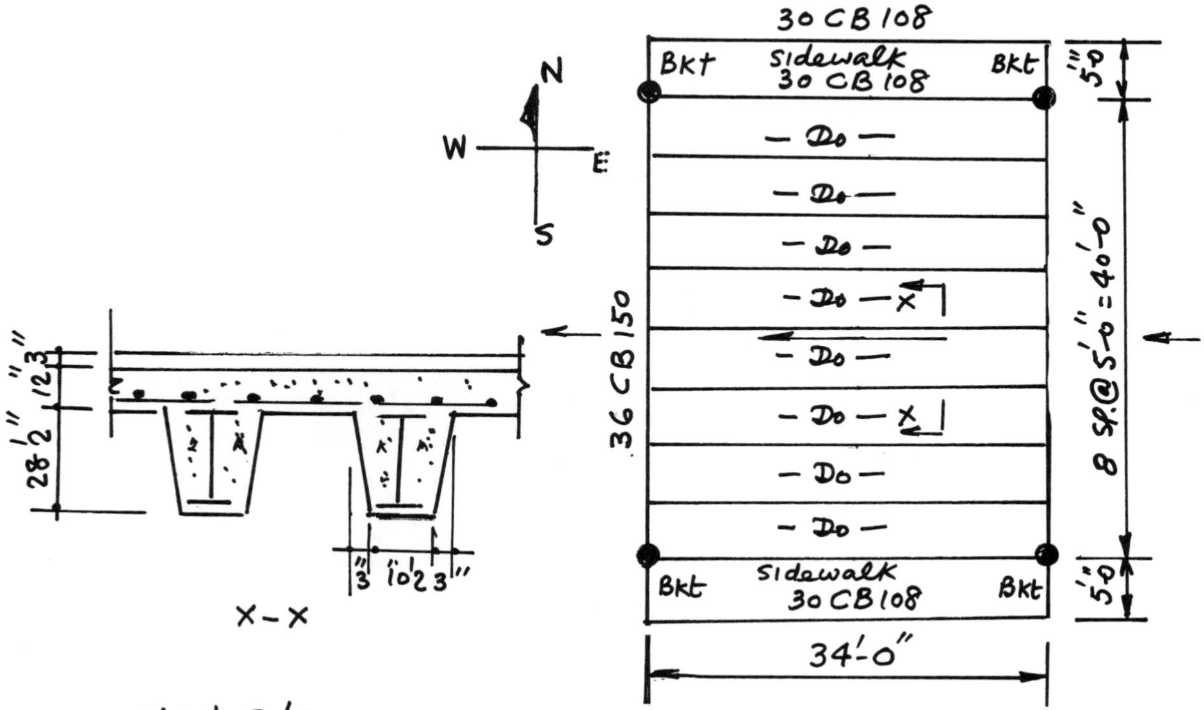

● Steel Cols

No Top steel reinf. shown on DWG.

∴ use simple span moment, span = 5'-0"

S.S.B.M @ ℄ $M_{DL} = \frac{0.222(5)^2}{8} = 0.694$ 'K/'

@ Curb $M_{DL} = \frac{0.185(5)^2}{8} = 0.578$ 'K/'

for Live load HS20	@ ℄	@ curb
$M_{LL} = \left(\frac{5.0+2}{32}\right)16$	= 3.50	3.50
$M_{Imp} = (0.30) \times 3.5$	= 1.05	1.05
M_{DL}	= 0.694	0.578
	5.244	5.128
M_T	5.24 'K/'	5.13 'K/'

Deck slab capacity (as built)

@ ℄ effective depth to reinforcement.

#5 @ 5 c/c $= 10.5 - \frac{0.625}{2} = 10.17"$

concrete strength unknown for inventory rating

Assume $f_c = 1300$ psi; $f_s = 18000$ psi; $n = 10$

$$K = 1/\left(1 + \frac{18000}{10 \times 1300}\right) = 0.419$$

$$J = 1 - K/3 = 0.860$$

$$R = \frac{1300}{2} \times 0.419 \times 0.860 = 234$$

$$R_{M_c} = \frac{0.34 \times 12 \times (10.19)^2}{12} = 24.3\ ^{'K}/_{'}$$

$$R_{M_s} = 0.74 \times 18 \times 0.860 \times \frac{10.19}{2} = 9.73\ ^{'K}/_{'}$$

@ curb $d_{eff.} = 7.5 - \frac{0.625}{2} = 7.19''$

$R_{M_c} = 12.1\ ^{'K}/_{'}$; $R_{M_s} = 6.86\ ^{'K}/_{'}$ ← use

Inventory

Total slab Capacity	= 6.86
Less DL Moment	= 0.58
Allow LL + Imp	= 6.28
Allow L.L	= 6.28/1.30 = 4.83 'K/'
Safe load capacity	$= \frac{4.83}{3.5} \times 36 = 49.68^T$

Operating

$R_{M_s} = \frac{25}{18} \times 6.86$	= 9.53 'K/'
Less D.L	= 0.58 'K/'
L.L + Imp	= 8.95 'K/'
Allow L.L	$= \frac{8.95}{1.30} = 6.88$ 'K/'
Safe load capacity	$= \frac{6.88}{3.50} \times 36 = 70.76^T$

Exterior Stringer 30 CB 105

Loads Conc. fence = 5 × 12.5 × 4 = 250 #/'

Post $= 3 \times 12.5 \times 4.17 \times \frac{8}{120} = 10$ #/'

= 260 #/'

Concret. walk $= 10.5 \times \frac{0.15}{2} \times 5 = 0.33$ #/'

fence Curb = [(1.0 × 1.19 + 0.67 × 0.25) 0.150] = 0.20 #/'

Haunch A $= \left[\frac{18 + 21.5}{2}\right] \times 33$ = 652 □"

Less Steel = 32 □"

620 □"

Dead load $= \frac{620 \times 0.150}{144} = 0.65^{K}/_{1}$

30" CB $=$ $0.11^{K}/_{1}$

Total D.L $= 1.55^{K}/_{1}$

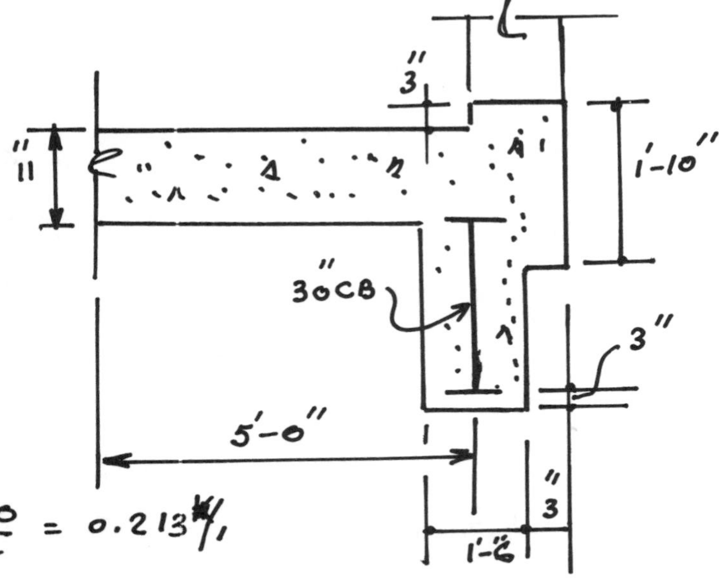

Live load $= 85 \times \frac{5.0}{2} = 0.213^{K}/_{1}$

Span $= 37\text{-}6'$

$M_{DL} = 1.55(37.6)^2/8 = 274'^{K}$

$M_{LL} = 0.213(37.6)^2/8 = 37.6$

M_{IMP} neglect

$M_{Total} = 312'^{K}$

As built rating factors

Inventory $M_{cap} = 405'^{k}$

Less D.L $= 274'^{k}$

L.L $= 131$

R.F $= \frac{131}{37.6} = 3.48$ or 296 psf.

Operating

$M_{cap} = 570'^{k}$

Less D.L $= 274'^{K}$

LL+I $= 296'^{K}$

LL $= 228$

RF $= \frac{228}{37.6} = 6.06$ or 515 psf

Girder Analysis

7/8" rivet with 15/16" ϕ holes

net flange area $= \frac{14.2}{14} = 0.857$

Reduction < 15%. use gross section.

Haunch Area = $\left(\frac{14+21}{2}\right)57$ = 998 in^2

Less steel area = − 73 in^2

925 in^2

weight = $\frac{925 \times 0.15}{144}$ = 0.96 k/1

+ girder 116×3.4 = 0.40 k/1

1.36 k/1

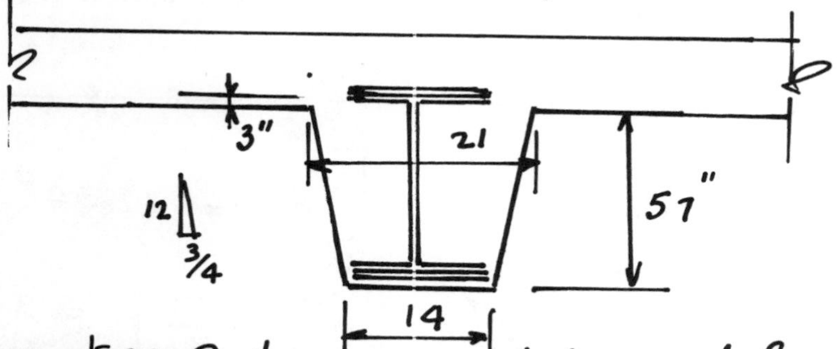

Section properties @ ℄ with 4 Plates each face

Elements		A	Y	AY^2	I_o	I_g
1 PL	60"×½"	30	? —		9000	-
4 ∠s	6×6×¾"	33.76	28.47	27363	113	-
2 PL	14×½	14.00	30.50	13024	-	-
2 PL	14×½	14.00	31.00	13454	-	-
2 PL	14×½	14.00	31.50	13892	-	-
2 PL	14×3/8	10.50	31.94	10792	-	-
	1) Σ	116.26		78445	9113	87558
W/3 PL	2) Σ	105.76		76846		
W/2 PL	3) Σ	91.76		62954		
W/1 PL	4) Σ	77.76		49500		

S_{c_1} = I/c = 2725; S_{c_2} = 2420; S_{c_3} = 2015; S_{c_4} = 1610

@ ℄ moment capacity — Inventory: $2725 \times \frac{16}{12} = 3633'^k$ — Operating: $2725 \times \frac{22.5}{12} = 5109'^k$

shear capacity — $30 \times 9.5 = 285^k$ — $30 \times 13.5 = 405^k$

Dead load

Stringer reaction span ② $1.59 \times \frac{34.7}{2}$ = 27.6

span ③ $1.59 \times \frac{19.3}{2}$ = 15.3

42.9 ÷ 5 = 8.58 k/1

Haunch + girder = 1.36 k/1

9.94 k/1

Live load

wheel load $P = 16\left(1 + \frac{20.7}{34.7}\right) + 4\left(\frac{5.3}{19.3}\right) = 26.6^k$

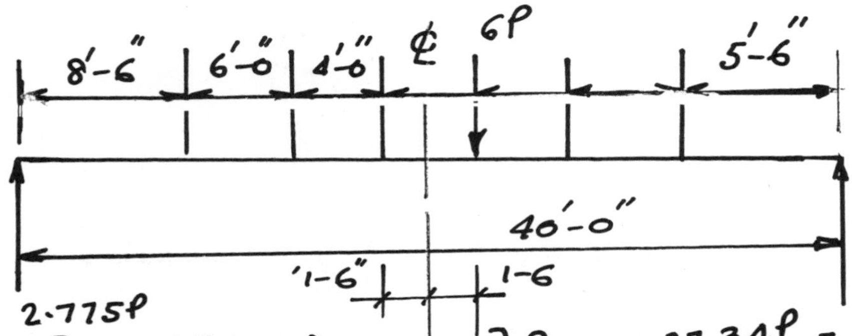

Max $M_{LL} = [2.775(18.5) - 10 - 4]P = 37.34P = 993'^k$

$= 894'^k$

For 3 Lanes use 90%

Max $V_{LL} = P\left[\frac{38}{40} + \frac{32}{40} + \frac{28}{40} + \frac{22}{40} + \frac{18}{40} + \frac{12}{40}\right] = 3.75P = 99.8^k$

GIRDER G2

M_{DL} ℄ $= 9.74 \times \frac{40^2}{8} = 1948'^k$; $198.8 = V$

M_{LL} $= 894'^k$; $89.8 = V$

$M_{Imp} = 0.30 M_{LL} = 268'^k$; $26.9 = V_{Imp}$

$M_{Total} = 3110'^k$; $315.5 = V_T$

Moments

Rating @ ℄		Inventory	Operating
	Mcap.	3633	5100
less D.L		1948	1948
		1685	3152
LL + IMP		1296.1	2121.6
R.F	$M_{LL}/894$ =	1.44	2.71
		or 51.84 T	97.56 T

Shear

		Inventory	Operating
Vcap		285	405
Less VDL		198.8	198.8
LL + IMP		86.2	206.2
LL.		66.3	158.6
RF	LL/89.8 =	0.74	1.77
		or 26.64 T ↑	63.72 T

Typical Interior stringer as built

Dead Load Deck $0.222 \times 5.0 = 1.11^k/'$, $0.185 \times 5 = 0.93^k/'$

30 CB

Haunch Area $\left(\frac{10.5 + 16.5}{2}\right) 28.5 = 385\square''$

$= -32$

Less steel area $= 0.37^k/'$, $353 \times \frac{0.150}{144} = 0.37$

30 CB 108

$t_w = 0.53''$, $S = 304\ in^3$

Mom. Cap (Inventory) $= \frac{304 \times 16}{12} = 405'^k$

Mom. cap (operating) $= 304 \times \frac{22.5}{12} = 570'^k$

Shear Cap (Inventory) $= 30 \times 0.53 \times 9.5 = 151^k$

Shear Cap (operating) $= 30 \times 0.53 \times 13.5 = 215^k$

span length $= 30'-2''$

wheel load fraction $= \frac{5.0}{5.5} = 0.91$

Impact $= 0.30$

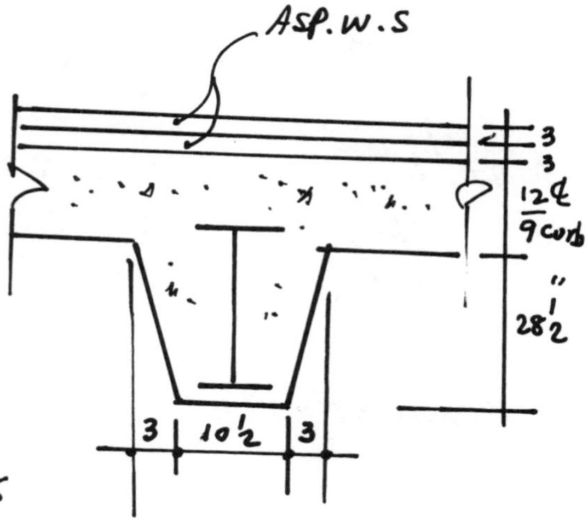

Moment $M_{DL} = 1.59 \times \frac{(30.2)^2}{8} = 181'^k$

$V_{DL} = 1.59 \times \frac{30.2}{2} = 24.0^k$

$M_{LL} = 282 \times \frac{0.91}{2} = 128'^k$

$V_{LL} = 41.6 \times \frac{0.91}{2} = 22.6^k$

$M_{imp} = 0.3 M_{LL} = 39'^k$

$V_{imp} = 0.3 V_{LL} = 6.8^k$

$M_{Total} = 348'^k$ $V_T = 53.4^k$

Rating factor

Inventory

Mcap	= 405		Vcap	= 151
Less D.L	= 181		Less D.L	= 24
LL + IMP	= 224		V_T	= 127
$LL = \frac{224}{1.3}$	= 172		LL V_T	= 97
$RF = \frac{172}{128}$	= 1.34		RF	$= \frac{97}{22.6} = 4.32$

↑ Governs

1.38 × 36 = 48.24 T.

Operating

Mcap	= 570
Less D.L	= 181
LL + IMP	= 389
LL	= 299
R.F	$= \frac{299}{128} = 2.34$ or 84.24 Tons.

Floor Beam 36 CB 150

Dead loads Stringer Reactions $1.59 \times \frac{11.22}{2} = 8.9^k$

27.6

36.5 K

$\frac{36.5}{5.0} = 7.3^{k}/_{1}$

Haunch + Beam = 0.66

$7.99^{k}/_{1}$

Live load wheel load $P = 16\left(1 + \frac{20.7}{34.7}\right) + 4\left(\frac{6.7}{34.7}\right)$

$= 26.3K$

Max. M_{LL}	=	10.2×26.3	=	268'k
V_{LL_1}	=	2.4×26.3	=	63.1k
V_{LL_2}	=	2.0×26.3	=	52.6k
M_{DL}	=	$7.9\,(20)^2/8$	=	395'k

Bracket's $M_{DL} = 1.5\left(\frac{11.22 + 34.7}{2}\right) 5.0 = 178'^{k}$

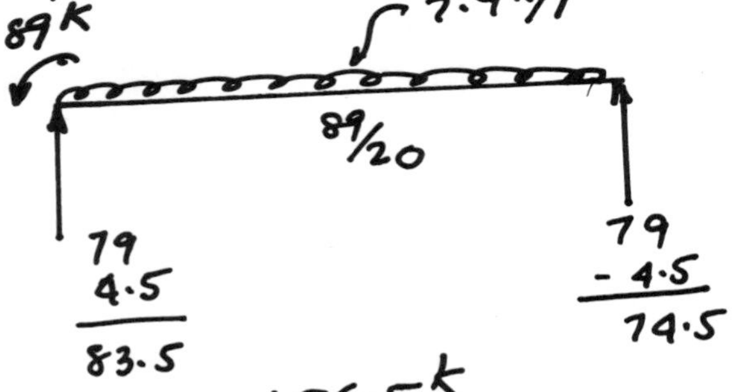

Moments

$M_{DL} = 395 - \frac{89}{2}$	=	351'k
M_{LL}	=	268'k
M_{IMP}	=	80'k
M_{Total}	=	699'k

Shear $V_1 = 74.5 + 63.1 + 0.3(63.1) = 156.5^k$

As Built RATING

	INVENTORY	operating
M_{cap}	677	953
Less DL	351	351
M LL + IMP	326	602
LL	251	463
R.F $\frac{LL}{268}$	0.94	1.73
or	33.84T	62.28T

Bracket @ side walk

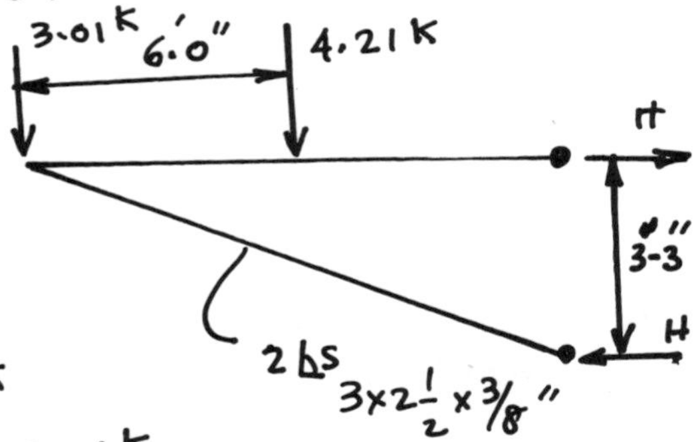

Dead Loads

9" Avg. conc. slab	619x5	= 3.10k
Bracket	222x5	= 1.11
		4.21k
Conc. spanderal	295x5	= 1.48k
Fence Post	326x5	= 1.63
		= 3.01k

Dead Load $H_{DL} = \frac{3.01 \times 6 + 4.21 \times 3}{3.25} = 9.44\,k$

Net area 2 Ls $3 \times 2\frac{1}{2} \times \frac{3}{8}$

$= 2(1.92 - \frac{3}{8} \times 1.0) = 3.09\ in^2$

Live load @ 85 psf

$= 0.085 \times 5.2 \times 5.0 = 2.21\,k$

L.L $H_{LL} = 2.21 \times \frac{3}{3.25} = 2.04\,k$

Impact

Total HDL $= 9.44 + 2.04 = 11.48\,k$

$f_t = \frac{11.48}{3.09} = 3.72\ ksi < 16\ ksi$ ok

Compressed Strut force $= 11.48 \times \frac{6.82}{6} = 13.06\,k$

$f_c = \frac{13.06}{2 \times 1.92} = 3.46\ ksi < 14$ ok.

During the period of 46 years, the bottom flange of stringer was corroded @ 1/16" to 3/8" due to weather effect and leaching of salt through concrete. Due to loss of area, reduction in capacity for stringer found out.

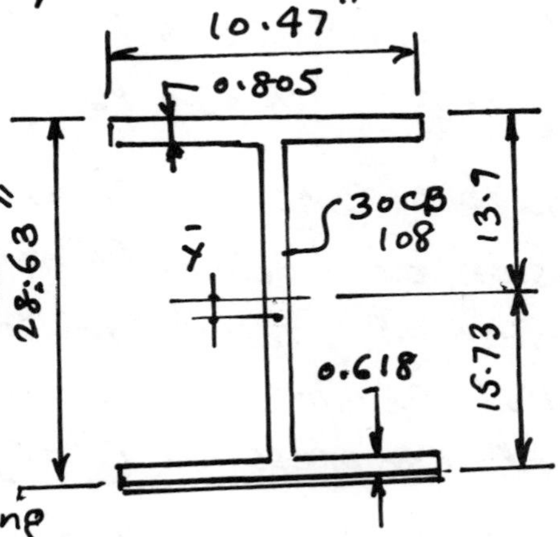

$-A = 10.47 \times \frac{3}{16} = 1.963\ in^2$

$A = 32\ in^2$

$\bar{Y} = \frac{1.963 \times 14.99}{32} = 0.919$

$I = (4554.2 - 1.963[15.73]^2 - 32(0.919)^2)$

$= 4041.48\ in^4$

$S_T = \frac{4041.48}{15.73} = 256.94\ in^3$

Capacity

		INV.	Oper'ling
Mcap		$256 \times \frac{16}{12} = 342.5$	$256 \times \frac{22.5}{12} = 481.6$
Less DL		181.0	181.0
LL + IMP		161.5	300.6
LL		124.12	231.2
R.F	LL/128	0.97	1.81
	or	34.92T	65.16T.

From the rating, it is inferred that the structure itself is good for HS 20-44 loading except there is heavy leaching on account of the high salt content (sodium chloride) on the bottom of the deck and stringers. Secondly, the North abutment is in the broken and cracked position at its bridge seat. The main feature of rehabilitation is that the present clearance of the underpass from the railroad tracks to the bottom of the deck is less than 18' 6". Hence, the complete rehabilitation of the existing bridge with solid / hollow slab prestressed unit is recommended.

EXAMPLE 6-02

Given:- Design a P.C.I. beam BI- 48x27 for the following design data.

Loading:- HS 20-44 Loading
54'-3" span
Wearing surface + future wearing surface

$$BI-48;\ \frac{6\times48}{144}\times150+\frac{2\times48}{144}\times150=400^{\#}/'$$

Prestressing Steel :- 27" deep beam:- with 22 - $\frac{1}{2}$" ϕ strands with nominal area of 0.1438 in^2 and an ultimate strength of 20000#.

f'_s = 270,000 Psi (ultimate strength)
f'_{si} = 189,000 Psi (Initial prestress)
f'_c = 5000 Psi (ultimate strength at 28 days)
f'_{ci} = 4000 Psi (ultimate strength at time of prestressing)

Allowable Concrete stresses:-

Tension at Bottom (Final) = $6\sqrt{f'_c}$ = 424 Psi
Tension at Top (Initial) = $0.04 f'_c$ = 200 Psi
Initial Compression (Bott) = $0.6 f'_{ci}$ = 2400 Psi
Final Compression (top) = $0.4 f'_{ci}$ = 2000 Psi
Live load Distribution E = 4 + 0.06 (S) = 7.255'
E_c = 4,100,000 psi for computing L.L deflection.

Properties of B.I-48

$A = 692.5\ in^2,\ Y_B = 13.37\ in,\ Y_T = 13.63\ in,\ I = 65941\ in^4$

$S_B = 4932\ in^3;\ S_T = 4838\ in^3,\ W = 721\ ^{\#}/ft.$

$$M_{DL} = (721+400)\times54.25^2\times\frac{12}{8} = 4948760''^{\#}$$

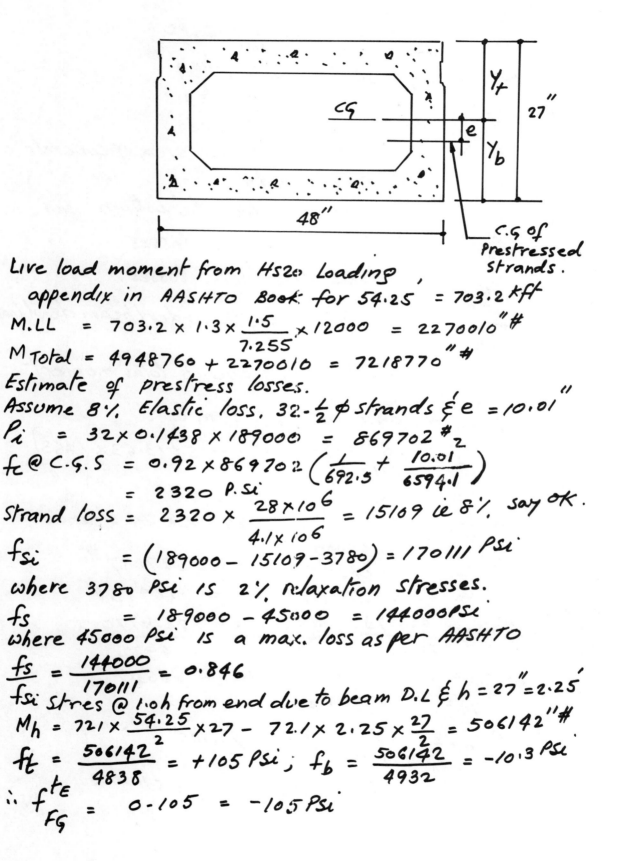

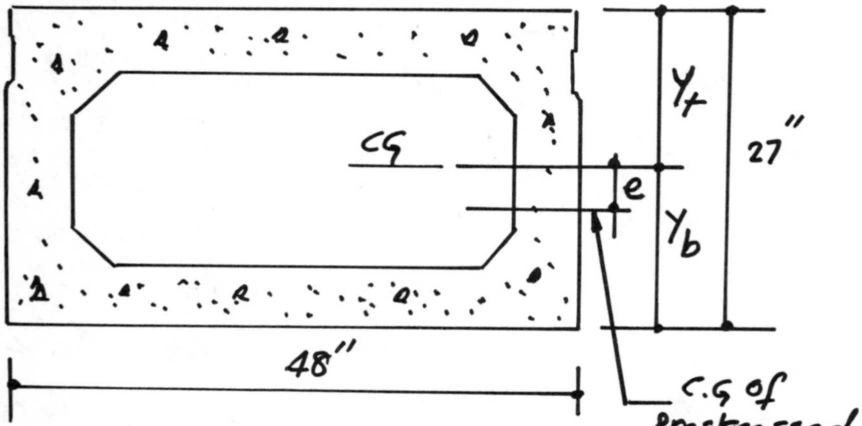

Live load moment from HS20 Loading, appendix in AASHTO Book for 54.25' = 703.2 kft

$M.LL = 703.2 \times 1.3 \times \frac{1.5}{7.255} \times 12000 = 2270010''\#$

$M_{Total} = 4948760 + 2270010 = 7218770''\#$

Estimate of prestress losses.

Assume 8% Elastic loss, 32-$\frac{1}{2}$" ϕ strands & e = 10.01"

$P_i = 32 \times 0.1438 \times 189000 = 869702\#_2$

$f_c @ C.G.S = 0.92 \times 869702 \left(\frac{1}{692.5} + \frac{10.01}{6594.1}\right)$

$= 2320\ P.Si$

Strand loss $= 2320 \times \frac{28 \times 10^6}{4.1 \times 10^6} = 15169$ ie 8% say ok.

$f_{si} = (189000 - 15109 - 3780) = 170111\ Psi$

where 3780 Psi is 2% relaxation stresses.

$f_s = 189000 - 45000 = 144000 Psi$

where 45000 Psi is a max. loss as per AASHTO

$\frac{f_s}{f_{si}} = \frac{144000}{170111} = 0.846$

Stres @ 1.0h from end due to beam D.L & h = 27" = 2.25'

$M_h = 721 \times \frac{54.25}{2} \times 27 - 72.1 \times 2.25 \times \frac{27}{2} = 506142''\#$

$f_t = \frac{506142}{4838} = +105\ Psi$; $f_b = \frac{506142}{4932} = -10.3\ Psi$

$\therefore f^{tE}_{FG} = 0 - 105 = -105\ Psi$

Required prestressed force

$$f_{FG}^{bE} = \frac{M_T}{S_B} = \frac{7218770}{6932} = 1463 \text{ PSi}$$

$$F = \frac{A}{h}\left[Y_b \times \frac{f_s}{f_{si}} \times f_{FG}^{tE} + Y_t\, f_{FG}^{bE}\right]$$

where F = applied prestress force

A = Gross cross sectional area of concrete.

h = Total height of box

Y_b = distance of C.G.C from the bottom

f_s = steel stress after final losses

f_{si} = steel stress after intial losses.

f_{FG}^{tE} = top fiber stress due to girder/beam dead load moment.

f_{FG}^{bE} = bottom fiber stress due to total moment.

Y_t = distance of C.G.C from top.

$$F = \frac{692.5}{27}\left[13.37 \times 0.846 \times -105 + 13.63 \times 1463\right]$$

$$= 481005\#$$

$$N = \frac{481005}{0.1438 \times 144000} = 23.22 \text{ use 24 strands.}$$

$$F_i = 24 \times 0.1438 \times 170111 = 587087\#$$

$$F = 24 \times 0.1438 \times 144000 = 496973\#$$

$$e_{min} = \frac{496973}{692.5} + \frac{496973e}{4932} - \frac{7218770}{4932}$$

$$0 = 717.65 + 100.77e - 1463.7$$

$$e_{min} = 7.40 \text{ inches}$$

$$e_{max} = \frac{4838}{692.5} - \frac{4838}{587087} \times -105$$

$$= 6.98 + 0.87 = 7.85 \text{ inches}$$

$e_{avg} = 7.62$ in.

Summation of stresses
at release

$$\frac{F_i}{A} = \frac{587087}{692.5} = 848$$

$$\frac{F_i e}{z_t} = \frac{587087 \times 7.62}{4838} = 922$$

$$\frac{F_i e}{z_b} = \frac{587087 \times 7.62}{4932} = 907$$

$$\frac{M_G}{z_t} = \frac{3182922}{4838} = 658$$

$$\frac{M_S}{z_t} = \frac{1765838}{4838} = 365$$

$$\frac{M_L}{z_t} = \frac{2270010}{4838} = 469$$
$$\overline{1492}$$

final stress.

$$\frac{F}{A} = \frac{496973}{692.5} = 718$$

$$\frac{Fe}{z_t} = \frac{496973 \times 7.62}{4838} = 783$$

$$\frac{Fe}{z_b} = \frac{496973 \times 7.62}{4932} = 768$$

$$\frac{M_G}{z_b} = \frac{3182922}{4932} = 645$$

$$\frac{M_S}{z_b} = \frac{1765838}{4932} = 358$$

$$\frac{M_L}{z_b} = \frac{2270010}{4932} = 460$$
$$\overline{1463}$$

Stage I @ release

Mid span
$$f_t = +848 - 922 + 658 = 584 > -190 \text{ ok}$$
$$f_b = +848 + 907 - 645 = 1110 < 2400 \text{ ok}$$

At 1.0 h from end
$$f_t = 848 - 922 + 105 = 31 > -190 \text{ ok}$$
$$f_b = 848 + 907 - 103 = 1652 < 2400 \text{ ok}$$

Stage III

Mid span
$$f_t = 718 - 783 + 1492 = 1398 < 2000 \text{ ok}$$
$$f_b = 718 + 768 - 1463 = 23 > -424 \text{ ok}$$

Required ultimate moment.
$$M_U = 1.892 \, DL + 2.3 (LL + I)$$
$$= 1.892 \times 4948760 + 2.3 \times 2270010$$
$$= 14584077 \text{ in lbs}$$

Ultimate moment capacity
$$A_s = 24 \times 0.1438 = 3.45 \,\square"$$

$$d = 13.63 + 7.62 = 21.25 \text{ in}$$

$$p = \frac{3.45}{48 \times 21.25} = 0.0034$$

$$q = p\frac{f_s'}{f_c'} = 0.0034 \times \frac{270}{5} = 0.1836$$

$$f_{su} = f_s'\left(1 - 0.5\frac{pf_s'}{f'c}\right)$$

$$= 270000\left(1 - 0.5 \times \frac{0.0034(270)}{5}\right)$$

$$= 270000(1 - 0.5 \times 0.1836) = 245214 \text{ Psi}$$

$$M_U = 0.85 f_c'(b - b')t(d - 0.5t)f_{su}$$

$$= 0.85 \times 5000(48 - 10)5.5 \times (21.25 - 2.75)245214$$

$$= 16421981 > 14584077 \quad \text{ok}.$$

Shear reinforcement.

Max Shear @ 1/4 Point

$$V_G = \frac{wL}{4} = \frac{400 \times 54.25}{4} = 5400^{\#}$$

$$V_S = \frac{721 \times 54.25}{4} = 9778^{\#}$$

$$V_{LL+I} = 59800^{\#}$$

$$V_{Total} = 74978^{\#}$$

$$V_{ult} = 1.892 \times 15178 + 2.3 \times 74978 = 201166^{\#}$$

$$V_c = 180\ b'Jd = 180 \times 10 \times \frac{7}{8} \times 21.25 = 33469^{\#}$$

$$V_u - V_c = 201166 - 33469 = 167697$$

$$A_V = \frac{1}{2}(V_u - V_c)s/f_yJd = \frac{167697 \times 12}{2 \times 40000 \times \frac{7}{8} \times 21.25} = 0.35 \text{ in}^2$$

Use #4 @ 12" o/c.

To compute mid span deflection of beam

a, prestress deflection:- $\Delta = \dfrac{-0.125 P_e L^2}{EI}$

$$= \frac{-0.125 \times 481 \times 7.62 \times 54.25^2 \times 12^2}{4.1 \times 10^3 \times 65941}$$

$$= 0.717''$$

b, D.L. deflection:- $\Delta = \dfrac{5wL^4}{384EI} = \dfrac{5 \times 0.721 \times 54.25^4 \times 12^3}{384 \times 4.1 \times 10^3 \times 65941}$

$$= 0.520''$$

net Instataneous deflection $= 0.717 - 0.520 = 0.197''$

Camber $= \dfrac{L^2}{48EI}\left(6P_e - 5M_B\right)$

$$= \frac{54.25^2 \times 12^2}{48 \times 4.1 \times 10^6 \times 65941}\left(\begin{array}{l}6 \times 487000 \times 7.62 \\ -5 \times 3182922\end{array}\right) = 0.198''$$

L.L. Moment deflection

$$\Delta = \frac{5}{48}\frac{M_L L^2}{EI} = \frac{5}{48} \times \frac{189.170 \times 54.25^2 \times 12^3}{4.1 \times 10^3 \times 65941} = 0.370''$$

deflection due to Slab wt

$$\Delta = \frac{5}{384} \times \frac{0.350 \times 50.25^4 \times 1728}{4.1 \times 10^3 \times 65941} = 0.251''$$

deflection due to superimposed load

$$\Delta = \frac{5}{384} \times \frac{0.533 \times 54.25^4 \times 1728}{4.1 \times 10^3 \times 65941} = 0.383''$$

deflection due to wearing surface

$$\Delta = \frac{5}{384} \times \frac{0.150 \times 54.25^4 \times 1728}{4.1 \times 10^3 \times 65941} = 0.1090''$$

net Camber upward $= 0.351''$

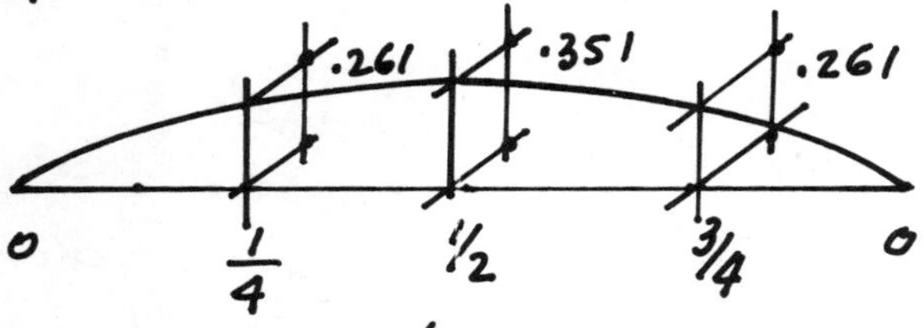

Theoretical Camber diagram.

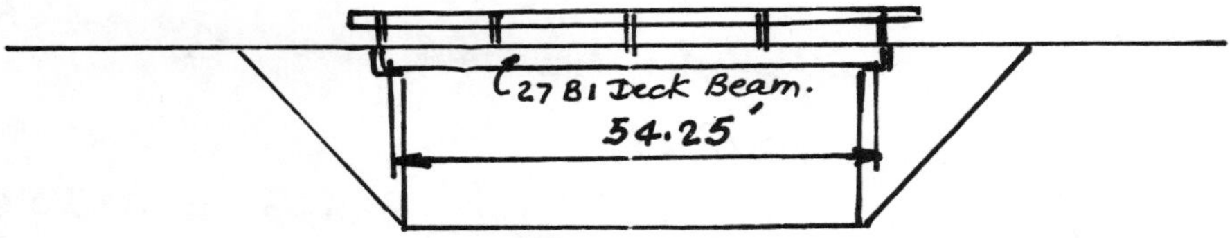

ELEVATION

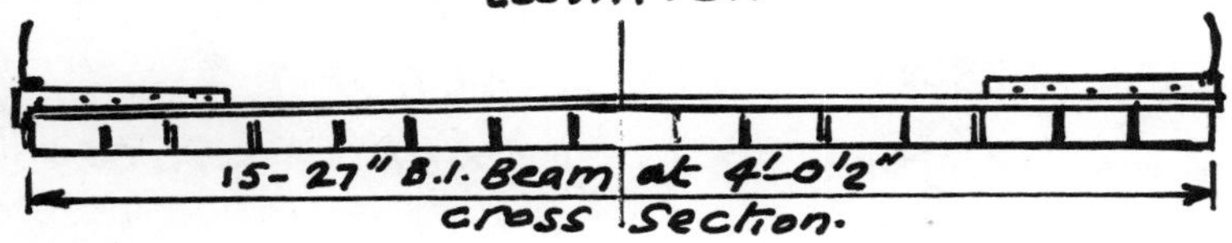

cross Section.

EXAMPLE 6-03

Given:- Design a Typical Box Beam as per prevailent practical method being used in most of the state highway departments in the United States.

Design Data

L.L = HS20-44

Prestressing steel = $\frac{3}{8}''\phi$ strands

$A = 0.080\ in^2$

U.S = 20000 psi

f_s' = 250,000 P.S.I (ultimate strength)

f_{si}' = 175000 P.S.I (Initial)

Prestressed Concrete $f_c' = 5000$ psi, $f_{ci}' = 4000$ psi

Try 17" deep Beam with 26 No strands.

size of beam = 36"×17"

Properties of Beam:- Wt. 378 #/ft; $A = 363\ in^2$; $Y_T = 8.27\ in$; $S_B = 1435\ in^3$

$Y_B = 8.73\ in$; $S_T = 1515\ in^3$;

$I = 12{,}530\ in^4$.

Allowable concrete stresses

Ten @ Top	=	400 psi
" @ Bott.	=	200 psi
Initial comp	=	2400 psi
final comp	=	2000 psi.

Load:- Wearing surface 5" Max. = 0.4167×150×3 = 187 #/ft

F.W.S = 25×3 = 75 #/ft

262 #/ft

for beam depth 17" & 26 No strands

assume e = 3.69" Losses = 33 k/in²

effective span length = 39'-0" (Anchor dowel to anchor dowel).

$$M_{DL} = \frac{(378+262)(39^2)}{8} = 121680\ \#ft = 121.680\ kft$$

L.L Distribution $E = 4 + 0.06 \times 39 = 6.34$

L.L Moment from Appendix H20-44 Loading AASHTO

for 39' span = 336.0 kft

$$M_{LL}\ \text{distributed} = 336 \times 1.3 \times \frac{1.5}{6.34} \times 1000 = 103500\ \#ft = 103.5\ kft$$

$$P_i = 26 \times (175000) \times 0.08 = 364{,}000\ \#$$

$$P_f = 26 \times (175000 - 33000) \times 0.08 = 295000\ \#$$

		1 P/A	2 Pe/S	3 1+2	4 M_{DL}/S	5 3+4	6 M_{LL}/S	7 5+6	
Initial	Top	1000	−1368	−368					> −400 ok
	Bott.	1000	1442	+2442					≃ 2400 ok
Final	Top	814	−1108	−294	+965	+671	+820	+1491	< 2000 ok
	Bott.	814	+1169	+1983	−1018	+965	−866	+99	> −200

(+1983) < 2000 ok

$$p = \frac{26 \times 0.080}{36 \times (8.27 + 5.69)} = 0.00414$$

$$\text{ULT. capacity } M = \frac{26 \times 0.08 \times 22500 \times 13.96}{12000}\left(1 - \frac{0.6 \times 0.00414 \times 22500}{5000}\right)$$

$$= 483.66^{\,kft}$$

$$\text{Actual } M_U = 1.5\,(121.68) + 2.5\,(103.5)$$

$$= 441.27 < 483.66 \text{ ok}$$

Beam Camber

Live load Deflection:-

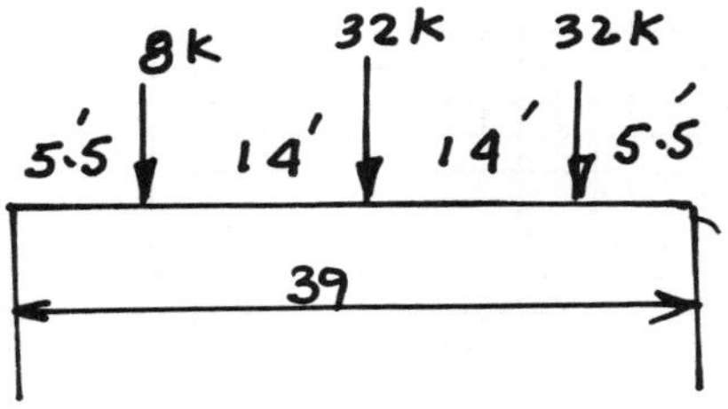

At ℄ per Lane Δ

$$= \frac{32 \times 39^3}{48EI} + \frac{40 \times 5.5 \times 19.5}{6 \times E.I\,(39)}\left(39^2 - 5.5^2 - 19.5^2\right)$$

$$= 0.125$$

At ℄ Total Δ for 3 lanes

$$= 0.125 \times 3 = 0.375 < \frac{L}{800} = \frac{39 \times 12}{800} = 0.585''$$

D.L. Deflection due to additional slab + curb + Parapet.

(SLAB + curb + Parapet) = 1854 + 1112 = 2966#/ft

$$\Delta = \frac{5}{384} \times \frac{2966 \times 39^4 \times 1728}{4.0 \times 10^6 \times 12530} = 0.226''$$

Camber due to prestress (Interior beam)

$$M_{Beam} = 378 \times (39)^2 \times \frac{12}{8} = 863000''\#$$

$$\text{Camber} = \frac{L^2}{48EI}\left(6\,Pe - 5M_B\right)$$

$$= \frac{(39)^2 \times 144}{48 \times 4.0 \times 10^6 \times 12530}\left(6 \times 364000 \times 5.69 - 5 \times 863000\right)$$

$$= 0.74'' \text{ Say } 3/4''$$

PRESTRESSED CONCRETE BOX BEAMS

HS 20 LOADING

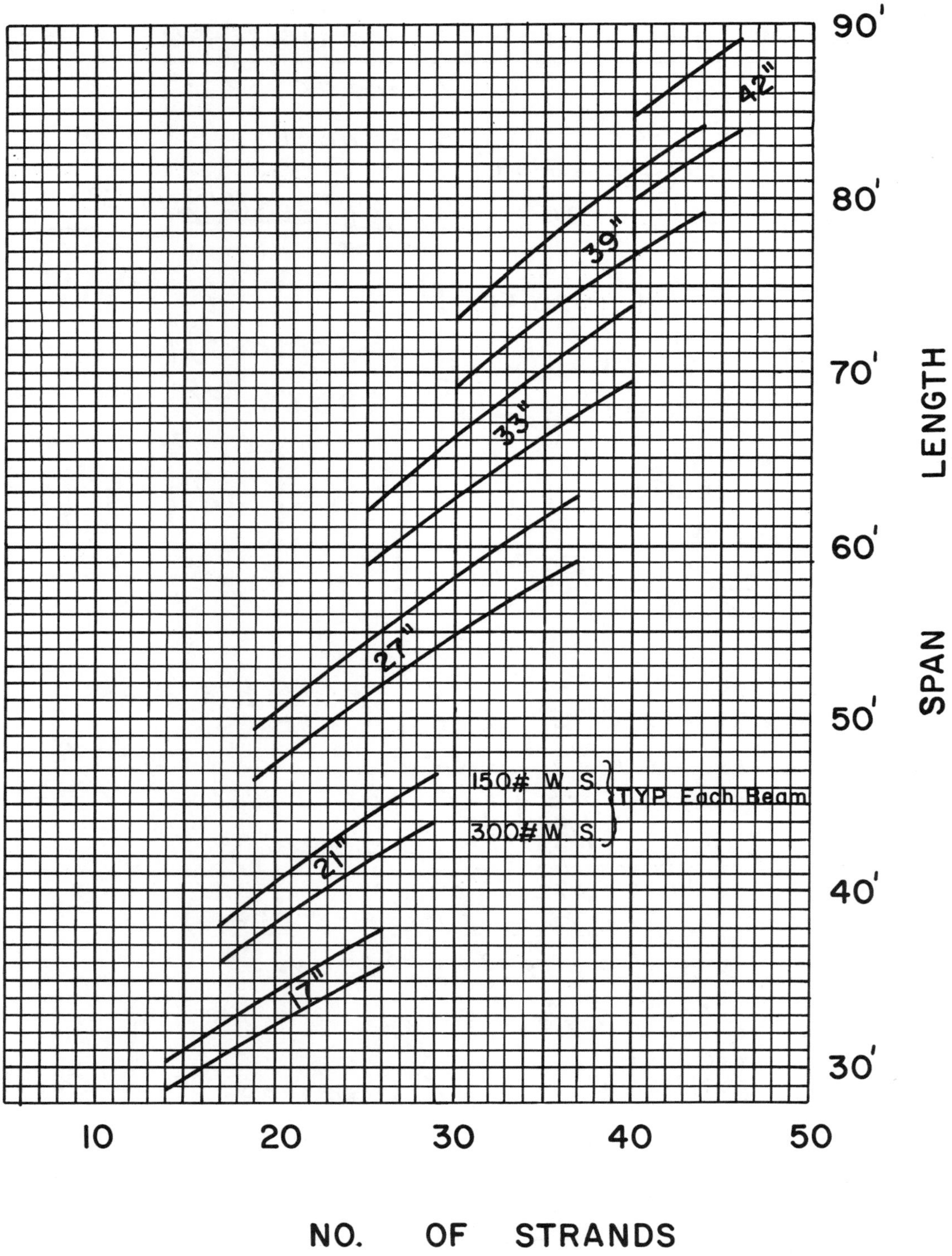

STRAND PATTERNS

Beam Depth	No. of Strands	ROW 1	2	3	4	5	6	7	8	9	e	Losses Elast. Comp.	Losses Total	f_{su}
	14	14									7.23	4	27	250
	15	13	2								6.96	4	27	246
	16	13	3								6.86	5	28	244
	17	12	5								6.64	5	28	240
	18	14	3			1					6.45	5	29	238
	19	14	4			1					6.39	5	29	236
17	20	14	5			1					6.33	5	30	235
	21	16	3			2					6.18	5	30	233
	22	15	5			2					6.05	6	31	231
	23	17	4				2				6.01	6	31	230
	24	18	3			2	1				5.90	6	32	228
	25	18	4			2	1				5.87	6	33	227
	26	18	5				3				5.69	6	33	225
	17	15		2							8.82	4	26	244
	18	16			2						8.62	4	27	242
	19	16		1	2						8.45	4	27	240
	20	16		2	2						8.29	5	28	238
	21	16		3	2						8.15	5	28	236
	22	16		4	2						8.02	5	29	234
21	23	17		2	4						7.90	5	29	232
	24	17		3	4						7.79	5	30	231
	25	17		4	4						7.69	5	30	229
	26	17		5	4						7.60	6	31	228
	27	17	1	4	5						7.51	6	31	227
	28	17	1	5	5						7.43	6	32	226
	29	15	4	5	5						7.29	6	32	225
	19	19									12.07	4	24	250
	20	18	2								11.87	4	24	248
	21	17	4								11.69	4	25	246
	22	15	7								11.43	4	25	244
	23	13	10								11.20	4	26	242
	24	12	12								11.07	4	26	240
	25	12	11	2							10.87	4	26	238
	26	12	12		2						10.69	4	27	237
27	27	13	10	2	2						10.59	4	27	236
	28	12	12	2	2						10.50	5	28	235
	29	12	13	2		2					10.35	5	28	234
	30	12	12	4		2					10.20	5	28	232
	31	13	12	2	2	2					10.13	5	29	231
	32	13	11	4	2	2					10.01	5	29	230
	33	14	11	2	4	2					9.95	5	30	229
	34	14	12	2	2	4					9.83	5	30	228
	35	15	12		4	4					9.78	5	30	227
	36	15	11	2	4	4					9.68	6	31	226
	37	13	14	2	4	4					9.58	6	31	225

STRAND PATTERNS

Beam Depth	No. of Strands	ROW 1	2	3	4	5	6	7	8	9	e	Losses Elast. Comp.	Total	f_{su}
33"	25	13	10	2							13.93	4	25	241
	26	12	12	2							13.82	4	25	240
	27	13	12		2						13.72	4	26	239
	28	13	13			2					13.55	4	26	238
	29	13	12		2	2					13.26	4	26	236
	30	13	11	2	2	2					13.12	4	27	235
	31	10	15	2	2	2					12.92	4	27	233
	32	14	12		2	2	2				12.80	5	28	232
	33	14	11	2	2	2	2				12.69	5	28	231
	34	12	14	2	2	2	2				12.58	5	28	230
	35	14	15			2	2	2			12.48	5	29	229
	36	14	14	2		2	2	2			12.38	5	29	229
	37	14	15		2	2	2	2			12.29	5	29	228
	38	14	14	2	2	2	2	2			12.21	5	30	227
	39	14	15		4	2	2	2			12.13	5	30	227
	40	14	14	2	4	2	2	2			12.05	6	31	226
39"	30	14	10	2	2		2				16.05	4	25	237
	31	14	11	2		2	2				15.92	4	26	236
	32	14	14				2		2		15.68	4	26	235
	33	14	13	2			2		2		15.57	4	26	234
	34	14	12	2		2	2	2			15.34	4	26	233
	35	14	13		2	2	2	2			15.25	4	27	232
	36	14	14	2			2	2	2		15.05	4	27	230
	37	14	15		2		2	2	2		14.97	4	27	230
	38	14	14	2		2	2	2	2		14.79	5	28	229
	39	14	13	4		2	2	2	2		14.72	5	28	228
	40	14	14	2	2	2	2	2	2		14.65	5	28	228
	41	14	13	2	4	2	2	2	2		14.49	5	29	227
	42	14	12	4	4	2	2	2	2		14.43	5	29	226
	43	14	13	4	2	2	4	2	2		14.28	5	29	225
	44	15	11	4	2	4	4	2	2		14.10	5	30	224
42"	39	15	14		2	2	2		2	2	16.06	4	27	228
	40	15	15		2		2	2	2	2	15.90	5	28	227
	41	15	14	2		2	2	2	2	2	15.75	5	28	226
	42	15	15		2	2	2	2	2	2	15.69	5	28	226
	43	15	14		4	2	2	2	2	2	15.55	5	29	225
	44	15	15		2	2	4	2	2	2	15.41	5	29	224
	45	15	14	2	2	2	4	2	2	2	15.37	5	29	224
	46	14	16	2	2	2	2	2	4	2	15.20	5	30	223

Typical layout of Box Beam with strands is shown below.

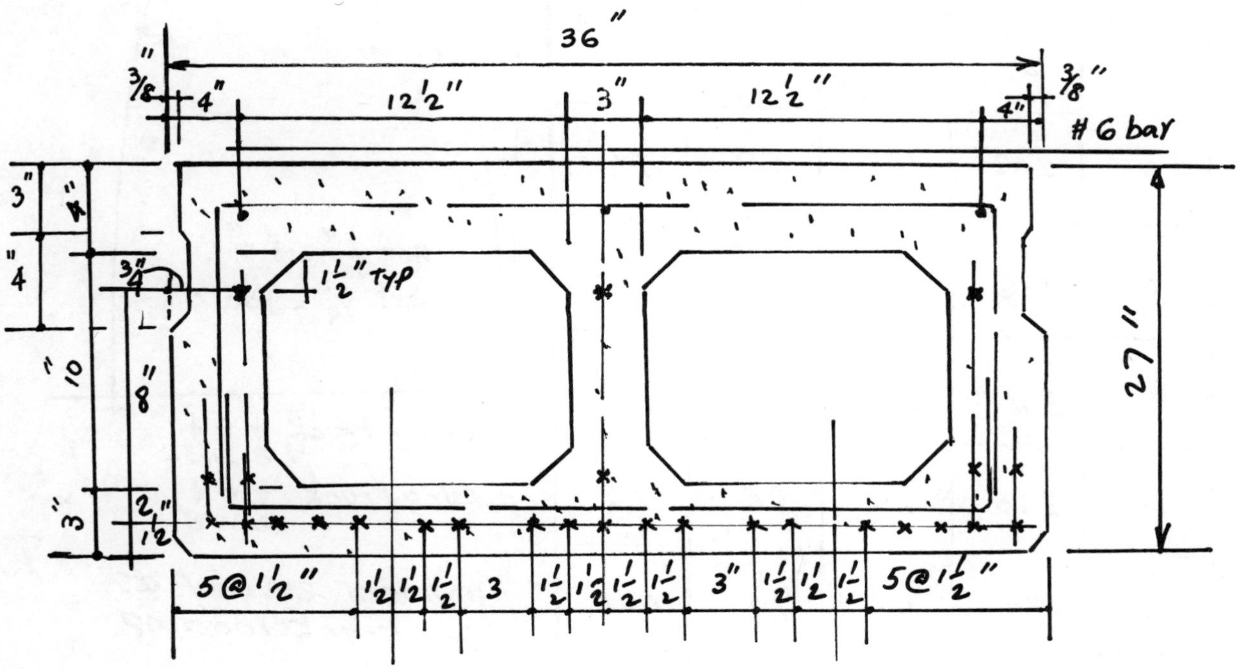

EXAMPLE 6-04

Given:- Design the deck of Example 6-01 with 21" deep x 3' wide precast voided slab bridge in New York.
The structure is to built of three unequal spans of 37', 54'6" and 34'9", which are made continuous for composite dead load and live load by means of contiuity reinforcement in the deck slab and diaphragm at the central piers.

Design data HS20-44 Loading $P = 16^K$

Wt. of 21" deep x 3'-0 wide deck slab = 1.305 K/ft.

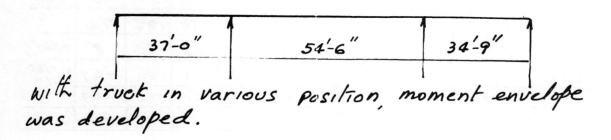

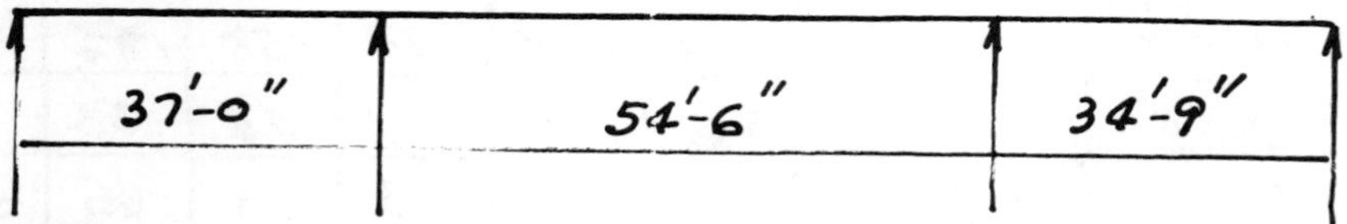

with truck in various position, moment envelope was developed.

Portion Ft ①	M per truck ②	M per ½ truck ③	M per stringer ④	M. per stringer + Imp.
		②÷2	③x0.58	④x1.3
1	29	15	9	11
5	202	101	59	77
8	276	138	80	104
9.6	301	151	88	114
14	330	165	96	125
19	324	162	94	122
23.6	292	146	85	111
29.	189	85	55	72
33	-4	111	-1.16	-1.5

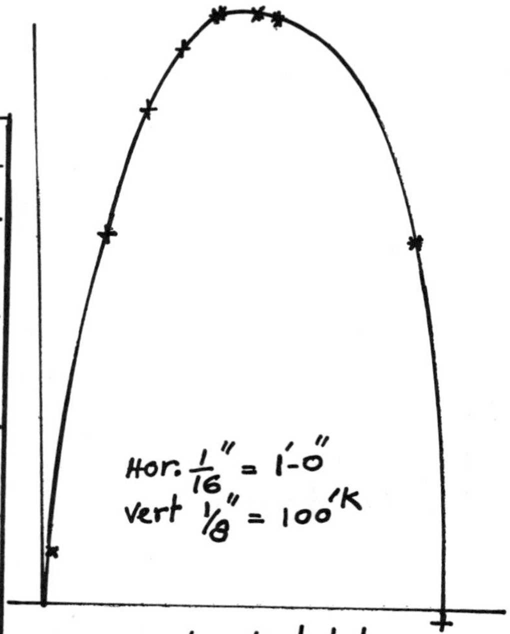

* using truck ↓8 ↓32 ↓32

+ using truck ↓32 ↓32 ↓8

moment envelop as per truck loading.

DESIGN +M Envelope for 37 span $l = 37'$

Location	5	8	9.6	14	19	23.6	29	33	
MLL - stringer	59	80	88	96	94	85	55	-1.16	
1.3 MLL	77	104	114	125	122	111	72	-1.5	
$M_{Bottom} = 0.79 M_{1.3}$	61	82	90	99	96	88	57	-1.2	
$M_{D.L}$ due to 4' Bm	60	87	98	121	129	172	91	+56	0.732 K/f
$M_{D.L}$ due to 4' BM + 6" SLAB	84	122	139	170	182	170	129	78	0.3 K/1
MDL + Mbott + M6" Slab	145	204	229	269	278	258	186	76	
Simple span MDL of 3" F.O.Lay	22	32	36	44	47	44	33	8	0.267 K/1
-ve Moment from Table 3.4 of AISC	-8	-13	-15	-22	-30	-38	-46	-57	0.1585 wl²
Continueous Beam	14	21	21	22	17	6	-13	-49	
Total Moment	159	225	250	291	295	264	173	27	

Also assumed prestressed effective ratio based on $\frac{F_o}{F} = 1.31$ Governed by AASHTO

Try $e = 5.5''$

$$\text{Req'd } F = \frac{295 \times 12}{5.5 + 4.67} = 348$$

$$F_o = 348 \times 1.31 = 456$$

$$N = \frac{456}{28.9} = 15.7 \text{ use 16 Cables (strands) } \tfrac{1}{2}''\phi$$

$$\text{Exact } e = \frac{2\times2 + 2\times4 + 2\times6 + 8\times8}{16} = 5.5 = \text{assumed ok}$$

Check stage I at continuous end

for $f_{top} \le 3\sqrt{f_{ci}'} = 3\sqrt{4000}$

$$e \le 4.67 + \frac{703 \times 4.67 \times 0.19}{456} = 6.0'' > 5.5'' \text{ ok}$$

for $f_{bott} \le 0.6 f_{ci}' = 0.6 \times 4000$

$$e \le -4.67 + \frac{703 \times 4.67 \times 2.4}{456} = 12.6 > 5.5'' \text{ ok}$$

Check stage II at continuous end Bottom Stress.

$f_{bott} \le 0.6 f_c' = 0.6 \times 5000$

$$e \le -4.67 + \frac{-224 \times 12}{348} + \frac{703 \times 4.67 \times 3}{348} = 15.9'' > 5.5'' \text{ ok}$$

Check stage III at simply supported end Top stress

$f_{top} \le 3\sqrt{f_c'} = 3\sqrt{5000}$

$$e \le 4.67 + \frac{703 \times 4.67 \times 0.212}{348} = 6.6'' > 5.5'' \text{ ok}$$

$$\text{Check } \frac{E_c\,\text{slab}}{E_c(\text{pre})} = \frac{\sqrt{3000}}{\sqrt{5000}} = 0.77 \text{ ok.}$$

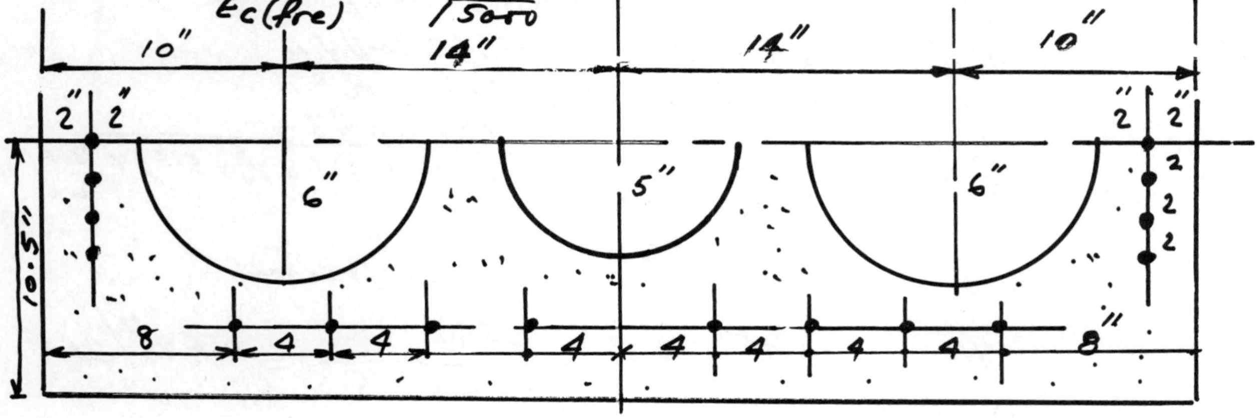

EXAMPLE 6-05

Given:- Design a four-lane highway bridge with simply supported, rolled-beam stringers. Structural steel to be used is A-36. Loading is HS20-44. Concrete to be used for the deck is cass A, with 28-day strength f'_c = 3,000 psi and allowable compressive stress f_c = 1,200 psi.

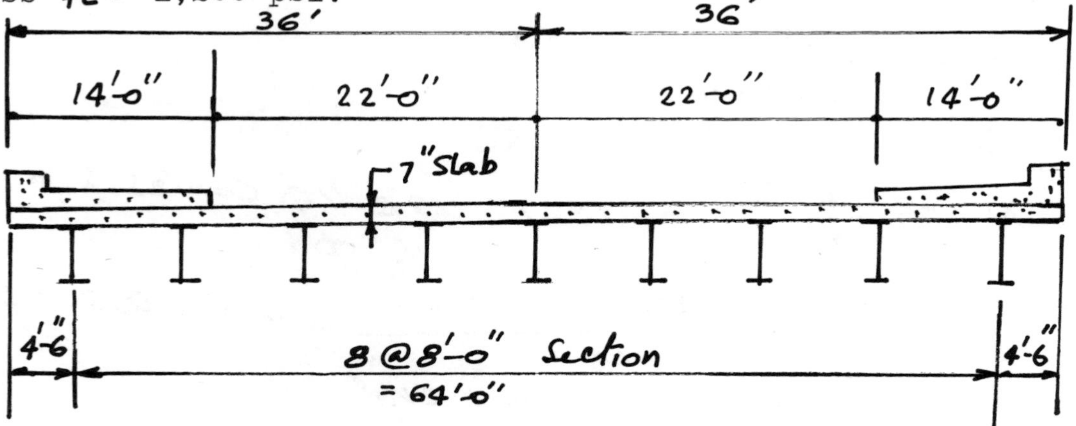

Concrete slab:- It is designed to span transversely between stringers as in non composite design

S. effective span = Distance between flange edges + $\frac{1}{2}$ fl. width

det-flange width = 1'

then $S = 8 - 1 + \frac{1}{2} = 7.5$ ft

assume 7" thick slab $= \frac{7}{12} \times 150 = 88$ psf and a $1\frac{1}{2}$ inch f.w.s weighs 20 psf.

Total D.L = 88 + 20 = 108 psf.

$$M_{D.L} = \frac{w_D S^2}{10} = \frac{108(7.5)^2}{10} = 608 \text{ ft-lb/ft}$$

Live load moment with reinforcement perpendicular to traffic, per ft of width in concrete slab as AASHTO

$$M_{LL} = 0.4(S+2) = 400(7.5+2) = 3800 \text{ ft-lb/ft}$$

$$M_{LL} + \text{IMPACT} = 3800 + 1140 = 4940 \text{ ft-lb/ft}$$

$$\therefore M_T = 608 + 4940 = 5548 \text{ ft-lb/ft}.$$

d_{eff} = 5.5" & Strip of slab = 12"

$$\therefore f_c = \frac{12M}{(kd)(Jd)\,b/2} = \frac{12 \times 5548}{(0.36 \times 5.5)(0.88 \times 5.5) \times \frac{12}{2}}$$

$$= 1158 < 1200 \text{ Psi}$$

Hence 7" thick slab is satisfactory

$$A_s = \frac{12M}{f_s J d} = \frac{12 \times 5548}{20000 \times 0.88 \times 5.5} = 0.69 \text{ in}^2/\text{ft}$$

5 @ 6" o/c & # 4 @ 6" o/c

Loading = HS20-44

Structural Steel = A36, $F_b = 20$ ksi, $F_v = 12$ ksi

Clear span = 50'-0, effective span = 53'-0"

Dead Load $= \frac{7}{12} \times 8 \times 0.15 = 0.70$

steel beam, haunch & diaphragm $= 0.20$

Load/stringer 0.90 k/ft

Curb $= 14 \times 0.5 \times 0.15 \times 2 = 2.10$ k/'

Railing $= 0.06$

Total $= 2.16$ k/ft

Load on 9 stringers = 2.16 k/'

Curb, Railing Load/stringer $= \frac{2.16}{9} = 0.24$ k/'

Total load per stringer $= 0.90 + 0.24 = 1.14$ k/ft

Live load

L.L distribution $= \frac{S}{5.5} = \frac{8}{5.5} = 1.45$ wheels

$= 0.725$ axle

Impact $= \frac{50}{53 + 125} = 0.28 < $ Max = 30%

Max. Moment

$M_{DL} = \frac{wL^2}{8} = \frac{1.14 \times 53^2}{8} = 400$'k

LLM $= 0.725 \times 681.45 = 494$'k

Impact $= 0.28 \times 494 = 138$'k

1032'k

Max shear

DL V $= 1.14 \times 26.5 = 30$

LL V $= 0.725 \times 59.35 = 43$

IMP V $= 0.28 \times 43 = 12$

85 KIPS.

$S_{required} = \frac{1032 \times 12}{20} = 619.2$ in^3

Use W 36 × 182 ($S = 622$ in^3, $I = 11300$ in^4)

check $f_b = \frac{1032 \times 12}{622} = 19.91 < 20$ ksi ok

$f_v = \frac{85}{36.32 \times .725} = 3.23 < 12$ ksi ok.

Deflection due to D.L $w = 1.14\ ^k/_{ft}$

$$\Delta = \frac{45\, w L^4}{2\, E_s I}$$

$$= \frac{45 \times 1.14 \times 53^4}{2 \times 29 \times 10^3 \times 11300} = 0.617''$$

Deflection due to Live load + Impact.

$$\Delta = \frac{324}{E_s I_s} P_T \left(L^3 - 555L + 4780\right)$$

(U.S.S.H Vol 2)

$P_T = 4 \times 9 \times 1.30 = 46.8$ kips
(Concentrated load on nine stringers = wt of front truck wheel × distribution factor plus impact)

$I_s = 9 \times 11300 = 101700\ in^4$

$$\Delta = \frac{324 \times 46.8}{29 \times 10^3 \times 101700} \left(53^3 - 555 \times 53 + 4780\right)$$

$$= 0.639\ in.$$

$$\frac{\text{Live load } \delta}{\text{Span}} = \frac{0.639}{53 \times 12} = \frac{1}{1000} < \frac{1}{800} \text{ O.K.}$$

EXAMPLE 6-06

Given:- Design an access bridge of span 51'-6" as per A.A.S.H.T.O. requirement to approach Rio Vallenciana Dam, in South America.

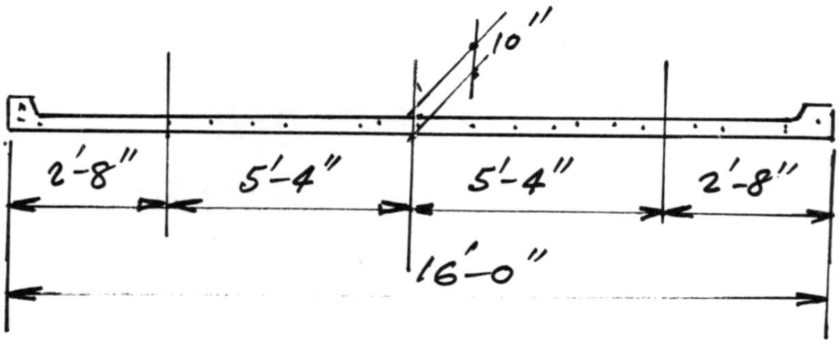

Beam design

assume slab 10" thick, span 51'-6"

Loading H20-S16 Steel corten type

Dead load carried by Steel

slab $= \frac{10}{12} \times 5.33 \times 0.15 = 0.63\ ^k/_1$

steel assumed $= 0.13$ Total $= 0.76\ ^k/_1$

L.L distribution factor $= \dfrac{5.33}{5.5} = 0.97$ wheel

Impact $= \dfrac{50}{5.33+125} = 38.3$ use 30%.

Max. moment for span 51.5′ from Gaylord Stl H/Book

$= 18L + \dfrac{392}{L} - 280$

$= 18 \times 51.5 + \dfrac{392}{51.5} - 280 = 654'^{k}$

Moment due to impact $= 654 \times \dfrac{30}{100} = 196'^{k}$

$M_T = 850'^{k}$

Trial Section $= \dfrac{850 \times 12}{33} = 309.9''$

use W 24×120

wheel load $= 16^{k}$

P+I $= 16 \times 1.3 = 20.8^{k}$

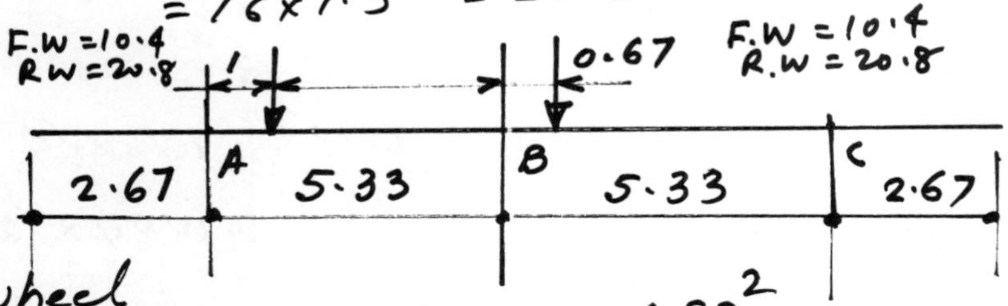

Rear wheel

$M_{AB} = \dfrac{20.8 \times 1 \times 4.33^2}{5.33^2} = 13.73'^{k}$

$M_{BA} = \dfrac{20.8 \times 1^2 \times 4.33}{5.33^2} = 3.17'^{k}$

$M_{BC} = \dfrac{20.8 \times 0.67 \times 4.66}{5.33^2} = 10.65'^{k}$

$M_{CB} = \dfrac{20.8 \times 0.67^2 \times 4.66}{5.33^2} = 1.53'^{k}$

By moment distribution:-

D.F	0	1	0.5	0.5	1	0
		+13.73	−3.17	+10.65	−1.53	
		−13.73	−6.62			
			−0.33	−0.33	−0.17	
		−0.17	−0.09	−0.85	+1.70	
		+0.24	+0.47	+0.47	+0.24	
		−0.24	−0.12	−0.12	−0.24	
		0	−9.82	+9.82	0	

∴ Rear wheel.

$R_B\,(\text{left}) = \dfrac{20.8 \times 12}{5.33^3}\left[5.33 + 2 \times 4.33\right] + \dfrac{9.82}{5.33} = 3.78^k$

$R_B\,(\text{right}) = \dfrac{20.8 \times 4.66^2}{5.33^3}\left[5.33 + 2 \times 0.67\right] + \dfrac{9.82}{5.33} = 21.65^k$

$\overline{\qquad 25.43^k}$

$\therefore$ Front wheel $= \dfrac{25.43}{2} = 12.72^k$

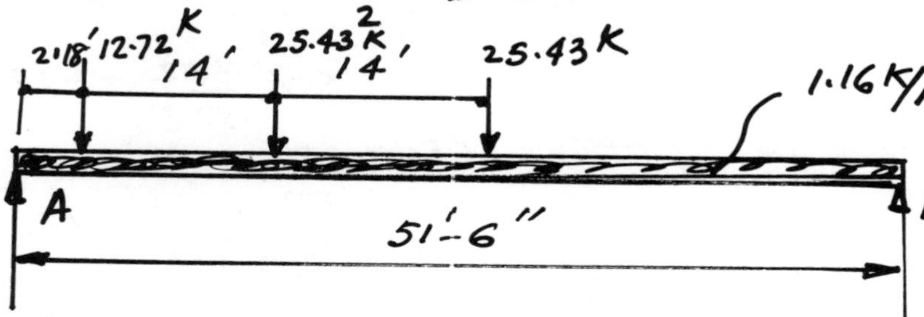

$R_B \times 51.5 = 1.16 \times 51.5 \times 25.75 + 12.72 \times 2.18 + 25.43 \times 16.18 + 25.43 \times 30.18$

$R_B = 52.23^k\ ;\ R_A = 69.0^k$

Point of shear being zero $= 16.18'$

$\therefore M = 69.0 \times 16.18 - 1.16 \times \dfrac{16.18^2}{2} - 12.72 \times 14 = 790'^k$

$S_{req'd} = \dfrac{790 \times 12}{33} = 288\ in^3$ use W24X120

Lateral bracing system.

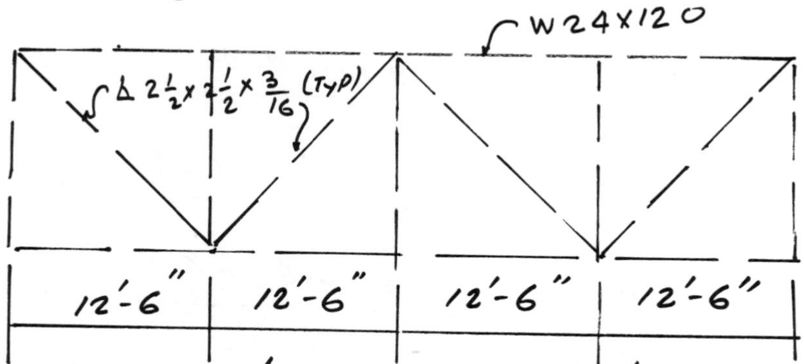

Design of transversly reinforced slab.

$f_c = 1350$ Psi; $f_s = 20000$ Psi; $t = 10''$

S = c to c stringer distance − ½ FLG width

$= 5.33 - 0.58 = 4.75$

L.L moment/ft of slab width $= 0.8P(S+2)/32$

where $P = 16K$; Impact $= \dfrac{50}{4.75+125} = 38.8$ use 30%

Design moment/ft width of slab.

D.L Moment $= \left(\frac{10}{12} \times 0.15\right) \times \frac{4.75^2}{10} = 0.282$

LL moment $= \frac{1}{32}\left(1.3 \times 0.8 \times 0.16(4.75+2)\right) = 3.52$

$3.802'^{k}$

$d = \sqrt{\frac{3.802 \times 1000}{226}} = 4.10''$ use $D = 10''$

$As = \frac{3.802}{1.44 \times 7.5} = 0.352\ \square''$

Use # 4@6" Transversely, & # 4@14 long. top & bott.

D.L. deflection:-

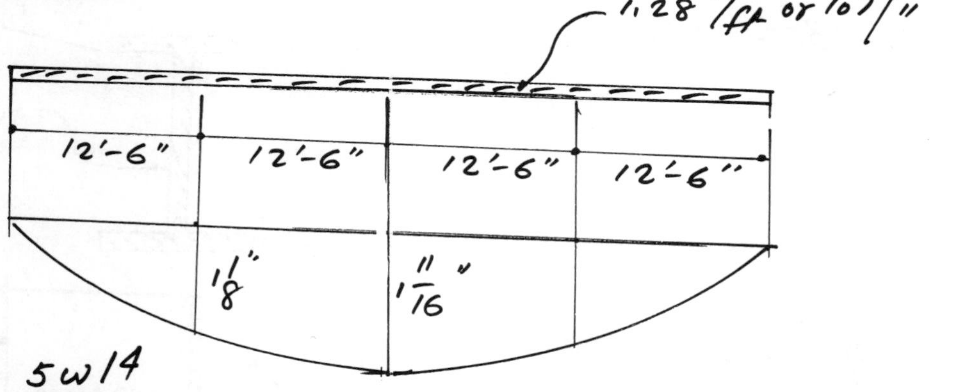

$\Delta_{max} = \frac{5wl^4}{384EI}$

$= \frac{5 \times 107 \times 600^4}{384 \times 30 \times 10^6 \times 3635.3} = 1.67''$

$\Delta_{x\frac{1}{4}} = \frac{Wx}{24EI}\left[L^3 - 2Lx^3 + x^3\right] = \frac{107 \times 150}{24 \times 30 \times 10^6 \times 3135.3}\left(6 \times 10^3 - 2700 + 337.5\right)$

$= 1.08''$

Cross bracing

Unbraced length of girder $= \frac{50.0}{4} = 12.5'$

Wind load = 50 PSF

Exposed Area of bridge/ft = 6.58 ft

Wind force on structure = $50 \times 6.58 = 329\ \#/ft$

Since the wind is uniform, reaction at support from D.L

$= 71.5 \times \frac{0.329}{1.28} = 18.38^k$ Say 20^k

Hence $\frac{1}{2}$ of $20^k = 10^k$ acts at each upper corner of end cross frame.

stress in AB $= 10^k C$; Stress in CB $= \frac{10 \times 73.76}{72} = 10.24^k T$

use $\angle\ 2\frac{1}{2} \times 2\frac{1}{2} \times 3/16$ good for $27^k > 10.24$ ok

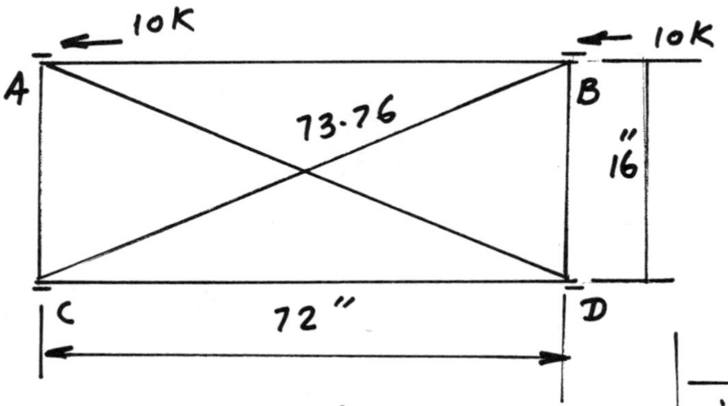

X-Bracing

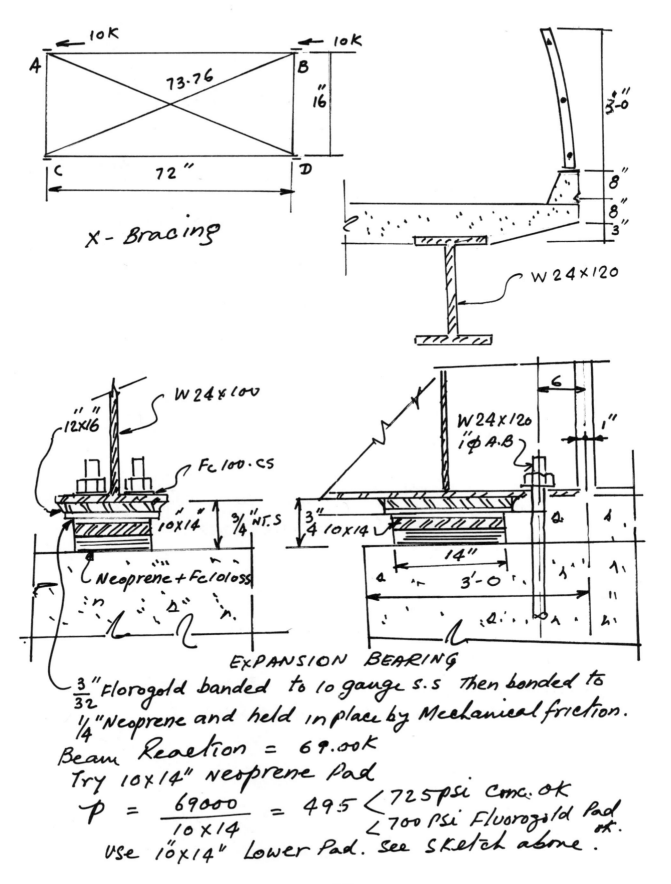

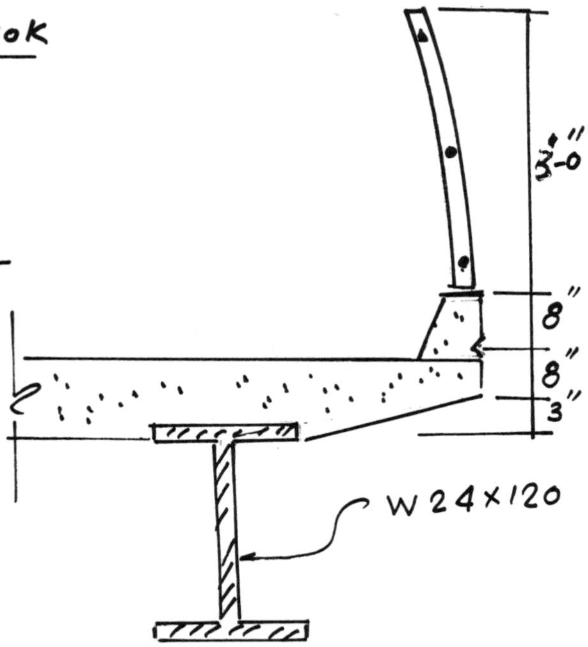

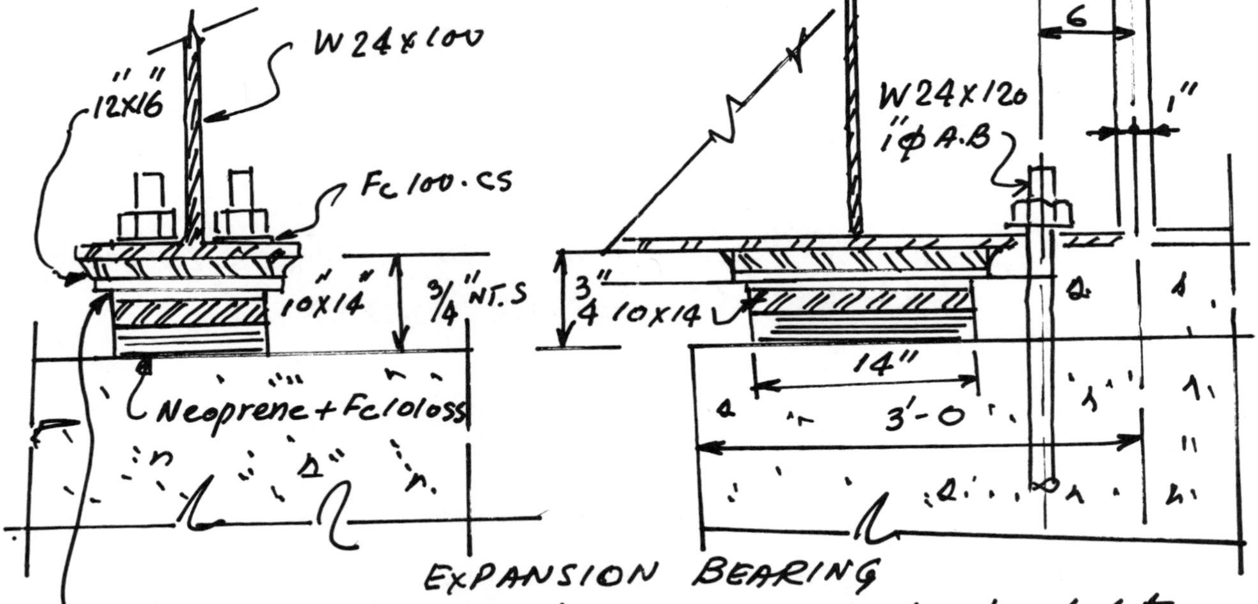

EXPANSION BEARING

$\frac{3}{32}$" Florogold banded to 10 gauge s.s then bonded to 1/4" Neoprene and held in place by Mechanical friction.

Beam Reaction = 69.00K

Try 10×14" Neoprene Pad

$$p = \frac{69000}{10 \times 14} = 495 < 725 \text{ psi Conc. OK}$$
$$< 700 \text{ psi Fluorogold Pad ok.}$$

Use 10"×14" Lower Pad. See sketch above.

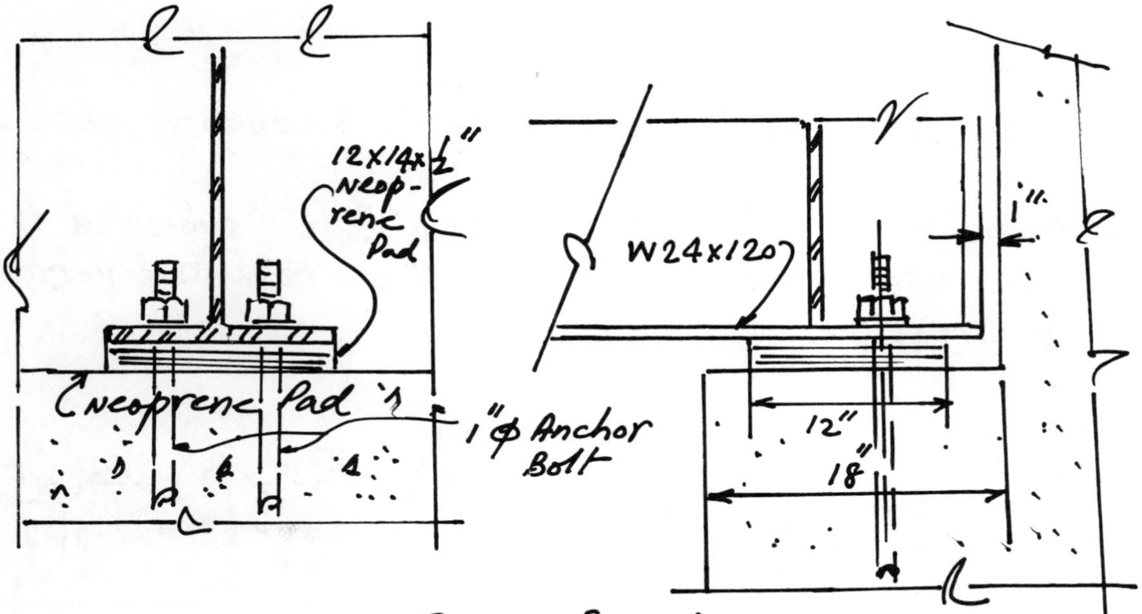

FIXED BEARING

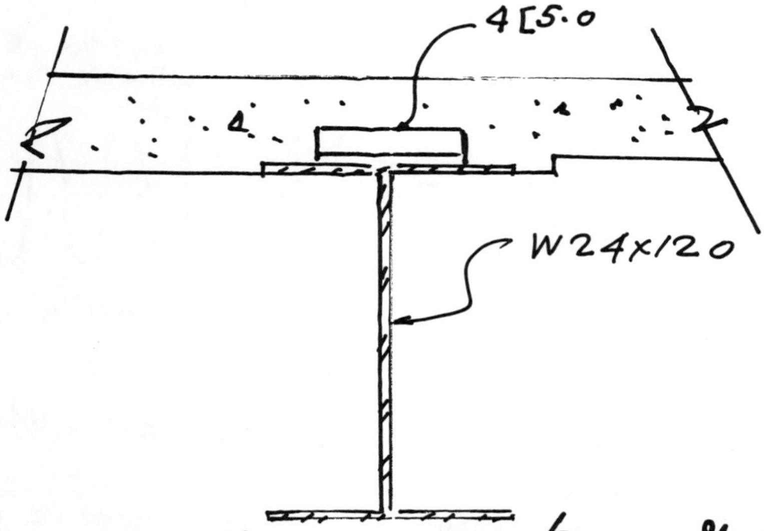

Design of shear connectors:- It is omitted except to emphasize their importance. Their purpose is to insure composite action between the concrete slab and the steel beam by preventing the slab from sliding along the steel flange and lifting off the flange. The welds should be designed to resist the shear carried by the connectors, including fatigue due to repeated loads. Shear connectors must have atleast 1" cover in all sides.

A. Values of R

1. From table 1.7.3 A/AASHTO for H.S. Loading, Case I no. of cycles = 500,000.

2. Since beam is continuous, splice is subjected to reversals of stress rather than repeated variations of stress as in case 4 below

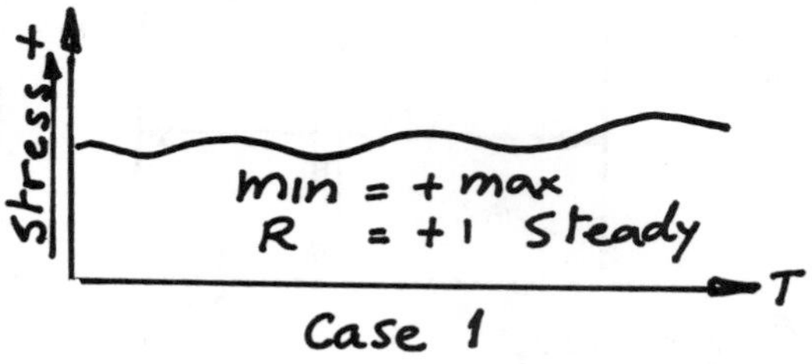

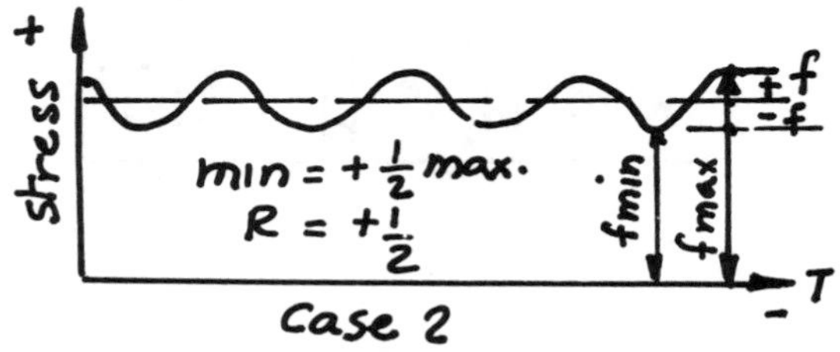

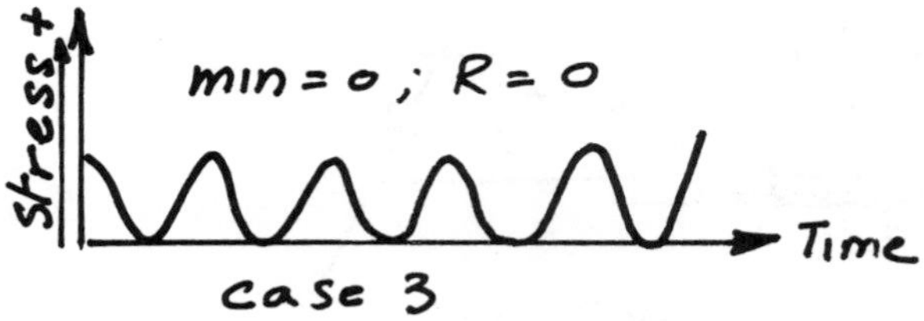

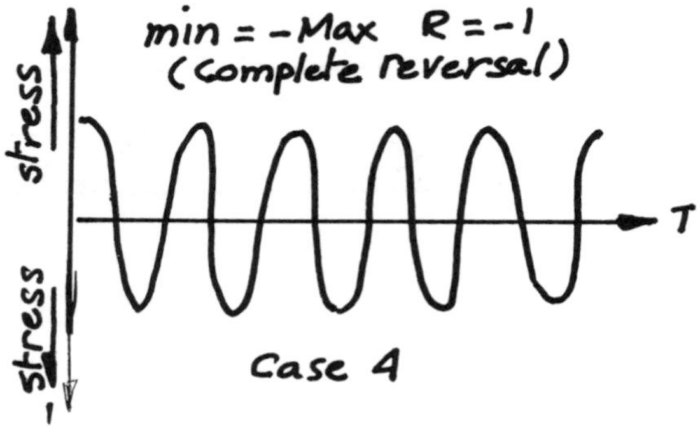

$$R = \frac{f\,min}{f\,max.}$$

3. Since case 4 apples to continueous beams, Max - Moment is always greater than max. + Mom.
and $R = \frac{\text{max.} - \text{Mom (min)}}{\text{Max} + \text{Mom (max.)}}$ = is negative ie < 0
At splice location (0.2 L or more) in any span R is negative

4. Since $R < 0$, splice design should be based on allowable fatigue stress as given in Section 1.7.3 AASHTO which would reduce allowable stress in the ratio of $\frac{\text{fallow. fatigue stress}}{\text{fallow. basic unit stress}}$
A36 = 20000 psi bending, 12000 psi shear

or Increase actual moments or shear by ratio of $\dfrac{f_{allow.}\ \text{basic unit}}{f_{allow.}\ \text{fatigue stress}}$

5. From fig. 1.7.3.A/AASHTO, min $R = -1$ and max $R = +1$. This is also verified from four cases shown above. It means that member is stressed from tension to an estimated compression. This is not the case @ field splice but we assume so.

B. Allowable Fatigue Stress Fr.

1. for field splice. Fr is calculated from table 1.7.3, N = 500,000

	from	a	k_2	
Tension :-	20500 psi	0.78	0.55	note 4
Comp :	13300 psi	0.78	–	note 1

2. note 4. Allow f tension from graph 1.7.3 A for A36 for $R = -1$ curve 1 gives $F_r = 13300$ psi

or for low alloy steel for $N = 500{,}000$, $k_1 = 1.16$ for $t < \frac{3}{4}''$

$$F_r = \frac{k_1(20500)}{1 - 0.55R} = \frac{1.16(20500)}{1 + 0.55} = 15{,}350 \text{ P.S.I}$$

3. note 1. Allow f comp from $F_r = \dfrac{0.55\,F_y}{1 - \left(\dfrac{0.55F_y}{k_1} - 1\right)R} = \dfrac{0.55 \times 36000}{1 - \left(\dfrac{0.55 \times 36000}{1 \times 13300} - 1\right)(-1)}$

where $k_1 = 1.0 + a\left(\dfrac{F_y}{58000} - 1\right) \leq 1$

$$= 1.0 + .78\left(\frac{58000}{58000} - 1\right) = 1$$

$$\therefore F_r = \frac{19800}{1 - (0.4887)(-1)} = \frac{19800}{1.4887} = 13300 \text{ psi}$$

for tension & compression, $f_{r\,allow}$:- 13300 psi

4. Ratio of $\dfrac{f_{allow}\ \text{fatigue stress}}{f_{allow}\ \text{basic unit stress}} = \dfrac{13{,}300}{20{,}000} = 0.665$ T

& $= \dfrac{13{,}300}{18700} = 0.712$ C.

Design Criteria:-

1. a. Find max. moment @ splice location (could be +M or -M) from computer output of Beam Design. Call this Msplice

   b. Calculate resisting Moment of Beam, call this R.M. beam. Since ftension = 20000 would give larger value than fcomp (= 18700 psi) use moments obtained by f = 20000

$$R.M.\,beam = \frac{20000 \times \text{Section Modulus of beam}}{12000}$$

   c. Find average of above two moments:- Call this Mavg

$$M_{avg} = \frac{M_{splice} + R.M.\,beam}{2}$$

2. Calculate Modified Moment due to fatigue unit stress call this $M_{fatigue}$. $M_{fatigue} = \frac{f_{allow.} \times M_{splice}}{F_r}$

   a. $M_{fatigue}$ tension $= \frac{20000}{13{,}300} \times M_{splice} = 1.51\, M_{splice}$

   b. " " Compression $= \frac{18700}{13{,}300} \times M_{splice} = 1.37\, M_{splice}$

3. Calculate 75% of Beam Resisting Moment. Call this 0.75 R.M. beam

4. Compare Mave. and $M_{fatigue}$ with 0.75 R.M. beam

   a. If 0.75 RM beam > Mave or $M_{fatigue}$ can be bolted Beam splice

   b. If 0.75 R.M. beam < Mave or $M_{fatigue}$ splices are to be designed per AASHO

Note:-
The above analysis is based on fallow. for tension which gives maximum resisting moment of beam. It can also be compared with fallow & Fr for compression.

EXAMPLE 6-07

Given:-Select field splice for interior beam W 33 x 141 of U.S.26 Lt.Bridge for computer output M splice -321'K

Beam size = W33x141, S = 446.8 in^3; Span = 75'

splice @ 0.2L of 75' span.

$$R.M.\ beam = \frac{20}{12} \times 446.8 = 745'^{K}$$

$$M_{ave.} = \frac{321 + 745}{2} = \frac{1066}{2} = 533'^{K}$$

$$M_{fatigue\ tension} = 1.51 \times 321 = 485'^{K}$$

$$0.75\ R.M\ Beam = 0.75 \times 745 = 558'^{K}$$

$> M_{ave}$ 533'K

$> M_{fatigue}$. 485'K

use standard splice.

EXAMPLE 6-08

Given:- Design an Elastromeric Bearing Pad for span of 86.8' of bridge carrying a total load of 2.0 k/ft. on the entire span.

Elastomeric Bearing:- Hardness 60, Modulus $M_{70}^{\circ F} = 160$

$M_{20}^{\circ F} = 1.9 \times 160$

Temp. change = +35°F to -45°F

For other properties, refer to DuPont Design of Neoprene Pads.

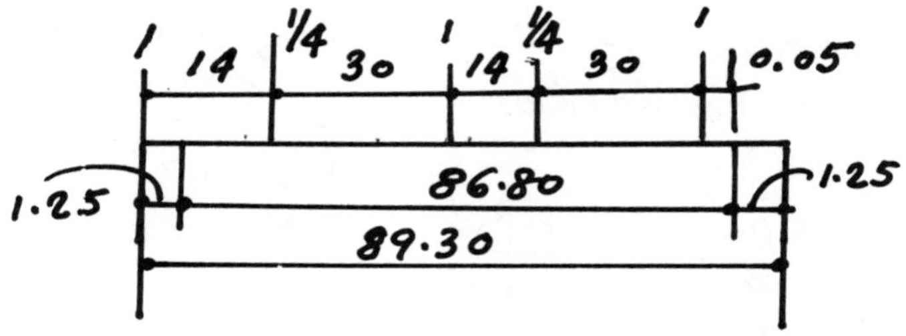

D.L Int. Beam

$= 2.0 \times 89.3 = 178.6^{K}$

$$R_{D.L} = \frac{178.6}{2} = 89.3^{K}$$

$L.L$, $I = \frac{50}{86.8+125} = 0.236$

$\frac{R_U}{P} = \frac{88.05+44.05+0.05}{86.80} + \frac{74.05+30.05}{4 \times 86.80}$

$= 1.523 + 0.300 = 1.823$

$R_{LL}+I = 1.823 \times 32 \times 1.236 = 72^K$

$R_{LL}+I+R_{DL} = 72 + 89.3 = 161.3^K$

Size of Pad = $48 \times 5 \times 2''$

Max. Pressure $= \frac{R}{A} = \frac{175000}{48 \times 5}$

$= 730\text{ psi} < 800$ ok

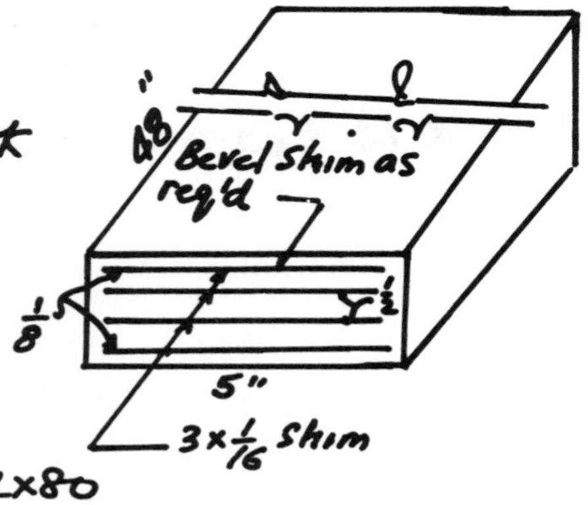

Length change at 45°F

$\Delta_{45} = 0.000006 \times 86.8 \times 12 \times 45$

$= 0.281''$

$\Delta_{max} = \Delta_{35+45} = 0.000006 \times 86.8 \times 12 \times 80$

$= 0.500''$

$T \leq \frac{W}{5}$ Lamination $1/2 \leq 5/5$

$T \geq 2\Delta_{max}$ Pad $2'' > 2 \times 0.5 = 1.0$ ok

$T \geq 1''$ $2'' > 1.''$ ok

Shear force $F = \frac{M_{20}^{\circ F} \times W \times L \times \Delta_{45}^{\circ F}}{T} = \frac{1.9 \times 160 \times 5 \times 48 \times 0.281}{2}$

$= 10.3^K$

$20\%\ R_{DL} = 20\%\ (89.3) = 17.86 > 10.3$ ok

Check for bevel requirement.

Shape factor $= \frac{48 \times 5}{2(48+5) \times \frac{1}{2}} = 4.53$ use 4

$\frac{R_{DL}}{A} = \frac{89.3^K}{48 \times 5} = 372$ psi

∴ for 60 Hardness & 4.00 shape factor, Compressive strain = 5% as per dupont charts.

EXAMPLE 6-09

Given:- Perform the settlement analysis of 10'x 10'x 2'-9" footing designed for the center pier of Example 6-01. Also find the maximum load allowable acting on the center column by two span rigid frame analysis method.

Settlement analysis

$$P_c = P_o + SP_1 \times C_w \times C_d$$

wher P_c = Contact pressure (tsf) between bottom of footing & soil pressure.

P_o = Confining pressure (tsf) provided by the soil to the side of the footing.

S = Settlement in inches

C_W = correction factor for the effect of ground water table.

P_1 = Pressure (tsf) empirically developed to fit data

C_d = Correction factor for the effect of depth of footing max. value 2.

$0.5 \leq C_W \leq 1.0$

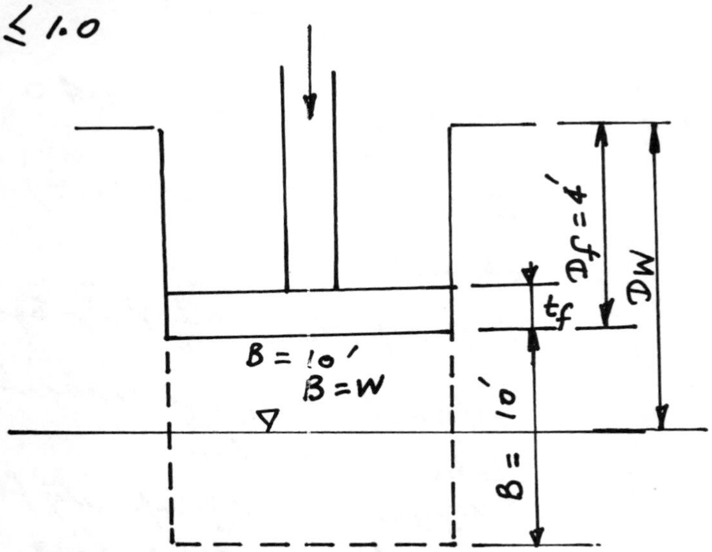

$P_c = (P_{col} + W_f + W_b) \div (B \times W)$

$= (125 + 20.63 + 6.83) \div 100 = 1.52$ TSF

$P_o = 0.0625 \times 4 = 0.25$

$P_1 = 0.36(N_{ca} - 3)$

$N_C = C_n N$

$C_n = 0.77 \log_{10}\left(\frac{20}{p}\right) = 1.47$ wher $p = 0.25$

$N_{c_1} = 1.47 \times 12 = 17.58$ for sand above/below gr. water

$N_{c_2} = 1.47 \times 25 = 36.75$ for silty sand below gr. water

$N_C = C_n N'$

$N' = 15 + (N - 15) \div 2$

$N_{c_1} = 1.47 \times 13.5 = 19.85$ $\quad N_{c_1 avg} = \frac{17.58 + 19.85}{2} = 18.72$ Say 19

Also

$N_{c_2} = 1.47 \times 20 = 29.4$ $\quad N_{c_2} avg = \frac{36.75 + 29.4}{2} = 33.08$ Say 33

Hence N_{ca} of boring ① & ② $= \frac{19 + 33}{2} = 26$

Hence $P_1 = \frac{1}{4}\left[0.36\,(N_{ca} - 3)\right]$

$= \frac{1}{4}\left[0.36\,(26 - 3)\right] = 2.07$

$C_W = 0.5\left(1.0 + \frac{D_W}{D_f + B}\right) = 1.04$

$C_d = 1.0 + \frac{D_f}{B} = 1.40$

$\therefore \quad 1.52 = 0.25 + S(2.07 \times 1.04 \times 1.4)$

$S = 0.42 < 1''$

Now $P_{c_{ult}} = C N_c S_c + P_o N_p S_p + \frac{1}{2} \gamma N_\gamma S_\gamma B$

where $P_{c_{ult}}$ = ultimate bearing capacity of soil

C = cohesive factor

N_c = Terzaghi bearing capacity factor $\propto \phi^0$

S_c = shape factor depending B/W

N_p = Terzaghi bearing capacity factor

S_p = shape factor depending upon B/W

γ = avg. unit weight (tcf)

N_γ = Terzaghi bearing capacity factor

S_γ = shape factor depending upon B/W

B = minimum footing width (ft).

$C = 0$ $\quad N_q = 40 \quad N_\gamma = 21$

$P_o = 0.25 \quad S_q = 1 \quad S_\gamma = 1 - \frac{0.2B}{W} = 0.8$

$\therefore P_{c_{ult}} = 0.25 \times 40 \times 1 + \frac{1}{2} \times 90 \times 21 \times 0.8 \times 10$

$= 10 + 7560 = 7570\ \#/\square'$

$= 3.79\ T/sf$

$P_{c_{allow}} = 0.25 + \frac{(3.79 - 0.25)}{2.5\ (S.F)} = 1.67\ TSf > 1.52$ ok

$P_{c_{col\ all.}} = (1.67 \times 100) - 20.63 - 6.83 = 139.54 > 125^T$ ok

Check of Column loading

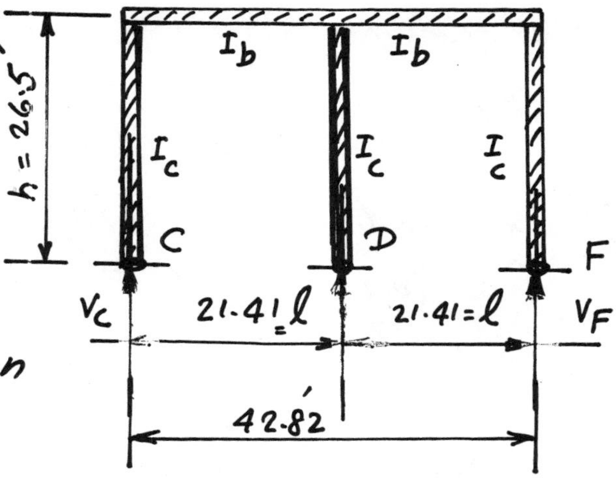

Both truck & Lane loading applied on roadway. Truck loading as per span ratio of $L : nL = 1.4$ & $L = 99'$, Reaction is 63.K concentrically. For equivalent uniform Loading on pier, one can take $w_1 = 0.70\ ^k/ft$

Also D.L of stringer Void slab $w_2 = 1.032\ ^k/'$

Total $w = w_1 + w_2 = 1.732\ ^k/ft$

Pier Cap size assumed is $4.5' \times 4.5'$, $I_b = 34.17\ ft^4$

Col size assumed is $3' \times 3'$, $I_c = 6.75\ ft^4$

then $n_1 = \frac{I_b}{I_c} \times \frac{h}{l} = \frac{34.17}{6.75} \times \frac{26.5}{21.41} = 6.27$

Then $V_C = V_F = \frac{wl}{2} \times \frac{3n_1+3}{4n_1+3}$

$$= \frac{1.732 \times 21.41}{2} \times \frac{3 \times 6.27+3}{4 \times 6.27+3}$$

$$= 14.40^k$$

Also $V_D = wl \times \frac{5n_1+3}{4n_1+3}$

$$= 1.732 \times 21.41 \times \frac{5 \times 6.27+3}{4 \times 6.27+3}$$

$$= 45.3^K$$

Since there are max 11 stringers on whole Pier cap & Central Col. takes $5\frac{1}{2}$ max stringers reactions. There is no wind acting on Center Column

$\therefore R_D = V_D = 45.3 \times 5.5 = 249.15^k = 124.57^T$

Say $125^T < 139.54$ ok

Check Loads on exterior Cols. C & F. P due to wind = 17.39^k

Reaction $V_C = V_F$ due to wind $= \frac{1}{2}\frac{Ph}{l} =$

$$= \frac{1}{2} \times \frac{17.39 \times 26.5}{21.41}$$

$$= 10.76^K$$

Since there is max 3 stringers acting on each Col.

Hence $V_C = V_F$ due to wind $= 10.76 \times 3 = 32.28^K$

& $V_C = V_F$ due to truck $= 14.40 \times 3 = 43.20^k$

Total 75.48^k

Say 37.24^T

Size of footing provided for end Columns of Pier is $7' \times 7' \times 2'\text{-}9''$.

EXAMPLE 6-10

Given:- Design an abutment for two spans continuous bridge of 39.85' and having a four lane traffic for city street. Loading is HS20-44 and depth of footing is 24'-3". The soil is sandy gravel with angle of internal friction 34°.

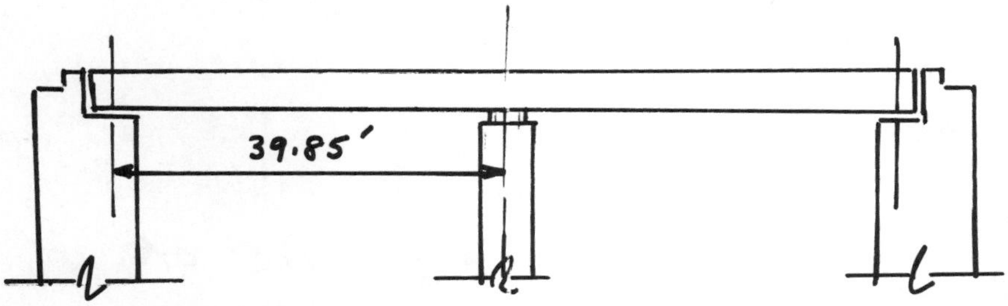

Dead Load 2" W.S = 0.1 K/1

6" Conc. = 0.3 K/1

Box. BM 27" S. wt = 0.72 K/1

1.12 K/4 for 4' stringer

Dead Load $= \frac{1.12}{4} = 0.28$ K/1

$R_A = R_B = \frac{0.28 \times 39.85}{2} = 5.58^K$

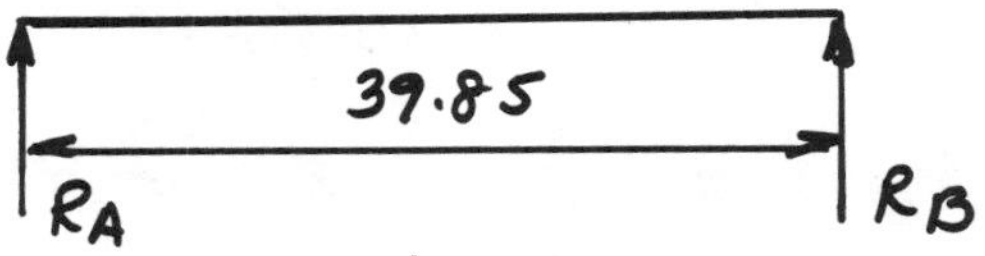

Live Load due to truck

$R_A = \frac{4 \times 11.85 + 16 \times 25.85 + 16 \times 39.85}{39.85}$

$= 27.56$ K

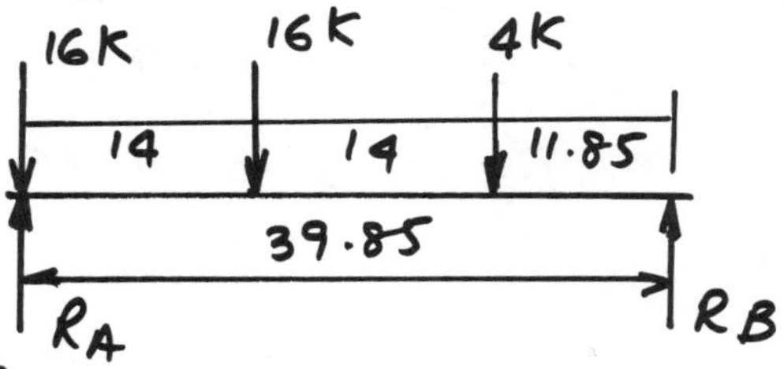

Live load due to Lane loading

$R_A = 26 + \frac{0.64 \times 39.85}{2} = 38.75^K$

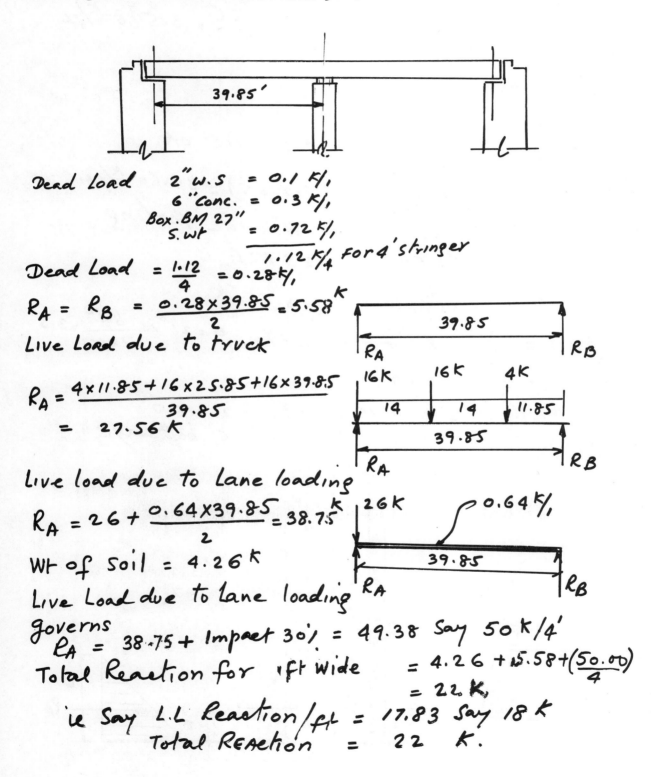

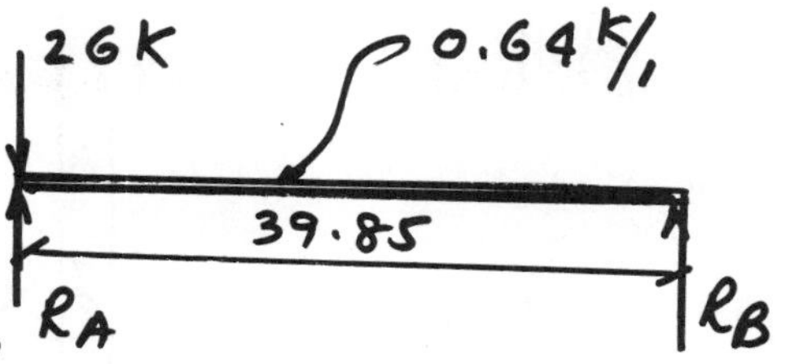

Wt of soil $= 4.26^K$

Live Load due to Lane loading governs

R_A = 38.75 + Impact 30% = 49.38 Say 50 K/4'

Total Reaction for 1 ft wide $= 4.26 + 5.58 + \left(\frac{50.00}{4}\right)$

$= 22$ K

ie Say L.L Reaction/ft = 17.83 Say 18 K

Total Reaction = 22 K.

Bearing Area of footing $= \frac{22 \times 1000}{4400} = 5.0\,\square'$

Assume the depth of footing $= 2'\text{-}3''$

The net upward pressure

$$= \frac{22 - 4.26}{5.0} = 3.548\ ^{k}/_{ft}.$$

Assumptions

$f_c' = 3000$ Psi

$V_c = 2\sqrt{f_c'} = 110$ Psi

$v = \frac{3548}{12 \times .85 \times 21} = 16.56 < 110$ ok.

$W_U = 1.4(9.84) + 1.7(12.25) = 34.60\ ^{k}/_{ft}$

Net soil pressure over 8' wide footing

$$= \frac{34.60}{8} = 4.325 \text{ ksf}.$$

$M_U = \frac{4.325 \times (2.0)^2}{2} = 8.65'^{k}$

$K_U = \frac{M_U}{F}$ & F for $b_w = 96''$, $d = 21''$ is $\frac{bd^2}{12000} = 3.5$

$= \frac{8.65}{3.5} = 2.47$

$\therefore$ Min. steel $= 0.0015 \times 96 \times 21 = 2.016\,\square''$

use #9 @ 6 both ways

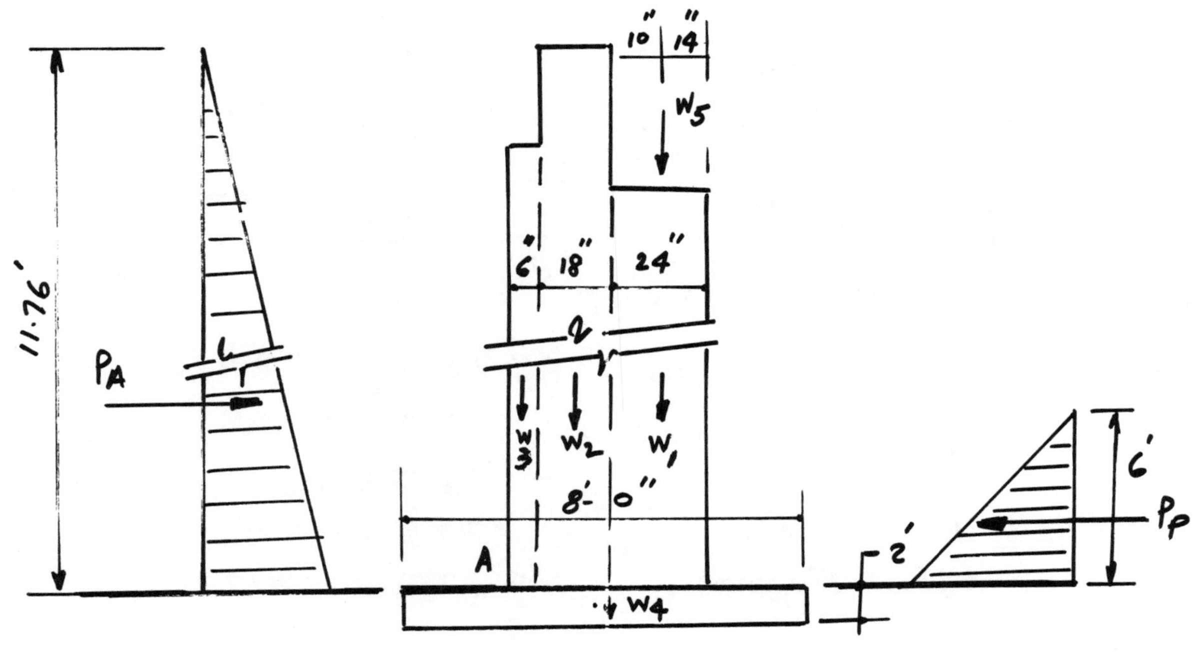

$k_p = \tan^2(45° + \frac{34}{2}) = 3.53$

$k_A = \tan^2(45 - \frac{34}{2}) = 0.2827$

$P_A = 0.2827 \times \frac{1}{2} \times 120 \times 11.76^2 = 2.345\,k$

$P_p = 3.53 \times \frac{1}{2} \times 120 \times 6^2 = 7.625^k$

$W_1 = 8.76 \times 2 \times 150 \times 1'-0 = 2.628k$

$W_2 = 11.76 \times 1.5 \times 150 \times 1'-0'' = 2.646\,k$

$W_3 = 10.76 \times 0.5 \times 150 \times 1'-0'' = 0.807\,k$

$W_4 = 8.00 \times 2.0 \times 150 \times 1'-0'' = 2.400\,k$

Force	Arm x from A	Moment ft-k
W1 = 2.628	3.00′	+7.884
W2 = 2.646	1.25′	+3.308
W3 = 0.807	0.25′	+0.202
W4 = 2.400 k	2′-0″	+4.800
W5 = 18 k	2.83′	+50.940
PA = 2.345	3.92′	+9.192
Pp = 7.625	2′-0	-15.25
Σ 26.481		+61.076

overturning moment = 6.08

F.S against O.T $= \frac{61.076}{6.058} =$ >2.0 ok

F.S against sliding =

$x = \frac{61.076}{26.481} = 2.31$

$e = 2.34 - 2.31 = 0.03 < 1.33$ ok

$f = \frac{P}{A}\left(1 \pm \frac{6e}{b}\right) = \frac{26.481}{8.0}\left(1 \pm \frac{6 \times .03}{8}\right)$

$= 3.310(1 \pm 0.025) = 3.392$ or 3.227 ok

Design of structural Steel:

$As = 0.0010 \times 12 \times 44.5'' = 0.334$ as min. steel when d is 48″.

Use #5 @ 12″ c/c Horizontal & #5 @ 24″ c/c vertically.

7

DAMS AND SPILLWAY

GRAVITY DAM

It is a solid concrete/masonary structure designed and shaped so that its weight is sufficient to insure stability against the effects of all imposed forces. It usually has trapezoidal profile with the upstream face vertical. Dams upto 100' high are generally considered as Low Dams. Dams from 100'-300' high as Medium Dams. Over 300' high as High Dams.
Structural Height:- It is the difference in elevation between the top of the dam and the lowest point in the excavated foundation area. The level of the crown of the roadway is considered to be the top of the dam.
Hydraulic Height:- To which the water is raised by the structure and is the difference in the elevation between the lowest point of the original steambed at the axis of the dam and the highest controlled water surface.

EXAMPLE 7-01
Given:- Design a gravity dam 29 meters high and 24 meters wide at the base, for Rio Vallenciano, South America.
For stability of Non Overflow Section, the dam must resist tendencies to destruction:
1. overturning
2. sliding
3. overstressing

Criteria for safe functions of the dam against the above tendencies are:
1. Vertical stress @ upstream edge of horizontal section com-

puted without uplift must be greater than the uplift pressure at that point or e should fall within the middle third of the base.

2. $\Sigma H / \Sigma W-U \leq 0.8$ for sound rock.

3. Unit stresses in the concrete and foundation

Forces to be considered are:

1. uplift
2. slit pressure
3. earth pressure
4. weight of the structure
5. resulting reaction of the foundation

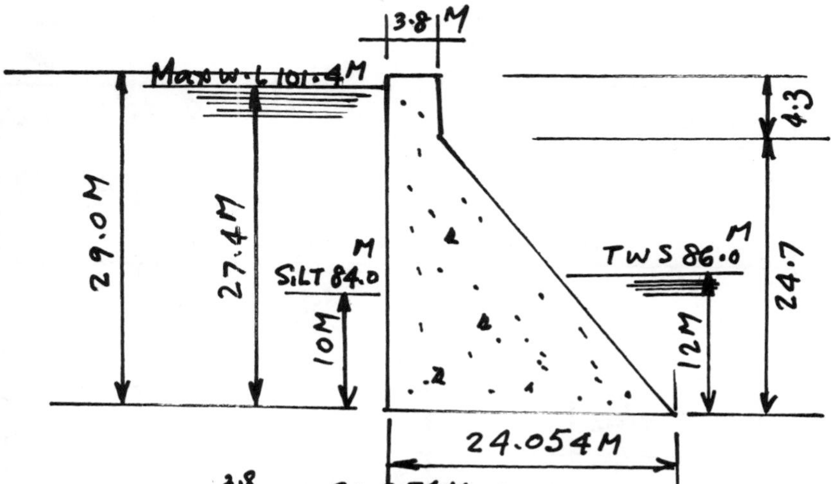

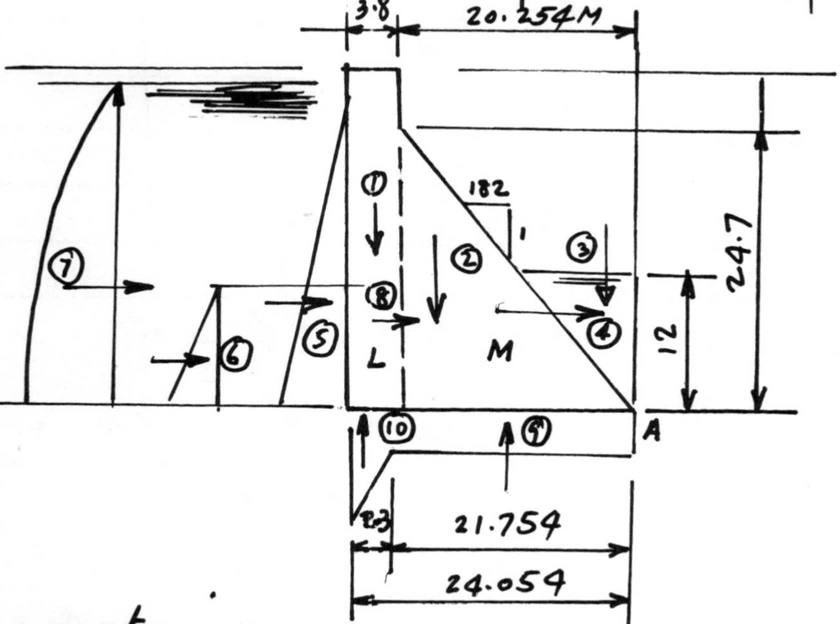

Check for overturning

Consider strip of base section 1 M & take moments about A.

WT of structure ① $3.8 \times 29 \times 2.4 = 264.48$ MT

② $\frac{1}{2} \times 24.7 \times 20.254 \times 2.4 = 600.33$ MT

⑧ Veb = 944776.8 × 0.1 = 944.777 MT

Meb = 94477.68 × 10.485 = 990.561 MT

Line	Item	Force	Horiz'l arm	vert. arm	Moment	moment
Vert. Forces					Mx	My
A	Portion L	264.48 ①	22.154	14.5	5859.29	3334.96
B	Portion M	600.33 ②	14.50	8.233	8704.76	4942.50
	Σ W	864.81		Σ	14564.05	8777.46
∴ X	= Σ Mx/Σ W	= 14564.053/864.81 = 16.841 M				
∴ Y	= Σ My/Σ W	= 8777.46/864.81			= 10.1496 M	
C	= Tailwater	59.37 ③	3.298		195.8299	
d	uplift	288.65 ⑨	12.03		-3471.57	
e	uplift	-17.00	23.52		-399.84	
Horizontal	forces					
f	Tailwater	72.0 ④		4.00		+288.0
g	Hd. water	375.38 ⑤		9.133		-3428.35
h	E/Q H_2O	40.06 ⑦		11.3		452.69
J	E/Q Mass	94.472 ⑧		10.15		958.911
K	Silt Pr.	33.39 ⑥		3.333		-111.2898

Without Earthquake But silt & water

Vertical forces

	Σ W−U ↓ +	Σ M +
① + ②	864.81	14564.05
③	59.37	195.83
⑨	-288.65	− 3471.57
⑩	- 17.00	− 399.84
Horizontal forces		
④		+ 288.00
⑥		− 111.29
⑤	Σ 618.53	− 3428.35
		Σ 7638.87

Σ H = 375.38 + 33.39 − 72.0 = 336.77

$$\tan\theta = \frac{\Sigma H}{\Sigma W-U} = \frac{336.77}{618.53} = 0.545 < 0.8 \text{ ok}$$

Vertical Tail water ③ $\frac{1}{2} \times 12 \times 9.895 \times 1.0$ = 59.37 MT

Horizontal Tail water ④ $\frac{1}{2} \times 1.0 \times (12)^2$ = 72.00 MT

Horizontal Head water ⑤ $\frac{1}{2} \times 1.0 \times 27.4^2$ = 375.38 MT

Silt Pressure ⑥ $\frac{w_s h^2}{2}\left(\frac{1 - \sin\phi}{1 + \sin\phi}\right)$ =

$\frac{1.362 \times 10^2}{2} \times \frac{0.658}{1.342}$ = 33.39 MT

Earthquake water ⑦* = 40.06 MT

Earthquake mass ⑧* = 94.48 MT

uplift ⑨ $1 \times 12 \times 24.1$ = 288.65 MT

uplift ⑩ $(1.0 \times 27.4) - 12$ = 15.40 MT

*Earthquake forces

a) Earthquake effect on water mass.

$P_e = C \lambda w h$

From the chart Fig 164 (Design of small dams by U.S.D.O.I B.O.R)

Pressure coefficient for φ (angle of face from vertical) is 0.735

λ = Earthquake Intensity = $\frac{\text{Earthquake acc.}}{\text{acc. of gravity}} = 0.1$

w = unit wt of water = 1000 kg/m3

h = Total depth of Reservoir @ section.

= 27.40 M

P_e = $0.735 + 0.1 \times 1000 \times 27.40$ = 2013.9

⑦ $V_{earthquake} = 0.726\, P_e h = 0.726 \times 2013.9 \times 27.40 = 40.06$ MT

$M_{eQ} = 0.299\, P_e h^2 = 0.299 \times 2013.9 \times 27.40^2 = 45.21$ MT

b) Earthquake effect on Concrete mass.

@ C.G. of mass

	339439.2 × 14.5	=	4921868.4
	605337.6 × $\frac{24.7}{3}$	=	4983744.4
Σ	944776.8		Σ 9905612.8

C.G. of mass = $\frac{9905612.8}{944776.8} = 10.485$ M

Point of resultant intersect at base

$\bar{x}$ from ℄ $= \frac{7636.8678}{618.5317} = 12.35^M$

with Earthquake, silt & water

	↓+	↶+	ΣH
	618.53	7636.87	336.77
E/Q. H_2O	–	– 452.69	40.06
E/Q Mass	–	– 958.91	94.48
	618.53	6225.27	471.31

$\tan Q = \frac{471.31}{618.53} = 0.762 < 0.8$ ok

Point of resultant intersect @ base $\bar{x}$ from ℄ $= \frac{6225.27}{618.53} = 10.06$ M

∴ e 1) for case w/o (E/Q + Silt + H_2O) from ℄ of base

$= \frac{24.053}{2} - 12.35 = -0.308$ M

2) for case w/ (E/Q + Silt + H_2O) from ℄ of base

$= \frac{24.053}{2} - 10.065 = 1.962$ M

Since e in both cases, lies within middle third, Dam is safe against overturning & sliding

$\Sigma H / \Sigma W - U < 0.8$.

Also shear friction $Q = [(\Sigma W - U) \times f'] + (b + q) / \Sigma H$

where $q = \frac{400}{14.15} \times \frac{104}{10^3} = 282.6$ then Q for 1) = 22.436

& Q for 2) = 16.0276 > 5 ok.

SPILLWAY

Due to high discharge efficiency of overflow portion of concrete gravity dam, the Nappe shaped profile is used. This approximate profile of the nappe of jet flowing over sharp crested weir providing the ideal form for obtaining optimum discharge. Elements of Nappe Shaped Crest Profile are:-

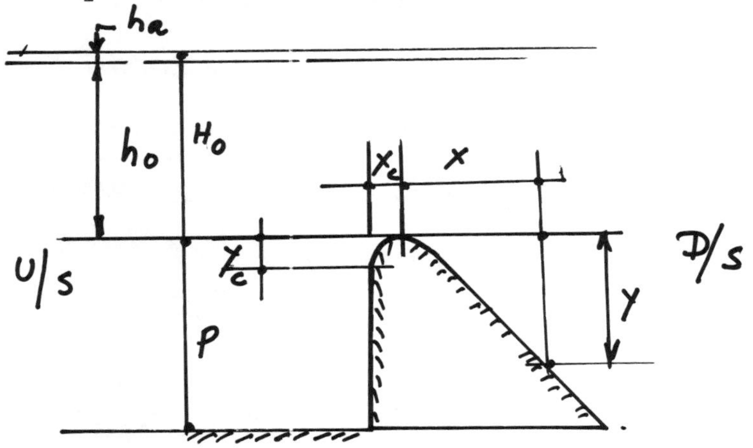

1. The portion upstrem from the origin is defined as a compound circular curve.
2. The portion downstream is given by

$$\frac{Y}{Ho} = -k\left(\frac{X}{Ho}\right)^n \text{ where values of } k, n \text{ are } 0.5 \; \& \; 1.87$$

Design Head H_o can be found out from

$$Q = C L Ho^{3/2}$$

where
Q = discharge in C.FS
C = Coefficient of discharge = 3.6
L = Effective length of crest
Ho = Total Head on Crest, including Velocity of approach Head.

EXAMPLE 7-02
Given:- Design a spillway section of Rio Vallenciano Dam. for a discharge of 38000 cfs by the formula explained above.

$$Q = C L Ho^{3/2}$$

$$Ho = \left(\frac{Q}{CL}\right)^{2/3}$$

$$= \left(\frac{38000}{3.6 \times 200}\right)^{2/3} = 4.345^M$$

Use $Ho = 3.98M$ as required by authority

$$He = \frac{4}{3}(3.98) = 5.307M$$

Elevation max = 101.314 M.

Determination of Elevations of Ogee Crest shaped defined by compound curve @ tangential points

$$Y = K\, Ho \left(\frac{X}{Ho}\right)^n$$

$$\frac{dy}{dx} = \frac{nK}{Ho^{n-1}} X^{n-1}$$

$$= \frac{1}{0.82} = 1.2195$$

$$n = 1.87$$

$$K = 0.5$$

$$\text{then } X^{0.87} = \frac{1.2195 \times \left(\frac{3.98}{0.3048}\right)^{0.87}}{0.5 \times 1.87}$$

$$x = (12.1948)^{\frac{1}{0.87}} = 12.1948^{1.15} = 17.746 \text{ ft}$$

$$= 5.4089 \text{ M}$$

Similarly

$$Y = \frac{3.98}{0.348} \times 0.5 \left(\frac{17.746 \times .3048}{3.98} \right)^{1.87}$$

$$= 3.532$$

Elevation @ tangent Point (Dam axis as origin)

$x = 5.409$ M , $Y = 3.532$ M

	X (D/S)	Y (D/S)
1	0.4 × 3.98 − 1.194 = 0.398	0.007 × 3.98 = 0.0279
2	0.6 × 3.98 − 1.194 = 1.194	0.063 × 3.98 = 0.2507
3	0.8 × 3.98 − 1.194 = 1.990	0.153 × 3.98 = 0.6089
4	1.0 × 3.98 − 1.194 = 2.786	0.267 × 3.98 = 1.0626
5	1.2 × 3.98 − 1.194 = 3.582	0.410 × 3.98 = 1.6318
6	1.4 × 3.98 − 1.194 = 4.398	0.590 × 3.98 = 2.3482
7	1.7 × 3.98 − 1.194 = 5.572	0.920 × 3.98 = 3.6616
8	2.0 × 3.98 − 1.194 = 6.766	1.310 × 3.98 = 5.2138
9	2.5 × 3.98 − 1.194 = 8.756	2.10 × 3.98 = 8.3580
10	3.0 × 3.98 − 1.194 = 10.746	3.11 × 3.98 = 12.3778
11	3.5 × 3.98 − 1.194 = 12.736	4.26 × 3.98 = 16.9548

Rating curve for tailwater

Assume $n = 0.025$, $S_b = 0.0035$

$C = \frac{1}{n} = 40$ $S_b^{\frac{1}{2}} = 0.059$.

n = coefficient of roughness in manning formula.

S_b = mean bed slope D/S.

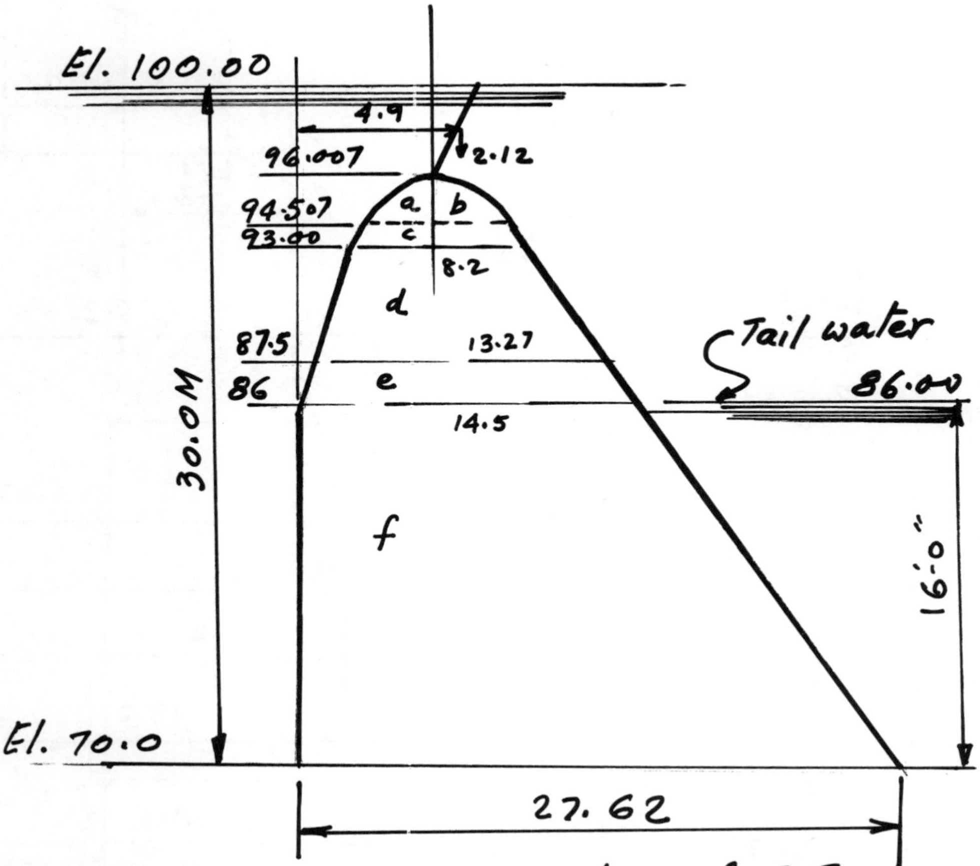

To find C.G of various parts of O.Gee shaped crest & to find C.G of whole mass.

a) Quarter elipse.

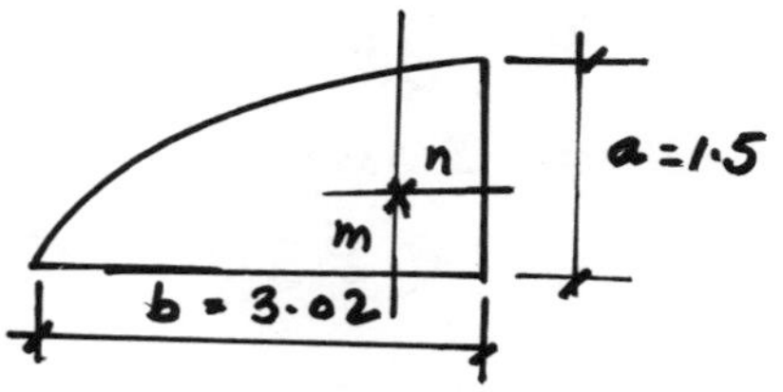

$$m = \frac{4a}{3\pi} = 0.6366\,M$$

$$n = \frac{4b}{3\pi} = 1.28\,M$$

$$A = \frac{\pi ab}{4} = 3.55\,M^2$$

b) half Parabola

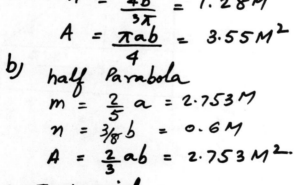

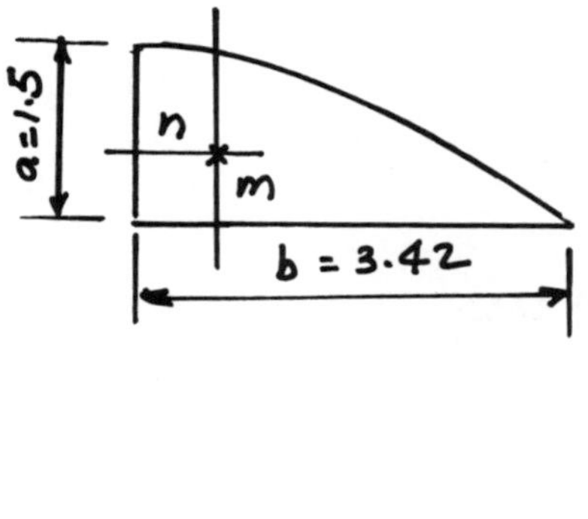

$$m = \frac{2}{5}a = 2.753\,M$$

$$n = \frac{3}{8}b = 0.6\,M$$

$$A = \frac{2}{3}ab = 2.753\,M^2.$$

c, Trapezoid

$$A = \frac{d}{2}(b + b_1)$$
$$= 11.0312\ M^2$$
$$C_1 = \frac{d(2b + b_1)}{3(b + b_1)} = 0.7836\ M$$
$$C_2 = \frac{1}{A}\left[\frac{1}{2}(L_2 \times d)\frac{L_2}{3}^2 + b_1 d\left[\frac{b_1}{2} + L_2\right] + \frac{1}{2}(L_1 d)\left[\frac{L_1}{3} + b_1 + L_2\right]\right]$$
$$= 5.3317\ M.$$

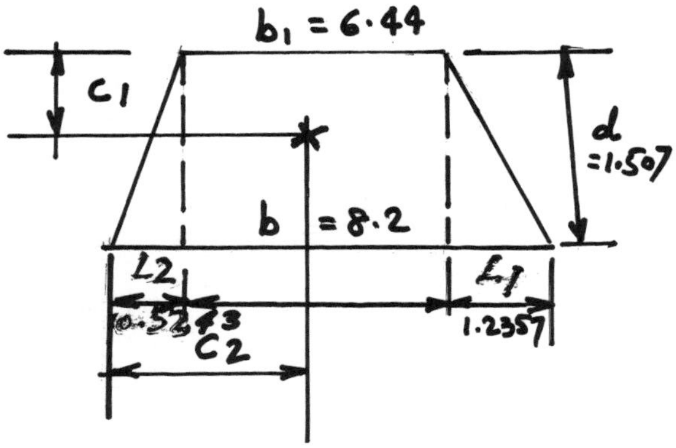

d) Trapezoid

$A = 59.042\ M^2$

$C_1 = 2.9665\ M$

$C_2 = 5.715\ M$

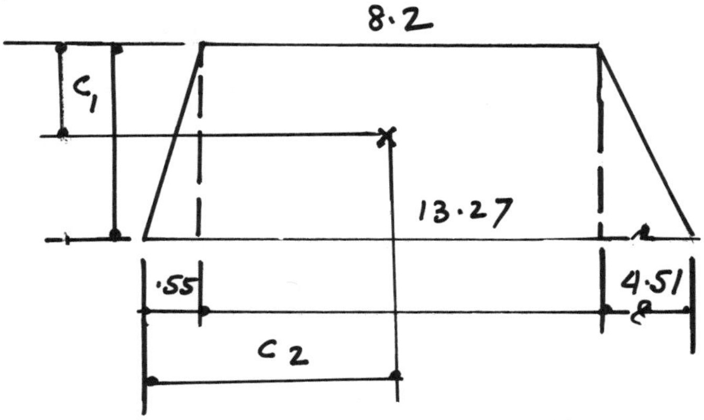

e) Trepezoid

$A = 20.8275\ M^2$

$C_1 = 0.7611\ M$

$C_2 = 6.9470\ M$

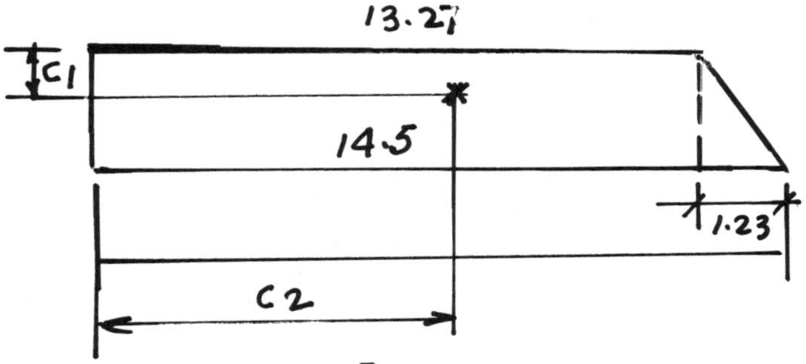

f) Trepezoid

$A = 336.96\ M^2$

$C_1 = 8.8306\ M$

$C_2 = 10.8705\ M$

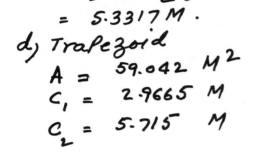

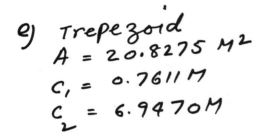

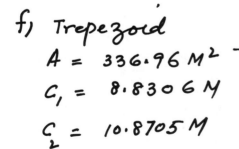

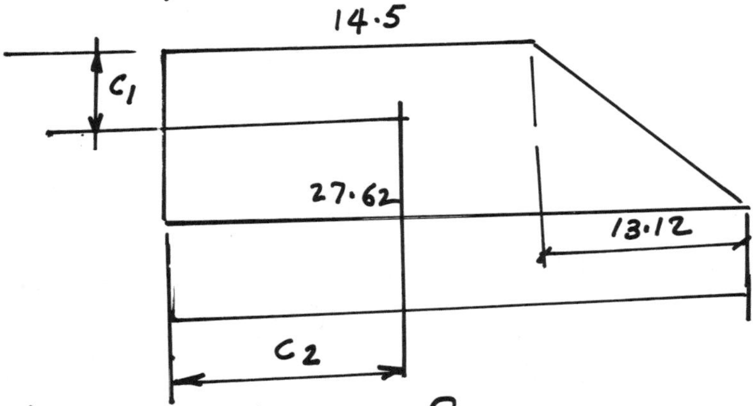

Total Area = a + b + c + d + e + f

= 434.1462 □m.

5, Horz. water head = $\frac{1}{2} \times 1.0 \times 30^2$ = 450 MT

6, Earth Quake (water) = $P_e = 0.735 \times .1 \times 1.0 \times 30$ = 2.205 T

$V_{ea} = 0.726 \times 2.205 \times 30$ = 48.024 MT

$M_{ea} = 0.299 \times 2.205 \times 30^2$ = 593.28 MT

e_{y_a} = 12.3538

7, Earth Quake (mass) $V_{eb} = 1041.994 \times 0.1$ = 104.1994

$M_{eb} = 104.1994 \times 10.0592$ = 1048.163

8, uplift

Tailwater = 16 M

water Head = 30 M

9, water (Gate) = 2.12

10, water (crest) = 12

12, water (face near crest) = 1.5

11, water (Face) = 7.64

13, water (over gate/crest) = 3.00

S.No	Item	force	Lever arm (Hor)	Lever arm verl.	Moment	Moment
1	mass	1041.99	4.105			4277.369
9	water (gate)	2.12	8.91			18.8892
10	water (crest)	12.00	11.51			138.1200
11	water (face)	7.69	13.01			99.3964
13	water (o.g.c.)	3.00	9.51			28.5300
8	uplift					
a)	$\frac{30+15}{2} \times 2.2$	-49.5	12.81			-634.095
b)	$\frac{15}{2} \times 25.42$	-190.65	$(13.81 - (\frac{25.4}{3} + 2.2)) = 3.1370$			-598.069
	ΣW	879.700				
5	H_2O	-450		10		-4500.00
4	SILT	-33.39		3.33		-111.189
6	E/Q. H_2O	-48.024		12.3538		-589.2249
7	E/Q Mass	-104.193		10.0592		-1048.163
	ΣW-U	826.6			Σ	-2922.497

$$434.1642\,(\bar{x}) = 3.55\left[0.7007 + (3.02 - 1.28)\right.$$
$$+ 2.7533\left[0.7007 + 3.02 + 1.2825\right]$$
$$+ 11.0312\left[0.55 \times 3.558\right]$$
$$+ 59.0425\,(5.7150) + 20.8275 \times 6.9470$$
$$+ 336.96 \times 10.8705 = 4213.5485$$
$$\bar{x} = 9.7058\,M$$
$$434.1642\,(\bar{y}) = 3.55\,(24.507 + 0.6366)$$
$$+ 2.753\,(24.507 + 0.6)$$
$$+ 11.0312\,(24.507 - 0.7836)$$
$$+ 59.0425\,(23.0 + 2.9665)$$
$$+ 20.8275\,(17.5 + 0.7611)$$
$$+ 336.96\,(16 - 8.8306)$$
$$= 4367.3669$$
$$\bar{y} = 10.0592\,M.$$

Rating curve for Tailwater

Max. possible flood $Q = 38000\ cfs = 1076\ M^3/s.$

ELEV.	a	p	r	$r^{2/3}$	c	Kd	$Sb^{1/2}$	Q
73.63	0.00	0	0	0	0	0	0	0
74.00	2.59	14	0.185	0.325	40	33.67	0.059	1.9865
75.00	21.09	22.36	0.943	0.961	40	810.6996	0.059	47.83
80.00	173.57	41.00	4.044	2.52	40	17497.87	0.059	1032.13
85.00	491.09	93.00	5.2805	3.03	40	59520.8	0.059	35111.69
90.00	1068.59	149.00	7.1717	3.72	40	159006.15	0.059	93813.65
95.00	1893.59	196.00	9.6612	4.53	40	343118.5	0.059	20243.9

Consider strip of base section 1 meter wide

Forces (Gates up position)

1, Weight of Structure = $434.1642 \times 2.4 = 1041.994\ MT$

2, 3, } No Tailwater

4, Silt pressure (Horiz'L) = $\dfrac{wh^2}{2}\left(\dfrac{1 - \sin\phi}{1 + \sin\phi}\right)$

$$= \frac{1.36 \times 10^2}{2}\left(\frac{1 - .3420}{1 + 0.3420}\right) = 33.3903\ MT$$

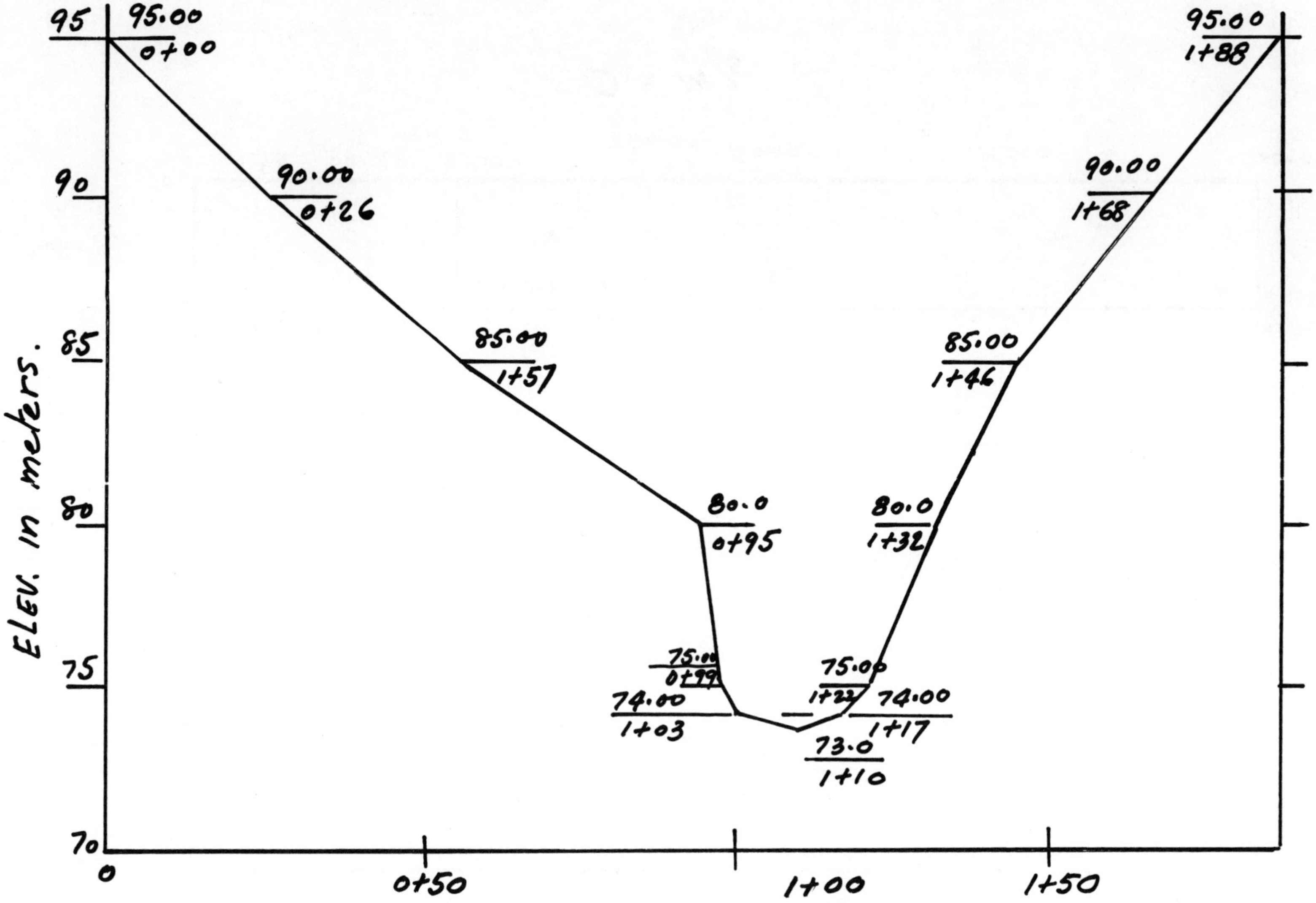

Cross Section along Dam Axis.

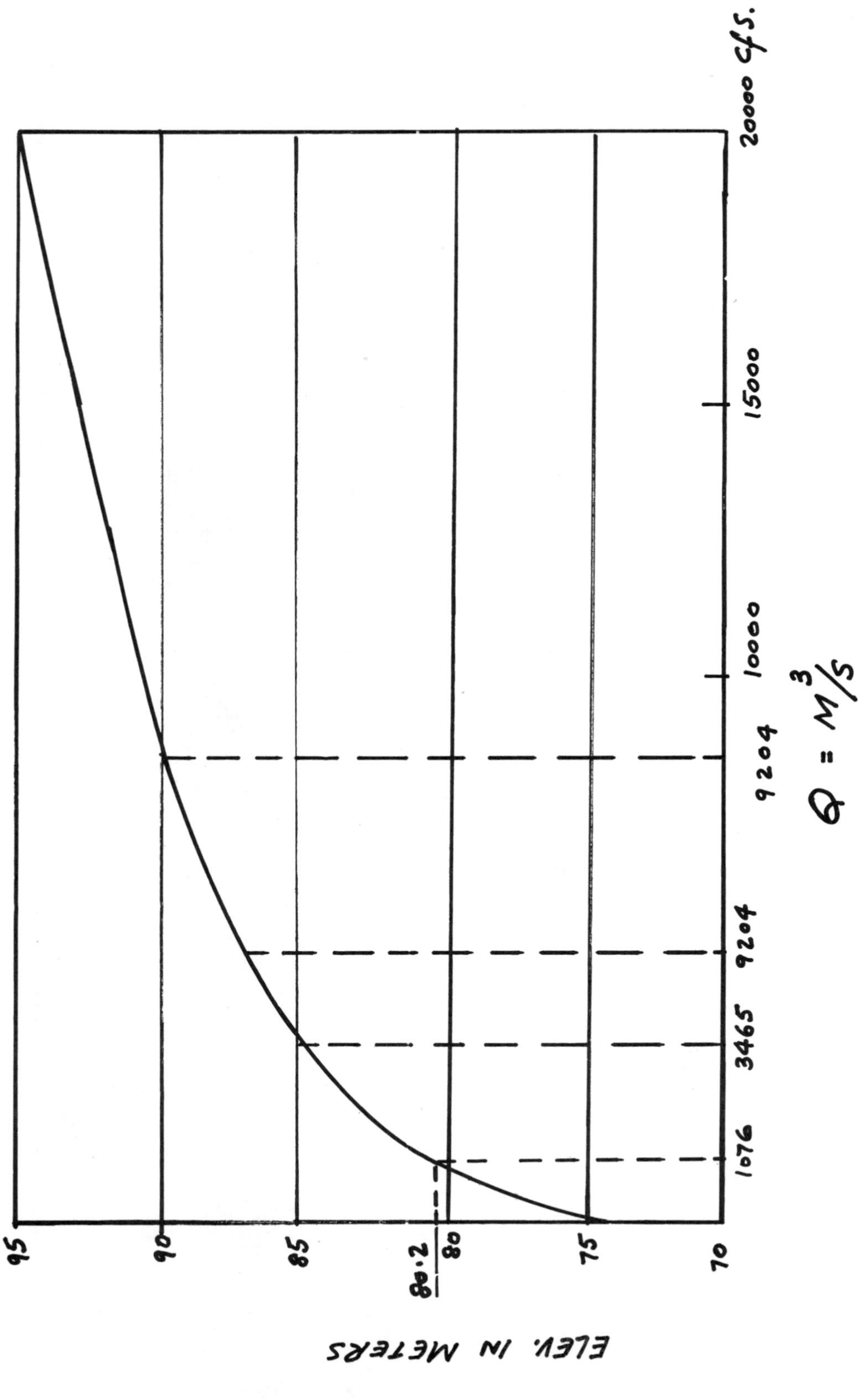

95
90
85
80.2
80
75
70
ELEV. IN METERS
1076
3465
9204
9204
10000
15000
20000 cfs.
Q = M3/S

$$e = \frac{-2922.491}{879.700} = -3.5355\text{ M}$$

$$\frac{b}{6} = 4.6033 > 3.5355 \text{ ok}$$

when gates are down, the max flood level will be 100.00 M & the tail water level will be 86.00

Hor' Load	Forces	Arm	Moment
1. Head water	$1 \times \frac{1}{2}(30+3.993) \times 26.007 = -449.026$	$26.009 - \frac{26.009(2\times30+3.99)}{3(30+3.99)} = 9.6873$	-4282.060
2. Tail water	$\frac{1}{2} \times 1.0 \times 16^2 = 128$	5.33	+ 684.00
3. Silt	− 33.36	3.33	− 111.189
4. Earth quake Mass. Vert. Load	−104.1994	10.0592	−1048.163
a) Mass	1041.994	4.105	4277.369
b) water (face)	7	13.01	91.07
c) uplift	$\frac{15+16}{2} \times 25.42 = -394.01$	$13.81 - \frac{[25.42(2\times16+15)]}{3(16+15)} + 2.2 = -1.23$	−649.00
d. Tail water	$\frac{1}{2} \times 13.12 \times 16 \times 1 = 104.96$	$13.81 - 4.37 = 9.44$	−986.624

$\Sigma W - U = 709.344$ $\qquad \Sigma M = -2139.4762$

$$e = \frac{-2139.4762}{709.344} = -3.01613 < 4.6033 \text{ ok}$$

sliding factor

when gates are up $\frac{\Sigma H}{\Sigma W - U} = \frac{635.609}{826.6} = 0.769 < 0.8$ ok

when gates are down $\frac{\Sigma H}{\Sigma W - U} = \frac{499.6137}{709.344} = 0.7093 < 0.8$ ok

Shear factor Q

when gates are up $= \frac{826.6 \times 0.65 + 27.62 \times 282.685}{635.609} = 12.28 > 5$ ok

when gates are down $= \frac{709.344 \times 0.65 + 27.62 \times 282.685}{499.6135} = 15.628 > 5$ ok

ARCH DAM

It is defined as a structure by which the total water load is transmitted to the abutments by the arch action. Also a part of the water load is usually carried by gravity elements of the structure. The gravity elements and vertical beam action introduce a complexity in the design and a true arch dam is produced by the intoduction of an articulated joint at the base of the dam. Keep in mind that it is not desirable to destroy any part of the structural strength of the dam in order to simplify its analysis. An economical ratio of length to height is 5:1. After that the arch will become quite massive, so it is advisable to take advantage of curved structure for analysis. The general conditions imposed by the theory of elasticity are: 1) each element in the dam must be in static equilibrium, 2) the continuity of the structure is undisturbed by loading, 3) the state of stress throughout the structure is determined by the state of stress on any mutually perpendicular coordinate system, which are usually cylindrical coordinates, in which vertical planes will cut radial slices through dam called cantilevers and horizontal planes will cut horizontal arches. The tabular coefficients and formulas for designing circular arches (as developed by Mr. R.S. Lieurance of the Bureau of Reclamation, US Dept. of Interior) has beem found quite useful. The following definitions as to the signs are used in the tables:

1) a positive thrust (H) produses compression.
2) a positive moment (M) tends to produce compression in the extrados of the arch.
3) a positive shear (V) tends to move a section of the arch upstream with respect to the section near the abutment.
4) a positive radial load acts downstream toward the center of the arch.
5) a positive deflection is a movement upstream.
6) a temperature rise ia assumed positive.

EXAMPLE 7-03

Given:- Design an intake structure for Riovallenciano Dam.

$E_c = 3.0 \times 10^6$ P.S.I

$E_c = 432 \times 10^6$ PSF

$r = 9.0130'$, $t = 1.6404'$

Design height $= (31 \times 3.2808') \times 0.9 = 91.5343'$

$$\frac{t}{r} = \frac{1.6404}{9.0130} = 0.1820$$

$\phi_A = 90^0$

By use of tables (see appendix), values of h at crown, m @ crown, h @ abutment, m @ abutment, value

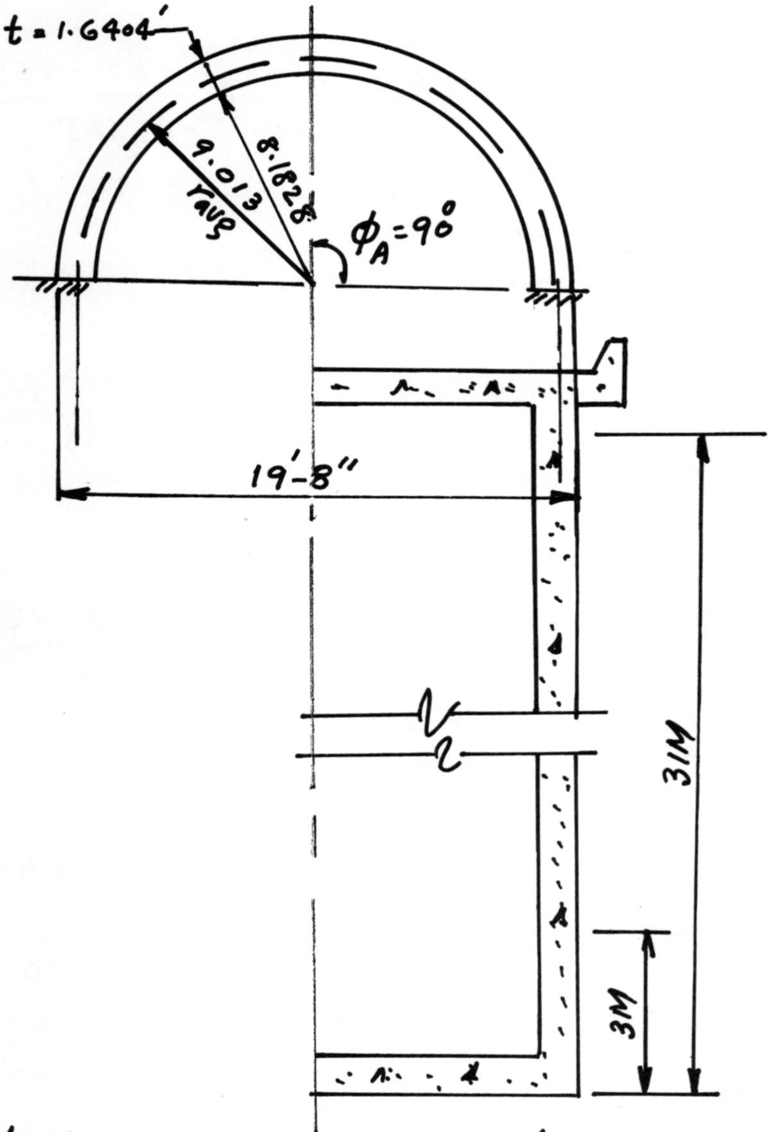

of V at abutment For $\phi_A = 90°$, $t/r = 0.182$

By interpolation $h_{extra} = \dfrac{1097 - 1055}{0.125} \times 0.057 = 19.15$

h_{crown} for t/r of 0.125 $= 1055.00$

$\therefore h_{crown}$ for $t/r = 0.182$ $\quad 1074.15$

Again m @ crown.

By interpolation $m_{extra} = \dfrac{11.39 - 3.056}{0.125} \times 0.057 = 3.8006$

m_{crown} for $t/r = 0.125$ $= 3.056$

$\therefore m_{crown}$ for $t/r = 0.182$ $\quad 6.8563$

Also h @ abutment

By interpolation $h_{extra} = \frac{1125-1063}{0.125} \times 0.057 = 28.27$

h_{abut} for $t/r = 0.125$ $= 1063.00$

∴ h_{abut} for $t/r = 0.182$ 1091.2720

again m @ abutment.

By interpolation $m_{extra} = \frac{-16.830+4.90}{0.125} \times 0.057 = -5.440$

m_{abut} for $t/r = 0.125$ $= -4.900$

∴ m_{abut} for $t/r = 0.182$ $= -10.3400$

V_{abut} for $t/r = 0.182$ $V_{extra} = \frac{-28.22+7.956}{0.125} \times 0.057 = -9.238$

V_{abut} @ $t/r = 0.125$ $= -7.956$

∴ $V_{abutment}$ for $t/r = 0.182$ $= -17.194$

$P_e = C \lambda w h = 0.735 \times 0.1 \times 62.5 \times 91.5343 = 420.4811$ #/□′

$P_W = 91.5343 \times 62.5 = 5720.8937$ #/□′

$P_e + P_W = 420.4811 + 5720.89 = 6141.3748$ #/□″

$= 6.15$ unit of 1000 #/□′

M @ crown $= 1074.15 \times 6.15 \times 9.013$

$= 59.54$ ′K

M @ crown $= -6.8563 \times 6.15 \times 9.01302$

$= 3425.3$ ′#

H @ abut $= 1091.27 \times 6.15 \times 9.013$

$= 60.489$ ′K

M @ abut $= -10.34 \times 6.15 \times 9.0130^2$

$= 5160$ ′#

V @ abut $= -17.1944 \times 6.15 \times 9.013$

$= 953.08$ #

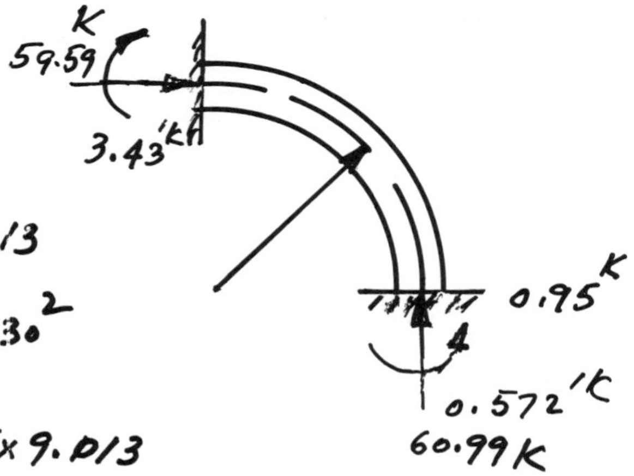

Thickness $t = 1.640 = 19.68''$ Say $= 19.75''$

∴ $d = 17''$

For steel $F_y = 60000$ Psi

$d = 17, \; b = 12, \; F = 0.289$

$K_U = \left(\dfrac{5.160 \times 1.7}{0.289} \right) = 24.47$

use $\rho_{min} = \dfrac{200}{F_y} = 0.003$

#6 @ 13" E.F ie #6 @ 0.33 M

$f_c = \dfrac{60489.2}{144} = 418 < 700$ Psi ok

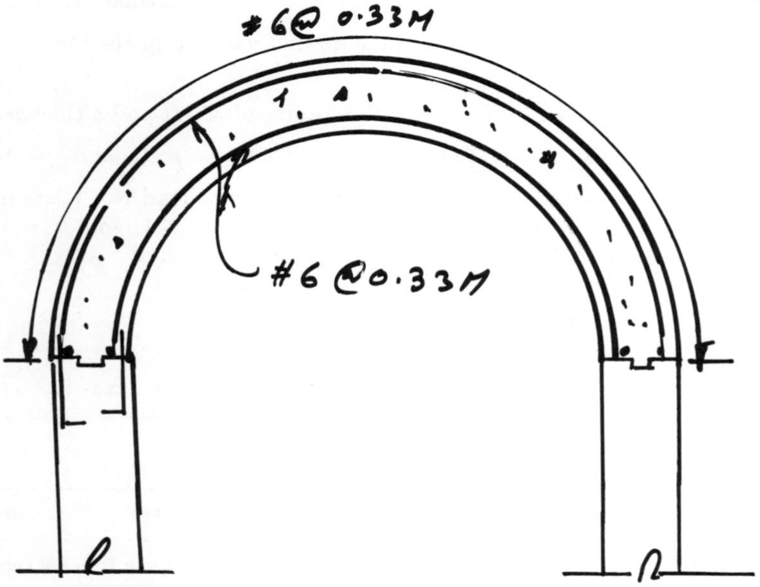

APPENDIX

The Use of the Tables

The caption of each table describes the load and the type of values to be found on that sheet (forces and moments, or deflections). In any table the extreme left column is designated ϕ_A and represents the half central angle of the arch. At the top of the tables are listed the values $\frac{t}{r}$, in which t is the arch thickness and r is the radius of the arch center line. Straight-line interpolation between the values $\frac{t}{r}$ and ϕ_A to obtain the desired value from the table will be sufficiently accurate for most cases.

For example, consider a 63° arch with a radius of 500 ft and a thickness of 40 ft: E_c = 4,000,000 lb per sq in. = 576,000,000 lb per sq ft; and $\frac{t}{r} = 0.080$. The thrusts at the crown and the quarter points, due to load No. 1, are interpolated as shown in Table 1. From Table 1(a), h = 1,024; and H = 1,024 × 500 = 512,000 lb. From Table 1(b), K_1 = − 23,210; and

$$\Delta = \frac{-\ 23{,}210 \times 500}{576{,}000{,}000} = -\ 0.02035.$$

TABLE 1.—Use of Tables 3 to 9; Illustrative Example

Values of ϕ_A, in degrees	Values of $\frac{t}{r}$: 0.075	0.080	0.100	0.075	0.080	0.100
	(a) Thrust at the Crown Due to Load No. 1			(b) Deflection at the Quarter Point Due to Load No. 1		
60	+1,022	+1,022	+1,022	−24,560	−23,440	−18,950
63	......	+1,024	......	......	−23,210	......
70	+1,030	+1,031	+1,035	−24,470	−23,360	−18,900

The variety of sections which are possible for cantilevers makes tabulations such as those presented for arches impossible.[6]

Radial Load Description.—Referring to Fig. 1, P is the total load at the abutment—in pounds per square feet when the load is distributed and in pounds when the load is concentrated. The loads indicated by the diagrams in Tables

[6] To compute cantilever stresses and deflections, refer to *Bulletin No. 1*, Part V, Technical Investigations, Boulder Canyon Final Reports, Bureau of Reclamation, U. S. Dept. of the Interior, Chapter IV, p. 63.

3 to 9 are unit radial loads applied at the upstream face (except the unit temperature load) and may be combined into any pattern that varies as a straight line between quarter points. The various loads are described in Table 2. The

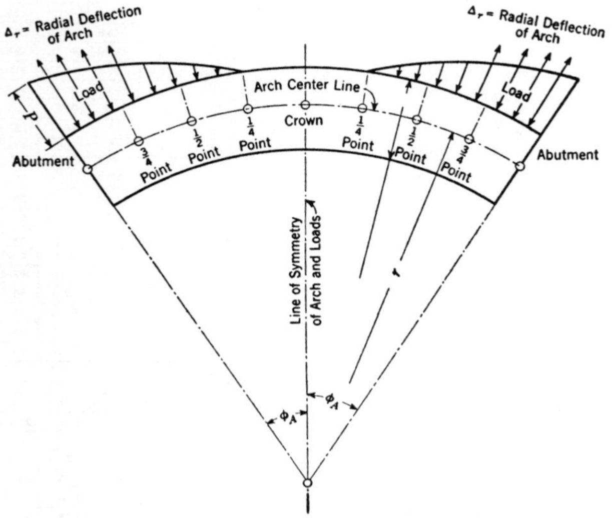

FIG. 1.—PROPERTIES OF A CIRCULAR ARCH

unit load shown in the diagrams in Tables 3 to 9 (Appendix) results in forces or moments determined by the corresponding formulas given in the tables.

TABLE 2.—DESCRIPTION OF RADIAL LOADS

Table No.	Load No.	Intensity, in pounds per square foot	Pattern	Variation; maximum at abutment to zero at:
3	1	10,000	Uniform	Uniform
4	2	10,000	Triangular	Three-quarter point
5	3	10,000	Triangular	Half point
6	4	10,000	Triangular	Quarter point
7	5	10,000	Triangular	Crown
8	Temperature	Uniform change of $-10°$ F		
9	Concentrated	1,000 lb, applied radially at the abutment		

Positive Sign Conventions.—Fig. 2 shows the direction of positive forces and moments, and the direction of forces and moments due to positive loads. Loads directed toward the arch center, or downstream, are positive. Deflections away from the arch center, or upstream, are positive. Thrusts are positive when they tend to produce compression; moments when they tend to produce compression in the extrados; and shears when they tend to move a section upstream with respect to a section nearer the abutment. The temperature table (Table 8, Appendix) is based on a drop in temperature.

TABLE 3(a).—Forces and Moments for Radial Load No. 1

VALUES OF t/r

VALUES OF h AT CROWN

ϕ_A	.025	.050	.075	.100	.125	.250	.375	.500	.625	.750	.875	1.000	1.125	1.250	1.375	1.500
10	310.1	117.5	67.91	48.84	39.69	27.65	26.22	26.46	27.20	28.14	29.18	30.28	31.41	32.56	33.73	34.91
20	880.6	656.0	477.5	360.7	286.2	153.4	124.8	116.8	115.4	116.6	119.2	122.5	126.2	130.2	134.4	138.7
30	983.1	919.3	831.9	740.8	657.4	407.6	318.0	283.7	270.7	267.4	269.1	273.6	279.8	287.1	295.1	303.7
40	1003	988.7	960.8	923.8	876.4	683.7	565.3	505.7	477.7	466.7	465.4	469.8	477.8	488.3	500.4	513.6
50	1009	1010	1005	993.8	978.9	877.1	786.6	728.3	696.4	682.4	679.9	685.6	696.3	710.6	727.4	746.1
60	1011	1018	1022	1022	1021	987.2	942.3	907.2	886.8	879.5	882.5	893.0	909.0	929.1	952.1	977.5
70	1012	1021	1029	1035	1039	1046	1039	1032	1031	1038	1056	1072	1096	1125	1156	1189
80	1012	1023	1033	1041	1049	1079	1097	1114	1132	1155	1182	1213	1249	1287	1328	1371
90	1012	1024	1035	1045	1055	1097	1132	1166	1200	1237	1277	1320	1366	1415	1466	1519

VALUES OF m AT CROWN

ϕ_A	.025	.050	.075	.100	.125	.250	.375	.500	.625	.750	.875	1.000	1.125	1.250	1.375	1.500
10	3.967	5.593	6.424	7.052	7.592	9.753	11.48	12.99	14.35	15.62	16.83	17.98	19.10	20.19	21.26	22.31
20	2.817	8.293	13.18	16.90	19.77	28.68	34.77	40.02	44.86	49.44	53.83	58.08	62.23	66.30	70.29	74.23
30	1.377	5.128	10.31	15.99	21.56	43.05	57.16	68.27	78.03	87.07	95.67	104.0	112.1	120.1	127.9	135.6
40	0.775	3.042	6.593	11.12	16.30	43.96	67.14	85.76	101.6	115.9	129.2	141.8	154.0	165.9	177.6	189.1
50	0.486	1.935	4.295	7.470	11.34	36.58	63.47	87.66	109.9	128.0	145.6	162.0	177.7	192.8	207.5	222.0
60	0.328	1.310	2.928	5.150	7.926	27.98	52.98	78.15	101.7	123.4	143.4	162.1	179.8	196.7	213.1	228.9
70	0.232	0.926	2.075	3.661	5.664	20.84	41.48	63.99	86.29	107.5	126.0	146.0	163.5	180.1	196.0	211.2
80	0.170	0.675	1.512	2.668	4.131	15.42	31.42	49.67	68.39	86.58	103.8	119.9	134.9	148.9	162.1	174.6
90	0.127	0.503	1.122	1.977	3.056	11.39	23.31	37.07	51.29	65.09	77.97	89.73	100.3	109.9	118.4	126.0

VALUES OF h AT ABUTMENT

ϕ_A	.025	.050	.075	.100	.125	.250	.375	.500	.625	.750	.875	1.000	1.125	1.250	1.375	1.500
10	320.8	131.3	82.64	64.06	55.23	44.32	43.86	45.05	46.73	48.60	50.58	52.61	54.67	56.76	58.85	60.96
20	888.6	678.3	511.2	402.3	333.0	212.0	188.9	185.2	187.6	192.5	198.7	205.5	212.8	220.3	228.0	235.9
30	987.0	933.5	859.5	782.3	711.7	503.7	434.5	413.1	410.3	415.8	425.6	437.9	451.7	466.3	481.7	497.4
40	1005	997.2	978.8	953.3	919.9	786.9	710.9	679.9	673.0	679.2	692.8	710.8	731.6	754.2	778.1	802.9
50	1010	1015	1016	1014	1009	965.7	929.8	914.6	916.5	929.8	950.6	976.5	1006	1037	1070	1105
60	1012	1021	1029	1036	1042	1056	1065	1079	1100	1127	1160	1196	1236	1277	1320	1364
70	1012	1024	1035	1045	1055	1098	1137	1176	1216	1260	1307	1353	1403	1454	1506	1558
80	1012	1025	1037	1049	1060	1117	1172	1226	1281	1337	1393	1450	1508	1566	1625	1684
90	1013	1025	1038	1050	1063	1125	1188	1250	1313	1375	1438	1500	1563	1625	1688	1750

VALUES OF m AT ABUTMENT

ϕ_A	.025	.050	.075	.100	.125	.250	.375	.500	.625	.750	.875	1.000	1.125	1.250	1.375	1.500
10	-6.704	-8.194	-8.306	-8.158	-7.947	-6.918	-6.159	-5.601	-5.175	-4.839	-4.569	-4.346	-4.160	-4.001	-3.865	-3.746
20	-5.136	-13.96	-20.60	-24.67	-27.05	-29.92	-29.32	-28.31	-27.33	-26.45	-25.68	-24.99	-24.39	-23.85	-23.38	-22.95
30	-2.563	-9.032	-17.23	-25.43	-32.71	-53.06	-59.33	-61.20	-61.55	-61.32	-60.86	-60.31	-59.74	-59.19	-58.65	-58.14
40	-1.447	-5.448	-11.34	-18.41	-27.24	-59.29	-78.42	-88.36	-93.66	-96.60	-98.28	-99.24	-99.78	-100.1	-100.2	-100.2
50	-0.903	-3.476	-7.468	-12.59	-18.54	-51.96	-79.74	-98.71	-110.1	-119.4	-125.0	-128.9	-131.8	-133.8	-135.4	-136.6
60	-0.602	-2.339	-5.089	-8.715	-13.07	-40.94	-69.64	-93.27	-111.2	-124.4	-134.1	-141.4	-146.9	-151.2	-154.6	-157.3
70	-0.419	-1.633	-3.574	-6.166	-9.329	-30.93	-56.01	-79.28	-98.75	-114.3	-125.0	-135.9	-143.3	-149.2	-153.8	-157.6
80	-0.299	-1.169	-2.564	-4.436	-6.738	-22.95	-43.00	-62.90	-80.60	-95.42	-107.4	-116.9	-124.4	-130.3	-134.9	-138.5
90	-0.217	-0.849	-1.863	-3.224	-4.900	-16.83	-31.96	-47.39	-61.42	-73.30	-82.87	-90.29	-95.87	-99.92	-102.7	-104.6

VALUES OF v AT ABUTMENT

ϕ_A	.025	.050	.075	.100	.125	.250	.375	.500	.625	.750	.875	1.000	1.125	1.250	1.375	1.500
10	-122.0	-157.6	-168.4	-173.8	-177.6	-190.6	-201.7	-212.5	-223.2	-233.9	-244.6	-255.2	-265.9	-276.5	-287.2	-297.8
20	-45.11	-126.2	-191.5	-235.8	-265.5	-332.3	-363.5	-387.6	-409.4	-430.4	-450.9	-471.1	-491.2	-511.3	-531.2	-551.1
30	-14.70	-52.85	-102.8	-154.6	-202.6	-358.7	-434.7	-483.2	-520.9	-553.8	-584.2	-613.2	-641.3	-669.0	-696.2	-723.2
40	-6.104	-23.33	-49.28	-81.14	-119.6	-283.7	-399.9	-478.4	-536.6	-583.8	-624.9	-662.2	-697.2	-730.7	-763.1	-794.7
50	-2.978	-11.60	-25.23	-43.01	-64.05	-189.9	-307.1	-399.7	-472.0	-530.6	-580.3	-623.9	-663.6	-700.5	-735.5	-769.1
60	-1.612	-6.319	-13.89	-24.01	-36.37	-119.4	-212.4	-296.9	-368.7	-429.1	-480.7	-525.7	-565.9	-602.7	-636.8	-669.0
70	-0.929	-3.655	-8.067	-14.03	-21.41	-73.93	-139.2	-204.6	-264.3	-316.7	-358.5	-402.6	-438.2	-470.2	-499.6	-526.7
80	-0.559	-2.198	-4.858	-8.466	-12.95	-45.73	-88.69	-134.2	-177.6	-216.9	-251.7	-282.2	-309.0	-332.8	-354.0	-373.1
90	-0.344	-1.352	-2.985	-5.201	-7.956	-28.22	-55.26	-84.45	-112.7	-138.4	-160.8	-180.0	-196.2	-209.8	-221.1	-230.6

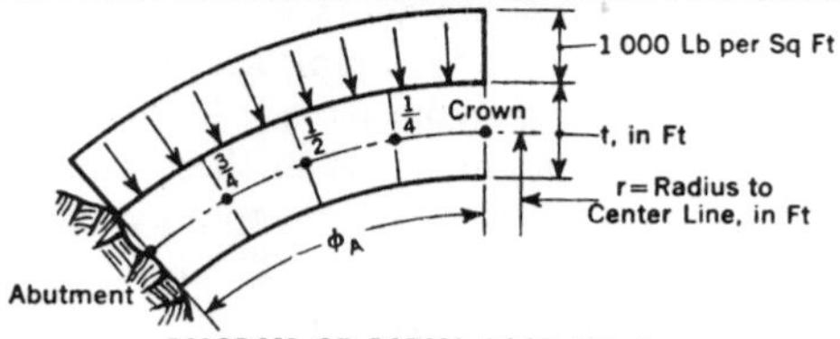

Thrust, Moment, Shear, in Lb, and Ft-Lb

$H = hr$
$M = mr^2$
$V = vr$

DIAGRAM OF RADIAL LOAD NO. 1

TABLE 3(*b*).—Radial Deflections for Radial Load No. 1

ϕ_A	Values of t/r															
	.025	.050	.075	.100	.125	.250	.375	.500	.625	.750	.875	1.000	1.125	1.250	1.375	1.500
Values of K_1 at Crown																
10	-27190	-5956	-2626	-1604	-1168	-628.7	-538.2	-511.8	-507.1	-511.5	-520.6	-532.5	-546.2	-561.1	-576.8	593.2
20	-71560	-28760	-15020	-9141	-6208	-2256	-1557	-1327	-1232	-1193	-1180	-1183	-1194	-1212	-1233	-1258
30	-77910	-38350	-28330	-17070	-12720	-4936	-3118	-2462	-2169	-2022	-1949	-1914	-1905	-1910	-1927	-1949
40	-78590	-40260	-27090	-20280	-16070	-7428	-4804	-3716	-3186	-2903	-2745	-2657	-2612	-2595	-2597	-2612
50	-78550	-40560	-27720	-21200	-17210	-8900	-6085	-4779	-4061	-3695	-3463	-3324	-3244	-3202	-3187	-3191
60	-78510	-40540	-27820	-21400	-17530	-9560	-6823	-5485	-4737	-4293	-4017	-3846	-3741	-3682	-3654	-3648
70	-78460	-40490	-27780	-21400	-17560	-9798	-7168	-5869	-5126	-4671	-4374	-4199	-4082	-4015	-3980	-3969
80	-78540	-40470	-27730	-21350	-17520	-9849	-7289	-6033	-5313	-4867	-4582	-4397	-4280	-4209	-4161	-4160
90	-78730	-40480	-27700	-21310	-17470	-9821	-7299	-6071	-5369	-4935	-4657	-4476	-4360	-4290	-4254	-4241
Values of K_1 at $\frac{1}{4}$ Point																
10	-24270	-5403	-2418	-1496	-1100	-608.6	-525.5	-503.2	-500.2	-505.5	-515.3	-527.7	-541.7	-556.8	-572.9	-589.3
20	-63370	-25680	-13520	-8290	-5680	-2124	-1490	-1283	-1199	-1165	-1156	-1160	-1173	-1192	-1215	-1240
30	-68780	-34040	-21710	-15310	-11470	-4558	-2930	-2341	-2041	-1949	-1885	-1858	-1853	-1862	-1874	-1906
40	-69230	-35610	-24060	-18080	-14390	-6777	-4452	-3486	-3015	-2764	-2626	-2552	-2516	-2505	-2511	-2530
50	-69080	-35790	-24550	-18830	-15330	-8054	-5581	-4431	-3806	-3479	-3278	-3159	-3092	-3060	-3052	-3061
60	-68960	-35700	-24560	-18950	-15560	-8602	-6210	-5042	-4332	-4002	-3765	-3619	-3532	-3485	-3466	-3466
70	-68800	-35580	-24470	-18900	-15550	-8777	-6485	-5356	-4712	-4319	-4062	-3916	-3826	-3765	-3740	-3737
80	-68740	-35470	-24370	-18810	-15470	-8790	-6565	-5476	-4853	-4469	-4225	-4069	-3972	-3915	-3887	-3883
90	-68730	-35400	-24280	-18720	-15390	-8738	-6548	-5486	-4880	-4507	-4268	-4115	-4019	-3962	-3934	-3928
Values of K_1 at $\frac{1}{2}$ Point																
10	-16520	-3903	-1843	-1193	-908.9	-550.2	-490.8	-477.7	-479.4	-487.6	-499.3	-513.1	-528.2	-544.1	-560.6	-577.7
20	-41800	-17460	-9474	-5982	-4214	-1749	-1299	-1153	-1099	-1081	-1082	-1094	-1112	-1135	-1160	-1188
30	-44840	-22660	-14750	-10610	-8106	-3513	-2401	-1996	-1819	-1737	-1702	-1694	-1702	-1720	-1746	-1777
40	-44800	-23420	-16070	-12270	-9906	-5002	-3474	-2835	-2526	-2366	-2284	-2246	-2235	-2243	-2261	-2290
50	-44420	-23330	-16210	-12590	-10380	-5774	-4202	-3466	-3072	-2868	-2749	-2685	-2657	-2651	-2663	-2685
60	-44100	-23100	-16080	-12540	-10410	-6040	-4548	-3823	-3422	-3190	-3054	-2976	-2936	-2922	-2927	-2945
70	-43730	-22860	-15890	-12400	-10300	-6067	-4651	-3962	-3575	-3344	-3195	-3123	-3081	-3060	-3061	-3076
80	-43420	-22640	-15710	-12240	-10150	-6001	-4633	-3972	-3601	-3378	-3241	-3159	-3113	-3092	-3085	-3101
90	-43110	-22430	-15530	-12080	-10030	-5905	-4563	-3919	-3557	-3340	-3205	-3122	-3074	-3050	-3044	-3051
Values of K_1 at $\frac{3}{4}$ Point																
10	-6869	-1931	-1054	-760.9	-628.8	-458.0	-434.8	-435.9	-445.2	-458.1	-473.0	-489.0	-505.7	-522.9	-540.5	-558.4
20	-15790	-7256	-4305	-2954	-2243	-1201	-1005	-950.3	-939.1	-946.6	-963.7	-968.3	-1012	-1041	-1071	-1101
30	-16350	-8833	-6122	-4676	-3750	-2064	-1629	-1476	-1420	-1406	-1414	-1433	-1461	-1494	-1530	-1568
40	-16000	-8820	-6359	-5084	-4292	-2630	-2104	-1890	-1798	-1763	-1759	-1773	-1798	-1830	-1868	-1910
50	-15630	-8586	-6218	-5022	-4296	-2810	-2323	-2109	-2006	-1968	-1959	-1969	-1992	-2023	-2060	-2102
60	-15330	-8352	-6029	-4865	-4169	-2782	-2344	-2153	-2063	-2025	-2016	-2026	-2047	-2077	-2113	-2153
70	-15020	-8142	-5851	-4708	-4026	-2684	-2260	-2095	-2012	-1978	-1960	-1978	-1996	-2023	-2055	-2091
80	-14740	-7952	-5694	-4566	-3893	-2576	-2171	-1997	-1915	-1878	-1866	-1870	-1883	-1904	-1928	-1958
90	-14460	-7778	-5552	-4442	-3778	-2476	-2072	-1895	-1807	-1764	-1734	-1740	-1745	-1757	-1773	-1792
Values of K_1 at Abutment																
10	-217.7	-281.3	-300.5	-310.3	-317.0	-340.1	-360.0	-379.3	-398.4	-417.5	-436.5	-455.6	-474.6	-493.6	-512.6	-531.6
20	-80.51	-225.3	-341.9	-420.8	-473.9	-593.2	-648.8	-691.8	-730.9	-768.3	-804.8	-841.0	-876.9	-912.6	-948.2	-983.7
30	-26.25	-94.33	-183.5	-275.9	-361.6	-640.2	-776.0	-862.5	-929.8	-988.5	-1043	-1095	-1145	-1194	-1243	-1291
40	-10.90	-41.64	-87.97	-144.8	-207.5	-506.4	-713.9	-853.9	-957.8	-1042	-1115	-1182	-1245	-1304	-1362	-1419
50	-5.316	-20.71	-45.03	-76.77	-114.3	-338.9	-548.2	-713.4	-842.5	-947.1	-1036	-1114	-1184	-1250	-1313	-1373
60	-2.877	-11.28	-24.79	-42.87	-64.92	-213.1	-379.1	-530.0	-658.1	-765.9	-858.0	-938.4	-1010	-1076	-1137	-1194
70	-1.658	-6.524	-14.40	-25.05	-38.22	-132.0	-248.5	-365.2	-471.7	-565.3	-639.9	-718.6	-782.1	-839.4	-802.5	-940.2
80	-0.9976	-3.923	-8.672	-15.11	-23.12	-81.63	-158.3	-239.5	-317.0	-387.2	-449.3	-503.8	-551.6	-594.0	-631.8	-666.0
90	-0.6140	-2.413	-5.328	-9.284	-14.20	-50.38	-98.64	-150.7	-201.2	-247.0	-287.1	-321.3	-350.2	-374.4	-394.7	-411.6

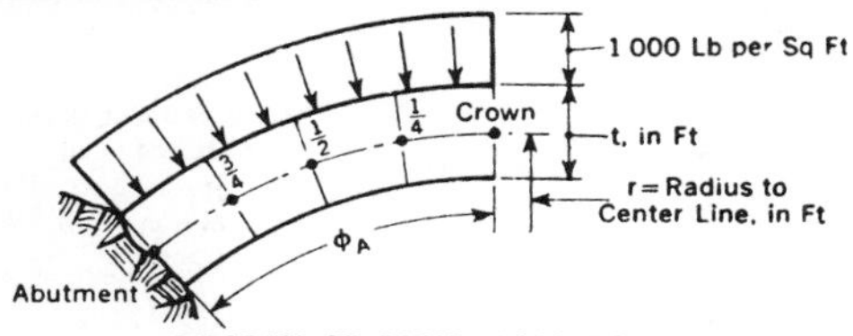

Radial Deflection, in Ft

$$\Delta_r = \frac{K_1 r}{E_c}$$

E_c = Modulus of Elasticity of Concrete in Direct Stress, in Lb per Sq Ft

DIAGRAM OF RADIAL LOAD NO. 1

TABLE 4(*a*).—Forces and Moments for Radial Load No. 2

ϕ_A	Values of t/r															
	.025	.050	.075	.100	.125	.250	.375	.500	.625	.750	.875	1.000	1.125	1.250	1.375	1.500
	Values of h at Crown															
10	6.046	3.198	2.885	2.873	2.949	3.477	3.924	4.302	4.641	4.954	5.252	5.541	5.822	6.097	6.369	6.637
20	10.28	10.29	9.976	9.850	9.921	11.42	13.14	14.71	16.13	17.46	18.71	19.92	21.08	22.21	23.32	24.43
30	10.44	11.94	13.14	14.18	15.16	19.68	23.75	27.38	30.67	33.70	36.56	39.29	41.92	44.46	46.95	49.38
40	10.22	11.75	13.25	14.74	16.25	23.99	31.33	37.93	43.88	49.35	54.45	59.29	63.91	68.38	72.72	76.95
50	10.08	11.46	12.85	14.30	15.78	24.53	34.15	43.60	52.48	60.77	68.54	75.94	82.98	89.76	96.33	102.7
60	10.05	11.27	12.52	13.82	15.21	23.51	33.70	44.72	55.81	66.60	76.97	86.93	96.51	105.8	114.7	123.5
70	10.09	11.19	12.32	13.49	14.74	22.24	31.95	43.23	55.33	67.68	79.98	92.06	103.9	115.4	126.6	137.6
80	10.19	11.20	12.23	13.30	14.43	21.16	30.01	40.75	52.85	65.76	79.08	92.52	105.9	119.2	132.3	145.3
90	10.35	11.28	12.24	13.23	14.27	20.34	28.30	38.18	49.69	62.39	75.90	89.90	104.2	118.6	133.0	147.3
	Values of m at Crown															
10	-.0152	.0336	.0489	.0615	0.727	0.118	0.153	0.183	0.209	0.234	0.256	0.278	0.298	0.318	0.338	0.357
20	-0.104	-.0803	-.0496	-.0233	-.0221	.0633	0.105	0.141	0.172	0.202	0.230	0.257	0.283	0.308	0.333	0.483
30	-0.255	-0.290	-0.315	-0.336	-0.356	-0.475	-0.611	-0.749	-0.885	-1.017	-1.145	-1.271	-1.395	-1.516	-1.636	-1.754
40	-0.441	-0.517	-0.596	-0.681	-0.773	-1.330	-1.960	-2.594	-3.214	-3.820	-4.413	-4.995	-5.569	-6.136	-6.697	-7.253
50	-0.669	-0.776	-0.892	-1.022	-1.169	-2.162	-3.486	-4.897	-6.365	-7.832	-9.284	-10.73	-12.16	-13.57	-14.98	-16.38
60	-0.942	-1.075	-1.221	-1.384	-1.569	-2.870	-4.767	-7.036	-9.576	-12.19	-14.86	-17.54	-20.23	-22.92	-25.61	-28.30
70	-1.259	-1.418	-1.590	-1.781	-1.994	-3.502	-5.813	-8.818	-12.32	-16.14	-20.16	-24.32	-28.55	-32.83	-37.15	-41.50
80	-1.620	-1.804	-2.001	-2.217	-2.468	-4.106	-6.677	-10.17	-14.44	-19.30	-24.59	-30.21	-36.04	-42.04	-48.17	-54.39
90	-2.024	-2.232	-2.454	-2.693	-2.955	-4.714	-7.436	-11.22	-15.99	-21.62	-27.94	-34.80	-42.09	-49.71	-57.59	-65.68
	Values of h at Abutment															
10	6.275	3.475	3.170	3.163	3.241	3.782	4.241	4.633	4.987	5.315	5.629	5.932	6.229	6.520	6.807	7.091
20	10.94	10.97	10.69	10.59	10.67	12.16	13.86	15.41	16.83	18.15	19.41	20.62	21.79	22.93	24.06	25.17
30	11.93	13.26	14.34	15.28	16.16	20.25	23.96	27.28	30.30	33.11	35.77	38.31	40.76	43.14	45.47	47.76
40	12.96	14.20	15.41	16.61	17.83	24.08	30.02	35.39	40.27	44.78	49.00	53.02	56.88	60.62	64.26	67.82
50	14.49	15.48	16.47	17.50	18.55	24.67	31.35	37.92	44.12	49.94	55.43	60.68	65.70	70.56	75.27	79.88
60	16.55	17.30	18.07	18.87	19.70	24.56	30.37	36.59	42.85	48.95	54.85	60.54	66.04	71.38	76.57	81.65
70	19.12	19.69	20.27	20.86	21.48	25.02	29.30	34.13	39.23	44.43	49.60	54.70	59.71	64.62	69.43	74.16
80	22.21	22.63	23.06	23.50	23.95	26.38	29.18	32.31	36.17	39.17	42.75	46.34	49.93	53.50	57.04	60.55
90	25.82	26.14	26.46	26.78	27.10	28.69	30.29	31.88	33.47	35.07	36.66	38.26	39.85	41.44	43.04	44.63
	Values of m at Abutment															
10	-0.245	-0.243	-0.236	-0.228	-0.220	-0.186	-0.164	-0.148	-0.137	-0.127	-0.120	-0.114	-0.109	-0.105	-0.101	-0.098
20	-0.769	-0.760	-0.764	-0.761	-0.752	-0.675	-0.609	-0.558	-0.520	-0.490	-0.465	-0.445	-0.429	-0.414	-0.402	-0.264
30	-1.745	-1.615	-1.515	-1.432	-1.363	-1.048	-0.817	-0.648	-0.521	-0.424	-0.348	-0.287	-0.237	-0.196	-0.161	-0.132
40	-3.183	-2.963	-2.756	-2.555	-2.357	-1.420	-0.649	-0.056	0.399	0.756	1.040	1.272	1.464	1.624	1.761	1.879
50	-5.080	-4.796	-4.513	-4.225	-3.942	-2.302	-0.684	0.783	1.993	2.994	3.823	4.526	5.120	5.631	6.074	6.462
60	-7.445	-7.111	-6.774	-6.425	-6.059	-3.922	-1.435	1.069	3.388	5.452	7.263	8.846	10.23	11.46	12.54	13.51
70	-10.29	-9.920	-9.543	-9.152	-8.741	-6.277	-3.170	0.282	3.774	7.114	10.21	13.05	15.62	17.95	20.06	21.99
80	-13.64	-13.24	-12.84	-12.42	-11.99	-9.330	-5.851	-1.723	2.737	7.291	11.73	15.97	19.96	23.68	27.13	30.34
90	-17.50	-17.09	-16.67	-16.24	-15.79	-13.06	-9.420	-4.912	0.217	5.695	11.29	16.84	22.23	27.41	32.34	37.00
	Values of v at Abutment															
10	-21.04	-21.80	-22.13	-22.40	-22.66	-23.94	-25.22	-26.52	-27.82	-29.13	-30.44	-31.76	-33.07	-34.39	-35.70	-37.02
20	-40.64	-41.18	-41.83	-42.42	-42.94	-45.15	-47.29	-49.48	-51.71	-53.99	-56.28	-58.60	-60.92	-63.26	-65.61	-67.96
30	-60.95	-61.02	-61.24	-61.53	-61.86	-63.69	-65.73	-68.01	-70.45	-73.00	-75.67	-78.39	-81.16	-83.97	-86.82	-89.68
40	-81.57	-81.67	-81.80	-81.92	-82.04	-82.50	-83.23	-84.42	-86.04	-87.96	-90.12	-92.46	-94.92	-97.50	-100.1	-102.9
50	-102.3	-102.6	-102.9	-103.1	-103.4	-103.4	-102.9	-102.4	-102.4	-102.8	-103.7	-104.8	-106.2	-107.8	-109.6	-111.4
60	-123.1	-123.6	-124.2	-124.7	-125.1	-126.1	-125.4	-124.0	-122.5	-121.3	-120.4	-120.0	-119.8	-119.9	-120.3	-120.8
70	-144.0	-144.8	-145.6	-146.4	-147.2	-149.6	-149.9	-148.8	-146.9	-144.8	-142.7	-140.8	-139.2	-137.8	-136.7	-135.8
80	-164.9	-166.1	-167.2	-168.3	-169.4	-173.5	-175.6	-175.8	-174.7	-172.8	-170.5	-168.0	-165.6	-163.3	-161.2	-159.3
90	-185.9	-187.4	-188.9	-190.3	-191.7	-197.7	-201.9	-204.1	-204.7	-204.1	-202.7	-200.9	-198.7	-196.4	-194.1	-191.9

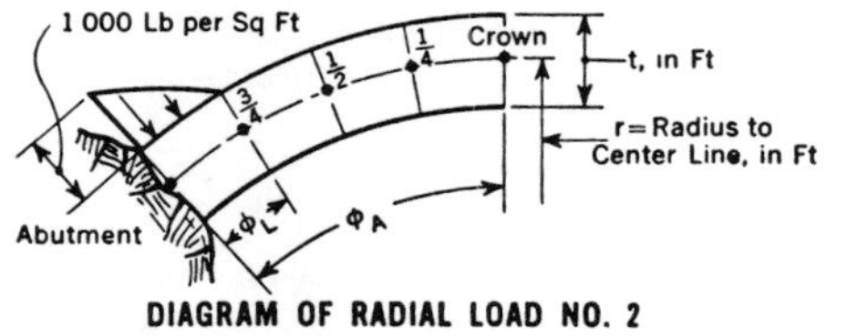

DIAGRAM OF RADIAL LOAD NO. 2

Thrust, Moment, Shear, in Lb, and Ft-Lb

$H = hr$
$M = mr^2$
$V = vr$

TABLE 4(*b*).—Radial Deflections for Radial Load No. 2

ϕ_A	Values of t/r: 025	.050	.075	.100	.125	.250	.375	.500	.625	.750	.875	1.000	1.125	1.250	1.375	1.500
	VALUES OF K_1 AT CROWN															
10	-499.9	-114.1	-74.89	-61.34	-55.24	-48.35	-48.69	-50.24	-52.17	-54.28	-56.47	-58.72	-61.01	-63.32	-65.64	-67.98
20	227.8	-208.6	-181.2	-150.8	-131.4	-100.8	-97.09	-98.36	-101.2	-104.7	-108.6	-112.7	-116.9	-121.1	-125.5	-129.7
30	3720	331.7	-13.00	-89.20	-111.5	-122.9	-125.4	-129.6	-134.7	-140.2	-146.0	-151.9	-157.9	-163.9	-170.0	-176.1
40	12580	1719	5048	183 7	60.25	-78.65	-108.3	-125.7	-137.9	-148.2	-157.4	-166.1	-174.4	-182.5	-190.4	-198.2
50	30800	4434	1474	682.3	355.0	25.97	-46.75	-79.82	-103.4	-121.3	-136.1	-148.1	-160.3	-170.9	-180.9	-190.5
60	63850	9204	3116	1494	864.5	176.0	55.03	-0.3403	-35.84	-61.98	-82.73	-100.0	-115.0	-128.4	-140.6	-151.9
70	118900	16990	5733	2752	1603	372.4	179.7	101.8	85.83	21.88	-3.959	-25.11	-43.04	-58.66	-72.56	-85.20
80	205300	29020	9713	4631	2621	628.4	329.4	221.2	161.7	122.6	92.92	69.19	49.48	32.64	17 96	4.873
90	334700	46870	15550	7353	41.48	963.6	510.0	358.5	283.1	236.2	202.9	1776	157.3	140.3	125.9	113.4
	VALUES OF K_1 AT $\frac{1}{4}$ POINT															
10	-3971	-111.1	-736.3	-60.68	-54.90	-48.27	-48.46	-50.21	-52.22	-54.24	-56.53	-58.69	-61.06	-63.27	-65.70	-67.93
20	-63.74	-237.9	-187.2	-152.5	-1319	-100.9	-97.16	-98.38	-101.2	-104.7	-108.5	-112.5	-116.7	-120.9	-125.2	-129.5
30	2097	96.48	-91.04	-125.7	-132.3	-127.5	-127.6	-131.0	-135.6	-140.8	-146.3	-151	-157 9	-163.8	-169.8	-175.8
40	7520	968.4	243.4	-54 70	-16.84	-98.08	-118.9	-132.0	-142.4	-151.5	-160.0	-168.1	-175.9	-183.6	-191.2	-198.7
50	18580	2645	856.0	378.0	177.1	-21.49	-71.40	-96.91	-116.1	-131.2	-144.1	-155.4	-165.8	-175.6	-184.9	-193.8
60	38480	5553	1873	890.2	508.4	85.62	5.504	-34.72	-62.22	-83.35	-100.6	-115.4	-128.4	-140.2	-151.0	-161.2
70	71380	10250	3470	1669	972.8	220.5	97.12	43.48	9.271	-16.26	-36.77	-53.96	-68.83	-81.99	-93.85	-104.8
80	122500	17440	5869	2814	1580	390.0	202.9	131.9	90.73	62.34	40.04	21.75	6.240	-7.238	-19.14	-29.89
90	198600	27990	9346	4449	2575	605.5	326.0	229.8	180.2	148.2	125.9	106.4	91.28	78.55	67.62	57.99
	VALUES OF K_1 AT $\frac{1}{2}$ POINT															
10	-307.8	-101.6	-69.69	-58.65	-53.64	-48.03	-48.72	-50.11	-52.20	-54.14	-56.46	-58.57	-60.96	-63.14	-65.56	-67.78
20	-707.7	-296.9	-197.0	-154.2	-132.1	-100.9	-97.26	-98.39	-101.1	-104.4	-108.2	-112.1	-115.6	-120.3	-124.8	-128.7
30	-1569	-437.4	-269.1	-209.7	-179.8	-138.9	-133.4	-134.6	-138.0	-142.3	-147.3	-152.5	-157.9	-163.4	-169.0	-174.7
40	-3879	-7416	-358.9	-246.7	-199.6	-1471	-144.9	-149.0	-154.6	-160.6	-167.0	-173.4	-180.0	-186.6	-193.2	-199.9
50	-8833	-1406	-559.9	-327.9	-244.5	-140.1	-136.9	-142.3	-150.2	-158.2	-166.0	-173.6	-181.0	-188.4	-195.4	-202.8
60	-18080	-2652	-948.0	-494.5	-319.0	-136.7	-121.2	-124.8	-132.4	-140.8	-149.1	-1571	-164.9	-172.4	-179.7	-186.8
70	-33880	-4778	-1616	-788.8	-473.0	-147.0	-100.3	-106.8	-111.0	-117.4	-113.1	-131.6	-138.5	-145.2	-151 7	-158.0
80	-59250	-8181	-2689	-1265	-635.8	-176.7	-109.5	-94.62	-92.91	-95.25	-99.43	-104.2	-109.1	-114.0	-118.8	-123.5
90	-98200	-13390	-4330	-1997	-1121	-231.8	-120.8	-90.98	-81.23	-78.49	-78.68	-80.16	-82.23	-84.54	-86.92	-89.33
	VALUES OF K_1 AT $\frac{3}{4}$ POINT															
10	-206.9	-84.00	-62.65	-55.06	-51.53	-47.61	-48.33	-49.95	-51.87	-53.98	-56.14	-58.38	-60.64	-62.92	-65.22	-67.54
20	-1015	-299.6	-185.8	-145.5	-126.3	-100.2	-97.13	-98.26	-100.8	-104.0	-1076	-1114	-115.3	-119.3	-123.4	-127.5
30	-3719	-760.6	-380.9	-265.3	-214.9	-150.2	-140.2	-139.1	-141.0	-144.3	-148.4	-152.8	-157.6	-162.6	-167.7	-172.9
40	-10550	-1815	-767.8	-468.7	-345.1	-198.6	-176.0	-170.7	-170.7	-173.0	-176.5	-180.7	-185.4	-190.4	-195.7	-2011
50	-24540	-3888	-1496	-833.0	-569.4	-260.6	-213.3	-198.9	-194.5	-194.0	-195.7	-198.4	-201.9	-206.0	-210.4	-215.0
60	-49750	-7525	-2740	-1440	-925.3	-351.0	-262.0	-232.9	-220.7	-215.2	-213.2	-213.1	-214.3	-216.1	-218.7	-221.6
70	-91360	-13420	-4718	-2386	-1476	-480.5	-332.6	-279.7	-256.5	-244.0	-254.5	-232.6	-261.8	-229.2	-269.0	-229.4
80	-155900	-22430	-7703	-3795	-2288	-659.7	-422.3	-343.2	-306.2	-385.1	-271.8	-262.8	-256.4	-251.7	-248.3	-245.9
90	-251500	-35640	-12030	-5815	-3434	-901.4	-542.8	-425.8	-375.2	-340.6	-320.7	-306.7	-296.2	-288.1	-281.6	-276.3
	VALUES OF K_1 AT ABUTMENT															
10	-37.55	-38.92	-39.50	-39.99	-40.46	-42.73	-45.02	-47.34	-49.67	-52.00	-54.34	-56.69	-59.03	-61.38	-63.73	-66.08
20	-72.53	-73.50	-74.66	-75.71	-76.64	-80.59	-84.41	-88.32	-92.31	-96.36	-100.5	-104.6	-108.8	-112.9	-117.1	-121.3
30	-108.8	-108.9	-109.3	-109.8	-110.4	-113.7	-117.3	-121.4	-125.7	-130.3	-135.1	-139.9	-144.9	-149.9	-155.0	-160.1
40	-145.6	-145.8	-146.0	-146.2	-146.4	-147.3	-148.6	-150.7	-153.6	-157.0	-160.9	-165.0	-169.4	-174.0	-178.8	-183.6
50	-182.6	-183.1	-183.6	-184.1	-184.5	-184.6	-183.6	-182.8	-182.8	-183.6	-185.1	-187.1	-189.6	-192.4	-195.6	-198.9
60	-219.7	-220.7	-221.7	-222.6	-223.3	-225.0	-223.8	-221.3	-218.7	-216.5	-215.0	-2141	-213.8	-214.0	-214.7	-215.7
70	-256.9	-258.5	-260.0	-261.4	-262.7	-267.0	-267.6	-265.6	-262.2	-258.4	-254.7	-251.3	-248.4	-246.0	-244.0	-242.5
80	-294.3	-296.4	-298.5	-300.4	-302.3	-309.7	-313.5	-313.9	-311.9	-308.4	-304.3	-299.9	-295.6	-291.6	-287.8	-284.3
90	-331.9	-334.5	-337.1	-339.7	-342.2	-352.9	-360.4	-364.3	-365.4	-364.4	-361.9	-358.5	-354.7	-350.6	-346.5	-342.5

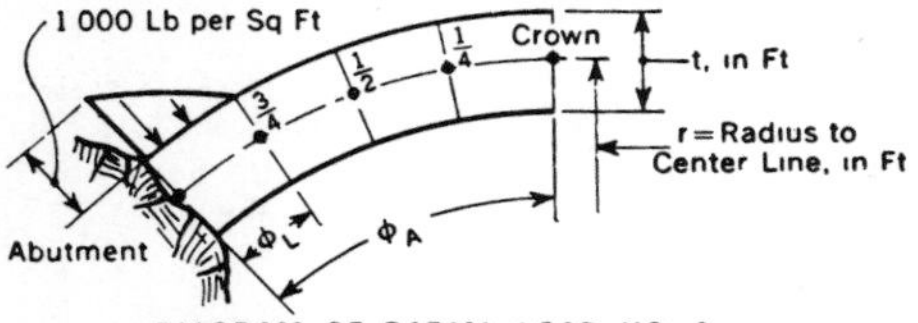

DIAGRAM OF RADIAL LOAD NO 2

Radial Deflection, in Ft

$$\Delta_{\mathfrak{c}} = K_1 \frac{r}{E_c}$$

E_c = Modulus of Elasticity of Concrete in Direct Stress, Lb per Sq Ft

TABLE 5(a).—Forces and Moments for Radial Load No. 3

ϕ_A	VALUES OF t/r															
	.025	.050	.075	.100	.125	.250	.375	.500	.625	.750	.875	1.000	1.125	1.250	1.375	1.500
VALUES OF h AT CROWN																
10	22.85	11.32	8.388	7.387	7.014	7.146	7.741	8.330	8.893	9.429	9.951	10.46	10.96	11.46	11.95	12.43
20	57.27	48.56	40.40	34.91	31.51	27.19	28.30	30.26	32.37	34.49	36.57	38.62	40.63	42.62	44.58	46.58
30	61.73	62.89	62.07	60.41	58.64	54.73	56.69	60.55	64.96	69.50	74.04	78.53	82.97	87.34	89.84	95.95
40	62.30	65.52	67.91	69.69	71.07	76.56	83.16	90.82	98.82	106.9	114.8	122.6	130.3	137.9	145.4	152.8
50	62.69	66.14	69.28	72.17	74.89	87.56	100.3	113.3	126.2	138.8	151.1	163.2	174.9	186.5	197.8	208.9
60	63.31	66.64	69.84	72.96	76.05	91.69	108.4	125.9	143.6	161.0	178.1	194.7	211.0	226.9	242.5	257.9
70	64.21	67.36	70.46	73.56	76.66	93.02	111.3	131.3	152.2	173.5	194.7	215.6	236.3	256.5	276.4	296.0
80	65.38	68.37	71.35	74.35	77.38	93.54	112.0	132.8	155.3	178.9	202.9	227.2	251.3	275.4	299.1	322.6
90	66.81	69.68	72.55	75.45	78.38	94.09	112.2	132.8	155.6	180.0	205.6	231.9	258.6	285.3	312.1	338.9
VALUES OF m AT CROWN																
10	.0958	0.216	0.286	0.342	0.391	0.586	0.739	0.870	0.986	1.093	1.193	1.289	1.380	1.469	1.555	1.639
20	-0.450	-0.182	.0905	0.313	0.491	1.071	1.472	1.815	2.127	2.420	2.699	2.967	3.228	3.481	3.729	4.215
30	-1.249	-1.195	-1.044	-0.846	-0.637	0.201	0.715	1.084	1.390	1.661	1.913	2.153	2.384	2.608	2.828	3.043
40	-2.256	2.369	-2.421	-2.426	-2.401	-2.170	-2.090	-2.174	-2.350	-2.575	-2.828	-3.096	-3.373	-3.655	-3.941	-4.229
50	-3.512	-3.743	-3.946	-4.129	-4.300	-5.146	-6.178	-7.402	-8.777	-10.16	-11.61	-13.09	-14.57	-16.06	-17.55	-19.05
60	-5.030	-5.360	-5.680	-6.000	-6.326	-8.180	-10.54	-13.35	-16.44	-19.71	-23.08	-26.51	-29.98	-33.47	-36.98	-40.50
70	-6.820	-7.239	-7.661	-8.095	-8.546	-11.22	-14.77	-19.15	-24.18	-29.64	-35.40	-41.36	-47.45	-53.64	-59.90	-66.21
80	-8.884	-9.390	-9.908	-10.44	-11.00	-14.34	-18.84	-24.56	-31.33	-38.94	-47.18	-55.87	-64.91	-74.19	-83.68	-93.31
90	-11.22	-11.82	-12.43	-13.06	-13.72	-17.62	-22.87	-29.62	-37.81	-47.25	-57.71	-68.99	-80.91	-93.34	-106.2	-1.9.3
VALUES OF h AT ABUTMENT																
10	23.78	12.45	9.577	8.607	8.256	8.465	9.130	9.790	10.42	11.03	11.62	12.20	2.78	13.34	13.91	14.46
20	58.95	50.83	43.23	38.13	35.00	31.26	32.62	34.77	37.07	39.38	41.65	43.89	46.10	48.28	50.45	52.65
30	64.99	66.13	65.56	64.27	62.88	60.21	62.61	66.67	71.20	75.85	80.49	85.09	89.64	94.14	97.02	103.0
40	68.16	70.88	72.96	74.58	75.89	81.36	87.67	94.80	102.2	109.6	117.0	124.2	131.4	138.5	145.4	152.4
50	72.12	74.73	77.14	79.39	81.54	91.64	101.8	112.1	122.4	132.4	142.3	152.0	161.6	170.9	180.2	189.3
60	77.29	79.52	81.68	83.81	85.91	96.55	107.7	119.3	130.9	142.5	153.8	165.0	175.9	186.7	197.3	207.8
70	83.77	85.61	87.43	89.25	91.08	100.5	110.6	121.2	132.2	143.3	154.6	165.3	176.2	186.9	197.6	208.1
80	91.62	93.13	94.64	96.15	97.67	105.4	113.6	122.2	131.0	140.1	149.2	158.4	167.5	176.6	185.7	94.8
90	100.9	102.2	103.4	104.7	105.9	112.1	118.4	124.6	130.8	137.1	143.3	149.5	155.8	162.0	168.2	174.4
VALUES OF m AT ABUTMENT																
10	-0.842	-0.913	-0.903	-0.878	-0.851	-0.733	-0.650	-0.589	-0.544	-0.508	-0.479	-0.456	-0.436	-0.419	-0.405	-0.392
20	-2.128	-2.449	-2.732	-2.904	-2.995	-2.992	-2.841	-2.696	-2.574	-2.470	-2.383	-2.308	-2.243	-2.186	-2.137	-1.846
30	-4.505	-4.433	-4.540	-4.707	-4.875	-5.274	-5.209	-5.033	-4.849	-4.680	-4.531	-4.402	-4.288	-4.189	-4.099	-4.024
40	-8.117	-7.729	-7.475	-7.317	-7.219	-6.966	-6.604	-6.158	-5.722	-5.327	-4.981	-4.679	-4.416	-4.187	-3.985	-3.806
50	-12.94	-12.33	-11.81	-11.35	-10.94	-9.228	-7.677	-6.230	-4.960	-3.792	-2.809	-1.940	-1.187	-0.526	0.058	0.577
60	-19.01	-18.24	-17.52	-16.84	-16.19	-13.04	-9.855	-6.733	-3.820	-1.186	1.164	3.250	5.103	6.755	8.230	9.562
70	-26.38	-25.49	-24.63	-23.79	-22.96	-18.69	-14.00	-9.048	-4.123	0.575	5.201	8.955	12.61	15.95	8.99	21.76
80	-35.12	-34.15	-33.19	-32.24	-31.29	-26.22	-20.39	-13.88	-7.021	-0.136	6.558	12.93	18.93	24.53	29.74	34.58
90	-45.34	-44.32	-43.30	-42.28	-41.25	-35.68	-29.09	-21.46	-13.07	-4.271	4.622	13.39	21.89	30.02	37.77	45.10
VALUES OF v AT ABUTMENT																
10	-40.18	-42.73	-43.78	-44.50	-45.11	-47.82	-50.44	-53.06	-55.69	-58.32	-60.95	-63.59	-66.23	-68.87	-71.51	-74.15
20	-68.55	-72.61	-76.49	-79.46	-81.71	-88.62	-93.69	-98.46	-103.2	-107.9	-112.6	-117.4	-122.1	-126.9	-131.6	-136.4
30	-100.9	-102.0	-104.0	-106.5	-109.0	-119.1	-126.2	-132.4	-138.3	-144.2	-150.1	-156.0	-161.9	-167.8	-174.7	-179.8
40	-134.9	-135.0	-135.6	-136.6	-137.9	-145.2	-151.7	-157.6	-163.2	-168.9	-174.6	-180.3	-186.2	-192.1	-198.1	-204.1
50	-169.4	-169.4	-169.7	-170.2	-170.8	-174.5	-178.2	-181.6	-185.2	-188.9	-192.9	-197.1	-201.5	-206.1	-210.8	-215.7
60	-204.2	-204.6	-205.0	-205.5	-206.0	-208.4	-210.0	-210.8	-211.5	-212.4	-213.6	-215.2	-217.1	-219.3	-221.7	-224.4
70	-239.4	-240.2	-240.9	-241.7	-242.5	-245.6	-246.9	-246.7	-245.5	-244.0	-242.6	-241.4	-240.6	-240.0	-239.8	-239.9
80	-274.9	-276.2	-277.4	-278.6	-279.9	-284.9	-287.5	-288.1	-286.9	-284.6	-281.9	-279.0	-276.1	-273.4	-270.9	-268.7
90	-310.8	-312.6	-314.4	-316.1	-317.8	-325.4	-330.7	-333.4	-333.9	-332.7	-330.4	-327.5	-324.1	-320.6	-317.2	-313.7

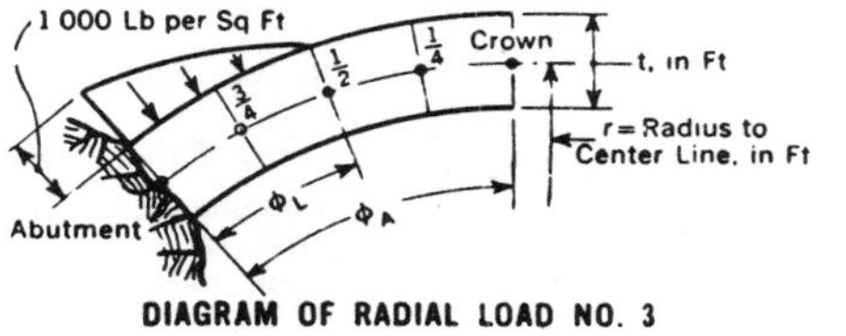

DIAGRAM OF RADIAL LOAD NO. 3

Thrust, Moment, Shear, in Lb, and Ft-Lb

$H = hr$
$M = mr^2$
$V = vr$

TABLE 5(*b*).—RADIAL DEFLECTIONS FOR RADIAL LOAD No. 3

ϕ_A	VALUES OF t/r															
	.025	050	.075	.100	.125	.250	375	500	625	.750	.875	1.000	1.125	1250	1.375	1.500
	VALUES OF K_1 AT CROWN															
10	-1614	-456.5	-246.3	-177.3	-146.6	-109.0	-104.9	-106.1	-108.9	-112.5	-116.5	-120.6	-125.0	-129.4	-133.9	-138.5
20	-374.3	-1337	-904.9	-642.8	-494.8	-272.7	-233.4	-224.1	-220.8	-227.6	-233.5	-239.8	-247.1	-254.8	-262.8	-270.8
30	14770	489.8	-600.1	-701.0	-654.4	-423.9	-351.8	-329.2	-323.7	-325.7	-331.5	-339.4	-348.6	-358.6	-369.0	-380.3
40	55080	6197	1271	132.9	-228.4	-419.9	-390.0	-376.4	-374.9	-379.7	-387.9	-398.3	-409.9	-422.4	-435.5	-449.0
50	139900	17970	5168	1974	824.4	-211.5	-305.3	-332.9	-351.8	-367.3	-383.4	-399.4	-415.5	-431.8	-448.0	-464.3
60	295900	39250	12080	5194	2652	186.2	-104.8	-198.2	-248.3	-283.5	-312.1	-337.0	-359.8	-381.1	-401.4	-421.0
70	558800	74640	23430	10400	5564	784.7	197.6	13.14	-78.28	-136.9	-180.6	-216.0	-237.5	-273.3	-298.0	-320.9
80	974700	130200	41070	18400	9984	1634	606.0	293.4	148.1	61.25	0.733	-45.74	-83.75	-116.2	-144.7	-170.4
90	1603000	213700	67390	29680	16470	2814	1143	647.4	428.3	305.2	224.5	165.9	120.2	88.77	51.10	23.47
	VALUES OF K_1 AT $\frac{1}{4}$ POINT															
10	-1543	-4371	-238.7	-173.5	-144.5	-108.6	-104.7	-105.9	-108.8	-112.4	-116.4	-120.6	-124.7	-129.3	-133.8	-138.4
20	-1615	-1402	-897.1	-630.4	-484.8	-270.1	-232.2	-223.5	-223.5	-227.2	-232.9	-239.3	-246.6	-254.3	-262.2	-270.3
30	6935	-465.0	-855.9	-793.7	-693.9	-425.9	-352.4	-329.6	-323.9	-325.7	-331.3	-338.9	-348.0	-357.8	-368.3	-379.1
40	29620	2811	225.1	-321.5	-469.4	-455.1	-407.0	-384.6	-383.5	-383.5	-394.1	-400.1	-414.7	-423.0	-439.6	-448.6
50	76930	9496	2483	765.7	165.4	-326.9	-354.5	-362.3	-371.9	-382.6	-395.4	-408.9	-423.2	-437.8	-452.8	-468.0
60	163300	21450	6428	2636	1247	-70.18	-215.4	-266.9	-297.1	-321.2	-342.5	-362.3	-381.2	-399.4	-417.3	-434.7
70	307800	41110	12810	5605	2934	307.1	-9.847	-116.3	-171.7	-210.3	-241.2	-267.6	-291.3	-313.1	-333.5	-352.9
80	534600	71680	22620	10100	5449	826.1	255.2	77.92	-8.391	-63.07	-103.4	-136.0	-163.7	-188.2	-210.4	-230.8
90	874500	117200	37090	16670	9083	1528	328.0	314.4	186.9	112.6	52.71	23.25	-7.828	-34.08	-56.91	-77.33
	VALUES OF K_1 AT $\frac{1}{2}$ POINT															
10	- 1299	- 376.8	- 215.5	-161.9	-137.7	-107.3	-104.2	-105.6	-108.5	-112.1	-116.1	-120.3	-124.6	-129.0	-133.5	-138.1
20	- 4056	- 1461	- 840.4	-581.0	-449.3	-261.8	-229.1	-221.6	-222.0	-225.9	-231.4	-237.9	-245.1	-252.7	-263.5	-268.5
30	- 9509	- 2430	- 1360	-963.9	-758.8	-425.6	-352.3	-329.7	-323.8	-325.2	-330.3	-337.4	-345.9	-355.2	-365.2	-375.6
40	- 23970	- 4344	- 1989	-1284	-972.2	-532.1	-436.5	-404.3	-394.0	-393.3	-397.6	-404.9	-413.9	-424.1	-435.2	-446.8
50	- 55040	- 8399	- 3234	-1828	-1263	-590.8	-534.9	-435.7	-423.9	-422.4	-426.7	-434.0	-443.3	-453.9	-465.3	-477.4
60	-113100	-15960	- 5561	-2838	-1791	-655.9	-487.8	-438.0	-421.9	-419.0	-422.4	-429.3	-438.2	-448.4	-459.4	-471.1
70	-212200	-28880	- 9531	-4569	-2702	-771.7	-510.6	-434.5	-407.4	-398.8	-398.8	-403.1	-410.0	-418.4	-427.8	-437.8
80	-371000	-49530	-15880	-7342	-3145	-972.4	-562.7	-443.0	-396.8	-377.5	-370.5	-369.7	-372.4	-377.1	-383.2	-390.2
90	-613700	-81020	-25560	-11580	-6411	-1293	-660.1	-476.1	-401.7	-366.6	-349.0	-340.4	-336.9	-336.3	-337.6	-340.3
	VALUES OF K_1 AT $\frac{3}{4}$ POINT															
10	- 779.9	- 261.6	- 169.4	- 137.3	- 122.3	-103.0	-101.8	-103.8	-107.0	-110.8	-114.9	-119.1	-123.5	-127.9	-132.4	-137.0
20	- 3978	- 1094	- 616.3	- 441.7	- 357.0	-237.7	-217.1	-213.4	-215.5	-220.1	-226.0	-232.7	-239.9	-247.5	-255.2	-263.2
30	- 14380	- 2770	- 1310	- 862.0	- 661.7	-386.2	-332.3	-316.4	-313.1	-315.5	-320.8	-327.9	-336.1	-345.0	-354.6	-364.4
40	- 41310	- 6668	- 2668	- 1549	-996.0	-535.6	-436.4	-403.7	-392.3	-390.1	-392.7	-398.3	-405.6	-413.4	-423.6	-433.7
50	- 97470	- 14550	- 5303	- 2808	- 1825	-718.8	-541.3	-482.3	-458.0	-448.0	-445.6	-447.2	-451.7	-458.0	-465.6	-474.1
60	- 199900	- 28670	- 9932	- 4975	- 3058	-984.8	-674.1	-571.2	-524.0	-503.1	-491.9	-487.1	-486.3	-488.2	-492.2	-497.2
70	- 370800	- 51940	-17460	- 8449	- 5006	- 1378	-859.1	-689.8	-612.7	-571.6	-546.5	-533.4	-524.9	-520.3	-518.4	-518.5
80	- 638300	- 88030	-29020	-13730	- 7946	- 1942	- 1117	-852.6	-732.3	-666.3	-625.9	-599.3	-580.3	-568.4	-559.4	-553.2
90	-1038000	-141600	-46050	-21460	-12210	- 2730	- 1467	- 1071	-893.1	-795.5	-734.9	-693.9	-664.7	-642.8	-626.1	-613.0
	VALUES OF K_1 AT ABUTMENT															
10	-71.73	-76.27	-78.15	-79.44	-80.53	-85.35	-90.03	-94.71	-99.40	-104.1	-108.8	-113.5	-118.2	-122.9	-127.6	-132.4
20	-122.4	-129.6	-136.5	-141.8	-145.8	-158.2	-167.2	-175.7	-184.2	-192.6	-201.0	-209.5	-218.0	-226.5	-235.0	-243.5
30	-180.1	-182.0	-185.6	-190.0	-194.5	-212.5	-225.3	-236.4	-247.0	-257.4	-267.9	-278.4	-289.0	-299.6	-310.2	-320.9
40	-240.8	-240.9	-242.0	-243.9	-264.0	-259.1	-270.8	-281.3	-291.4	-301.4	-311.6	-321.9	-332.3	-342.9	-353.6	-364.4
50	-302.4	-302.4	-302.9	-303.8	-304.8	-311.5	-318.0	-324.8	-330.5	-337.2	-344.4	-351.8	-359.7	-367.9	-376.4	-385.1
60	-364.6	-365.1	-365.9	-366.8	-367.7	-372.1	-374.8	-376.3	-377.5	-379.1	-381.3	-384.1	-387.4	-391.4	-395.8	-400.6
70	-427.4	-428.7	-430.1	-431.5	-432.9	-438.5	-440.8	-440.3	-438.2	-435.6	-433.1	-431.0	-429.4	-428.5	-428.1	-428.2
80	-490.7	-492.9	-495.2	-497.4	-499.6	-508.5	-513.4	-514.2	-512.1	-508.1	-503.2	-498.0	-492.8	-488.0	-483.6	-479.6
90	-544.7	-557.9	-561.1	-564.3	-567.4	-580.9	-590.3	-595.1	-596.0	-593.9	-589.8	-584.5	-578.6	-572.4	-566.1	-560.0

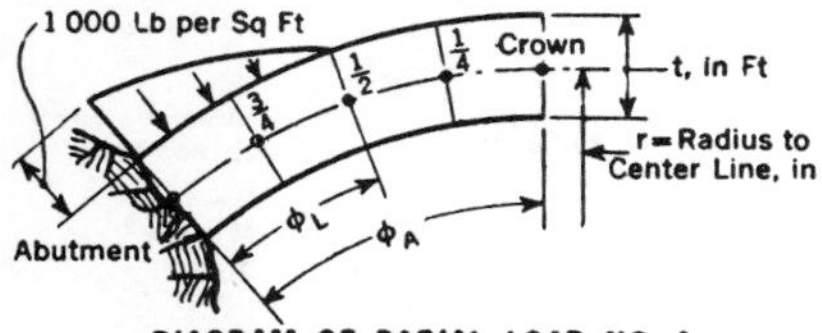

DIAGRAM OF RADIAL LOAD NO. 3

Radial Deflection, in Ft

$$\Delta_r = K_1 \frac{r}{E_c}$$

E_c = Modulus of Elasticity of Concrete in Direct Stress, Lb per Sq Ft

TABLE 6(*a*).—Forces and Moments for Radial Load No. 4

ϕ_A	Values of t/r: .025	.050	.075	.100	.125	.250	.375	.500	.625	.750	.875	1.000	1.125	1.250	1.375	1.500
	VALUES OF h AT CROWN															
10	56.39	24.62	16.38	13.33	11.97	10.83	11.31	11.97	12.66	13.34	14.01	14.68	15.35	16.01	16.67	17.32
20	150.7	119.8	93.43	75.86	64.69	46.42	44.63	45.89	48.01	50.42	52.95	55.52	58.10	60.69	63.27	65.98
30	165.9	161.8	153.0	142.6	132.7	103.8	96.81	97.45	100.9	105.5	110.6	115.9	121.4	127.0	132.5	138.1
40	169.0	172.0	172.6	171.5	169.4	157.0	152.7	155.2	161.1	168.8	177.3	186.3	195.6	205.0	214.4	223.9
50	170.9	175.5	179.1	181.9	184.0	189.8	195.7	204.6	215.7	228.3	241.6	255.5	269.6	283.7	297.9	312.1
60	173.0	178.0	182.5	186.6	190.4	206.7	222.2	238.8	256.8	275.6	296.0	314.6	334.3	354.0	373.6	393.2
70	175.6	180.6	185.4	189.9	194.4	215.6	237.0	259.7	283.7	308.6	333.9	359.5	385.1	410.6	436.1	461.4
80	178.7	183.6	188.4	193.2	198.2	221.2	245.7	272.1	300.2	329.6	359.9	390.6	421.6	452.6	483.5	514.3
90	182.4	187.2	192.0	196.8	201.6	225.8	251.7	280.0	310.4	342.8	376.4	411.0	446.2	481.7	517.4	553.1
	VALUES OF m AT CROWN															
10	0.357	0.654	0.817	0.943	1.052	1.490	1.834	2.129	2.394	2.637	2.866	3.084	3.295	3.499	3.698	3.893
20	-0.781	.0594	0.818	1.433	1.916	3.452	4.508	5.411	6.236	7.011	7.750	8.463	9.156	9.832	10.49	11.49
30	-2.499	-2.112	-1.469	-0.714	0.052	3.080	5.047	6.556	7.856	9.044	10.17	11.24	12.29	13.31	14.31	15.30
40	-4.642	-4.611	-4.383	-4.001	-3.513	-0.679	1.641	3.362	4.716	5.855	6.865	7.793	8.666	9.502	10.31	11.10
50	-7.313	-7.521	-7.608	-7.590	-7.484	-6.274	-4.967	-4.059	-3.532	-3.279	-3.200	-3.273	-3.420	-3.627	-3.877	-4.159
60	-10.56	-10.95	-11.27	-11.53	-11.74	-12.37	-12.94	-13.87	-15.19	-16.85	-18.75	-20.83	-23.04	-25.34	-27.72	-30.16
70	-14.40	-14.95	-15.47	-15.95	-16.42	-18.66	-21.22	-24.40	-28.20	-32.52	-37.25	-42.28	-47.54	-52.97	-58.54	-64.21
80	-18.85	-19.56	-20.25	-20.93	-21.70	-25.20	-29.54	-34.90	-41.27	-48.53	-56.50	-65.02	-73.98	-83.29	-92.86	-102.6
90	-23.92	-24.79	-25.65	-26.51	-27.39	-32.14	-37.99	-45.24	-53.95	-63.98	-75.15	-87.26	-100.1	-113.6	-127.6	-142.0
	VALUES OF h AT ABUTMENT															
10	58.42	27.17	19.09	16.12	14.82	13.88	14.53	15.36	16.21	17.06	17.90	18.74	19.57	20.40	21.23	22.05
20	153.2	124.2	99.60	83.24	72.88	56.43	55.45	57.35	60.05	63.03	66.12	69.25	72.39	75.53	78.66	81.92
30	169.5	166.3	158.9	150.2	142.0	118.6	114.1	116.3	120.8	126.4	132.4	138.7	145.0	151.4	157.8	164.2
40	175.1	177.9	179.0	178.7	177.6	171.0	170.5	175.2	182.6	191.2	200.6	210.3	220.2	230.2	240.3	250.4
50	180.6	184.5	187.6	190.3	192.5	200.6	208.8	218.9	230.4	242.8	255.8	269.1	282.5	295.9	309.4	322.9
60	187.4	191.2	194.7	198.0	201.1	225.5	229.5	244.0	259.2	274.9	291.3	306.8	322.9	339.0	355.0	371.1
70	195.9	199.3	202.6	205.8	209.0	224.7	240.4	256.6	273.1	290.0	307.5	324.2	341.3	358.5	375.6	392.6
80	206.2	209.2	212.2	215.2	218.2	233.0	248.1	263.5	279.2	295.1	311.2	327.3	343.5	359.7	375.9	392.1
90	218.5	221.2	223.9	226.6	229.3	242.8	256.2	269.7	283.2	296.7	310.2	323.7	337.2	350.6	364.1	377.6
	VALUES OF m AT ABUTMENT															
10	-1.675	-1.897	-1.895	-1.851	-1.797	-1.556	-1.382	-1.256	-1.169	-1.084	-1.023	-0.972	-0.950	-0.895	-0.864	-0.837
20	-3.218	-4.405	-5.358	-5.946	-6.279	-6.555	-6.319	-6.052	-5.811	-5.602	-5.421	-5.265	-5.128	-5.008	-4.901	-4.452
30	-6.098	-6.578	-7.438	-8.392	-9.275	-11.71	-12.27	-12.27	-12.10	-11.90	-11.68	-11.48	-11.30	-11.13	-10.98	-10.84
40	-10.73	-10.57	-10.77	-11.21	-11.78	-14.65	-16.15	-16.68	-16.75	-16.64	-16.44	-16.22	-16.00	-15.79	-15.58	-15.40
50	-17.02	-16.45	-16.12	-16.00	-16.02	-17.09	-18.03	-18.33	-18.18	-17.80	-17.34	-16.82	-16.32	-15.84	-15.38	-14.96
60	-24.99	-24.13	-23.44	-22.89	-22.45	-21.18	-20.24	-19.05	-17.63	-16.09	-14.05	-13.05	-11.64	-10.33	-9.111	-7.976
70	-34.73	-33.67	-32.72	-31.86	-31.08	-27.77	-24.61	-21.21	-17.62	-13.98	-9.978	-7.022	-3.821	-0.830	1.954	4.541
80	-46.37	-45.16	-44.03	-42.96	-41.78	-37.06	-31.95	-26.31	-20.25	-14.01	-7.785	-1.740	4.055	9.552	14.74	19.61
90	-60.06	-58.76	-57.50	-56.29	-55.10	-49.13	-42.53	-35.03	-26.74	-17.94	-8.920	.0813	8.903	17.44	25.63	33.44
	VALUES OF v AT ABUTMENT															
10	-56.38	-62.72	-64.96	-66.31	-67.36	-71.64	-75.65	-79.62	-83.58	-87.55	-91.52	-95.48	-99.45	-103.4	-107.4	-111.4
20	-80.23	-92.44	-103.1	-110.7	-116.2	-130.6	-139.3	-147.0	-154.4	-161.7	-169.0	-176.2	-183.5	-190.7	-198.0	-205.2
30	-113.3	-117.8	-124.6	-132.2	-139.6	-166.2	-181.8	-193.6	-204.0	-213.8	-223.4	-232.8	-242.2	-251.5	-260.8	-270.2
40	-150.4	-151.7	-154.6	-158.4	-163.0	-186.9	-205.7	-220.1	-232.3	-243.4	-253.9	-264.0	-274.1	-284.0	-294.0	-303.9
50	-188.8	-189.2	-190.3	-192.2	-194.5	-209.8	-225.0	-237.9	-249.1	-259.2	-268.8	-277.9	-286.8	-295.7	-304.6	-313.4
60	-227.8	-228.1	-228.8	-230.0	-231.3	-240.5	-250.4	-259.3	-267.1	-274.0	-279.7	-286.9	-293.2	-299.4	-305.7	-312.0
70	-267.3	-268.0	-268.8	-269.8	-271.0	-277.8	-284.3	-289.6	-293.8	-297.1	-300.0	-302.7	-305.3	-308.0	-310.8	-313.7
80	-307.5	-308.6	-309.8	-311.1	-312.2	-319.3	-325.0	-328.9	-331.0	-331.9	-331.9	-331.5	-330.9	-330.2	-329.6	-329.0
90	-348.2	-349.9	-351.6	-353.4	-355.2	-363.7	-370.5	-375.0	-377.3	-377.7	-376.8	-375.0	-372.5	-369.8	-366.9	-363.9

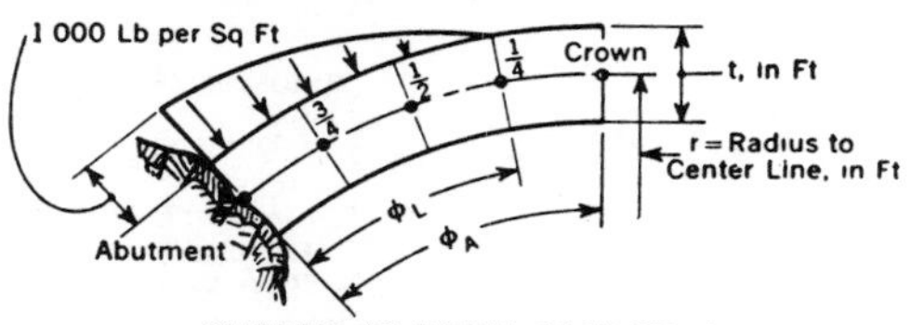

Thrust, Moment, Shear, in Lb, and Ft-Lb

$H = hr$
$M = mr^2$
$V = vr$

DIAGRAM OF RADIAL LOAD NO. 4

TABLE 6(b).—Radial Deflections for Radial Load No. 4

ϕ_A	Values of t/r															
	025	.050	.075	.100	.125	.250	.375	.500	.625	.750	.875	1.000	1.125	1.250	1.375	1.500
VALUES OF K_1 AT CROWN																
10	-4316	-1078	-527.7	-352.7	-276.4	-182.1	-168.6	-167.4	-170.2	-174.6	-179.9	-185.7	-191.9	-198.3	-204.8	-211.5
20	-4885	-3974	-2383	-1572	-1141	-521.2	-410.2	-377.6	-370.3	-368.5	-373.5	-381.1	-390.4	-400.7	-411.8	-423.0
30	21420	-1507	-2514	-2216	-1850	-937.7	-690.0	-605.1	-569.1	-557.5	-557.0	-562.6	-572.0	-583.8	-597.3	-612.0
40	93330	-8255	441.3	-1083	-1418	-1131	-881.4	-770.5	-720.9	-700.5	-695.3	-698.9	-707.9	-720.6	-735.6	-752.4
50	245700	28910	7088	1937	221.0	-944.9	-875.5	-807.1	-771.1	-756.5	-754.9	-761.1	-772.6	-787.6	-805.0	-824.2
60	527400	66620	19120	7422	3263	-408.4	-657.9	-690.9	-698.3	-706.4	-712.3	-734.0	-752.2	-772.4	-794.0	-816 7
70	1003000	129800	39050	16420	-8212	522.9	-249.1	-436.0	-510.6	-554.6	-588.5	-618.5	-647.0	-674.7	-711.9	-729.1
80	1759000	229300	70240	30390	16020	1882	351.8	-55.27	-222.4	-314.2	-376.0	-424.7	-465.7	-502.2	-535.9	-567 8
90	2902000	379400	117000	51200	27090	3815	1176	456.2	161.6	6.154	-91.88	-162.5	-217.8	-264.1	-304.4	-340.8
VALUES OF K_1 AT $\frac{1}{4}$ POINT																
10	-4053	-1018	-505.9	-342.0	-270.0	-181.0	-168.2	-167.2	-170.0	-174.4	-179.8	-185.6	-191.7	-198.1	-204.6	-211 3
20	-6963	-3954	-2298	-1510	-1098	-511.8	-406.5	-375.6	-366.9	-367.4	-372.5	-380.2	-389.4	-399.7	-410.7	-422.0
30	6153	-3150	-2866	-2298	-1857	-922.7	-686.1	-599.1	-566.4	-555.3	-554.9	-560.6	-569.9	-581.6	-594.9	-609.4
40	42350	1833	-1409	-1820	-1766	-1155	-885.7	-772.1	-721.8	-700.7	-695.0	-698.1	-706.6	-718.6	-733.1	-749.3
50	118400	12370	2043	-234.0	-906.9	-1095	-926.6	-834.0	-788.6	-768.9	-764.1	-767.8	-777.4	-790.7	-806.6	-824.6
60	258100	31380	8222	2637	713.5	-797.4	-806.4	-773.0	-753.2	-746.9	-744.4	-759.4	-772.9	-789.3	-811.4	-827.7
70	492600	62910	18330	7275	3308	-263.1	-557.7	-610.7	-629.4	-644.1	-660.0	-677.9	-697.2	-717.9	-747.9	-761.8
80	862100	112200	33960	14370	6678	494.5	-196.9	-367.9	-437.0	-447.7	-509.0	-536.6	-562.5	-587.5	-612.0	-636.3
90	1418000	185800	57170	24810	12950	1544	283.2	-51.13	-186.9	-260.6	-314.0	-348.5	-381.0	-410.0	-436.8	-462.2
VALUES OF K_1 AT $\frac{1}{2}$ POINT																
10	-3180	-831.0	-435.4	-306.7	-248.9	-176.3	-165.8	-165.6	-168.7	-173.3	-178.7	-184.6	-190.8	-197.2	-203.8	-210.4
20	-9897	-3548	-1954	-1287	-950.7	-477.3	-391.2	-366.2	-360.0	-361.6	-367.3	-375.3	-384.7	-395.0	-406.0	-417.3
30	-21290	-5799	-3265	-2272	-1742	-853.8	-649.2	-578.6	-551.6	-543.0	-543.9	-550.0	-559.5	-571 1	-584.2	-598.3
40	-51040	-9779	-4647	-3039	-2293	-1150	-866.3	-757.2	-709.7	-689.8	-684.1	-686.7	-694.4	-705.4	-718.8	-733.9
50	-114900	-18070	-7212	-4190	-2939	-1340	-1002	-870.6	-810.5	-782.7	-772.2	-771.4	-777.0	-786.8	-799.5	-814.3
60	-234200	-33500	-1194	-6250	-4031	-1528	-1087	-929.6	-858.1	-824.0	-804.6	-805.5	-808.3	-816.8	-828.0	-841 4
70	-437400	-59760	-19970	-9744	-5873	-1782	-1173	-968.1	-877 4	-833.0	-811.6	-803.3	-802.8	-807 7	-822 1	-827.0
80	-762000	-101600	-32780	-15320	-8654	-2198	-1304	-1019	-895.3	-833.2	-800.7	-784.3	-777.6	-777 1	-780.8	-787 4
90	-1257000	-165400	-52270	-23800	-13290	-2841	-1486	-1107	-933.3	-844.3	-794.8	-766.4	-750.3	-742.0	-738.9	-739.5
VALUES OF K_1 AT $\frac{3}{4}$ POINT																
10	-1627	-449.3	-300.7	-232.9	-201.7	-161.0	-156.7	-158.8	-163.1	-168.4	-174.3	-180.5	-187.0	-193.5	-200.2	207.0
20	-7014	-2093	-1172	-816.8	-684.1	-390.2	-344.7	-333.9	-334.3	-339.7	-347.6	-357.0	-367 4	-387.4	-389.9	-401.6
30	-22640	-4661	-2303	-1540	-1181	-653.3	-541.3	-505.1	-494.2	-494.3	-500.2	-509.5	-520.9	-533.7	-547.5	-562.2
40	-63290	-10440	-4297	-2553	-1824	-898.1	-715.0	-650.5	-624 4	-617 1	-618.2	-624.8	-634.7	-649.8	-660.1	-675.8
50	-148600	-22230	-8174	-4380	-2877	-1160	-870.6	-769.8	-726.5	-707.8	-702.0	-703.3	-709.4	-718 7	-730.2	-743.3
60	-306000	-43520	-15060	-7556	-4660	-1528	-1048	-888.5	-817.6	-782.7	-762.6	-758.9	-758.5	-762.3	-769.2	-778.1
70	-567200	-78820	-26350	-12710	-7519	-2065	-1286	-1038	-925.0	-865.5	-832.0	-813.0	-802.8	-798.4	-798.1	-800.6
80	-979400	-133900	-43840	-20620	-11810	-2857	-1633	-1245	-1071	-977.2	-921.3	-885.9	-862.8	-847.7	-838.0	-832.2
90	-1598000	-216100	-69780	-32290	-18260	-3983	-2110	-1529	-1272	-1133	-1048	-992.9	-954.3	-926.5	-906.0	-890.7
VALUES OF K_1 AT ABUTMENT																
10	-100.6	-111.9	-116.0	-118.4	-120.2	-127.9	-135.0	-142.1	-149.2	-156.3	-163.4	-170.4	-177.5	-184.6	-191.7	-198.8
20	-143.2	-165.0	-184.0	-198.6	-206.8	-233.0	-248.0	-262.4	-274.9	-288.7	-300.9	-314.6	-326.7	-340.5	-352.5	-366.3
30	-202.3	-210.3	-222.5	-236.1	-249.2	-296.6	-324.5	-345.5	-364 1	-381.6	-398.7	-415.5	-432.3	-449.0	-465.6	-482.3
40	-268.5	-270.8	-275.9	-282.8	-291.0	-333.7	-367.1	-392.9	-414.6	-434.4	-453.1	-471.3	-489.3	-507.0	-524.7	-542.4
50	-336.9	-337.6	-339.8	-343.1	-347.3	-374.5	-401.6	-424.7	-444.7	-462.7	-479.7	-496.0	-512.0	-527.9	-543.7	-559.5
60	-406.6	-407.2	-408.5	-410.5	-412.9	-429.4	-447.1	-462.9	-476.7	-489.2	-499.3	-512.2	-523.3	-534.5	-545.7	-557.0
70	-447.2	-478.3	-479.8	-481.7	-483.8	-495.9	-507.5	-517.0	-524.4	-530.4	-535.5	-540.3	-545.0	-549.8	-554.7	-559.9
80	-548.8	-550.8	-553.0	-555.3	-557.2	-570.0	-580.2	-587.0	-590.8	-592.4	-592.5	-591.7	-590.6	-589.4	-588.3	-587.3
90	-621.5	-624.5	-627.6	-630.8	-634.0	-649.2	-661.4	-669.5	-673.5	-674.3	-672.6	-669.3	-665.0	-660.1	-654.9	-649.6

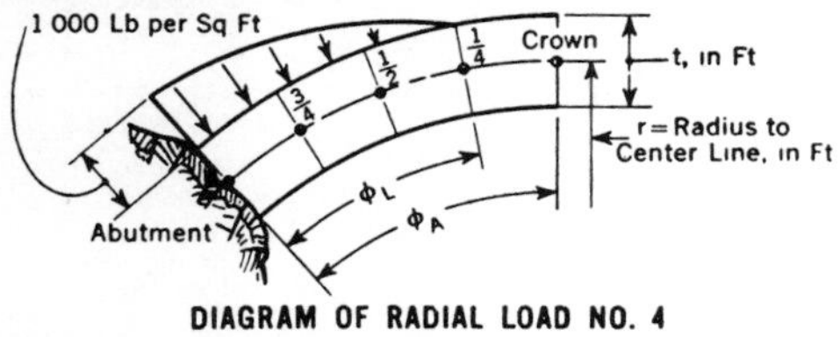

DIAGRAM OF RADIAL LOAD NO. 4

Radial Deflection, in Ft

$$\Delta_r = \frac{K_1 r}{E_c}$$

E_c = Modulus of Elasticity of Concrete in Direct Stress, Lb per Sq Ft

TABLE 7(*a*).—Forces and Moments for Radial Load No. 5

ϕ_A	Values of t/r															
	.025	.050	.075	.100	.125	.250	.375	.500	.625	.750	.875	1.000	1.125	1.250	1.375	1.500
VALUES OF h AT CROWN																
10	103.2	42.02	26.21	20.22	17.44	14.33	14.49	15.10	15.83	16.58	17.36	18.13	18.91	19.69	20.46	21.24
20	284.5	218.8	164.9	129.3	106.6	67.56	60.99	60.67	62.25	64.57	67.21	70.03	72.93	75.88	78.86	82.11
30	315.7	301.3	278.6	253.9	230.9	162.4	140.7	135.2	135.9	139.3	144.1	149.5	155.4	161.5	167.7	174.1
40	322.4	322.7	318.5	311.3	302.3	257.5	233.3	225.0	225.3	230.0	237.3	245.9	255.4	265.4	275.7	286.3
50	325.6	330.0	332.4	333.1	333.0	320.5	310.2	307.9	312.1	320.7	332.9	345.0	359.1	374.0	389.3	405.0
60	328.5	334.3	339.1	343.0	346.1	355.2	361.3	370.0	382.3	397.6	415.1	434.2	454.2	475.0	496.2	517.8
70	331.9	338.1	343.8	349.0	353.9	374.2	392.3	411.4	432.4	455.5	480.2	506.2	533.2	560.3	588.1	616.2
80	335.8	342.1	348.2	354.1	359.7	385.9	411.3	437.8	466.0	496.0	527.5	560.1	593.5	627.5	661.9	696.5
90	340.3	346.7	353.0	359.1	365.2	394.5	424.1	455.3	488.5	523.7	560.5	598.7	637.9	677.8	718.2	759.0
VALUES OF m AT CROWN																
10	0.921	1.462	1.748	1.967	2.157	2.912	3.511	4.028	4.492	4.923	5.328	5.716	6.091	6.455	6.810	7.160
20	-0.508	1.151	2.674	3.855	4.772	7.651	9.621	11.31	12.86	14.32	15.71	17.06	18.38	19.66	20.92	22.59
30	-2.648	-1.676	-0.230	1.403	3.029	9.370	13.51	16.73	19.54	22.12	24.56	26.92	29.22	31.46	33.66	35.84
40	-5.174	-4.779	-3.989	-2.894	-1.591	5.600	11.59	16.28	20.17	23.59	26.73	29.68	32.52	35.26	37.95	40.58
50	-8.267	-8.235	-7.939	-7.409	-6.682	-1.400	4.291	9.187	12.63	16.71	19.75	22.46	24.98	27.35	29.61	31.80
60	-12.00	-12.23	-12.28	-12.17	-11.93	-9.234	-5.596	-2.201	0.586	2.771	4.463	5.775	6.801	7.612	8.267	8.777
70	-16.42	-16.85	-17.17	-17.39	-17.51	-17.16	-16.12	-15.25	-14.93	-15.24	-16.11	-17.46	-19.26	-21.22	-23.49	-25.95
80	-21.54	-22.16	-22.70	-23.19	-23.61	-25.22	-26.64	-28.52	-31.18	-34.68	-38.94	-43.87	-49.35	-55.28	-62.02	-68.22
90	-27.39	-28.18	-28.94	-29.65	-30.33	-33.58	-37.15	-41.60	-47.20	-54.00	-61.93	-70.86	-80.62	-91.11	-102.2	-113.8
VALUES OF h AT ABUTMENT																
10	106.7	46.58	31.07	25.24	22.56	19.81	20.29	21.21	22.24	23.30	24.38	25.46	26.54	27.63	28.71	29.79
20	287.8	226.3	175.9	142.7	121.6	86.19	81.28	82.24	84.99	88.43	92.18	96.08	100.1	104.1	108.2	112.5
30	319.1	307.2	288.1	267.2	247.8	191.3	175.3	173.4	176.9	182.6	189.6	197.1	205.0	213.1	221.3	229.6
40	327.2	329.4	326.3	321.8	315.8	286.4	272.8	271.5	276.6	285.2	295.7	307.3	319.5	332.1	345.0	358.1
50	333.0	337.4	340.4	342.4	343.8	343.4	344.5	350.6	361.0	374.1	389.6	405.0	421.8	439.0	456.4	474.2
60	339.4	344.5	349.0	353.1	356.9	372.2	386.1	401.3	418.2	436.7	456.3	476.6	497.4	518.6	540.0	561.6
70	347.2	352.2	357.1	361.8	366.3	387.7	408.3	429.3	450.9	473.2	496.8	519.4	543.1	566.8	590.7	614.7
80	356.7	361.5	366.2	370.9	375.5	398.5	421.4	444.4	467.8	491.3	515.3	539.3	563.6	587.8	612.3	636.6
90	367.9	372.5	377.0	381.6	386.1	408.8	431.5	454.2	476.9	499.6	522.4	545.1	567.8	590.5	613.2	635.9
VALUES OF m AT ABUTMENT																
10	-2.644	-3.096	-3.113	-3.048	-2.964	-2.573	-2.288	-2.079	-1.920	-1.796	-1.695	-1.612	-1.543	-1.484	-1.433	-1.389
20	-3.788	-6.344	-8.324	-9.540	-10.24	-10.98	-10.67	-10.26	-9.878	-9.541	-9.247	-8.990	-8.765	-8.566	-8.389	-7.783
30	-5.983	-7.502	-9.659	-11.90	-13.93	-19.58	-21.16	-21.49	-21.41	-21.19	-20.92	-20.65	-20.39	-20.15	-19.92	-19.71
40	-10.02	-10.55	-11.71	-13.30	-15.10	-23.34	-27.97	-30.17	-31.17	-31.59	-31.72	-31.70	-31.61	-31.47	-31.32	-31.16
50	-15.67	-15.58	-15.95	-16.70	-17.56	-24.37	-30.00	-33.56	-36.24	-36.73	-36.97	-37.57	-37.72	-37.59	-37.48	-37.34
60	-22.90	-22.41	-22.24	-22.35	-22.69	-26.28	-30.38	-33.44	-35.31	-36.29	-36.66	-36.66	-36.42	-36.04	-35.59	-35.10
70	-31.79	-31.02	-30.48	-30.14	-29.96	-30.64	-32.12	-33.15	-33.39	-32.93	-31.33	-30.68	-29.15	-27.66	-26.08	-24.51
80	-42.44	-41.48	-40.68	-40.02	-39.53	-37.81	-36.74	-35.12	-32.93	-29.98	-26.72	-23.06	-19.42	-15.62	-12.41	-8.358
90	-55.01	-53.92	-52.95	-52.07	-51.26	-47.87	-44.54	-40.53	-35.64	-29.98	-23.76	-17.21	-10.51	-3.802	2.810	9.260
VALUES OF v AT ABUTMENT																
10	-70.22	-81.92	-85.76	-87.89	-89.46	-95.44	-100.8	-106.2	-111.5	-116.8	-122.1	-127.4	-132.7	-138.0	-143.3	-148.6
20	-77.63	-102.3	-122.9	-137.2	-147.1	-171.3	-184.3	-195.2	-205.5	-215.5	-225.4	-235.2	-245.0	-254.8	-264.6	-274.3
30	-101.2	-111.6	-126.1	-141.7	-156.4	-206.7	-233.5	-252.2	-267.9	-282.2	-295.8	-309.0	-322.1	-335.0	-347.9	-360.7
40	-132.1	-136.1	-142.9	-151.8	-161.8	-211.5	-248.0	-274.3	-295.0	-312.9	-329.2	-344.6	-359.5	-374.0	-388.3	-402.4
50	-165.0	-166.8	-170.0	-174.6	-179.9	-215.0	-248.5	-275.8	-298.2	-317.2	-333.4	-349.7	-364.5	-378.7	-392.5	-406.1
60	-198.9	-199.9	-201.7	-204.3	-207.6	-229.6	-254.1	-276.4	-295.6	-312.1	-326.8	-340.2	-352.7	-364.6	-376.0	-387.2
70	-233.4	-234.3	-235.7	-237.5	-239.7	-254.2	-270.9	-286.7	-300.5	-312.5	-321.1	-332.2	-340.5	-348.6	-356.2	-363.5
80	-268.6	-269.7	-271.1	-272.7	-274.6	-285.7	-297.7	-308.7	-317.9	-325.3	-331.3	-336.2	-340.3	-343.8	-346.9	-349.8
90	-304.3	-305.8	-307.5	-309.3	-311.2	-321.7	-331.9	-340.5	-347.1	-351.7	-354.6	-356.2	-356.8	-356.7	-356.1	-355.1

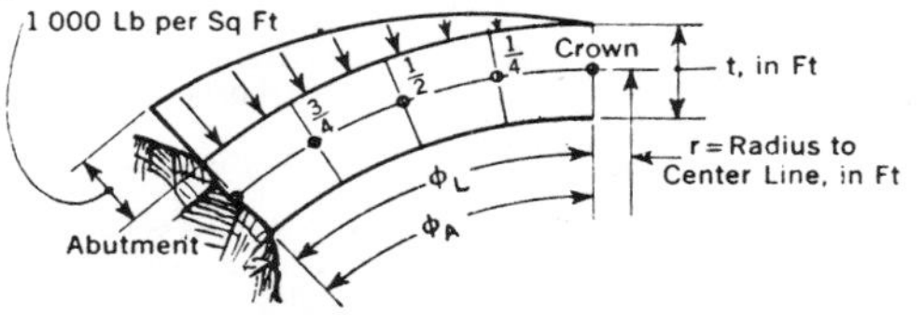

Thrust, Moment, Shear, in Lb, and Ft-Lb

$H = hr$
$M = mr^2$
$V = vr$

DIAGRAM OF RADIAL LOAD NO. 5

TABLE 7(*b*).—Radial Deflections for Radial Load No. 5

ϕ_A	VALUES OF t/r .025	.050	.075	.100	.125	.250	.375	.500	.625	.750	.875	1.000	1.125	1.250	1.375	1.500
VALUES OF K_1 AT CROWN																
10	- 8417	- 1964	- 912.1	- 583.6	- 442.0	-267.0	-239.6	-234.2	-235.8	-240.5	-246.7	-253.9	-261.6	-269.8	-278.2	-286.9
20	- 15690	- 8320	- 4640	- 2936	- 2061	-8422	-625.3	-557.6	-533.3	-526.8	-529.1	-536.2	-546.3	-558.4	-569.0	-585.8
30	- 10020	- 7305	- 6198	- 4794	- 3764	-1662	-1137	-948.5	-870.7	-833.7	-821.3	-820.0	-826.3	-838.0	-852.6	-869.6
40	83040	2256	- 3662	- 4163	- 3857	-2243	-1587	-1307	-1174	-1108	-1077	-1066	-1066	-1075	-1088	-1106
50	238200	23130	2931	- 1283	- 2187	-2297	-1788	-1514	-1385	-1290	-1246	-1232	-1230	-1236	-1249	-1267
60	525400	61380	15060	4197	587.7	-1865	-1700	-1520	-1407	-1343	-1309	-1295	-1294	-1302	-1317	-1336
70	1011000	125500	35240	13270	5551	-1001	-1421	-1342	-1296	-1265	-1250	-1248	-1255	-1269	-1289	-1312
80	1781000	226700	66860	27380	21480	335.5	-797.5	-1005	-1055	-1073	-1087	-1103	-1122	-1145	-1173	-1198
90	2949000	379400	114300	48430	24570	2260	7.967	-518.5	-699.4	-783.3	-834.5	-873.6	-910.0	-940.9	-988.3	-1006
VALUES OF K_1 AT $\frac{1}{4}$ POINT																
10	- 7736	- 1827	- 862.1	- 558.9	- 427.5	-263.7	-238.0	-233.1	-235.0	-239.8	-246.1	-253.3	-261.1	-269.2	-277.7	-286.4
20	- 16810	- 7876	- 4346	- 2756	- 1945	-816.4	-614.4	-550.8	-528.4	-522.8	-525.6	-533.0	-543.5	-555.5	-566.8	-583.1
30	- 5330	- 8488	- 6219	- 4644	- 3604	-1598	-1106	-930.5	-859.3	-823.6	-812.1	-812.1	-819.2	-830.8	-856.0	-862.6
40	28840	- 4057	- 5242	- 4656	- 4002	-2183	-1547	-1281	-1155	-1093	-1064	-1053	-1054	-1063	-1076	-1094
50	101000	5855	- 2078	- 3296	- 2232	-2343	-1738	-1499	-1356	-1277	-1231	-1220	-1216	-1223	-1235	-1252
60	233500	23860	3744	- 620.5	- 3500	-2153	-1851	-1549	-1421	-1349	-1310	-1293	-1290	-1296	-1309	-1326
70	456400	53760	13310	3759	5574	-1700	-1597	-1457	-1366	-1313	-1285	-1274	-1274	-1283	-1298	-1316
80	808100	100600	28150	10480	4269	-998.5	-1280	-1259	-1218	-1191	-1178	-1176	-1182	-1195	-1214	-1232
90	1338000	170700	50200	20390	9686	-10.23	-835.0	-972.3	-997.5	-1003	-1008	-1017	-1030	-1047	-1080	-1087
VALUES OF K_1 AT $\frac{1}{2}$ POINT																
10	- 5676	- 1410	- 703.7	- 477.1	- 377.1	-249.9	-230.2	-227.6	-230.5	-235.9	-239.9	-250.1	-258.1	-266.4	-274.9	-283.7
20	- 16330	- 6193	- 3375	- 2176	- 1571	-723.7	-568.9	-521.2	-505.9	-504.0	-509.0	-517.8	-529.1	-542.1	-554.4	-570.3
30	- 28570	- 9291	- 5509	- 3875	- 2958	-1364	-988.9	-855.4	-803.6	-777.9	-772.1	-775.8	-785.2	-798.3	-814.0	-831.6
40	- 59350	- 13520	- 7138	- 4917	- 2638	-1891	-1323	-1161	-1053	-1018	-993.8	-992.9	-995.5	-1008	-1022	-1040
50	-125400	- 22070	- 9809	- 6157	- 4450	-2208	-1622	-1374	-1259	-1189	-1448	-1146	-1145	-1152	-1165	-1181
60	-248700	- 37980	-14670	- 8276	- 5673	-2439	-1768	-1494	-1358	-1285	-1247	-1229	-1224	-1228	-1238	-1253
70	-458900	- 65050	-22920	-11860	- 7556	-2717	-1878	-1562	-1408	-1325	-1280	-1257	-1247	-1248	-1254	-1266
80	-794400	-108300	-36100	-17570	-10560	-3138	-2014	-1622	-1437	-1338	-1282	-1251	-1236	-1230	-1233	-1239
90	-1306000	-174000	-56150	-26280	-15150	-3785	-2220	-1709	-1475	-1350	-1278	-1235	-1210	-1197	-1203	-1193
VALUES OF K_1 AT $\frac{3}{4}$ POINT																
10	- 2632	- 775.1	- 447.1	- 336.3	- 285.7	-220.1	-212.0	-214.1	-219.4	-226.3	-234.0	-242.1	-250.6	-259.4	-268.2	-277.2
20	- 9142	- 3128	- 1785	- 1234	- 953.8	-550.3	-476.0	-456.6	-454.8	-460.7	-470.5	-482.6	-496.1	-510.6	-525.0	-541.2
30	- 23980	- 5792	- 3136	- 2186	-1704.8	-932.8	-757.1	-698.3	-682.1	-676.0	-682.2	-693.6	-708.2	-725.0	-742.9	-762.7
40	- 62370	- 11230	- 5043	- 3197	- 2386	-1250	-993.8	-898.6	-859.6	-846.1	-827.2	-853.9	-866.7	-882.9	-901.4	-921.6
50	-143100	- 22320	- 8665	- 4898	- 3336	-1521	-1172	-1043	-989.0	-962.2	-952.7	-957.4	-966.5	-979.8	-996.2	-1015
60	-291500	- 42420	-15130	- 7859	- 5018	-1852	-1337	-1158	-1078	-1039	-1022	-1017	-1020	-1028	-1040	-1055
70	-540500	- 75850	-25770	-12690	- 7683	-2338	-1541	-1285	-1166	-1106	-1074	-1058	-1051	-1052	-1057	-1065
80	-932700	-128100	-42310	-20150	-11770	-3058	-1847	-1457	-1283	-1190	-1137	-1105	-1086	-1076	-1071	-1071
90	-1522000	-206300	-66910	-31180	-17780	-4095	-2271	-1701	-1448	-1312	-1231	-1179	-1145	-1121	-1111	-1095
VALUES OF K_1 AT ABUTMENT																
10	-125.3	-146.2	-153.1	-156.9	-159.7	-170.4	-180.0	-189.5	-199.0	-208.5	-218.0	-227.4	-238.9	-246.4	-255.9	-265.3
20	-138.6	-182.5	-219.3	-244.9	-262.6	-305.7	-329.0	-348.4	-366.8	-384.6	-402.3	-419.8	-437.3	-454.8	-472.3	-489.6
30	-180.7	-199.2	-225.2	-253.0	-278.5	-368.9	-415.8	-450.2	-480.5	-503.7	-526.6	-551.6	-573.5	-589.1	-619.5	-643.9
40	-235.8	-242.9	-255.1	-270.9	-288.7	-377.5	-442.7	-489.6	-526.6	-558.5	-587.7	-615.1	-641.7	-667.6	-693.1	-718.3
50	-294.6	-297.6	-303.5	-311.7	-321.1	-383.8	-443.5	-492.3	-532.2	-566.2	-595.1	-624.2	-650.6	-675.9	-700.6	-724.9
60	-355.1	-356.8	-360.1	-364.7	-370.5	-409.8	-453.5	-493.3	-527.6	-557.2	-583.4	-607.3	-629.5	-650.7	-671.2	-691.1
70	-416.7	-418.3	-420.8	-424.0	-427.9	-453.8	-483.6	-511.7	-536.4	-557.7	-576.4	-593.0	-607.8	-622.3	-635.8	-648.8
80	-479.4	-481.4	-483.9	-486.8	-490.1	-510.0	-531.4	-551.0	-567.3	-580.6	-591.3	-600.1	-607.3	-613.6	-619.1	-624.4
90	-543.1	-545.9	-548.9	-552.1	-555.6	-574.2	-592.4	-607.8	-619.5	-627.7	-633.0	-635.8	-636.9	-636.7	-635.6	-633.9

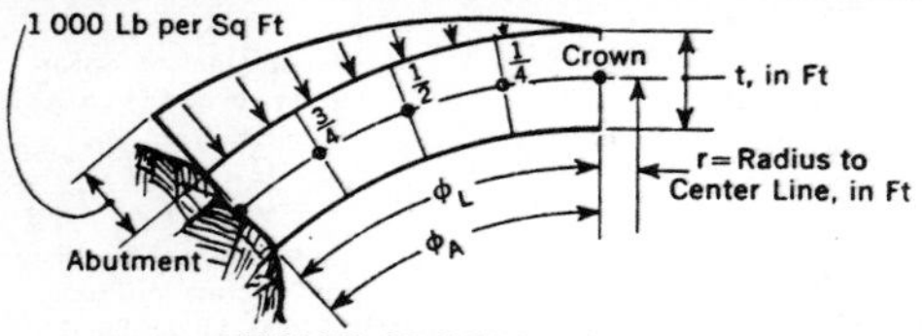

DIAGRAM OF RADIAL LOAD NO. 5

Radial Deflection, in Ft

$$\Delta_r = \frac{K_1 r}{E_c}$$

E_c = Modulus of Elasticity of Concrete in Direct Stress, Lb per Sq Ft

TABLE 8(*a*).—Forces and Moments for Temperature Load

ϕ_A	.025	.050	.075	.100	.125	.250	.375	.500	.625	.750	.875	1.000	1.125	1.250	1.375	1.500
	VALUES OF t/r															
	VALUES OF h AT CROWN															
10	$-.0^{6}710$	$-.0^{5}154$	$-.0^{5}211$	$-.0^{5}253$	$-.0^{5}286$	$-.0^{5}380$	$-.0^{5}426$	$-.0^{5}452$	$-.0^{5}470$	$-.0^{5}482$	$-.0^{5}491$	$-.0^{5}499$	$-.0^{5}504$	$-.0^{5}509$	$-.0^{5}513$	$-.0^{5}516$
20	$-.0^{6}147$	$-.0^{6}741$	$-.0^{5}153$	$-.0^{5}230$	$-.0^{5}298$	$-.0^{5}522$	$-.0^{5}645$	$-.0^{5}722$	$-.0^{5}776$	$-.0^{5}816$	$-.0^{5}846$	$-.0^{5}870$	$-.0^{5}890$	$-.0^{5}906$	$-.0^{5}920$	$-.0^{5}932$
30	$-.0^{7}340$	$-.0^{6}227$	$-.0^{6}618$	$-.0^{5}116$	$-.0^{5}178$	$-.0^{5}476$	$-.0^{5}683$	$-.0^{5}823$	$-.0^{5}924$	$-.0^{4}100$	$-.0^{4}106$	$-.0^{4}111$	$-.0^{4}115$	$-.0^{4}118$	$-.0^{4}121$	$-.0^{4}123$
40	$-.0^{7}112$	$-.0^{7}810$	$-.0^{6}243$	$-.0^{6}507$	$-.0^{6}863$	$-.0^{5}335$	$-.0^{5}579$	$-.0^{5}772$	$-.0^{5}921$	$-.0^{4}104$	$-.0^{4}113$	$-.0^{4}120$	$-.0^{4}127$	$-.0^{4}132$	$-.0^{4}136$	$-.0^{4}140$
50	$-.0^{8}465$	$-.0^{7}347$	$-.0^{6}108$	$-.0^{6}236$	$-.0^{6}423$	$-.0^{5}208$	$-.0^{5}425$	$-.0^{5}631$	$-.0^{5}808$	$-.0^{5}954$	$-.0^{4}108$	$-.0^{4}118$	$-.0^{4}128$	$-.0^{4}134$	$-.0^{4}140$	$-.0^{4}145$
60	$-.0^{8}224$	$-.0^{7}170$	$-.0^{7}543$	$-.0^{6}121$	$-.0^{6}222$	$-.0^{5}125$	$-.0^{5}289$	$-.0^{5}473$	$-.0^{5}649$	$-.0^{5}807$	$-.0^{5}946$	$-.0^{4}107$	$-.0^{4}117$	$-.0^{4}127$	$-.0^{4}134$	$-.0^{4}141$
70	$-.0^{8}120$	$-.0^{8}922$	$-.0^{7}298$	$-.0^{7}673$	$-.0^{6}125$	$-.0^{6}766$	$-.0^{5}193$	$-.0^{5}339$	$-.0^{5}495$	$-.0^{5}645$	$-.0^{5}785$	$-.0^{5}912$	$-.0^{4}103$	$-.0^{4}113$	$-.0^{4}122$	$-.0^{4}130$
80	$-.0^{9}696$	$-.0^{8}537$	$-.0^{7}175$	$-.0^{7}398$	$-.0^{7}748$	$-.0^{6}483$	$-.0^{5}129$	$-.0^{5}240$	$-.0^{5}366$	$-.0^{5}498$	$-.0^{5}627$	$-.0^{5}750$	$-.0^{5}863$	$-.0^{5}968$	$-.0^{4}106$	$-.0^{4}115$
90	$-.0^{9}425$	$-.0^{8}330$	$-.0^{7}108$	$-.0^{7}248$	$-.0^{7}468$	$-.0^{6}314$	$-.0^{6}873$	$-.0^{5}169$	$-.0^{5}268$	$-.0^{5}377$	$-.0^{5}489$	$-.0^{5}600$	$-.0^{5}706$	$-.0^{5}807$	$-.0^{5}901$	$-.0^{5}988$
	VALUES OF m AT CROWN															
10	$.0^{8}401$	$.0^{8}946$	$.0^{7}140$	$.0^{7}178$	$.0^{7}212$	$.0^{7}338$	$.0^{7}421$	$.0^{7}480$	$.0^{7}525$	$.0^{7}559$	$.0^{7}587$	$.0^{7}610$	$.0^{7}629$	$.0^{7}646$	$.0^{7}659$	$.0^{7}672$
20	$.0^{8}314$	$.0^{7}167$	$.0^{7}361$	$.0^{7}564$	$.0^{7}758$	$.0^{6}154$	$.0^{6}211$	$.0^{6}225$	$.0^{6}291$	$.0^{6}321$	$.0^{6}346$	$.0^{6}367$	$.0^{6}386$	$.0^{6}402$	$.0^{6}416$	$.0^{6}429$
30	$.0^{8}159$	$.0^{7}110$	$.0^{7}310$	$.0^{7}600$	$.0^{7}949$	$.0^{6}286$	$.0^{6}449$	$.0^{6}582$	$.0^{6}692$	$.0^{6}786$	$.0^{6}867$	$.0^{6}938$	$.0^{5}100$	$.0^{5}106$	$.0^{5}111$	$.0^{5}115$
40	$.0^{9}914$	$.0^{8}679$	$.0^{7}209$	$.0^{7}447$	$.0^{7}779$	$.0^{6}334$	$.0^{6}625$	$.0^{6}890$	$.0^{5}112$	$.0^{5}132$	$.0^{5}150$	$.0^{5}166$	$.0^{5}180$	$.0^{5}192$	$.0^{5}204$	$.0^{5}214$
50	$.0^{9}581$	$.0^{8}443$	$.0^{7}141$	$.0^{7}315$	$.0^{7}573$	$.0^{6}306$	$.0^{6}673$	$.0^{5}106$	$.0^{5}143$	$.0^{5}176$	$.0^{5}207$	$.0^{5}234$	$.0^{5}259$	$.0^{5}282$	$.0^{5}302$	$.0^{5}322$
60	$.0^{9}396$	$.0^{8}306$	$.0^{8}991$	$.0^{7}225$	$.0^{7}419$	$.0^{6}254$	$.0^{6}626$	$.0^{5}108$	$.0^{5}155$	$.0^{5}201$	$.0^{5}244$	$.0^{5}285$	$.0^{5}322$	$.0^{5}356$	$.0^{5}388$	$.0^{5}418$
70	$.0^{9}282$	$.0^{8}220$	$.0^{8}719$	$.0^{7}165$	$.0^{7}311$	$.0^{6}203$	$.0^{6}540$	$.0^{6}997$	$.0^{5}152$	$.0^{5}206$	$.0^{5}259$	$.0^{5}311$	$.0^{5}359$	$.0^{5}406$	$.0^{5}449$	$.0^{5}489$
80	$.0^{9}208$	$.0^{8}163$	$.0^{8}535$	$.0^{7}124$	$.0^{7}235$	$.0^{6}160$	$.0^{6}450$	$.0^{6}874$	$.0^{5}139$	$.0^{5}196$	$.0^{5}255$	$.0^{5}314$	$.0^{5}371$	$.0^{5}426$	$.0^{5}480$	$.0^{5}530$
90	$.0^{9}156$	$.0^{8}123$	$.0^{8}406$	$.0^{8}941$	$.0^{7}180$	$.0^{6}127$	$.0^{6}368$	$.0^{6}741$	$.0^{5}122$	$.0^{5}178$	$.0^{5}237$	$.0^{5}299$	$.0^{5}361$	$.0^{5}423$	$.0^{5}482$	$.0^{5}540$
	VALUES OF h AT ABUTMENT															
10	$-.0^{6}700$	$-.0^{5}151$	$-.0^{5}208$	$-.0^{5}249$	$-.0^{5}282$	$-.0^{5}375$	$-.0^{5}419$	$-.0^{5}445$	$-.0^{5}463$	$-.0^{5}475$	$-.0^{5}484$	$-.0^{5}491$	$-.0^{5}497$	$-.0^{5}501$	$-.0^{5}505$	$-.0^{5}508$
20	$-.0^{6}138$	$-.0^{6}697$	$-.0^{5}144$	$-.0^{5}216$	$-.0^{5}280$	$-.0^{5}490$	$-.0^{5}606$	$-.0^{5}679$	$-.0^{5}729$	$-.0^{5}767$	$-.0^{5}795$	$-.0^{5}818$	$-.0^{5}836$	$-.0^{5}852$	$-.0^{5}864$	$-.0^{5}875$
30	$-.0^{7}295$	$-.0^{6}197$	$-.0^{6}535$	$-.0^{5}100$	$-.0^{5}154$	$-.0^{5}412$	$-.0^{5}591$	$-.0^{5}713$	$-.0^{5}800$	$-.0^{5}866$	$-.0^{5}917$	$-.0^{5}958$	$-.0^{5}992$	$-.0^{4}102$	$-.0^{4}104$	$-.0^{4}106$
40	$-.0^{8}858$	$-.0^{7}620$	$-.0^{6}186$	$-.0^{6}388$	$-.0^{6}661$	$-.0^{5}257$	$-.0^{5}444$	$-.0^{5}592$	$-.0^{5}705$	$-.0^{5}794$	$-.0^{5}864$	$-.0^{5}922$	$-.0^{5}969$	$-.0^{4}101$	$-.0^{4}104$	$-.0^{4}107$
50	$-.0^{8}299$	$-.0^{7}223$	$-.0^{7}697$	$-.0^{6}152$	$-.0^{6}272$	$-.0^{5}133$	$-.0^{5}273$	$-.0^{5}406$	$-.0^{5}519$	$-.0^{5}613$	$-.0^{5}691$	$-.0^{5}757$	$-.0^{5}812$	$-.0^{5}859$	$-.0^{5}899$	$-.0^{5}935$
60	$-.0^{8}112$	$-.0^{8}851$	$-.0^{7}271$	$-.0^{7}606$	$-.0^{6}111$	$-.0^{6}625$	$-.0^{5}145$	$-.0^{5}237$	$-.0^{5}325$	$-.0^{5}404$	$-.0^{5}473$	$-.0^{5}533$	$-.0^{5}585$	$-.0^{5}630$	$-.0^{5}670$	$-.0^{5}705$
70	$-.0^{9}412$	$-.0^{8}316$	$-.0^{7}102$	$-.0^{7}230$	$-.0^{7}428$	$-.0^{6}262$	$-.0^{6}660$	$-.0^{5}116$	$-.0^{5}169$	$-.0^{5}221$	$-.0^{5}270$	$-.0^{5}312$	$-.0^{5}351$	$-.0^{5}385$	$-.0^{5}416$	$-.0^{5}444$
80	$-.0^{9}121$	$-.0^{9}933$	$-.0^{8}303$	$-.0^{8}692$	$-.0^{7}130$	$-.0^{7}838$	$-.0^{6}224$	$-.0^{6}416$	$-.0^{6}636$	$-.0^{6}865$	$-.0^{5}109$	$-.0^{5}130$	$-.0^{5}150$	$-.0^{5}168$	$-.0^{5}185$	$-.0^{5}200$
90	0	0	0	0	0	0	0	0	0	0	0	0	0	0	0	0
	VALUES OF m AT ABUTMENT															
10	$-.0^{8}678$	$-.0^{7}139$	$-.0^{7}181$	$-.0^{7}206$	$-.0^{7}222$	$-.0^{7}240$	$-.0^{7}226$	$-.0^{7}207$	$-.0^{7}189$	$-.0^{7}173$	$-.0^{7}159$	$-.0^{7}147$	$-.0^{7}137$	$-.0^{7}128$	$-.0^{7}120$	$-.0^{7}113$
20	$-.0^{8}573$	$-.0^{7}280$	$-.0^{7}564$	$-.0^{7}823$	$-.0^{6}104$	$-.0^{6}161$	$-.0^{6}178$	$-.0^{6}180$	$-.0^{6}177$	$-.0^{6}172$	$-.0^{6}165$	$-.0^{6}158$	$-.0^{6}151$	$-.0^{6}145$	$-.0^{6}138$	$-.0^{6}133$
30	$-.0^{8}296$	$-.0^{7}194$	$-.0^{7}518$	$-.0^{7}954$	$-.0^{6}144$	$-.0^{6}352$	$-.0^{6}466$	$-.0^{6}521$	$-.0^{6}546$	$-.0^{6}553$	$-.0^{6}552$	$-.0^{6}544$	$-.0^{6}533$	$-.0^{6}521$	$-.0^{6}508$	$-.0^{6}494$
40	$-.0^{8}171$	$-.0^{7}122$	$-.0^{7}360$	$-.0^{7}740$	$-.0^{6}124$	$-.0^{6}450$	$-.0^{6}730$	$-.0^{6}917$	$-.0^{5}103$	$-.0^{5}110$	$-.0^{5}114$	$-.0^{5}116$	$-.0^{5}116$	$-.0^{5}116$	$-.0^{5}115$	$-.0^{5}114$
50	$-.0^{8}108$	$-.0^{8}796$	$-.0^{7}246$	$-.0^{7}530$	$-.0^{7}937$	$-.0^{6}435$	$-.0^{6}845$	$-.0^{5}119$	$-.0^{5}146$	$-.0^{5}165$	$-.0^{5}178$	$-.0^{5}186$	$-.0^{5}192$	$-.0^{5}196$	$-.0^{5}197$	$-.0^{5}198$
60	$-.0^{9}727$	$-.0^{8}546$	$-.0^{7}172$	$-.0^{7}381$	$-.0^{7}691$	$-.0^{6}371$	$-.0^{6}822$	$-.0^{5}129$	$-.0^{5}169$	$-.0^{5}203$	$-.0^{5}229$	$-.0^{5}248$	$-.0^{5}263$	$-.0^{5}274$	$-.0^{5}282$	$-.0^{5}287$
70	$-.0^{9}510$	$-.0^{8}387$	$-.0^{7}124$	$-.0^{7}278$	$-.0^{7}512$	$-.0^{6}301$	$-.0^{6}730$	$-.0^{5}124$	$-.0^{5}174$	$-.0^{5}219$	$-.0^{5}258$	$-.0^{5}289$	$-.0^{5}315$	$-.0^{5}336$	$-.0^{5}352$	$-.0^{5}365$
80	$-.0^{9}367$	$-.0^{8}281$	$-.0^{8}908$	$-.0^{7}206$	$-.0^{7}383$	$-.0^{6}239$	$-.0^{6}616$	$-.0^{5}111$	$-.0^{5}164$	$-.0^{5}216$	$-.0^{5}264$	$-.0^{5}306$	$-.0^{5}342$	$-.0^{5}373$	$-.0^{5}399$	$-.0^{5}421$
90	$-.0^{9}269$	$-.0^{8}207$	$-.0^{8}673$	$-.0^{7}154$	$-.0^{7}288$	$-.0^{6}187$	$-.0^{6}505$	$-.0^{6}948$	$-.0^{5}146$	$-.0^{5}200$	$-.0^{5}252$	$-.0^{5}301$	$-.0^{5}345$	$-.0^{5}384$	$-.0^{5}419$	$-.0^{5}448$
	VALUES OF v AT ABUTMENT															
10	$-.0^{6}123$	$-.0^{6}267$	$-.0^{6}366$	$-.0^{6}440$	$-.0^{6}497$	$-.0^{6}660$	$-.0^{6}739$	$-.0^{6}785$	$-.0^{6}816$	$-.0^{6}837$	$-.0^{6}853$	$-.0^{6}866$	$-.0^{6}876$	$-.0^{6}884$	$-.0^{6}891$	$-.0^{6}897$
20	$-.0^{7}503$	$-.0^{6}254$	$-.0^{6}524$	$-.0^{6}786$	$-.0^{5}102$	$-.0^{5}178$	$-.0^{5}207$	$-.0^{5}247$	$-.0^{5}265$	$-.0^{5}279$	$-.0^{5}289$	$-.0^{5}298$	$-.0^{5}304$	$-.0^{5}310$	$-.0^{5}315$	$-.0^{5}319$
30	$-.0^{7}170$	$-.0^{6}114$	$-.0^{6}309$	$-.0^{6}580$	$-.0^{6}891$	$-.0^{5}238$	$-.0^{5}341$	$-.0^{5}412$	$-.0^{5}462$	$-.0^{5}500$	$-.0^{5}529$	$-.0^{5}553$	$-.0^{5}573$	$-.0^{5}589$	$-.0^{5}603$	$-.0^{5}615$
40	$-.0^{8}720$	$-.0^{7}521$	$-.0^{6}156$	$-.0^{6}326$	$-.0^{6}555$	$-.0^{5}215$	$-.0^{5}372$	$-.0^{5}496$	$-.0^{5}592$	$-.0^{5}666$	$-.0^{5}725$	$-.0^{5}773$	$-.0^{5}813$	$-.0^{5}847$	$-.0^{5}876$	$-.0^{5}901$
50	$-.0^{8}356$	$-.0^{7}266$	$-.0^{7}830$	$-.0^{6}181$	$-.0^{6}324$	$-.0^{5}159$	$-.0^{5}326$	$-.0^{5}484$	$-.0^{5}619$	$-.0^{5}731$	$-.0^{5}824$	$-.0^{5}902$	$-.0^{5}968$	$-.0^{4}102$	$-.0^{4}107$	$-.0^{4}111$
60	$-.0^{8}194$	$-.0^{7}147$	$-.0^{7}470$	$-.0^{6}105$	$-.0^{6}192$	$-.0^{5}108$	$-.0^{5}251$	$-.0^{5}410$	$-.0^{5}562$	$-.0^{5}699$	$-.0^{5}819$	$-.0^{5}923$	$-.0^{4}101$	$-.0^{4}110$	$-.0^{4}116$	$-.0^{4}122$
70	$-.0^{8}113$	$-.0^{8}867$	$-.0^{7}280$	$-.0^{7}632$	$-.0^{6}118$	$-.0^{6}720$	$-.0^{5}181$	$-.0^{5}319$	$-.0^{5}465$	$-.0^{5}606$	$-.0^{5}741$	$-.0^{5}857$	$-.0^{5}964$	$-.0^{4}106$	$-.0^{4}114$	$-.0^{4}122$
80	$-.0^{9}685$	$-.0^{8}529$	$-.0^{7}172$	$-.0^{7}392$	$-.0^{7}737$	$-.0^{6}476$	$-.0^{5}127$	$-.0^{5}236$	$-.0^{5}361$	$-.0^{5}491$	$-.0^{5}618$	$-.0^{5}738$	$-.0^{5}850$	$-.0^{5}953$	$-.0^{4}105$	$-.0^{4}113$
90	$-.0^{9}425$	$-.0^{8}330$	$-.0^{7}108$	$-.0^{7}248$	$-.0^{7}468$	$-.0^{6}314$	$-.0^{6}873$	$-.0^{5}169$	$-.0^{5}268$	$-.0^{5}377$	$-.0^{5}489$	$-.0^{5}600$	$-.0^{5}706$	$-.0^{5}807$	$-.0^{5}901$	$-.0^{5}988$

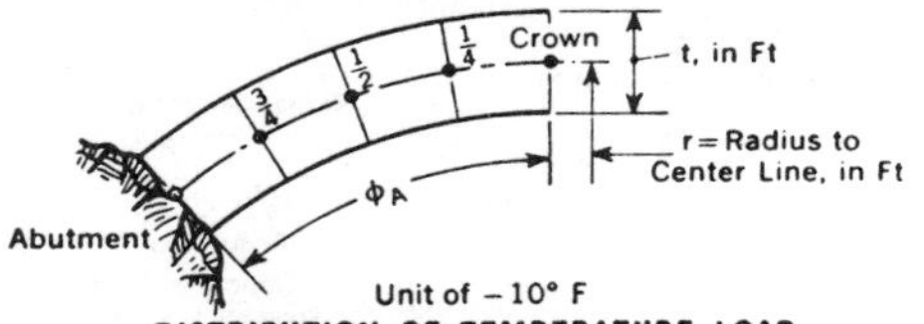

DISTRIBUTION OF TEMPERATURE LOAD
UNIFORM THROUGHOUT ARCH

Thrust, Moment, Shear in Lb, and Ft·Lb

$H = h r E_c$

$M = m r^2 E_c$

$V = v r E_c$

E_c = Modulus of Elasticity of Concrete in Direct Stress, Lb per Sq Ft

TABLE 8(*b*).—Radial Deflections for Temperature Load

ϕ_A	VALUES OF t/r															
	.025	.050	.075	.100	.125	.250	.375	.500	.625	.750	.875	1.000	1.125	1.250	1.375	1.500
VALUES OF K_1 AT CROWN																
10	- 5.47	- 1.97	- 1.08	- .69	- 0.43	- 0.33	- 0.28	- 0.25	- 0.24	- 0.23	- .225	- 0.22	- 0.22	- 0.22	- .215	- 0.21
20	-1 5.90	-1 1.45	- 8.07	- 5.91	- 4.52	- 2.09	- 1.56	- 1.29	- 1.13	- 1.06	- 1.01	- 0.97	- 0.95	- 0.93	- 9.15	0.90
30	-1 7.93	-1 6.30	-1 4.37	-1 2.48	-1 0.49	- 5.93	- 4.22	- 3.31	- 2.85	- 2.62	- 2.45	- 2.33	- 2.23	- 2.17	- 2.12	- 2.07
40	-1 8.41	-1 7.71	-1 6.82	-1 5.82	-1 4.80	-1 0.31	- 7.71	- 6.24	- 5.39	- 4.85	- 4.48	- 4.22	- 4.03	- 3.88	- 3.78	- 3.67
50	-1 8.61	-1 8.23	-1 7.76	-1 7.22	-1 6.67	-1 3.54	-1 1.05	- 9.37	- 8.22	- 7.43	- 6.87	- 6.46	- 6.15	- 5.91	- 5.72	- 5.56
60	-1 8.75	-1 8.50	-1 8.21	-1 7.88	-1 7.53	-1 5.52	-1 3.60	-1 2.04	-1 0.86	- 9.96	- 9.29	- 8.77	- 8.37	- 8.05	- 7.79	- 7.58
70	-1 8.86	-1 8.68	-1 8.48	-1 8.26	-1 8.02	-1 6.69	-1 5.32	-1 4.05	-1 3.00	-1 2.15	-1 1.47	-1 0.91	-1 0.47	-1 0.11	- 9.82	- 9.56
80	-1 8.97	-1 8.83	-1 8.68	-1 8.53	-1 8.36	-1 7.43	-1 6.43	-1 5.48	-1 4.63	-1 3.90	-1 3.28	-1 2.76	-1 2.32	-1 1.96	-1 1.66	-1 1.39
90	-1 9.08	-1 8.97	-1 8.86	-1 8.74	-1 8.62	-1 7.94	-1 7.22	-1 6.50	-1 5.84	-1 5.25	-1 4.74	-1 4.28	-1 3.88	-1 3.55	-1 3.27	-1 3.01
VALUES OF K_1 AT $\frac{1}{4}$ POINT																
10	- 4.88	- 1.78	- 0.99	- 0.69	- 0.52	- 0.32	- 0.28	- 0.25	- .024	- 0.24	- 0.23	- 0.23	- 0.22	- 0.22	- 0.22	- 0.22
20	-1 4.08	-1 0.21	-0 7.25	- 5.35	- 4.17	- 1.97	- 1.46	- 1.25	- 1.14	- 1.05	- 1.00	- 0.98	- 0.96	- 0.94	- .925	- 0.91
30	-1 5.82	-1 4.46	-1 2.81	-1 1.18	- 9.61	- 5.47	- 3.86	- 3.16	- 2.78	- 2.55	- 2.41	- 2.30	- 2.22	- 2.16	- 2.12	- 2.08
40	-1 6.21	-1 5.65	-1 4.92	-1 4.08	-1 3.20	- 9.38	- 7.15	- 5.86	- 5.11	- 4.65	- 4.33	- 4.10	- 3.94	- 3.81	- 3.72	- 3.63
50	-1 6.36	-1 6.07	-1 5.70	-1 5.26	-1 4.79	-1 2.22	-1 0.10	- 8.67	- 7.70	- 7.02	- 6.54	- 6.19	- 5.94	- 5.73	- 5.57	- 5.43
60	-1 6.44	-1 6.26	-1 6.05	-1 5.80	-1 5.52	-1 3.90	-1 2.32	-1 1.03	-1 0.04	- 9.29	- 8.73	- 8.30	- 7.97	- 7.70	- 7.48	- 7.31
70	-1 6.51	-1 6.38	-1 6.24	-1 6.08	-1 5.90	-1 4.87	-1 3.77	-1 2.75	-1 1.89	-1 1.20	-1 0.64	-1 0.20	- 9.84	- 9.55	- 9.31	- 9.10
80	-1 6.57	-1 6.47	-1 6.37	-1 6.26	-1 6.14	-1 5.45	-1 4.69	-1 3.94	-1 3.27	-1 2.69	-1 2.20	-1 1.79	-1 1.45	-1 1.16	-1 0.91	-1 0.72
90	-1 6.62	-1 6.55	-1 6.48	-1 6.40	-1 6.31	-1 5.82	-1 5.29	-1 4.75	-1 4.25	-1 3.80	-1 3.40	-1 3.06	-1 2.76	-1 2.51	-1 2.29	-1 2.10
VALUES OF K_1 AT $\frac{1}{2}$ POINT																
10	- 3.32	- 1.29	- .756	- .549	- 0.45	- .302	- 0.28	- 0.26	- 0.25	- 0.25	- 0.24	- 0.24	- 0.24	- 0.24	- 0.24	- 0.24
20	- 9.28	- 6.93	- 5.07	- 3.85	- 3.10	- 1.63	- 1.29	- 1.14	- 1.08	- 1.04	- 1.01	-0.994	- 0.98	- .972	- 0.96	- .958
30	-1 0.30	- 9.60	- 8.68	- 7.72	- 6.85	- 4.20	- 3.23	- 2.74	- 2.49	- 2.36	- 2.27	- 2.22	- 2.17	- 2.14	- 2.12	- 2.10
40	-1 0.47	-1 0.26	- 9.92	- 9.50	- 9.02	- 6.88	- 5.58	- 4.79	- 4.33	- 4.08	- 3.90	- 3.77	- 3.68	- 3.62	- 3.56	- 3.52
50	-1 0.49	-1 0.43	-1 0.31	-1 0.14	- 9.90	- 8.67	- 7.58	- 6.77	- 6.23	- 5.88	- 5.62	- 5.44	- 5.31	- 5.21	- 5.13	- 5.07
60	-1 0.48	-1 0.47	-1 0.43	-1 0.36	-1 0.26	- 9.62	- 8.92	- 8.28	- 7.80	- 7.45	- 7.18	- 6.99	- 6.83	- 6.72	- 6.62	- 6.55
70	-1 0.46	-1 0.46	-1 0.45	-1 0.43	-1 0.39	-1 0.08	- 9.68	- 9.27	- 8.92	- 8.64	- 8.43	- 8.25	- 8.11	- 8.00	- 7.92	- 7.85
80	-1 0.42	-1 0.43	-1 0.44	-1 0.43	-1 0.42	-1 0.29	-1 0.09	- 9.86	- 9.65	- 9.46	- 9.30	- 9.18	- 9.08	- 9.00	- 8.93	- 8.88
90	-1 0.38	-1 0.40	-1 0.40	-1 0.41	-1 0.41	-1 0.37	-1 0.28	-1 0.17	-1 0.06	- 9.96	- 9.87	- 9.81	- 9.76	- 9.71	- 9.68	- 9.65
VALUES OF K_1 AT $\frac{3}{4}$ POINT																
10	- 1.38	- .633	- .432	- .353	- 0.30	- 0.27	- 0.27	- 0.27	- 0.27	- 0.27	- 0.27	- 0.27	- 0.27	- 0.27	- 0.27	- 0.27
20	- 3.50	- 2.87	- 2.29	- 1.89	- 1.62	- 1.15	- 1.07	- 1.02	- 1.01	- 1.01	- 1.01	- 1.02	- 1.02	- 1.03	- 1.03	- 1.03
30	- 3.74	- 3.72	- 3.57	- 3.37	- 3.17	- 2.47	- 2.20	- 2.13	- 2.10	- 2.09	- 2.09	- 2.10	- 2.10	- 2.11	- 2.12	- 2.13
40	- 3.72	- 3.83	- 3.88	- 3.88	- 3.84	- 3.58	- 3.39	- 3.30	- 3.26	- 3.26	- 3.27	- 3.29	- 3.31	- 3.33	- 3.35	- 3.37
50	- 3.67	- 3.79	- 3.89	- 3.96	- 4.01	- 4.13	- 4.17	- 4.18	- 4.21	- 4.27	- 4.32	- 4.37	- 4.41	- 4.46	- 4.50	- 4.54
60	- 3.61	- 3.72	- 3.82	- 3.91	- 3.99	- 4.29	- 4.50	- 4.66	- 4.80	- 4.93	- 5.05	- 5.15	- 5.24	- 5.33	- 5.40	- 5.48
70	- 3.55	- 3.65	- 3.74	- 3.83	- 3.91	- 4.26	- 4.55	- 4.81	- 5.04	- 5.25	- 5.44	- 5.60	- 5.74	- 5.88	- 6.00	- 6.11
80	- 3.49	- 3.57	- 3.65	- 3.73	- 3.81	- 4.15	- 4.46	- 4.76	- 5.03	- 5.29	- 5.52	- 5.73	- 5.92	- 6.10	- 6.26	- 6.41
90	- 3.43	- 3.50	- 3.57	- 3.63	- 3.69	- 4.01	- 4.31	- 4.60	- 4.87	- 5.15	- 5.41	- 5.65	- 5.87	- 6.07	- 6.25	- 6.43
VALUES OF K_1 AT ABUTMENT																
10	-.0 440	-.0 952	- .131	- .157	- .177	- .236	- .264	- .280	- .291	- .299	-0.304	-0.309	- .313	- .316	- .318	- .32
20	-.0 180	-.0 905	- .187	- .281	- .364	- .637	- .739	- .882	- .946	- .996	- 1.03	- 1.06	- 1.09	- 1.11	- 1.12	- 1.14
30	$-.0^{2}607$	-.0 406	- .110	- .207	- .318	- .850	- 1.22	- 1.47	- 1.65	- 1.78	- 1.89	- 1.97	- 2.05	- 2.10	- 2.15	- 2.19
40	$-.0^{2}257$	-.0 186	-.0 558	- .116	- .198	- .769	- 1.33	- 1.77	- 2.11	- 2.38	- 2.59	- 2.76	- 2.90	- 3.05	- 3.13	- 3.22
50	$-.0^{2}127$	$-.0^{2}949$	-.0 296	-.0 647	- .116	- .568	- 1.16	- 1.73	- 2.21	- 2.61	- 2.94	- 3.22	- 3.46	- 3.65	- 3.82	- 3.98
60	$-.0^{3}694$	$-.0^{2}526$	-.0 168	-.0 375	-.0 685	- .387	- .896	- 1.46	- 2.01	- 2.50	- 2.92	- 3.30	- 3.61	- 3.90	- 4.14	- 4.36
70	$-.0^{3}404$	$-.0^{2}309$	$-.0^{2}999$	-.0 226	-.0 421	- .257	- .646	- 1.14	- 1.66	- 2.16	- 2.65	- 3.06	- 3.44	- 3.78	- 4.07	- 4.36
80	$-.0^{3}245$	$-.0^{2}189$	$-.0^{2}614$	-.0 140	-.0 263	- .170	- .453	- .842	- 1.29	- 1.75	- 2.21	- 2.64	- 3.03	- 3.40	- 3.75	- 4.04
90	$-.0^{3}152$	$-.0^{2}118$	$-.0^{2}385$	$-.0^{2}884$	.0 167	- .112	- .312	- .603	- .957	- 1.35	- 1.75	- 2.14	- 2.52	- 2.88	- 3.22	- 3.53

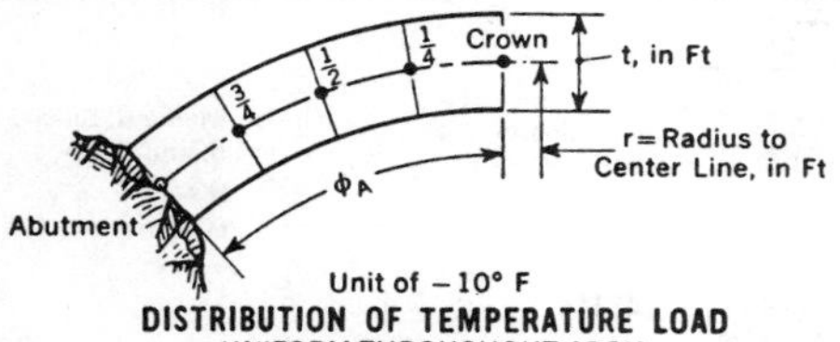

DISTRIBUTION OF TEMPERATURE LOAD
UNIFORM THROUGHOUT ARCH

Radial Deflection, in Ft
$\Delta_r = K_1 r c T$
C = Coefficient of Thermal Expansion of Concrete per Degree Fahrenheit Change in Temperature
T = Temperature Change in Degrees Fahrenheit ÷ (−10)
Example (Δ_r at Crown):
$\phi_A = 10°; \frac{t}{r} = 0.125; T = 25°$ F

$\Delta_r = (-0.43)\ (r)\ (c)\ (-2.5)$

TABLE 9(*a*).—FORCES AND MOMENTS FOR CONCENTRATED RADIAL LOAD AT ABUTMENT

ϕ_A	VALUES OF t/r															
	.025	.050	.075	.100	.125	.250	.375	.500	.625	.750	.875	1.000	1.125	1.250	1.375	1.500
	VALUES OF h AT CROWN															
10	25.36	54.83	75.29	90.41	102.1	135.8	151.9	161.4	167.7	172.1	175.4	178.0	180.1	181.7	183.1	184.3
20	5.251	26.47	54.72	82.09	106.2	186.3	230.1	257.9	276.5	291.3	302.1	310.8	317.7	323.5	328.4	332.6
30	1.214	8.110	22.07	41.40	63.64	170.0	243.8	293.9	329.9	356.9	378.0	395.0	408.9	420.5	430.4	438.8
40	.4000	2.891	8.685	18.10	30.83	119.6	206.9	275.7	328.6	369.9	402.8	429.5	451.7	470.4	486.4	500.2
50	.1660	1.238	3.870	8.443	15.10	74.13	151.7	225.4	236.6	340.7	384.0	420.3	450.9	477.0	499.6	519.2
60	.08014	.6079	1.938	4.325	7.929	44.65	103.4	168.9	231.8	288.2	337.6	380.5	417.7	450.1	478.4	503.4
70	.04297	.3293	1.063	2.403	4.469	27.34	68.89	121.2	176.5	230.3	281.3	325.5	366.1	402.3	434.7	463.7
80	.02484	.1918	.6237	1.423	2.671	17.24	46.03	85.53	130.8	177.8	223.9	267.6	308.2	345.5	379.6	410.6
90	.01517	.1178	.3852	.8842	1.671	11.19	31.15	60.30	95.81	134.7	174.7	214.2	252.2	288.0	321.6	352.8
	VALUES OF m AT CROWN															
10	-.1432	-.3379	-.4988	-.6368	-.7581	-1.207	-1.502	-1.713	-1.873	-1.997	-2.096	-2.178	-2.246	-2.304	-2.354	-2.398
20	-.1122	-.5949	-1.287	-2.013	-2.705	-5.498	-7.529	-9.108	-10.38	-11.44	-12.34	-13.10	-13.77	-14.35	-14.86	-15.32
30	-.05687	-.3935	-1.123	-2.141	-3.387	-10.20	-16.02	-20.76	-24.71	-28.06	-30.95	-33.49	-35.74	-37.73	-39.53	-41.15
40	-.03263	-.2424	-.7469	-1.595	-2.779	-11.92	-22.32	-31.77	-40.01	-47.20	-53.51	-59.11	-64.13	-68.65	-72.75	-76.49
50	-.02074	-.1582	-.5048	-1.123	-2.047	-10.94	-24.02	-37.87	-41.83	-62.98	-73.79	-83.60	-92.49	-100.6	-108.0	-114.8
60	-.01413	-.1091	-.3540	-.8032	-1.496	-9.064	-22.34	-38.50	-55.37	-71.77	-87.24	-101.6	-114.9	-127.2	-138.6	-149.2
70	-.01008	-.07842	-.2568	-.5891	-1.111	-7.241	-19.28	-35.61	-54.17	-73.45	-92.89	-110.9	-128.3	-144.8	-160.2	-174.7
80	$-.0^{2}7420$	-.05803	-.1911	-.4415	-.8388	-5.725	-16.06	-31.19	-49.62	-69.91	-90.93	-111.9	-132.5	-152.2	-171.2	-189.2
90	$-.0^{2}5577$	-.04378	-.1448	-.3360	-.6418	-4.517	-13.14	-26.47	-43.60	-63.37	-84.71	-106.8	-129.0	-150.8	-172.2	-192.8
	VALUES OF h AT ABUTMENT															
10	24.98	53.99	74.15	89.04	100.6	133.7	149.6	159.0	165.2	169.5	172.8	175.3	177.3	179.0	180.4	181.5
20	4.935	24.85	51.42	77.14	99.84	175.1	216.2	242.3	259.8	273.7	283.9	292.0	298.6	304.0	308.6	312.5
30	1.052	7.024	19.11	35.85	55.11	147.2	211.1	254.5	285.7	309.1	327.4	342.0	354.1	364.2	372.7	380.0
40	.3064	2.215	6.653	13.87	23.61	91.62	158.5	211.2	251.8	283.4	308.5	329.0	346.0	360.4	372.6	383.2
50	.1067	.7960	2.488	5.427	9.703	47.65	97.52	144.9	152.1	219.0	246.8	270.2	289.8	306.6	321.1	333.7
60	.04007	.3040	.9691	2.163	3.964	22.33	51.70	84.46	115.9	144.1	168.8	190.3	208.9	225.0	239.2	251.7
70	.01470	.1126	.3634	.8218	1.528	9.350	23.56	41.44	60.38	78.78	96.23	111.3	125.2	137.6	148.7	158.6
80	$.0^{2}4314$	.03330	.1083	.2470	.4637	2.993	7.993	14.85	22.72	30.88	38.89	46.47	53.51	59.99	65.91	71.31
90	0	0	0	0	0	0	0	0	0	0	0	0	0	0	0	0
	VALUES OF m AT ABUTMENT															
10	.2421	.4950	.6450	.7367	.7935	.8559	.8057	.7388	.6752	.6185	.5692	.5264	.4892	.4567	.4280	.4026
20	.2045	1.001	2.013	2.938	3.702	5.737	6.348	6.443	6.291	6.123	5.885	5.638	5.395	5.163	4.943	4.736
30	.1058	.6931	1.833	3.406	5.139	12.58	16.63	18.61	19.49	19.76	19.69	19.42	19.04	18.60	18.13	17.64
40	.06094	.4341	1.285	2.640	4.432	16.07	26.07	32.74	36.87	39.34	40.72	41.37	41.55	41.41	41.05	40.54
50	.03854	.2842	.8777	1.893	3.345	15.54	30.17	42.64	42.68	58.73	63.38	66.54	68.59	69.82	70.46	70.66
60	.02594	.1949	.6152	1.359	2.468	13.26	29.36	45.96	60.51	72.34	81.58	88.63	93.92	97.80	100.6	102.5
70	.01820	.1383	.4424	.9920	1.830	10.75	26.04	44.12	62.00	78.10	92.23	103.3	112.5	119.9	125.8	130.4
80	.01311	.1004	.3242	.7341	1.368	8.519	21.98	39.49	58.47	77.05	94.11	109.2	122.2	133.2	142.5	150.1
90	$.0^{2}9594$	.07397	.2404	.5481	1.029	6.677	18.01	33.83	52.21	71.37	90.04	107.4	123.2	137.1	149.4	160.0
	VALUES OF v AT ABUTMENT															
10	-995.6	-990.5	-986.9	-984.3	-982.3	-976.4	-973.4	-972.0	-970.9	-970.1	-969.5	-969.1	-968.7	-968.4	-968.2	-968.0
20	-998.2	-990.9	-981.3	-971.9	-963.7	-936.3	-921.3	-911.8	-905.4	-900.4	-896.7	-893.7	-891.3	-889.3	-887.7	-886.2
30	-999.4	-995.9	-989.0	-979.3	-968.2	-915.0	-878.1	-853.0	-835.0	-821.5	-811.0	-802.5	-795.6	-789.8	-784.8	-780.6
40	-999.7	-998.1	-994.4	-988.4	-980.2	-923.1	-867.0	-822.8	-788.7	-762.2	-741.1	-723.9	-709.6	-697.6	-687.3	-678.5
50	-999.9	-999.1	-997.0	-993.5	-988.4	-943.2	-883.8	-827.3	-818.8	-739.0	-705.9	-678.0	-654.6	-634.6	-617.3	-602.3
60	-999.9	-999.5	-998.3	-996.3	-993.1	-961.3	-910.5	-853.7	-799.3	-750.4	-707.6	-670.5	-638.3	-610.2	-585.7	-564.0
70	-1000.	-999.7	-998.5	-997.7	-995.8	-974.3	-935.3	-886.1	-834.1	-783.6	-735.6	-694.2	-656.0	-622.0	-591.5	-564.3
80	-1000.	-999.8	-999.4	-998.6	-997.4	-983.0	-954.7	-915.8	-871.2	-824.9	-779.5	-736.5	-696.5	-659.8	-626.2	-595.6
90	-1000.	-999.9	-999.6	-999.1	-998.3	-988.8	-968.8	-939.7	-904.2	-865.3	-825.3	-785.8	-747.8	-712.0	-678.4	-647.2

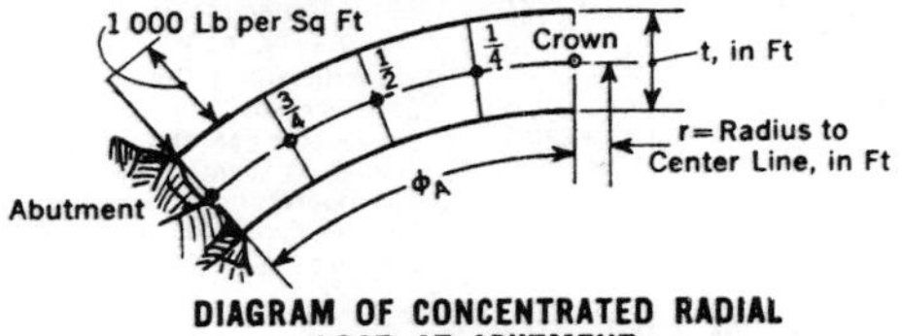

DIAGRAM OF CONCENTRATED RADIAL LOAD AT ABUTMENT

Thrust, Moment, Shear, in Lb, and Ft-Lb

H = h
M = m r
V = v

TABLE 9(b).—Radial Deflections for Concentrated Radial Load at Abutment

ϕ_A	Values of t/r															
	.025	.050	.075	.100	.125	.250	.375	.500	.625	.750	.875	.1000	1.125	1.250	1.375	1.500
Values of K_1 at Crown																
10	-808.3	-1434	-1592	-1653	-1633	-1726	-1736	-1740	-1742	-1744	-1745	-1745	-1746	-1746	-1746	-1747
20	1053	258.4	-344.8	-730.7	-974.1	-1412	-1518	-1561	-1583	-1596	-1605	-1611	-1616	-1619	-1622	-1624
30	1415	1125	708.4	442.5	143.2	-726.3	-1050	-1195	-1272	-1318	-1349	-1370	-1386	-1398	-1407	-1415
40	1501	1376	1217	1038	851.5	55.45	-410.9	-670.5	-823.2	-919.9	-985.1	-1031	-1066	-1092	-1113	-1129
50	1537	1469	1385	1288	1182	454.1	191.5	-112.6	-466.4	-459.8	-558.1	-631.2	-686.6	-729.7	-763.9	-791.7
60	1561	1517	1461	1407	1343	984.4	642.0	364.4	152.6	-6.501	-126.7	-218.8	-290.8	-347.9	-394.1	-432.1
70	1581	1550	1514	1475	1433	1194	946.0	740.5	535.4	383.3	264.8	163.3	83.97	19.18	-34.32	-78.99
80	1601	1576	1550	1522	1449	1326	1170	978.4	826.2	695.5	584.8	491.7	414.7	349.5	294.5	247.7
90	1621	1674	1581	1559	1537	1417	1288	1161	1043	937.2	844.2	763.6	694.0	633.6	582.4	537.7
Values of K_1 at $\frac{1}{4}$ Point																
10	-728.0	-1466	-1608	-1662	-1689	-1727	-1736	-1740	-1742	-1743	-1744	-1744	-1745	-1745	-1745	-1746
20	728.0	38.14	-490.2	-833.0	-1045	-1433	-1528	-1566	-1586	-1597	-1605	-1610	-1614	-1617	-1620	-1622
30	1039	796.3	459.6	210.8	-48.64	-809.3	-1094	-1221	-1289	-1330	-1357	-1375	-1389	-1399	-1407	-1414
40	1108	1009	878.5	728.7	571.5	-109.9	-514.0	-739.0	-871.8	-955.8	-1012	-1053	-1082	-1104	-1122	-1136
50	1089	1083	1017	939.4	853.4	395.8	22.35	-236.6	-591.9	-531.6	-617.0	-679.2	-726.3	-762.8	-791.7	-815.1
60	1150	1118	1079	1034	984.6	696.2	414.1	183.4	6.601	-126.3	-226.7	-303.5	-363.6	-411.0	-449.3	-480.6
70	1162	1140	1112	1086	1052	868.7	671.1	490.7	338.6	214.8	120.3	35.75	-28.63	-81.10	-124.3	-160.3
80	1172	1156	1138	1118	1096	972.3	835.6	703.0	583.3	480.1	392.8	382.3	258.5	207.9	161.8	127.7
90	1183	1170	1156	1141	1125	1037	931.8	826.4	721.8	629.7	546.0	524.1	493.2	447.2	408.8	373.9
Values of K_1 at $\frac{1}{2}$ Point																
10	-1192	-1556	-1650	-1687	-1705	-1731	-1737	-1739	-1740	-1741	-1741	-1741	-1742	-1742	-1742	-1742
20	-128.7	-547.1	-880.1	-1098	-1238	-1494	-1557	-1581	-1593	-1600	-1605	-1608	-1610	-1612	-1613	-1614
30	53.51	-70.71	-256.6	-407.3	-563.5	-1035	-1215	-1296	-1338	-1363	-1379	-1390	-1397	-1403	-1408	-1411
40	83.89	46.78	-13.45	-88.94	-172.3	-557.6	-795.8	-929.4	-1010	-1057	-1089	-1111	-1128	-1141	-1149	-1156
50	88.32	77.05	55.04	24.32	-6.701	-381.1	-436.3	-576.6	-841.5	-736.0	-781.4	-814.3	-838.9	-855.6	-869.6	-880.6
60	86.05	83.58	75.95	63.94	47.69	-68.13	-197.0	-306.7	-391.6	-455.2	-502.5	-538.1	-565.2	-586.1	-602.5	-615.5
70	81.20	82.10	80.30	76.07	69.68	14.41	-58.66	-130.2	-191.8	-241.9	-276.9	-312.9	-337.4	-356.7	-372.1	-384.4
80	75.10	77.21	77.89	77.23	75.36	68.01	14.71	-25.83	-35.79	-96.82	-124.3	-208.5	-243.4	-271.1	-295.6	-319.0
90	74.77	70.43	71.92	72.50	72.16	58.03	25.82	-11.79	-54.59	-96.56	-93.49	-74.73	-24.60	-52.55	-58.13	-62.74
Values of K_1 at $\frac{3}{4}$ Point																
10	-1539	-1672	-1708	-1722	-1729	-1737	-1737	-1737	-1737	-1737	-1737	-1737	-1736	-1736	-1736	-1736
20	-1177	-1273	-1376	-1448	-1495	-1580	-1598	-1603	-1604	-1604	-1603	-1605	-1602	-1602	-1601	-1636
30	-1117	-1121	-1154	-1184	-1221	-1344	-1388	-1404	-1410	-1412	-1411	-1410	-1409	-1408	-1406	-1405
40	-1121	-1102	-1093	-1092	-1097	-1,146	-1181	-1197	-1202	-1202	-1201	-1197	-1194	-1191	-1187	-1184
50	-1131	-1109	-1091	-1078	-1068	-1048	-1043	-1039	-1160	-845.0	-1015	-1006	-997.0	-988.9	-981.4	-974.5
60	-1141	-1121	-1103	-1087	-1073	-1019	-981.2	-953.5	-927.8	-904.7	-883.9	-865.1	-848.2	-832.9	-819.1	-806.5
70	-1153	-1135	-1119	-1103	-1089	-1026	-979.2	-927.9	-886.7	-849.8	-813.2	-785.4	-760.6	-736.8	-715.4	-696.0
80	-1162	-1147	-1133	-1119	-1106	-1044	-988.3	-917.3	-886.7	-841.2	-799.4	-761.4	-726.8	-695.4	-667.0	-641.1
90	-1174	-1161	-1149	-1137	-1126	-1080	-1045	-1019	-999.2	-982.7	-968.0	-830.1	-737.9	-702.0	-668.3	-637.7
Values of K_1 at Abutment																
10	-1777	-1768	-1762	-1757	-1753	-1743	-1738	-1735	-1733	-1732	-1731	-1730	-1729	-1729	-1728	-1728
20	-1782	-1769	-1752	-1735	-1720	-1671	-1645	-1628	-1616	-1607	-1600	-1595	-1591	-1587	-1584	-1582
30	-1784	-1778	-1765	-1748	-1728	-1633	-1567	-1523	-1491	-1466	-1448	-1432	-1420	-1410	-1401	-1393
40	-1785	-1782	-1775	-1764	-1750	-1648	-1548	-1469	-1408	-1361	-1323	-1292	-1267	-1245	-1227	-1211
50	-1785	-1783	-1780	-1773	-1764	-1684	-1578	-1477	-1462	-1319	-1260	-1210	-1168	-1133	-1102	-1075
60	-1785	-1784	-1782	-1778	-1773	-1716	-1625	-1524	-1427	-1339	-1263	-1358	-1139	-1089	-1045	-1007
70	-1785	-1784	-1783	-1781	-1778	-1739	-1669	-1648	-1489	-1399	-1313	-1239	-1171	-1110	-1056	-1007
80	-1785	-1785	-1784	-1782	-1780	-1755	-1704	-1635	-1555	-1472	-1391	-1315	-1243	-1178	-1118	-1063
90	-1785	-1785	-1785	-1784	-1784	-1777	-1762	-1738	-1707	-1672	-1634	1460	-1335	-1271	-1211	-1155

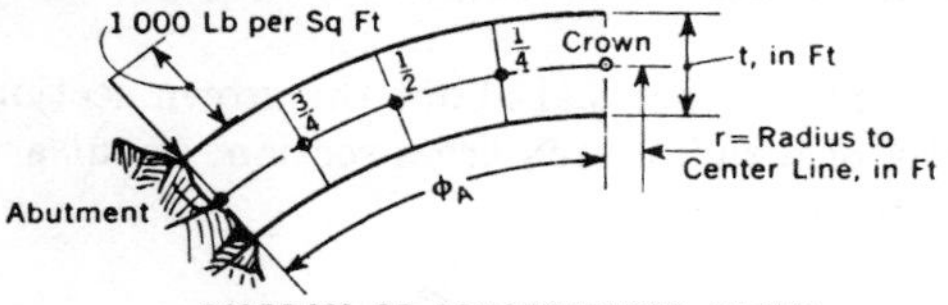

DIAGRAM OF CONCENTRATED RADIAL LOAD AT ABUTMENT

Radial Deflection, in Ft

$$\Delta_r = \frac{K_1}{E_c}$$

E_c = Modulus of Elasticity of Concrete in Direct Stress, Lb per Sq Ft

General Assumptions Made in Analyzing Arch Elements

In their paper in this Symposium, Messrs. Houk and Keener present a thoroughly inclusive list of assumptions that affect the design of masonry dams. Those that apply to circular arch dams of uniform depth are as follows:

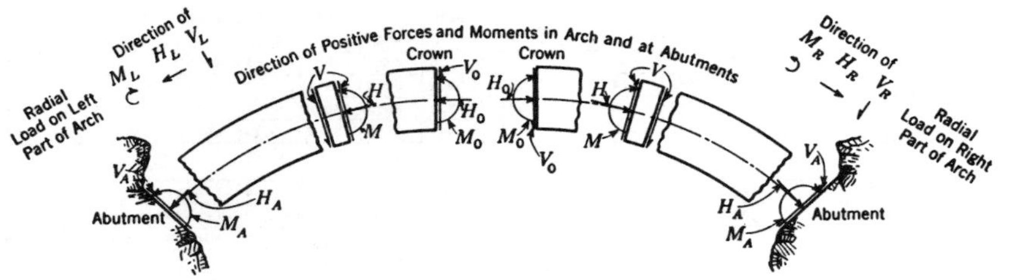

Fig. 2.—Direction of Forces and Moments

(*a*) The arch material is homogeneous and isotropic;

(*b*) Hooke's law applies, and the proportional elastic limit is not exceeded;

(*c*) A plane section before bending remains plane after bending;

(*d*) Direct stresses have a linear variation from extrados to intrados;

(*e*) The modulus of elasticity in direct stress is the same for tension and compression;

(*f*) Temperature strains are proportional to temperature changes;

(*g*) The temperature change occurs uniformly throughout an arch;

(*h*) The abutments of arch elements are radial planes;

(*i*) The ratio of the modulus of elasticity in direct stress (E) to the shearing modulus of elasticity (G) is expressed by

$$\frac{E}{G} = 2\,(1 + \mu) \quad \text{(2)}$$

in which μ = Poisson's ratio;

(*j*) The symbol K expresses the ratio of the detrusion caused by the actual shear distribution to that caused by an equivalent shear distributed uniformly. Assuming that $K = 1.25$ and $\mu = 0.2$, the ratio $\frac{K}{G} = \frac{1.25 \times 2.4}{E} = \frac{3}{E}$, which is the ratio included in Tables 3 to 9 (Appendix).

Further Assumptions Applying to the Tables.—In Tables 3 to 9, furthermore, it is assumed that:

(*k*) The arch is circular and of uniform thickness (that is, t and r are held constant), and 1 ft wide;

(*l*) The arch and its loads are symmetrical about the crown section;

(*m*) The moment of inertia of a radial arch cross section, about a vertical line through its center of gravity is,

$$I = \frac{t^3}{12} \quad \text{(3)}$$

8

THIN SHELL R.C. STRUCTURE AND ROOFS

Thin shell offers many of the attributes that architects and engineers are looking for an ideal structure.These structures are designed to enclose space and span distances.

EXAMPLE 8 -01
Given:Design an inverted Umberella "Hyperbolic Paraboloid"roof for a gasoline pumping station and to cover the service area of 60'x40'.

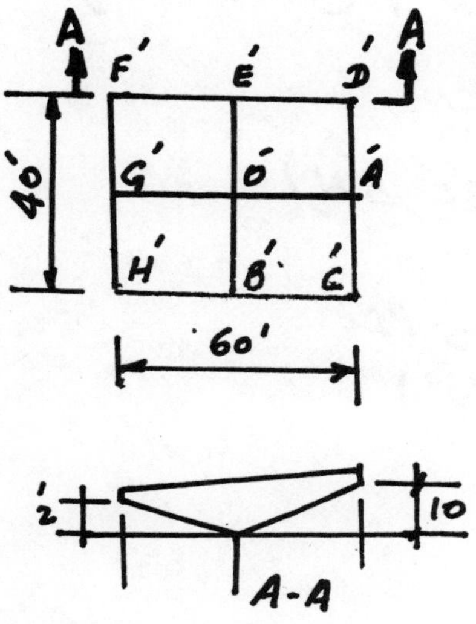

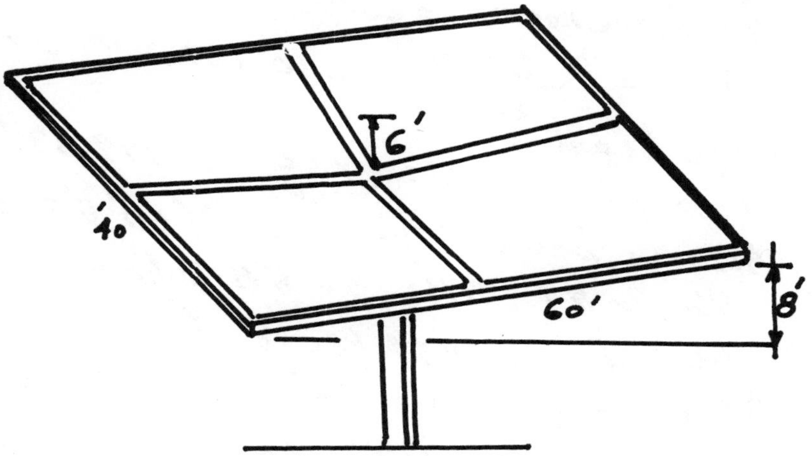

Length 2a = 60'
width 2b = 40'
depth f = 6'
Thickness d = $2\frac{1}{2}$"

Load
Dead Wt = 31 psf Shell surface
waterproof
Ribs = 9 psf shell surface
Live load = 15 psf shell surface
Total = 55 P.S.F

membrane shear $= \frac{qab}{2f} = \frac{55 \times 33 \times 20}{2 \times 6} = 2750$#/1

tension (Max) in edge Beam
F'E'D' / H'B'C' $= 2750\sqrt{30^2+4^2} = 83230$#

tension (Max) in H'G'F', C'A'D' $= 2750 \times 20 = 55000$#

Comp. (Max) in Rib G'OA' $= 2 \times 2750 \times \sqrt{30^2+10^2} = 173926$#

Comp. (Max) in Rib B'OE' $= 2 \times 2750 \times \sqrt{20^2+6^2} = 114840$#

The Bending moment induced in the rib because of live load on only one half of shell.

Unbalanced force in Ea. Edge Beam
$= \frac{1}{2} \times \frac{15}{55} \times 83230 = 11350$#

Moment to be resisted by rib O'A' & O'G'
$= \frac{1}{2}(2 \times 11.35)6 = 68.1$ Kft

Similarly moment to be resisted by rib O'B' & O'E' due to L.L. acting on Area G'A'C'H' = 45 Kft.

Reinforcement design:-

$A_s = \frac{2750}{20000} = 0.1375$ in² or # 4 @ 4" bothways

Edge beam moment $= 83.23 \times \frac{12}{2} = 499.38$ Kin

Assume beam size 10"×12" (E'D', E'F', B'C', B'H)
Use 2-#4 Top; 8-#8 Bottom.
Then $f_c = 1154$ Psi & $f_s = 19785$ Psi

again edge beam (A'D', A'C', G'F' & G'H')
assume beam size 7"×12"
moment $= 55 \times \frac{12}{2} = 330$ Kin

Use 2-#4 Top, 3-#7 & 3-#8 bottom.
Then stress f_c = 1023 Psi & f_s = 18945 Psi

Rib O'A' & O'G'

width of rib = 36" & clear outstand of rib 14",
Avg depth = 16.7"
Moment due to eccentricity of comp. force

$$= 173925 \times \frac{16.7}{2} = 1452270 \text{ \#''}$$

Use 9-#6 Top
15-#6 bott

Then f_c = 1088 Psi
f_s = 8403 Psi

Rib O'E' & OB'

Moment = $114840 \times \frac{15}{2}$ = 861300 Kin
d_{avg} = 15"

Use 6-#6 Top
10-#6 BOT.

Then f_c = 1021 Psi
f_s = 8330 Psi

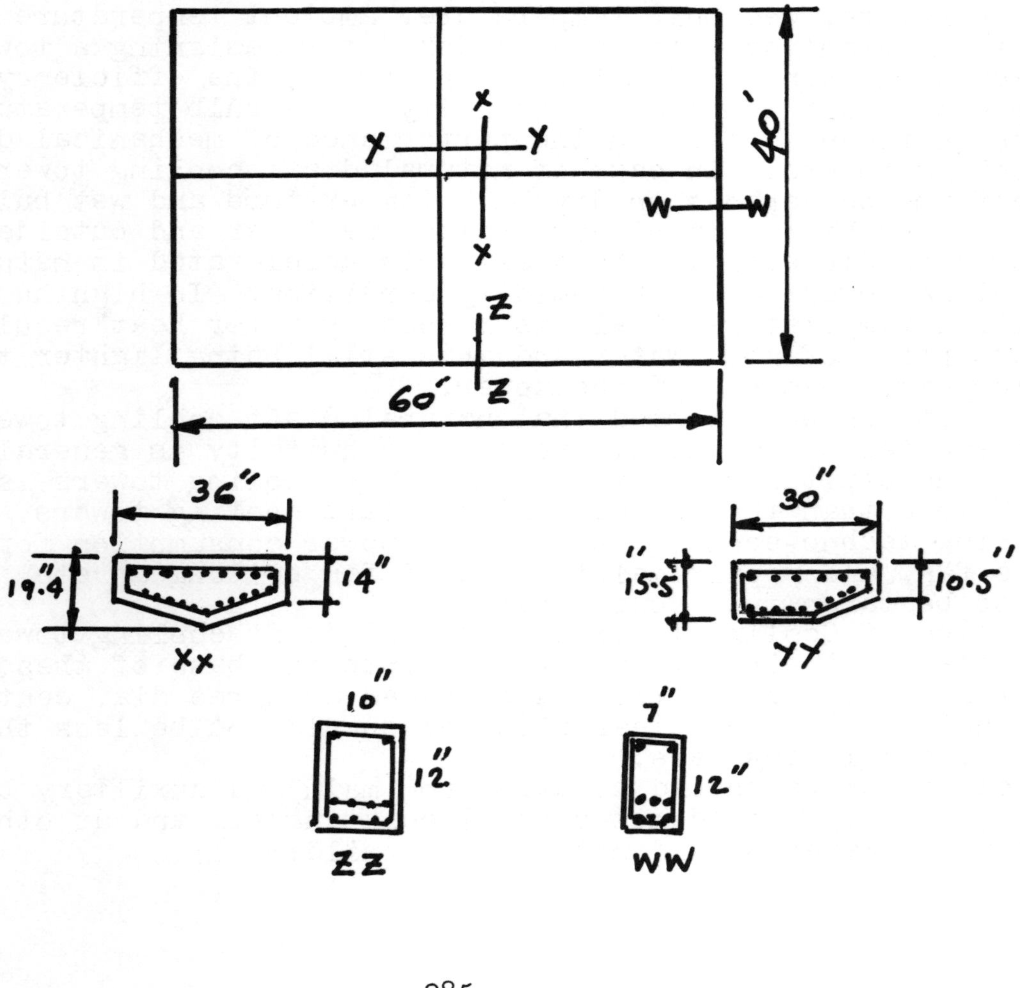

HYPERBOLIC NATURAL DRAFT COOLING TOWER

The first hyperbolic natural draft cooling tower was designed by Prof.Van Iteron of Dutch State Mines and was installed at Emona Colliery in 1916.

Towers of this type were built at Liverpool at Lister Drive Station.Since then,towers are being commonly used in thermal power plants.These are hyperbolic RCC structures supported on RCC columns.Most of the structure is empty shell but the lower portion contains a cooling stack over which hot water is distributed by RCC channel or pipe system,32' above ground level.The lower portion of the shell is open to allow the air to go to the cooling stack supported on the RCC columns which are designed for horizontal load due to wind.A pond is constructed below the tower to catch the cooled water and make up water for circulation.

As the warm water falls in the stack, it gives its heat to the air there which becomes lighter than ambient air and a draft is created due to chimney action. In this case, cooling is dependent on dry bulb temperature and wet bulb temperature, the draft for a given wet bulb temperature, i.e., being better in humid condition.

The quantity of water to be cooled per hour or duty of tower, temperature of hot water, temperature of cold water, i.e., degree of cooloing, direction of wind and its velocity, dry bulb temperature, wet bulb temperature, ambient temperature etc. are the important data to be considered for designing a tower. In case of mechanical draft cooling towers, the efficiency depends upon wet bulb temperature humidity. Dry bulb temperature has an insignificant effect on the performance of mechanical draft coolung towers. In case of natural draft cooling towers, the performance depends on dry bulb temperature and wet bulb temperature as the weight of air inside the tower and outside the tower is different. The draft gets accelerated in natural draft cooling towers at high humidity condition. In high humidiy condition temperature of air is raised by water heat resulting in absorption of more water and this still being lighter than inflow air, goes out of the tower.

Thus it can be inferred that natural draft cooling towers should be adopted near coastal areas where humidity is generally high. But the capital cost of natural draft cooling towers is about 60% more than that of mechanical draft cooling towers. While making techno-economic study, the power consumption for running the fan, and repair maintenance of fan switchgear etc. should also be taken into consideration.

Spacing of Cooling Towers:- Natural draft cooling towers are so located that air may pass freely into the base of these cooling towers. Generally, these are spaced at three dia. center at ground level. But clear distance should not be less than 30 to 40 meters in any case.

Cooling towers should be away from main and auxiliary buildings, so that they should not stop circulating air and at other times spray of water should not fall on buildings.

EXAMPLE 8-02

Given:- Design a cooling tower (Hyperboloid - Rotational) for a height of 100'.

Data $a = 30'$ $z_{base} = +100'$

$b = 70'$ $z_{top} = -30'$

Load = Dead WT = 150 #/ft³

Design factors

at base $r_0 = a\sqrt{1+\frac{z^2}{b^2}}$

$= 30\sqrt{1+\frac{100^2}{70^2}}$

$= 52.314'$

$\tan\phi = \frac{b}{a}\sqrt{\frac{r_0^2}{r_0^2 - a^2}}$

$= \frac{70}{30}\sqrt{\frac{52.314^2}{52.314^2 - 30^2}}$

$= 2.8482$

$\cos\phi = \frac{1}{\sqrt{1+2.8482^2}}$

$= 0.33127$

also $\cos\phi = \frac{a}{\sqrt{a^2+b^2}}\,\xi$

$\xi = \frac{\cos\phi\sqrt{a^2+b^2}}{a}$

$= \frac{0.33127\sqrt{30^2+70^2}}{30} = 0.8409$

$f(\xi) = 8.276$

at top $r_0 = 30\sqrt{1+\frac{(-30)^2}{70}} = 32.6391'$

$\tan\phi = \frac{70}{30}\sqrt{\frac{32.6391^2}{32.6391^2 - 30^2}} = 5.923$

$\cos\phi = \frac{1}{\sqrt{1+5.923^2}} = 0.16647$

$\xi_0 = \frac{0.16647\sqrt{30^2+70^2}}{30} = 0.4226$

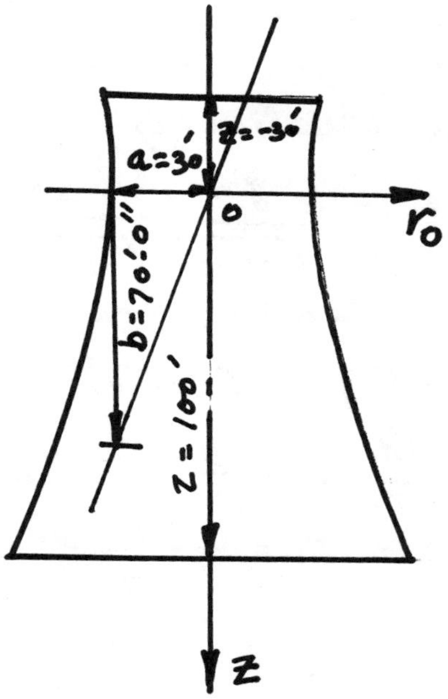

stress @ base

$N\phi = \frac{-g}{4}b^2\sqrt{a^2+b^2}\,\frac{\sqrt{1-\xi^2}}{a^2+b^2-a^2\xi^2}\left[f(\xi) - f(\xi_0)\right]$ — ①

$= \frac{-150}{4}\times 70^2\sqrt{30^2+70^2}\,\frac{\sqrt{1-0.8409^2}}{\left[30^2+70^2-(30^2\times 0.4809^2)\right]}\times(8.276-1.931)$

$= -9305.39\ ^K/ft$

$$\text{Again } N_\theta = -\frac{ga^2}{\sqrt{a^2+b^2}}\frac{\xi}{\sqrt{1-\xi^2}} + N_\phi \frac{a^2}{b^2}(1-\xi^2) \quad \text{— (11)}$$

$$= -\frac{150\times 30^2}{\sqrt{30^2+70^2}} \times \frac{0.8409}{\sqrt{1-0.8409^2}} + \left[-9305387\,\frac{30^2}{70^2}(1-0.8409^2)\right]$$

$$= -503.24\ ^{k}/ft$$

@ top using equation (1)

$N_\phi = 0$, Since $f(\xi_0) - f'(\xi_0) = 0$

using equation (2)

$$N_\theta = \frac{-ga^2}{\sqrt{a^2+b^2}}\frac{\xi_0}{\sqrt{1-\xi_0^2}} = -\frac{150\times 30^2}{\sqrt{30^2+70^2}}\frac{0.4226}{\sqrt{1-0.4226^2}}$$

$$= -0.827\ ^{k}/ft.$$

Check for static

$$\frac{N_\phi}{r_1} + \frac{N_\theta}{r_2} = -g\cos\phi$$

@ base $r_1 = \frac{r_0}{\sin\phi}$ where $\sin\phi = \tan\phi\cos\phi = 2.84819\times 0.33127$

$= 0.94352$

$$r_2 = \frac{r_0}{\sin\phi} = \frac{52.314}{0.94352} = 55.4454$$

$$r_1 = \frac{r_2^3}{\alpha a^2} \quad \text{wher } \alpha = \frac{a^2}{b^2}$$

$$= \frac{55.4454^3}{\frac{30^2}{70^2}\times 30^2} = 55.4454^3 \times \frac{70^2}{30^4} = -1031.1168'$$

$$\therefore \frac{N_\phi}{r_1} + \frac{N_\theta}{r_2} = \frac{-9305387}{-1031.1168} + \frac{-503235}{55445} = -51.5$$

and $-g\cos\phi = -150\times 0.33127 = -49.69 \simeq -51.5$ ok

@ Top $r_2 = \frac{r_0}{\sin\phi} = \frac{32.6391}{5.9233\times 0.16647} = 33.101'$

$$r_1 = -\frac{r_2^2}{\alpha a^2} = \frac{33.101^2\times 70^2}{30^4} = -219.398'$$

$$\therefore \frac{N_\phi}{r_1} + \frac{N_\theta}{r_2} = 0 + \frac{-826.548}{33.101} = -24.97$$

and $-g\cos\phi = -150\times 0.16607 = -24.97 \simeq -24.97$ ok

EXAMPLE 8-03

Given:- Design a Roof Shed to span 50 ft. for a snow load of 30 psf on roof surface to house animals.

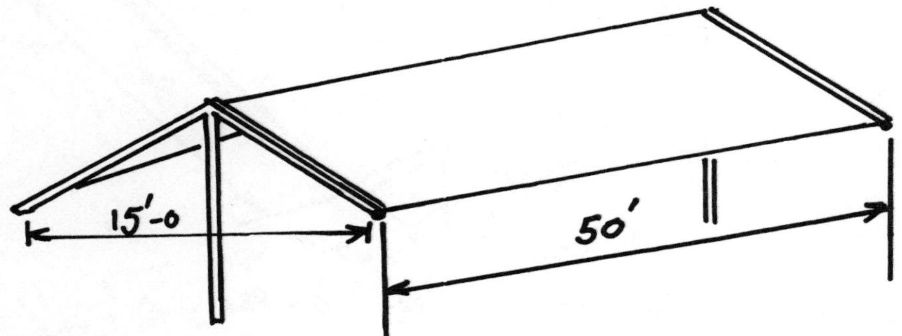

Slab 4" D.L = 50 #/□'

S.L = 30 #/□'

"p" Total = 80 #/□'

Load normal to slab p_n = 80 sin 60 = 69.3 #/□'

Load tangent point p_t = 80 sin 30 = 40.0 #/□'

Cross wise Bending moment @ ridge = $\frac{69.3 \times 8.66^2}{2}$ = 2600 ft-lb/ft

$As = \frac{m}{f_s Jd} = \frac{2600 \times 12}{20000 \times 2.5} = 0.624$ □"/'

#5 @ 6".

To find longitudenal moment in Plate M.

tangential Loading/ft = $P_t + R_{1t} + R_1$ from ℄ BC

$= \frac{40 \times 7.5}{\cos 30} + \frac{69.3 \times 8.66}{\cos 30} \sin 30$

$+ \frac{600}{\cos 30} = 1387$ #/ft

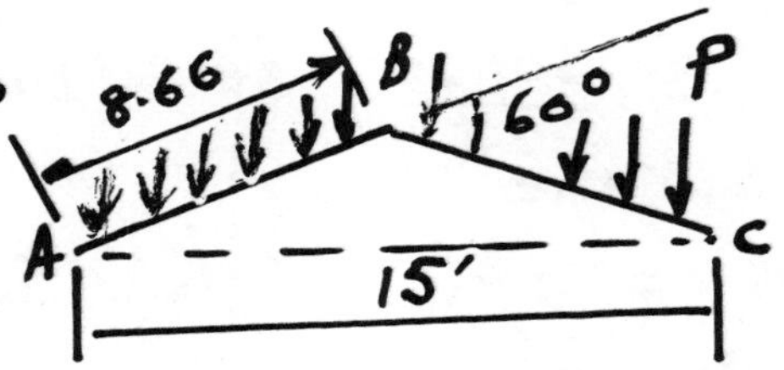

$M = \frac{1387 \times 50^2}{8} = 433000$ ftlbs

$As = \frac{433000}{19000 \times 7} = 3.26$ □"

use 4-#8

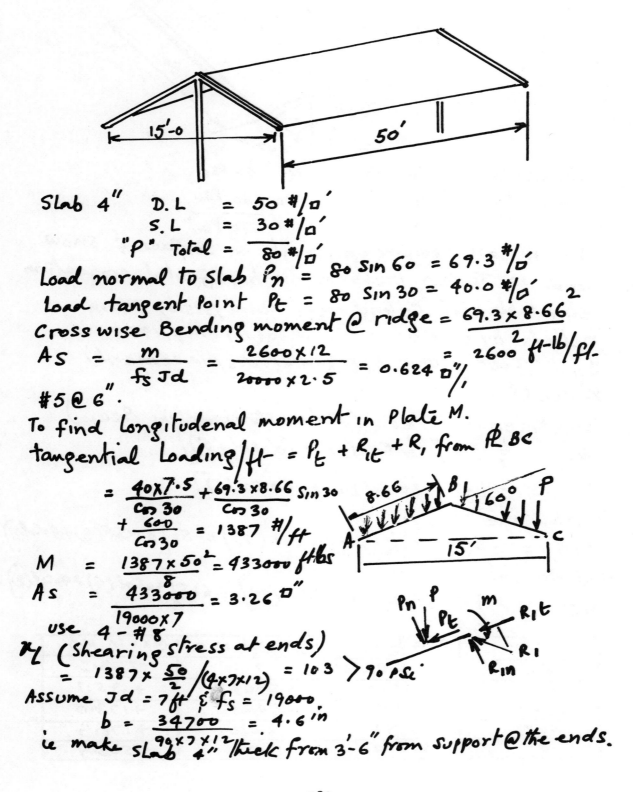

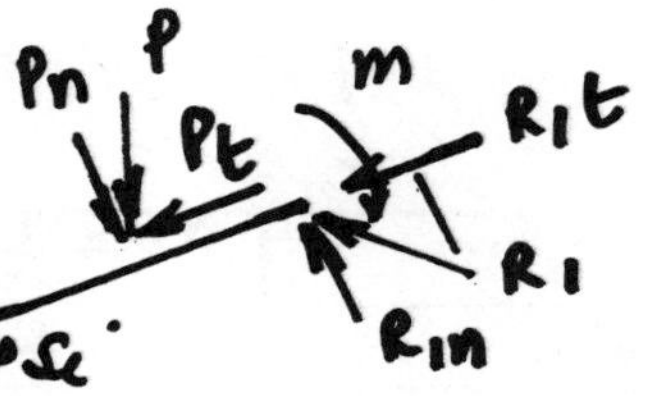

τ (Shearing stress at ends)

$= 1387 \times \frac{50}{2} / (4 \times 7 \times 12) = 103 > 90$ psi

Assume Jd = 7 ft & f_s = 19000

$b = \frac{34700}{90 \times 7 \times 12} = 4.6$ in

ie make slab 4" thick from 3'-6" from support @ the ends.

EXAMPLE 8-04

Given:- Design a Multiple Barrel Shell roof to span 50 ft. for the construction of shed for a gasoline station.

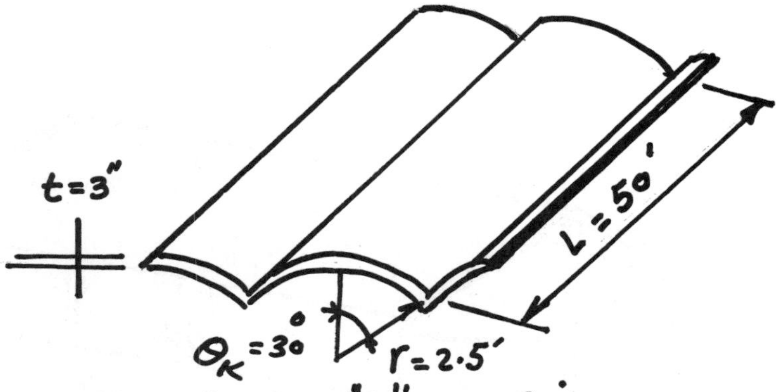

Dead Load Plus Roofing "Pd" = 40 Psi

Snow Load "Pu" = 30 Psi

70 Psi

D.L is distributed uniformly on surface & snow load is taken uniform on horizontal projection.

Using table Ref "Cylinderical analysis by Beam methods by CHINN A.C.I J 30(11) May, 1959.

A_H (Effect of unit Horizontal displacement) is negligible.

Longitudenal stress (Fiber stresses in Beam)

$$N_x = \frac{L}{r}(L)\left[P_u \, col(1) + P_d \, col(5)\right]$$

$$= \frac{50 \times 50}{25}\left[30 \, col(1) + 40 \, col(5)\right]$$

Memberane shear

$$N_{x\theta} = -L\left(P_u \, col(3) + P_d \, col(7)\right] = -50\left[30 \, col(3) + 40 \, col(7)\right]$$

Hoop Moment

$$M_\theta = r^2\left[P_u \, col(4) + P_d \, col(8)\right] = 625\left[30 \, col(4) + 40 \, col(8)\right]$$

	@ $x = \frac{L}{2}$ N_x	@ $x = 0, L$ $N_{x\theta}$	@ $x = L/2$ M_θ
θK	−24082	0	−223.6
$3/4 \theta K$	−19510	−5904	−85.1
$1/2 \theta K$	−5875	−9425	+178.0
$1/4 \theta K$	16592	−8210	+178.3
0	47504	0	−503.9

By placing steel @ 45° diagonal from the transverse supports toward shell, the shell shear force is handled by using #5@8".

$$NA(\bar{Y}) = \frac{r \sin \theta k}{\theta k} - r \cos \theta k$$

$= 2.2225.$ From the valley edge

By using linear variation to the N.A

Total Tensile force

$$T_s = \frac{1}{2} 5.56 \times 47.5 = 132^{ftk}.$$

9

ELEVATED WATER TANKS, PRESSURE VESSELS

OVERHAED WATER STORAGE TANK

EXAMPLE 9-01
Given: Design of overhead tank of capacity of 500,000 gallons at INDORE (INDIA).

Introduction:-The tank is overhead with capacity of 22.7 lakh litre water.Head to tank bottom shall be 18 M to top of base slab.The tank is to be located in INDORE city.The seismic coefficient is 0.02.
The tank is circular in shape with flat roof and flat bottom. The staging system is suitably braced at various levels as shown in the sketch.The tank and staging have been designed basically as per I.S.Codes.The staging system using ultimate strength design and container part on crack central conditions.
The tank is circular in shape with approximate diameter of 21 columns and tank wall.The walls are of varying thickness as shown in profile.The base slab is also of flat slab construction with drops supported on 37 columns.The columns are braced by grid system of rectangular beams at various levels.The columns are supported on 30 Cm.dia under reamed piles.
Materials:-Concrete, Cotainer portion:-1:1½:3
Foundation piles bracing etc. 1:2:4
Columns M 200 design mix
Steel :- Ribbed Tor Steel

Capacity calculations

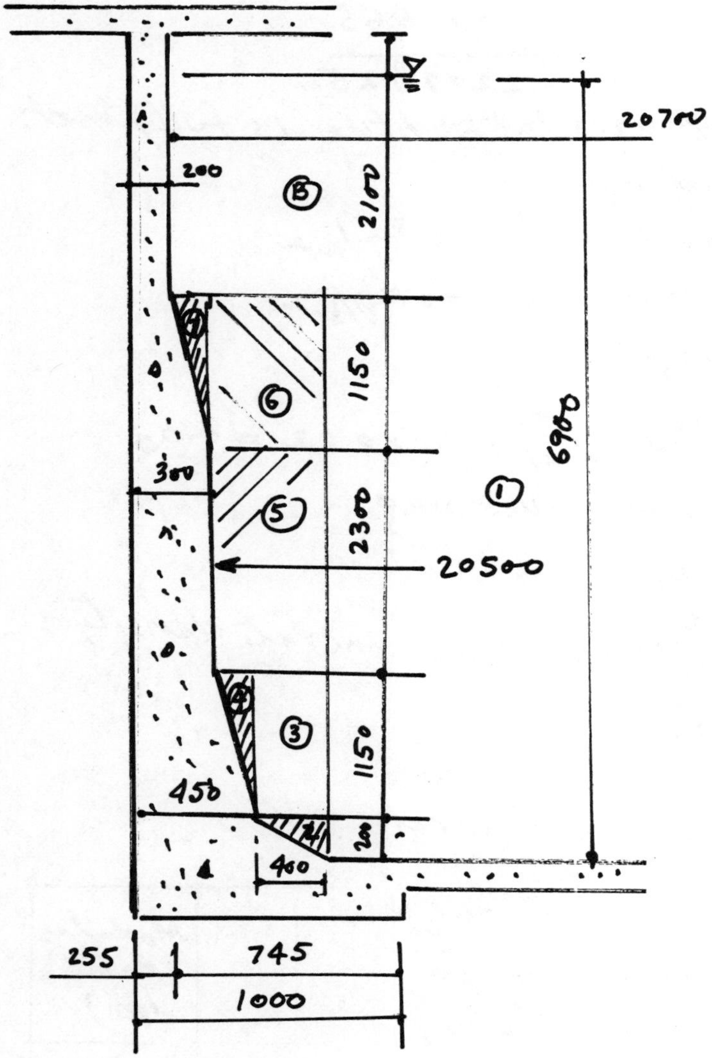

Volume

1. $\frac{\pi}{4}(20.7-1.3)^2 \times 4.8$ $= 1418.843$
2. $0.2 \times 0.2 \times \pi\left(19.4 + .4 \times \frac{2}{3}\right)$ $= 2.471$
3. $0.4 \times 1.15 \times \pi(19.4 + .4)$ $= 28.613$
4. $0.15 \times \frac{1.15}{2} \times \pi\left(19.4 + 0.4 + 0.4 + 0.15 \times 2/3\right)$ $= 5.50$
5. $0.55 \times 2.3 \times \pi(19.4 + 0.55)$ $= 79.283$
6. $0.55 \times 1.15 \times \pi(19.4 + 0.55)$ $= 39.641$
7. $0.10 \times \frac{1.15}{2} \times \pi\left(19.4 + 0.55 + 0.55 + 0.10 \times 2/3\right)$ $= 3.715$

8. $\frac{\pi}{4}(20.7)^2 \times 2.10$

$$\begin{array}{r} 1578.066 \\ = 706.724 \\ \hline 2284.790 \end{array}$$

less columns

$21 \times 0.23 \times .23 \times 6.9 \quad - \quad 7.665$

$$\overline{2277.125}$$

Hence capacity of 22.7 Lakh litre is fully met.

stressesses and loading

A a. Roof Live Load = 75 kg/m²

b. Balcony Live Load = 200 kg/m²

c. water load as per standard

d. Seismic force (αh_{max}) = $1.5 \times 0.02 = 0.03$

e, wind forces not governing

f, Seismic Conditions Load factor 1:4

g, Dead loads calculated on concrete density of 2400 kg/cu.M.

B Stresses:-

Permissable stress in concrete.

Grade of Conc.	Permissable stress kg/cm²					Modular Ratio (m)
	Comp. due to bending	Direct tension	Tension due to bending			
M250	85	13	18			11
M200	70	12	17			13

Permissable stresses in ribbed Tor steel in kg/cm²

1. Tensile stress in direct tension = 1500
2. Tensile stress in bending
   a, on liquid retaining face = 1500
   b, on face away t < 225 mm = 1500
   c, on face away t ≥ 225 mm = 1900

top, intermediate and bottom section.

$$K_1 = \frac{48 \times 6.9^4 \times 10^8}{20^2 \times 20.7^2 \times 10^4} = 6348$$

$$\text{Log } K_1 = 3.8026$$

$$K_2 = \frac{48 \times 6.9^4 \times 10^8}{30^2 \times 20.5^2 \times 10^4} = 2877$$

$$\text{Log } K_2 = 3.457$$

$$K_3 = \frac{48 \times 6.9^4 \times 10^8}{45^2 \times 20.2^2 \times 10^4} = 1316$$

$$\text{Log } K_3 = 3.1195$$

Table of Hoop Tension coefficient

	K=1000 =3	K=10000 =4	K1 =3.8026	K2 =3.457	K3 3.1195	$0.39K_1 + 0.5K_2 + 0.11K_3$
0.0	0.05	0.0	0.010	0.027	0.044	0.022
0.1	0.16	0.1	0.112	0.133	0.153	0.127
0.2	0.25	0.20	0.210	0.227	0.244	0.222
0.3	0.35	0.30	0.370	0.327	0.344	0.322
0.4	0.43	0.43	0.43	0.43	0.43	0.43
0.5	0.47	0.57	0.55	0.516	0.482	0.323
0.6	0.45	0.64	0.602	0.537	0.472	0.355
0.7	0.37	0.67	0.610	0.508	0.405	0.537
0.8	0.25	0.53	0.474	0.383	0.283	0.403
0.9	0.07	0.22	0.190	0.130	0.088	0.153

Requirement of hoop steel at various location are marked below:-

Location	Tension k.g	Total Steel cm²	Steel actual Provided	t = cm
0.0 H	1585	1.06	6.46 cm	20
0.1 H	9070	6.05	6.46 cm²	20
0.2 H	15868	10.58	11.90 cm²	20
0.3 H	23010	15.34	18.84 cm²	20
0.4 H	30708	20.47	22.62	20

3. Tensile stress in shear reinforcements
   a, for members $t < 225$ mm = 1500
   b. for members $t \geq 225$ mm = 1750

4. Compressive stress in columns subjected to direct load = 1750

5. Bond stress 40% more than plain M.S rounds.

Roof and roof supporting columns.

Container portion :- Mix $1:1\frac{1}{2}:3$

Roof slab is designed as flat slab construction.

Basic Grid 'L' = $20.59 \times 0.707 \times \frac{1}{4} = 3.64$

Load/sq.M

Self Weight = 0.125×2400 = 300 kg/m²

Live load = 75 "

375 kg/m²

Thickness required.

$t = 12.5$ cm or $\frac{L}{40} = 9$ 1 cm - provide 125 mm thick

Load on panel 'w' = $3.64 \times 3.64 \times 375 = 4969$ kg

Moment at any place $= k\frac{wL}{10}\left(1 - \frac{2}{3}\frac{D}{L}\right)^2$

$= k\frac{4969 \times 3.64}{10}\left(1 - \frac{2}{3} \times \frac{0.23}{3.64}\right)^2$

$= k \cdot 1660$ kgm where K

is coefficient

for middle strip +ve, −ve } = 0.16

for column strip +ve = 0.22

−ve = 0.46

then M @ middle strip ± = $0.16 \times 1660 = 266$ kgm

M @ column strip $= +0.22 \times 1660 = 368$ kgm

$= -0.46 \times 1660 = 764$ kgm.

$\therefore \frac{M}{bd^2} = \frac{764 \times 100}{182 \times 12.5^2} = 2.686$

Hence Section is safe.

Reinforcement required

$$\text{Middle Strip} = \frac{266 \times 100}{0.92 \times 1900 (12.5 - 2.5 - 1.0)} = 1.69\ \text{Cm}^2$$

Col. Strip

$$\text{Top} = 1.69 \times \frac{0.46}{.16} = 4.86\ \text{Cm}^2$$

$$\text{Bott.} = 1.69 \times \frac{.22}{.16} = 2.32\ \text{Cm}^2$$

$$\text{minimum steel} = 0.8 \left(0.3 - \frac{2.5}{3.5} \times 0.1\right) = 0.238\%$$

For 18.2 Cm x 12.5 Cm Section $As_{min} = 5.415\ \text{Cm}^2$

Provide min steel = ⌀ 8 @ 17 Cm c/c alternate bar cranked both in column & middle strip. steel provided = 5.41 Cm².

Columns

$$\text{Reaction of Column} = 375 \times 3.64 \times 3.64 = 4968\ \text{kg}$$

$$\text{S.Wt} = 0.23 \times 0.23 \times 7.2 \times 2400 = 914\ \text{kg}$$

$$5882\ \text{kg}$$

$$l/r = \frac{7.2 \times 0.7}{0.23} = 22$$

$$\text{Reduction factor} = 1.5 - \frac{22}{30} = 1.5 - 0.74 = 0.76$$

$$\text{Actual Stress} = \frac{5882}{23 \times 23} = 11.3\ \text{kg/cm}^2$$

$$\text{Allowable Stress} = 0.76 \times 50 = 38\ \text{kg/cm}^2\ \text{ok}$$

Provide 0.8% steel

reinforcement = 4.24 Cm²

Provide 4 No 12 ⌀ with ⌀6 links @ 250 c/c.

Peripheral Wall $(1 : 1\frac{1}{2} : 3)$

The peripheral wall has been designed considering the wall to be fixed at base.

The wall section has variable profile with transitional stiffness changes. with this, an effective stiffness factor 'K' has been found and tension value calculated. K is a function of stiffness of K_1, K_2 & K_3 of

0.5H	37166 kg	24.78 cm	26.78 cm	30
0.6H	39266 "	26.17 "	26.78 "	30
0.7H	37944 "	25.30 "	26.78 "	30
0.8H	28820 "	19.22 "	25.44 "	30
0.9H	10842 "	7.23 "	17.40 "	38.6

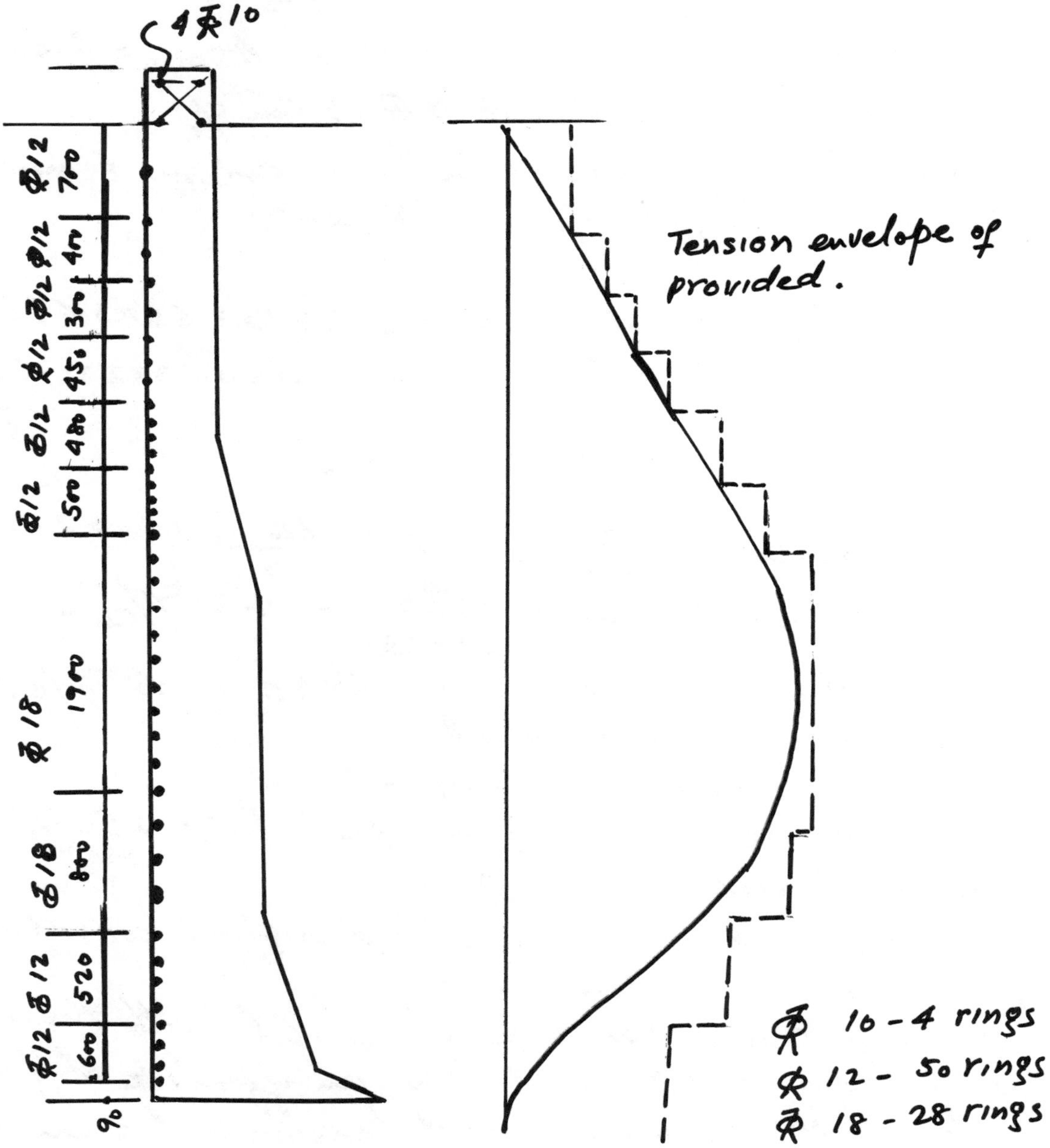

The momental effect has been computed from table 10 I.S. 3370- Part-IV - 1967

$$\frac{H^2}{Dt} = 7.2^2/20.2 \times 0.45 = 5.7$$

For 5.7, the moments are tabulated as under.

Location	M.Coefficient	Moment	Steel Req'd	Provided.
0.1H	0.00013	43	0.188 Cm^2	-
0.2H	0.00045	148	0.647 "	-
0.3H	0.00104	342	1.490 "	-
0.4H	0.00220	723	1.837 "	-
0.5H	0.00362	1190	2.568 "	-
0.6H	0.00499	1640	3.540 "	-
0.7H	0.00534	1755	3.781 "	-
0.8H	0.00287	943	2.0345 "	-
0.9H	-0.00461	-1514	3.180 "	-
0.97H	-0.01520	-4993	8.718 "	-
1.00H	-0.0.01975	-6488	-	-

$$A_{sr} = \frac{M \times 100}{0.92 \times 1500 (d-3.5)}$$

For positive moments and wall thickness greater than 22.5Cm, use 1900 Kg/cm^2 stress value.

Critical Section

20Cm thick wall ; $b = 100$ cm

$T = 23010$ Kg , $A_s = 15.34$ cm^2

$M = 342$ KgM

$t = 20$ cm

Due to moment water face is in Compression.

$A_c = 100 \times 20 + (13-1) \times 15.34 = 2184$ Cm^2

Tension direct $= \frac{23010}{2184.0} = 10.54$ $Kg/cm^2 < 12$ Kg/cm^2 ok.

30 Cm thick wall.

Maximum hoop tension. 39266 kg @ 0.6H

Moment = -1755 kgm ; Area of hoop steel = 26.80 Cm^2

t = 30 Cm ; $A_c = 30 \times 100 + 26.80 \times 12$

$= 3321.6$ □Cm.

Tensile stress $= \frac{39266}{3321.6} = 11.82$ kg/cm^2 < 12 kg/cm^2 ok

Moment effect without steel $= \frac{1755 \times 6}{(30)^2} = 11.7$ kg/cm^2

Moment causes compression on water face, hence ok

Minimum steel:-

Thickness — 20 Cm

$= 0.8\left(0.3 - \frac{10}{35} \times 0.1\right) = 0.216\%$

Area $= \frac{0.216 \times 20 \times 100}{100} = 4.32$ cm^2 or 2.16 cm^2 on each face.

Thickness — 30 Cm

$= 0.8\left(0.3 - \frac{20}{35} \times 0.1\right) = 0.194\%$

Area $= \frac{0.194}{100}(30)(100) = 5.82$

Thickness — 45 Cm

Area $= \frac{0.16}{100} \times 45 \times 100 = 7.2$ Cm^2

Reinforcement as required are marked in wall Section.

Tank floor slab:- The slab is designed as flat-slab with drop panels and Column heads by empirical methods. Dimension of Panel is shown in sketch.

DESIGN of INTERIOR PANEL - (A)

Assume slab thickness = 28 Cm

Drop thickness = 50 Cm.

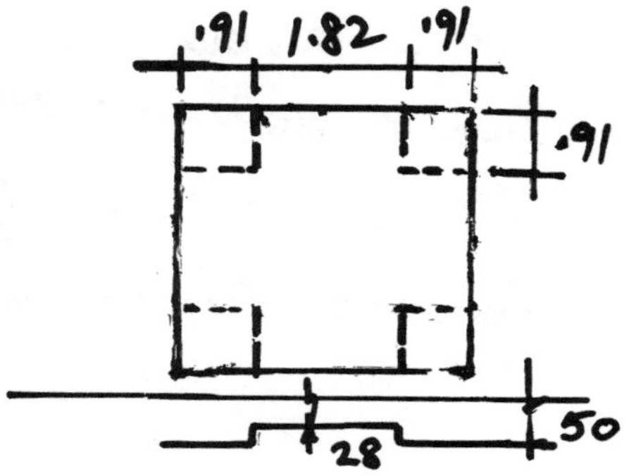

M''. Exterior $-ve\ M = \frac{1}{2} \times 0.45 \times 19074 \times \frac{0.745}{0.67} = 4772$ kgm

As the slab is resting on wall, the actual moment will be only $\frac{1}{2} = 4772 \times 0.5 = 2386$ kgM

$$A_t = \frac{2386 \times 100}{1500 \times 0.87 \times 45.5} = 4.00\ Cm^2$$

$$+ve\ M = \frac{1}{2} \times 0.25 \times 19074 \times \frac{0.745}{0.67} = 2651\ kgm$$

Since actual $+M = 1325$ kgM

$$A_t = \frac{1325 \times 100}{1900 \times 0.89 \times 45.5} = 1.736\ Cm^2$$

Middle strip width $= 2.68 - 0.67 - 0.745 = 1.265$

M' - Interior $-ve\ M = 0.15 \times 19074 = 2861$ kgM

$$A_t = \frac{2861 \times 100}{1500 \times 0.87 \times 23.5} = 9.33\ Cm^2$$

$M+ve = 0.13 \times 19074 = 3624$ kgM.

$$A_t = \frac{3624 \times 100}{1900 \times 0.89 \times 23.5} = 9.12\ Cm^2$$

Shorter span.

Take worst case

where span is 3.015.

B. width of Panel at right angles $= 4.44$M

$$M_{Total} = \frac{7704 \times 3.64}{10}\left(3.015 - \frac{2}{3} \times 0.9\right)^2 = 16355\ kgM$$

Half column strip

M' - interior $= \frac{1}{2} \times 0.5 \times 16355 = 4088$ kgM.

$$A_s = \frac{4088 \times 100}{1500 \times 0.87 \times 45.5} = 6.58\ Cm^2$$

$M+ve = \frac{1}{2} \times 0.25 \times 16355 = 2044$ kgm

$$A_s = \frac{2044 \times 100}{1900 \times 0.89 \times 23.5} = 5.14\ Cm^2$$

M' Exterior $-ve\ M = \frac{1}{2} \times 0.45 \times 16355 = 3680$ kgM.

Since the slab is directly resting on walls. The

Taking contribution of steel, the stress will be even lower.

Max -ve moment middle strip = 3887 kgm

Tensile stress in Concrete $= \dfrac{3887 \times 100 \times 6}{182 \times 28 \times 28}$

$= 16.34 \text{ kg/cm}^2$ ok.

Panel B.

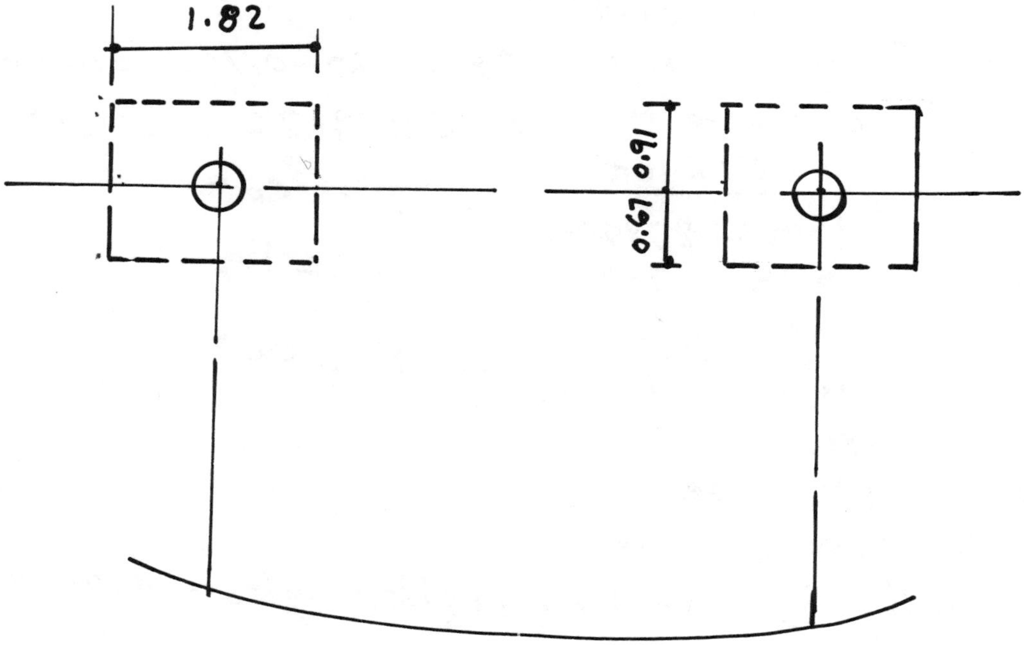

Longer span

Average width of Panel at right angles $= \dfrac{3.015 + 2.35}{2} = 2.68$ M

$M_{Total} = \dfrac{7704 \times 2.68}{10}\left(3.64 - \frac{2}{3} \times 0.90\right)^2 = 19074$ kgM

width of half column strip $= \dfrac{2.68}{4} = 0.67$ m.

M. Interior -ve M $= \frac{1}{2} \times 0.5 \times 19074 = 4768$ kgm.

$A_t = \dfrac{4768 \times 100}{1500 \times 0.87 \times 45.5} = 8.03 \text{ cm}^2$

$M_{+ve} = \frac{1}{2} \times 0.25 \times 19074 = 2384$ kgM.

$A_t = \dfrac{2384 \times 100}{1900 \times 0.89 \times 23.5} = 6.00 \text{ cm}^2$

MIDDLE STRIP

width of middle strip = 1.82 M

$-ve\ M = 0.15 \times 25915 = 3887\ kgm$

$-ve\ M = 3887\ kgm$

$$As\ -ve = \frac{3887 \times 100}{1500 \times 0.87 \times 2.35} = 12.67\ cm^2 \left(\begin{matrix}9-\Phi\ 12\\+6-\Phi\ 8\end{matrix}\right)$$

$$As\ +ve = \frac{3887 \times 100}{1900 \times 0.89 \times 23.5} = 9.8\ cm^2\ (9-\Phi\ 12)$$

$$\text{Min. steel in drop 0.91 m width} = \frac{0.8 \times 0.8 \times 50 \times 91}{100} = 7.28\ cm^2$$

Min. steel in 28 cm thick slab.

$$0.91\ m\ \text{width} = 5.06\ cm^2 = \frac{28 \times 91}{100} \times 0.8 \left(0.3 - \frac{18}{35} \times 0.1\right)$$

Check for shear.

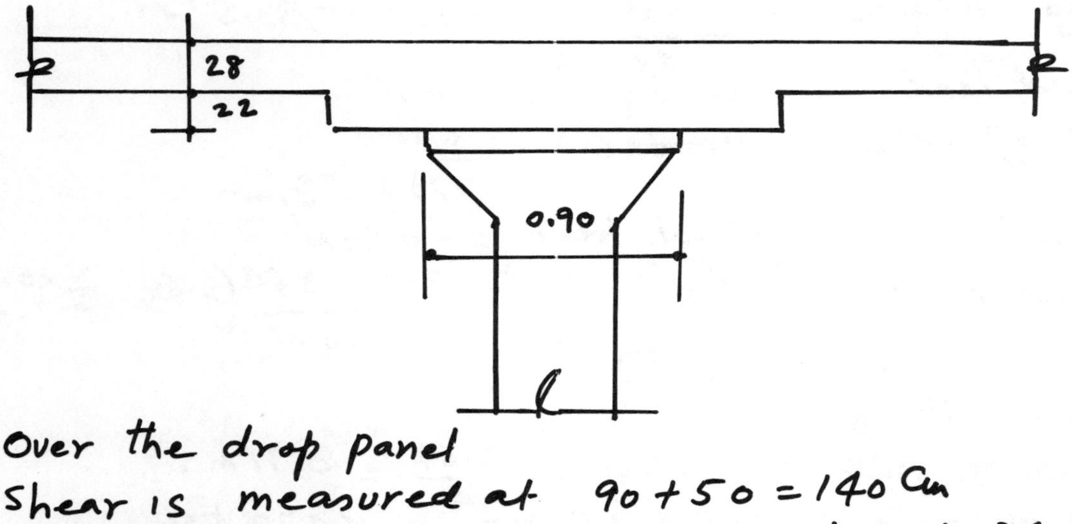

Over the drop panel

Shear is measured at 90 + 50 = 140 cm

Shear force :- $(3.64 \times 3.64 - 1.4 \times 1.4)\ 7704 = 86{,}978\ kgm$

$$\text{shear stress} = \frac{86978}{4 \times 140 \times 46 \times 0.9} = 3.75\ kg/cm^2$$

Check for no crack condition:-

Max. -ve M in column strip = 6478 kgm.

$$\text{Tensile stress in concrete} = \frac{6478 \times 100 \times 6}{91 \times 50 \times 50} = 17\ kg/cm$$ safe.

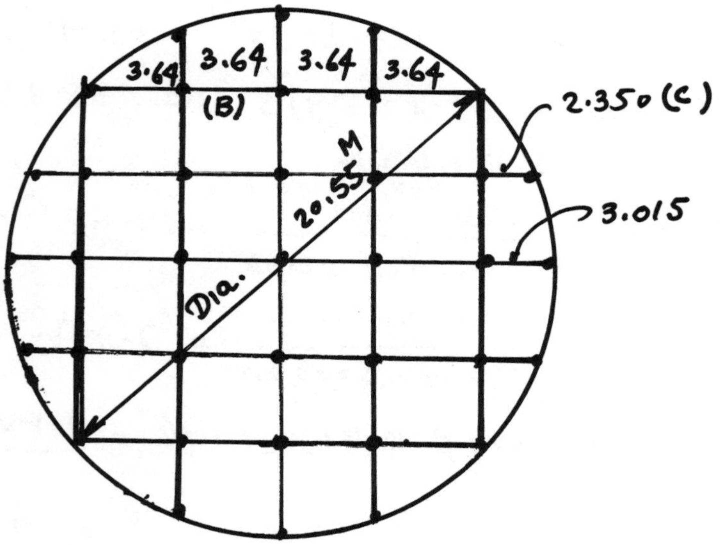

Avg thickness
is calculated as below:-

$3.64 \times 3.64 \times 0.28 = 3.7098$

$4 \times 0.91 \times 0.91 \times 0.22 = 0.7287$

4.4385

Avg Thickness $= \dfrac{4.4385}{3.64 \times 3.64} = 0.335$ or 33.5 Cm.

Dead Load $= 0.335 \times 2400 = 804$

WT. of water $= 1000 \times 6.9 = 6900$

7704 Kg/m²

Provide 'D' dia of Col. Head = 0.90 M.

Total $M = \dfrac{WL}{10}\left[L - \dfrac{2D}{3}\right]^2 = \dfrac{7704 \times 3.64}{10}\left(3.64 - \frac{2}{3} \times 0.9\right)^2$

$= 25915$ kgm.

Column Strip

width of half Col. strip $= \dfrac{3.64}{4} = 0.91$ m.

$-$ve $M = 0.5 \times 0.5 \times 25915 = 6478$ kgm.

Provide 500 mm thick drop panel

$As = \dfrac{6478 \times 100}{1500 \times 0.87 \times 45.5} = 10.9$ Cm² (8 ф - 12, 3 ф - 10)

$-$ve Moment $= 0.5 \times 0.2 \times 25915 = 2591.5$ kgm

$As = \dfrac{2591.5 \times 100}{1900 \times 0.89 \times 23.5} = 6.52$ Cm² (6 bars - 12 mm dia) actual exterior -ve Moments = 0.50 × 3680 = 1840 kgm

$$A_t = \frac{1840 \times 100}{1500 \times 0.87 \times 45.5} = 3.1 \text{ Cm}^2$$

Middle strip

M' - Interior -ve M = 0.15 × 16355 = 2453 kgm

$$M' \text{ +ve moment} = 2453 \times \frac{0.19}{0.15} = 3107 \text{ kgM}$$

$$A_t = \frac{3107 \times 100}{1900 \times 0.89 \times 23.5} = 7.82 \text{ Cm}^2$$

M" Exterior -ve M = 0.10 × 16355 = 1635 kgm.

Since slab is resting on wall, the actual exterior -ve Moment = 0.5 × 1635 = 817 kgM.

$$A_s = \frac{817 \times 100}{1500 \times 0.87 \times 45.5} = 1.35 \text{ Cm}^2$$

Panel C

The spans are smaller than the Panel 'B', however same design as per panel B may be adopted.

Design of columns

The load on various columns have been calculated after determination of load influence areas as marked.

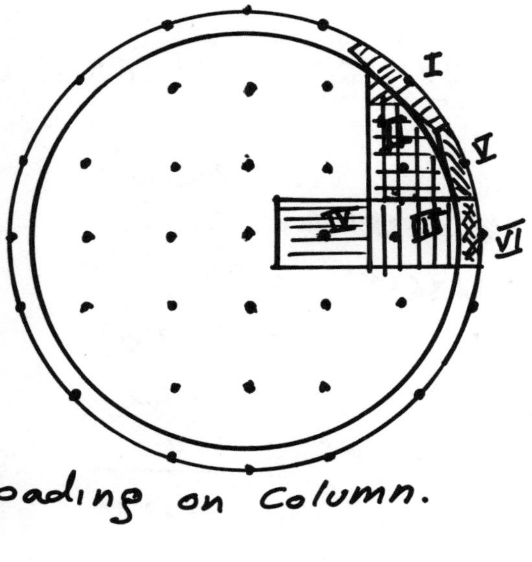

DETAILS OF Loading on Column.

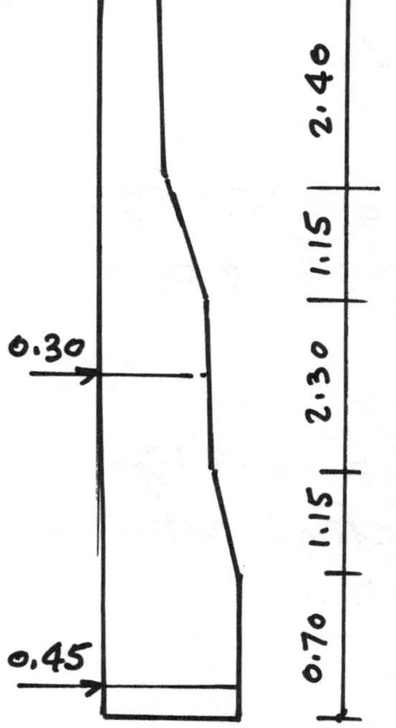

WALL Load $= 2.4 \times 0.20 = 0.48$
$= 1.15 \times 0.25 = 0.2875$
$= 2.30 \times 0.30 = 0.6900$
$= 1.15 \times 0.375 = 0.4310$
$= 0.70 \times 0.45 = 0.3150$

$2.2035\ M^3/M$

$2.2035 \times 2.4 = 5.288\ t/M.$

Calculation of Load on Group I

GROUP II

Roof Area $= \frac{3.64 \times 3.64}{2} = 6.63$

$= 6.63 + \frac{3.64}{2} \times \frac{1.4}{2} + \frac{3.62}{2} \times 1.4$

$= 10.452$

Roof Load $= 10.452 \times 0.375 = 3.9195$

Flat slab $= 10.452 \times 0.335 \times 2.4 = 8.403$
Water Load $= 10.452 \times 6.90 = 72.110$
Columns $= 0.783 \times 0.53 \times 0.53 \times 18.7 = 9.900$
Braces $= 3.700$
Wt. of Internal Columns $= 1.000$

Total :- 99.030 Tonne.

GROUP III

Roof area $= \frac{3.64 \times 3.64}{2} + 3.64 \times 1.5 = 6.6048 + 5.46$
$= 12.085$

$12.085 \times 0.375 = 4.53$
Flat slab $= 12.085 \times .335 \times 2.4 = 9.71$
Water Load $= 12.08 \times 6.9 = 83.35$
Columns $= 9.90$
Braces $= 3.70$
Wt of internal columns $= 1.00$

$= 112.19$ Tonnes.

Group IV

Roof area = 3.64 × 3.64 = 13.2496

Roof Load = 13.2496 × 0.375 = 4.968

FLAt slab = 13.2496 × 0.335 × 2.4 = 10.650

water Load = 13.2496 × 6.9 = 91.420

Columns = 0.785 × 0.53 × 0.53 × 18.7 × 2.4 = 9.900

Braces = 3(3.64 − 0.42) × 2 × 0.4 × 0.2 × 2.4 = 3.700

Wt of Internal Column = 1.300

121.640

Group V and VI

Roof area = 3.70 × 1.75 = 6.475 × 0.375 = 2.423

Balcony = 1 × 3.70 × 0.44 = 1.603

WALL Load = 3.7 × 5.288 = 19.568

Slab = 3.7 × 1.55 × 0.335 × 2.4 = 4.610

water Load = 3.7 × 1.55 × 6.9 = 39.570

Column = 0.785 × 0.42 × 0.42 × 18.7 × 2.4 = 2.500

76.500

Group I

Load on V & VI = 76.500

Extra roof and floor

$\frac{3.64}{2} \times \frac{3.64}{2} \times 0.6 \times \left[0.375 \times 6.9 + 0.364\right] = 16.000$

92.500 Tonnes.

Loads

I = 92.50 Tonne

II = 99.03 "

III = 112.19 "

IV = 121.64 "

V = 76.50 "

Determination of "As" in columns, for Direct Load only.

Group	DIA	Load	Load to be taken by Conc.	Load to be taken by STEEL	Area of Steel %	
I	42 Cm	92.5	79.60	12.9	7.37 Cm^2	
II	53 Cm	99.03	126.80	NIL	Nominal	
III	53 Cm	112.19	126.80	NIL	Nominal	
IV	53 Cm	121.64	126.80	NIL	Nominal	
V & VI	42 Cm	76.50	79.6	NIL	Nominal	

Load taken by Concrete Mix M200 ($1 : 1\frac{1}{2} : 3$)

6 months age factor (1.15)

i) 53 Cm dia column.

$$= \frac{\pi}{4} \times 53 \times 53 \times 50 \times 1.15 = 126.8 \text{ TONNES}$$

ii) 42 Cm dia column:-

$$= \frac{\pi}{4} \times 42 \times 42 \times 50 \times 1.15 = 79.60 \text{ TONNES}$$

SIESMIC COEFFICIENT. = 0.03

Load of tank with water = 3050.00 TONNES

Load of staging = 425.00 TONNES.

Moment at FOUNDATION LEVEL = $0.03 \times 3050 [18 + 1.15 + 3.5] + 0.03 \times 425 \times [9 + 1.15]$ = 2202 Tonnes M.

Z about XX of Columns.

$2 \times 1 \times 10.295^2$ = 211.974

$2 \times 2 \times 9.63^2$ = 370.947

$2 \times 5 \times 7.28^2$ = 529.958

$2 \times 7 \quad \times 3.64^2 \quad = 183.494$

$1 \times 7 \quad \times 0.00^2 \quad = 0.000$

1298.399 Say 1299

Forces :- $\frac{M}{I} \times Y$

For different Columns

I = 12.34 Tonnes

II = 12.34 "

III = 12.34 "

IV = 6.17 "

V = 16.32 Tonnes

VI = 17.45 Tonnes

Total Horizontal force $0.03 \times 34.75 = 104.25$ Tonnes.

Assume the end columns take ½ the shear taken by Internal columns.

$$= \frac{104.25}{3+5+6+6+5+3} = 3.066 \text{ Tonnes m}.$$

Bending moment in Internal Columns.

$$= 3.066 \left[\frac{4.75 - 0.40}{2}\right] = 6.67 \text{ Tonnes M}.$$

Bending moment in Internal Brace = 6.67 Tonnes M.

Bending moment in end Column = 3.33 " "

Bending moment in End Brace = 6.67 " "

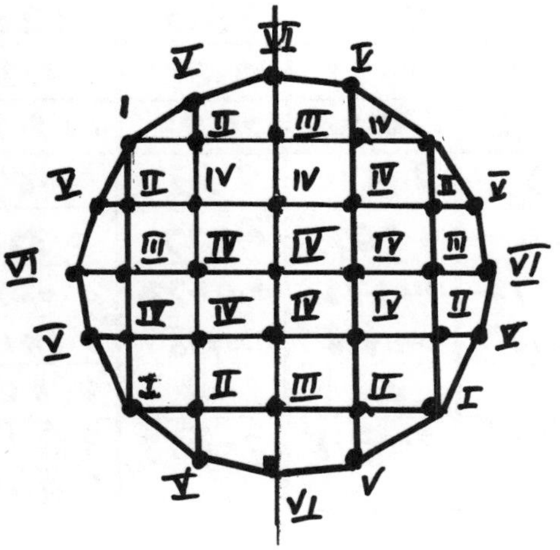

Considering the loading Pattern, Loads on various groups are determined as under:-

I = 92.5×4 = 370.00

II = 99.03×8 = 792.24

III = 112.19×4 = 448.76

IV = 121.64×9 = 1094.76

VI+V = 76.5×12 = 918.00

3603.76. > Total Load safe.

FINAL LOAD TABLE.

Group	LOAD	SEISMIC	TOTAL	1.4
I	92.50	12.34	104.84	146.77
II	99.03	12.34	111.37	155.92
III	112.19	12.34	124.53	174.34
IV	121.64	6.17	127.81	178.93
V	76.50	16.32	92.82	129.94
VI	76.50	17.45	93.95	131.53

Design of columns for seismic loads

Group	I	II	III	IV	V	VI	
Nos	4	8	4	9	8	4	
D	420	530	530	530	420	420	
D_1	320	430	430	430	320	320	
D_1/D	0.76	0.81	0.81	0.81	0.76	0.76	
1.4 Pu	146.77	155.92	174.34	178.93	129.94	131.53	
1.4 Mu	4.67	9.33	9.33	9.33	4.67	4.67	
$\frac{1.4P_u}{1.15\sigma_{cm}D^2}$	0.361	0.241	0.269	0.277	0.32	0.325	
$\frac{1.4M_u}{1.15\sigma_{cm}D^3}$	0.0274	0.0272	0.0272	0.0272	0.0274	0.0274	
$V/1.15\sigma_{cu}$	0.38×10^{-4}	0.0×10^{-4}	0.0×10^{-4}	0.0×10^{-4}	0.1×10^{-4}	0.1×10^{-4}	
As	12.0 cm^2	—	—	—	3.18 cm^2	3.18 cm^2	
	4-Φ18	7-Φ18	7-Φ18	7-Φ18	4Φ18	4Φ18	
	+2-Φ12				2Φ12	2Φ12	

Design of Brace:-

It will be seen that criteria for design of braces shall be seismic condition:

Max. moment (Ultimate) = 9.33 Tonnes

Shear force in Typical span = $\frac{9.33 \times 2}{3.64}$ = 5.12 Tonnes.

Assume section 400 x 200

Moment at the face of the Column = $\frac{9.33 \times [3.64 - 0.42]}{3.64}$

= 8.25 Tonnes M.

distance between tension and compression steel.

40 - 2 x 2.5 - 2 x 2 = 31, $A_s = \frac{825000}{31 \times 4250}$ = 6.26 cm^2

∴ Provide extra at top and bottom continueous.

Φ 20 + Φ 12 at top and bottom extra to be provided then to be curtailed @ 1.25 M from center of support.

Ultimate shear stress = $\frac{5120}{20 \times 31}$ = 8.25 kg/cm^2

Permissable = 2.5 x 7 = 17.5 kg/cm^2 Hence safe.

Provide φ 6 @ 300 c/c.

Design of foundation:-

Group I

'P' Load := 92.50 Tonn

'P_s' = 12.34 Tonne

'M' = 3.34 Tonn

Provide 4 No. 30 cm dia double reamed pile, 4.8 M long.
Each with load carrying capacity of 27 Tonne.

Self Wt. = 4 Tonne

Load per pile = $\frac{96.5}{4}$ = 24.12 Tonnes.

Under earthquake condition.

$\frac{92.5 + 4 + 12.34}{4} + \frac{3.34}{2 \times 1.13}$ = 27.21 ± 1.47

i.e. 28.68 Tonne & 25.74 Tonne.

Non seismic Governs design. shear at 30 Cm away from face of column.

$$= \frac{2 \times 92.5}{4} \times \frac{22.5}{30} = 31.60 \text{ Tonnes.}$$

Shear stress

$$= \frac{31.60 \times 1000}{163 \times 54 \times 0.9} = 3.99 \text{ kg/cm}^2$$

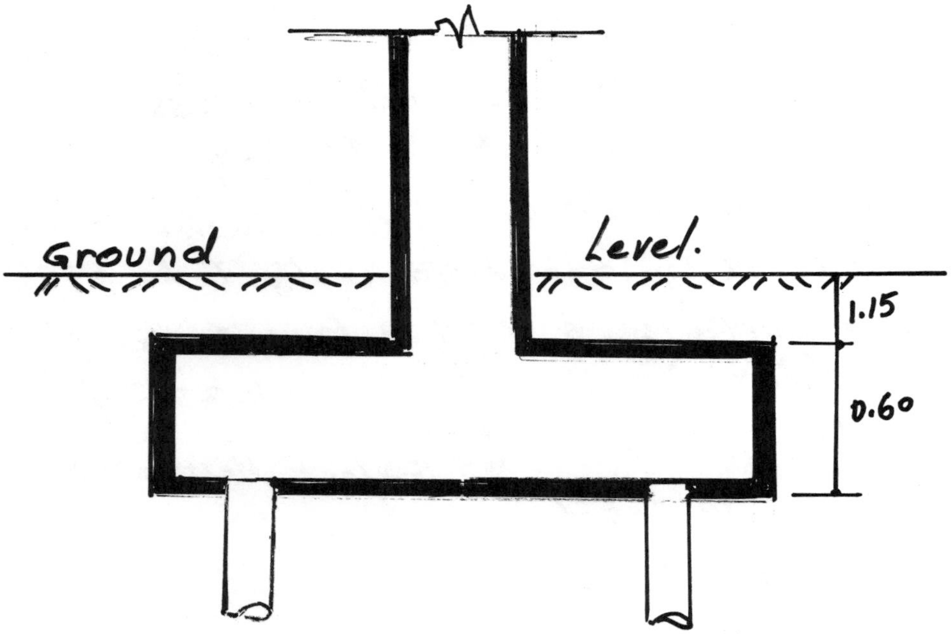

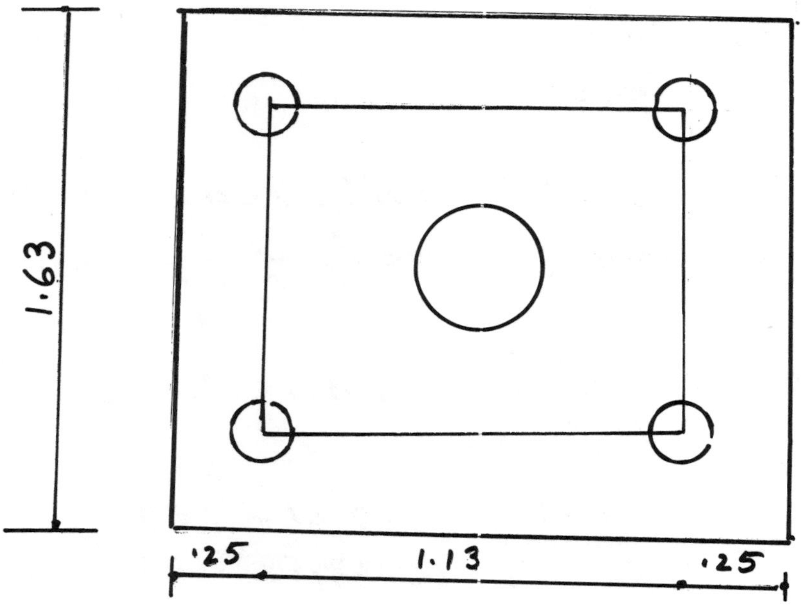

Moment at face of column $= \frac{2 \times 92.5 \times 35.5 \times 1000}{4}$

$= 16{,}41{,}875$ Kgm Cm

$$A_s = \frac{1641875}{4250 \times 0.9 \times 54} = 7.94 \text{ Cm}^2$$

$$\Sigma_0 = \frac{2 \times 92.5 \times 1000}{4 \times 14 \times 54 \times 0.9} = 67.9 \text{ Cm}$$

Provide - 23 No Φ10 Bars on either side.

Group II

$P = 99.03$ Tonnes

$P_s = 12.34$ Tonnes

$M_s = 6.66$ Tonnes

} Same as group I. Provide 23 No Φ10 Bars on either side.

Similarly for Group III & Group IV, V & VI can be handled & found 29-Φ10; 29-Φ10 & 18-Φ10, 18-Φ10 on each side of column needed.

Design of Balcony

Assume thickness 10 Cm

D.L $= 2400 \times 0.1 = 240$ kg/m

LL $= 150$ kg/m

Total 390 kg/m

$$B.M = 390 \times \frac{9 \times 9}{2} = 15795 \text{ kg cm.}$$

$$d = \sqrt{\frac{15795}{8.7 \times 100}} = 4.26 \text{ Cm}$$

used 10 Cm, $A_s = \frac{15795}{2300 \times 0.87 \times 7.5} = 1.05$

Provide Φ10 @ 25 cm c/c radially at top and 4-Φ10 ring at top to tie the radial bars.

Design of Stair case.

Provide tread of 250 mm & rise of 200 mm.

distance between c/c of Col. C & D = 4.34 m

" " " " " D & E = 3.70 m.

Size of Column = 42 Cm.

Stair flight CD = 4.34 − 0.42 = 3.92 M

" " DE = 3.70 − 0.42 = 3.28 M

Provide 16 treads of 245 mm each & 17 riser of 200 mm. Also 13 treads of 245 mm and 14 riser in D.E

Assum thickness 15 Cm.

Design Longer span only.

D.L of water = $0.15 \times 2400 \times 0.90 \times \left[3.42^2 + 3.4^2\right]^{1/2}$

= 1682 kgm.

D.L of steps = $\frac{16}{2} \times 0.245 \times 0.20 \times 0.9 \times 2400$ = 847 kg

L.L of Staircase = $150 \times 0.9 \times 3.92$ = 529 kg

3058 kg

Max. moment @ Support = $\frac{3058 \times \left[3.42 + .15\right] \times 100}{10}$

= 124450 kgCm.

$d = \sqrt{\frac{1.85 \times 124450}{0.185 \times 150 \times 90}} = 9.6$ Cm

$Ast = \frac{1.85 \times 124450}{4250 \times 0.87 \times 12} = 5.19$ Cm² at Support

At mid span Since M is $\frac{WL}{16}$ so area of steel

$= \frac{5.19 \times 10}{16} = 3.25$ Cm²

Provide 4 bars of Φ 12 at bottom throughout and 6 bars cut pieces at top of Φ 12 near support.

Average thickness = $15 + \frac{20}{2} = 25$ Cm.

Min. Steel per step = $0.0012 \times 100 \times 0.25 = 3.00$ Cm²

Provide Φ 8 @ 150 c/c both at top & bottom for each step take together.

Design of landing

Take thickness of landing $= 25$ Cm

D.L. of Landing $= 0.25 \times 2400 \left[\frac{0.42+0.90}{2}\right] \times 1.05$

$= 416$ kg

L.L on Landing $= 150 \times \left[\frac{0.42+0.90}{2}\right] \times 1.05$

$= 104$ kg

Load from staires $= 3058$ kg

Total 3578 kgm

$$B.M = 3578 \times \frac{1.05}{2} \times 100 = 187845 \text{ kg Cm}$$

$$d = \sqrt{\frac{187845 \times 1.85}{0.185 \times 150 \times 42}} = 17.26 \text{ Cm.}$$

$$A_s = \frac{1.85 \times 187845}{4250 \times .87 \times 22} = 4.27 \text{ Cm}^2$$

Min. steel for 25 Cm thick $= 0.0012 \times 25 \times 1.05$

$= 3.15 \text{ Cm}^2$

Provide 5 ϕ 12 @ top

2 ϕ 10 @ bottom.

EXAMPLE 9-02

Given:- Design an elevated Intze tank of 500,000 gallons for Lasdelicias, South America. Pedestal height is limited to 14 meter.

Specifications:-

$E_s = 2100000 \text{ k/cm}^2$

$f_s = 980 \text{ k/cm}^2$ (Ring steel)

$f'_c = 210 \text{ k/cm}^2 = 3000 \text{ \#/in}^2$

$f_c = 0.1 f'_c = 21 \text{ k/cm}^2$ (Tension)

$= 300 \text{ \#/□''}$

$\eta = 10$

shrinkage coefficient $C = 0.003$

$f_s = 1260 \text{ k/cm}^2 = 18000$ Psi.

Volume = 500,000 gals = ± 1700 M3

R = 8.00 Mts

h = 8.30 Mts.

r_i = $\frac{8.00}{\sqrt{2}}$ = 5.65 mts.

f = 8.00 − 5.65 = 2.35 mts

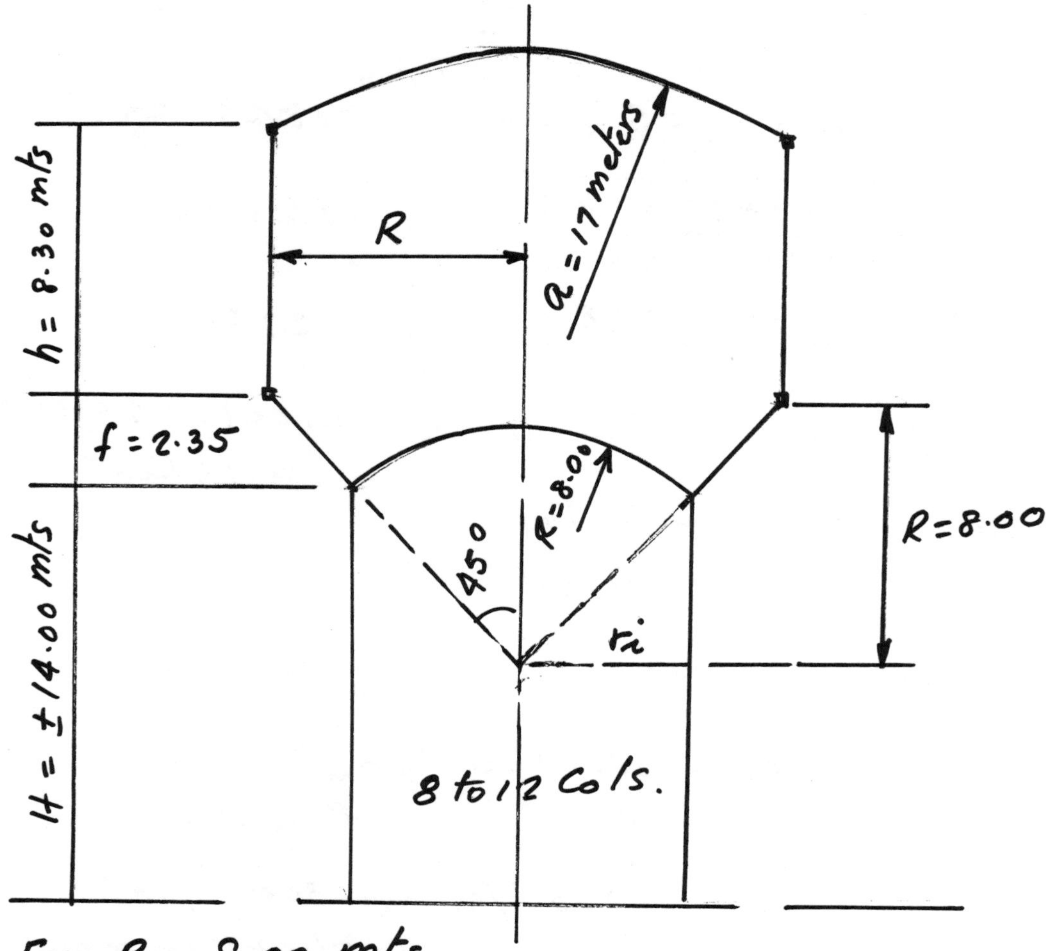

For R = 8.00 mts

$r_i = \frac{8}{\sqrt{2}} = 5.65$ m.

$V = \pi R^2 (h + 0.138R)$

$\therefore h = \frac{V}{\pi R^2} - 0.138R = 9.40 - 0.138 \times 8 = 8.3$ mts

Cover Dome

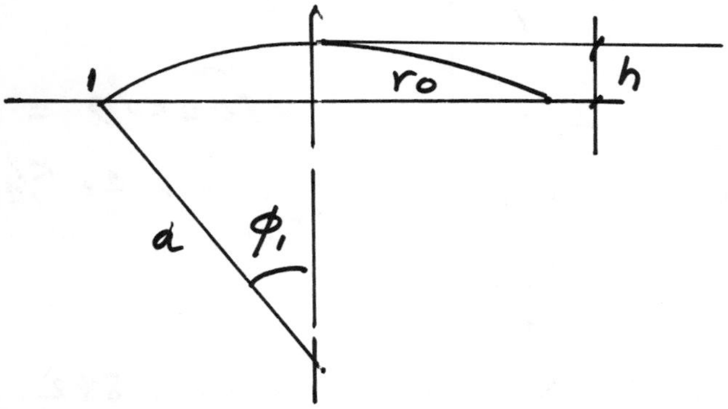

$\frac{h}{r_o} = \frac{1}{4}$, $h = \frac{8.00}{4.00} = 2.00$

Dome radius

$a = \frac{r_o^2 + h^2}{2h} = \frac{8^2 + 2^2}{2\times 2} = 17$ meter

$\sin\phi_1 = \frac{r_o}{a} = \frac{8}{17} = 0.4713$ or 0.49 radians

$\phi_1 = 28^\circ\text{-}7'$; $\sin^2\phi_1 = 0.221$

$\cos\phi_1 = 0.88199$

Try 4" thickness

L. Load = $150\ K/M^2$

D. Load = $250\ K/M^2$

$\omega = 400\ K/M^2$

@ 1

W(total load around 1) = Area × ω = $2\pi a^2(\cos\phi_0 - \cos\phi_1) \times \omega$

$= 6.28 \times 17^2(1.0 - 0.882)400$

$= 86000$ kgm.

$T_1 = \frac{W}{2\pi a \sin^2\phi_1} = \frac{86000}{2\pi \times 17 \times 0.221} = 3650\ K/Mt.$

$t_1 = \frac{3650}{100 \times 10} = 3.65\ K/cm^2$ compression @ point 1 meridianal

Hoop force

$H = -T + [\omega + \omega'(\phi_1 - \phi_0)]\, a_1 \cos\phi_1$

$H = -T + \omega\, a \cos\phi_1$ since $\omega' = 0$

$H = 3650 - 400 \times 0.7 \times 0.882 = -2350\ K/Mt.$

$h = -2.35\ K/cm^2$ compression.

@ crown

$T_0 = H_0 = \frac{1}{2} wa = \frac{1}{2} \times 400 \times 17 = -3400\ K/Mt$

$t_0 = h_0 = -3400/100 \times 1.0 = -3.40\ K/cm^2$ compression

$e = 10$ Cms ok

Ring tension @ base

$S_1 = \dfrac{W \cos\phi_1}{2\pi \sin\phi_1} = \dfrac{86000 \times 0.882}{2\pi \times 0.471} = 28500$ Kgms.

Ring steel

$As = \dfrac{28500}{100 \times 10} = 28.5\ Cm^2\ 8\ \phi\ 7/8''$

stresses at a point 1 meter above 1.

$\frac{h}{2} = 1.0$ mt, $r_0 = 5.75$ mts

$r_0^2 = a^2 - (a - \frac{h}{2})^2 = 289 - 256 = 33$

$\sin\phi_2 = \dfrac{5.75}{17} = 0.338 \quad \phi_2 = 19^\circ\text{-}46'$

$\cos\phi_2 = 0.741, \ \sin^2\phi_2 = 0.115$

$W = 2\pi \times 289 (1.000 - 0.941) \times 400 = 42{,}800$ Kg

$T_2 = \dfrac{42800}{6.28 \times 17 \times 0.115} = 3480\ K/mt$

$t_2 = \dfrac{3480}{100 \times 10} = 3.48\ K/cm^2$ Compression.

$H_2 = 3480 - (400 \times 17 \times 0.941) = 2920\ K/mt$

$h_2 = 2.92\ K/cm^2$ compression

Dome reinforcement.

$As = 0.0025 \times 100 \times 10 = 2.5\ Cm^2 - 3/8''\phi$ @ 25 Cm.

Dome weight.

Dome area $= 2\pi a^2 (\cos\phi_2 - \cos\phi_1) = 214\ M^2$

Dome Vol. $= 214 \times 0.10 = 21.4\ m^3$

Vol. Base beam:-

$V_{bb} = 16.35\pi \times 0.35 \times 0.45 = 8.1\ M3$

$29.5\ M3$

Concrete Live load $= 214 \times 150$ 32,000 kgs

Wt $= 29.5 \times 2500$ 74,000 "

106,000 kgs.

Weight per linear meter $= \dfrac{106,000}{16.35\pi} = 2070\ K/M'$.

Cylindrical

$f_s = 1000\ K/cm^2$, $f_c = 17.5\ K/cm^2 = 250$ psi

Tension at 0.7H

$0.7H = 0.7 \times 8.30 = 5.81$ mts $= H_1$

$T = pr = pD/2 = wH_1 D/2$

$= 1000 \times 5.81 \times 16/2 = 46480\ kgs/M = 31200\ \#/'$

$t = \dfrac{CE_s + f_s - nf_c}{12 f_c f_s} \times T = \dfrac{0.0002 \times 30 \times 10^6 + 14000 - 12 \times 250}{12 \times 250 \times 14000} \times 31200$

$= 12.5"$ use a total e of 14"

Note:- $C = 0.0002$ to be check for Blquilla's temp fluctuate between 18^{oC} to 40^{oC}.

$H^2/Dt = \dfrac{8.30^2}{16 \times .35} = 12.3$

Fixed base

Point	.0H	0.1H	0.2H	0.3H	0.4H	0.5H	0.6H	0.7H	0.8H	0.9H
Coefficient	-0.005	.097	.202	.312	.429	.543	.628	.633	.494	.211
T	-330	6460	13470	20700	28400	36000	41600	42000	32250	14000

Hinged base

Coefficient	-.002	.007	.197	.302	.417	.541	.664	.750	.720	.477
T	-135	6460	13200	20000	27800	36000	44000	49800	47700	31700

$T = \text{Coeff} \times wH = C \times 1000 \times 8.30 \times 8 = 66400\ C$

for sliding base

$T = \frac{1}{2} wHD = \frac{1}{2} \times 1000 \times 2.30 \times 16 = 66500$ kgs/m

from 1.0H to 0.6H use T = 49000 kgs.

$As = 49000/1000 = 49 \text{ Cm}^2 = 1'' @ 10$ Cm

from 0.6H to 0.4H use T = 44000 kgs

$As = 44000/1000 = 44 \text{ Cm}^2$, $1'' @ 11\frac{1}{2}$ cms.

From 0.4H to 0.2H use T = 28400 kgs

$AS = 28.4 \text{ Cm}^2$ $1'' @ 17$ Cms.

Shear at base table XVI Coeff. = 0.145

$V = 0.145 wH^2 = 0.145 \times 1000 \times 8.30^2$

$= 10{,}000$ kgs/m.

$v = \frac{10000}{100 \times 0.86 \times 32} = 3.5 \text{ K/cm}^2$ ok.

Moments at wall.

$M = \text{coefficient} \times wH^3 - c \times 1000 \times 8.3^3$

$= 575000\, c$ (K-m/mt).

Fixed base

Point	0.1H	0.2H	0.3H	0.4H	0.5H	0.6H	0.7H	0.8H	0.9H	1.0H
Coeff	0	-.0001	.0001	.0002	.0003	.0013	.0023	.0026	-.0005	-.0104
M	0	-57.5	57.5	115	173	748	1323	1496	-288	-5980

M(+) Tension in the outside

Interior force :- $f_s = 8000$ Psi $= 1260 \text{ K/cm}^2$

$As = \frac{M}{1260 \times .88 \times 32} = \frac{M}{11.3d}$

$= \frac{5980}{11.3 \times 32} = 16.6 \text{ Cm}^2$ $\frac{5}{8}''\phi @ 12$ Cm c/c

follow $\frac{1}{2}'' @ 48$ Cm to the tip.

Exterior face

$A_s = \frac{1496}{11.3 \times 32} = 4.14\ cm^2$ use $\frac{1}{2}''$ @ 20 cm c/c

Horizontal steel inside face $\frac{1}{2}''$ @ 50 cm c/c

Length of wall :- $16.35\pi = 51.50$ M/

Area :- $51.50 \times 8.30 = 428\ M^2$

Volume :- $428 \times 0.35 = 150\ M^3$

Wt. total = $150 \times 2500 = 37500$ kgs

WT/Lin. mt = $\frac{37500}{51.50} = 7250$ kg/Mt.

Bottom hopper design.

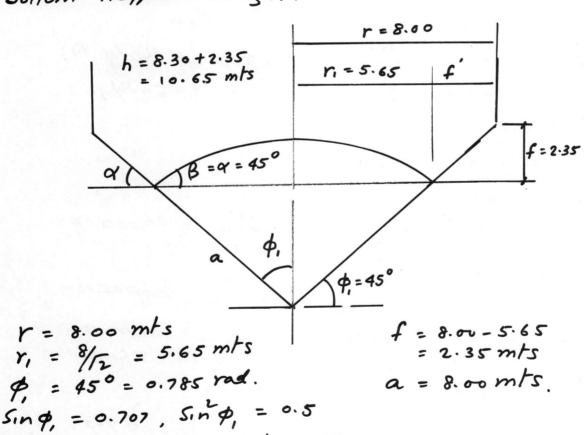

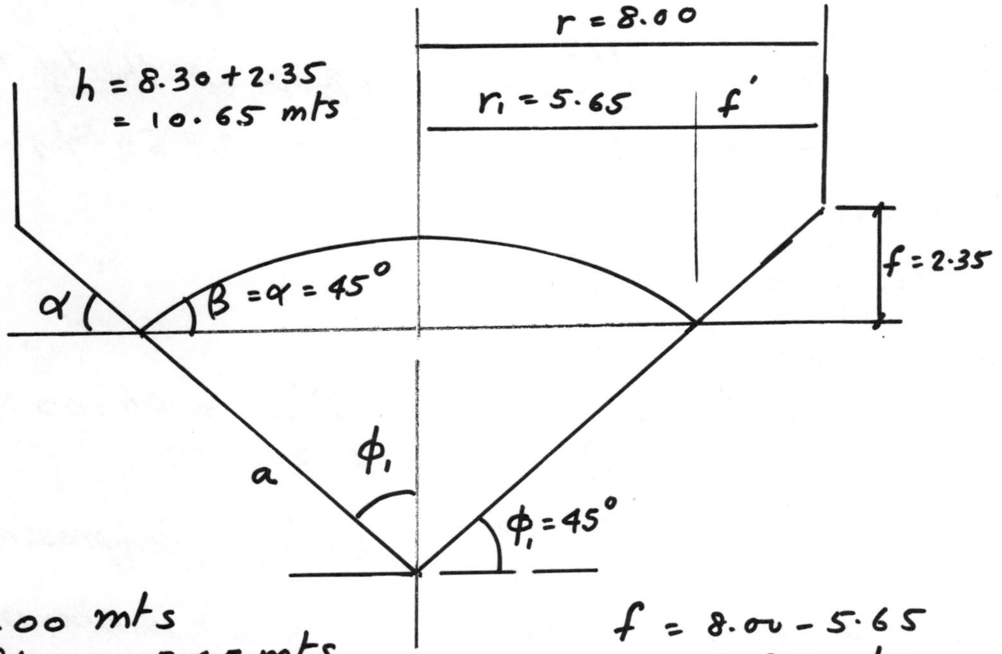

$r = 8.00$ mts

$r_1 = 8/\sqrt{2} = 5.65$ mts

$\phi_1 = 45^\circ = 0.785$ rad.

$\sin\phi_1 = 0.707$, $\sin^2\phi_1 = 0.5$

$f = 8.00 - 5.65$
$= 2.35$ mts

$a = 8.00$ mts.

Water weight on spherical dome:-

$$W_D = \pi w\left[r_1^2 h - f^2\left(a - f/a\right)\right]$$

$$= 1000 \times \pi\left[5.65^2 \times 10.65 - 2.35^2\left(8.00 - \frac{2.35}{8.00}\right)\right]$$

$W_D = 925{,}000$ kgs.

water wt on conical dome = 925000 kgs.

Dead load of spherical dome for e = 25 Cm, $w = 600\ K/M^2$

$W_L = 2\pi a^2 (\cos\phi_0 - \cos\phi_1)\, w$

$= 2\pi \times 64\ (1.000 - 0.707) \times 600 = 70000$ kgs

$W_{total} = W_D + W_L = 925000 + 70000 = 995{,}000$ kg

Uniform load on sph. dome:-

$70000 + \pi r_1^2 h p = 70000 + \pi \times 32 \times 8.30 \times 1000$

$= 905000$ kg

Area sph. dome

$2\pi a^2 (\cos\phi_0 - \cos\phi_1) = 6.28 \times 8^2 \times 0.293 = 118\ M^2$

$w = \dfrac{905000}{118} = 7700\ K/M^2$

Variable load increases from zero at the top to:-

$1.00 \times 1.00 \times 2.35 \times 1000 = 2350\ K/M^2$

Increase per radian

$\dfrac{2350}{0.785} = 3000\ K/M^2$

Stresses at bases:-

$T = \dfrac{W}{2\pi a \sin^2\phi} = \dfrac{995000}{6.28 \times 8 \times 0.5} = 40{,}000$ kgs

For e = 20 Cms

$t = 40000/20 \times 100 = 20\ K/cm^2$ compression

$A_s = 0.0025 \times 100 \times 20 = 5\ Cm^2$ minimum

$\frac{1}{2}$"@ 25 Cms

$H = T - [w + w'\phi_1] \cos\phi_1\, a$

$= 40000 - (7700 + 3000 \times 0.785)\, 8.0 \times 0.707$

$= -16500$ kgs.

$h = 16500/100 \times 20 = 8.3\ K/Cm^2$ Compression.

Stresses at top

$T_o = H_o = \frac{1}{2}\, w a = \frac{1}{2} \times 7700 \times 8 = 30800$ kgs

$t_o = h_o = \dfrac{30800}{100 \times 20} = 15.4$ K/cm^2 Comp

Stresses in conical dome:-

Taking load as uniform

Total load $= P_{water} + P_{DL} + P_{wall} + P_{cover}$

$= 925000 + 70000 + 375000 + 106000$

$= 1,476,000$ kg

Surface of conical dome

$\pi/\cos\phi\,(r_o^2 - r_i^2) = \pi(64-32)/0.707 = 142\ M^2$

Uniform load $w = \dfrac{1476000}{142} = 10400$ K/M^2

$p_n = w\cos\phi = 10400 \times 0.707 = 7350$ K/M^2

$T = \dfrac{W}{2\pi r_i^2 \sin\phi} = \dfrac{1476000}{6.28 \times 5.65 \times 0.707} = 59,000$ kgs

using $e = 35$ cms

$t = \dfrac{59000}{100 \times 35} = 17$ K/cm^2 comp.

$N = a\,p_n = 8 \times 7350 = 59000$ kgs

$n = 59000/35 \times 100 = 17$ K/cm^2 $5/8''\phi$ @ 22 cm c/c

$T = \dfrac{W}{2\pi \operatorname{tg}\phi} = \dfrac{1476000}{6.28} = 235,000$ kg (Total) comp.

For the sph. dome $T = -995000/6.28 = 158,000$ kgs tension.

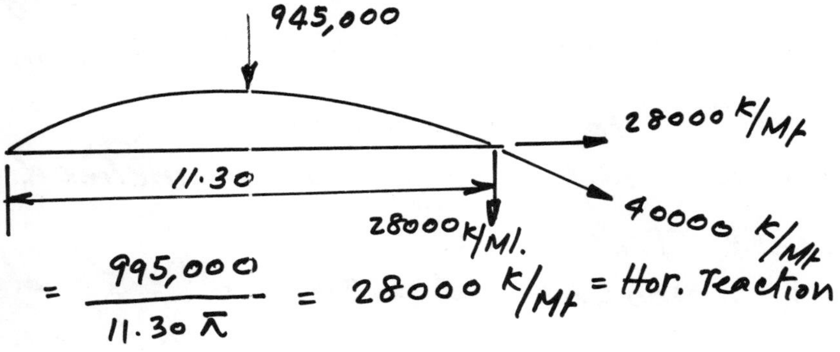

Vertical reaction $= \dfrac{995,000}{11.30\,\pi} = 28000$ K/Mt = Hor. reaction

Radial reinforcement

$A_S = 28000/1260 = 22.2\ Cm^2$

$\frac{3}{4}$" @ 13 Cms radial

$\frac{1}{2}$ @ 25 Cms Circumferential

$e = 20$ Cms.

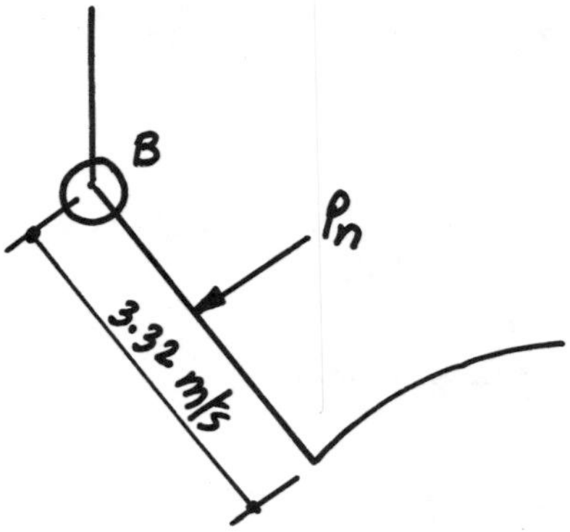

$P_n = 7350\ K/M^2$

$l = 2.35/0.707 = 3.32$ mts

$M(+) = 7350 \times \frac{3.32^2}{10} = 8200$ KM

$M(-) = 7350 \times \frac{3.32^2}{8} = 10,200$ KM

$d = \sqrt{\frac{10200}{12}} = 30$ Cms

$h = 35$ Cm

$d = 32$ Cm.

$As(+) = 8200/11.3 \times 3^2 = 22.7\ Cm^2/Mt$ $\frac{7}{8}$" @ 17 or $\frac{3}{4}$" @ 12 Cm

$As(-) = 10200/11.3 \times 3^2 = 28.0\ Cm^2/Mt$ $\frac{7}{8}$" @ 14 Cms c/c

Forces on (B)

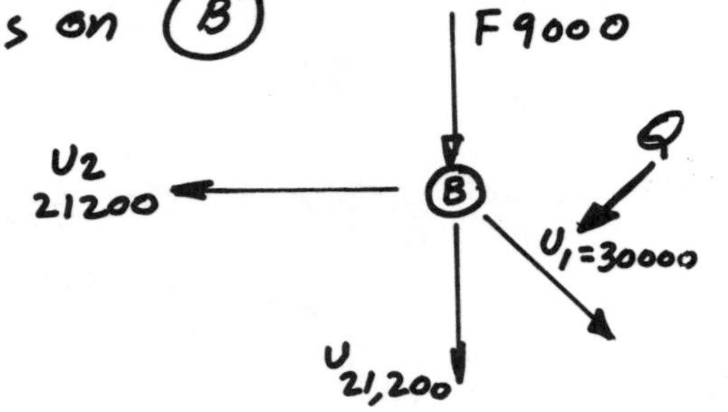

$Q = P_n l$

$= 7350 \times 3.32 = 24400\ K/Mt.$

$F = P_{cover} + P_{wall}$

$= 1720 + 7250 = 9000\ K/Mt$

$U_1 = U/\cos\phi = \frac{21200}{0.707} = 30000\ K/M$

$U_2 = U = 21200\ K/Mt.$

Total hoop $= 21200 \times 8 = 169,600$ kgs.

Circumferential Steel $A_S = 169600/1000 = 169.6\ Cm^2$

34 ϕ 1"

10 - 1" in the beam

and 1" ϕ @ 12 Cms c/c in inclined slab.

Check stresses:-

$b = 100$ Cms ; $d = 30$, $d' = 5$, $d = 10$ Cms

$A_S = 23\ Cm^2$; $A_S' = 28\ Cm^2$; $M = 10$ T-M, $N = 30$ T.

$e = \frac{10^7 M}{30 cm} + 10 = 44$ cm ; $e/d = \frac{44}{30} = 1.47$

$J = 0.87$

Table 10 ACI handbook $i = 2.43$

$m = 12 \times 23 \times 2.43/3000 + 23 \times 28/3000$

$= 0.438$

$q = 0.224 + 0.214 \times 5/30 = 0.260$

Table 11 $K = 0.40$, $\frac{1/k\,(2n-1)\,A_s'}{bd} = \frac{0.214}{0.400} = 0.535$

$\frac{1}{k}\frac{d'}{d} = 0.415$, table 12 $\therefore Z = 0.37$

Table 13: $J = 0.85$, Table 10 $= \frac{l}{d} = 1.47$, $J = 0.85$

$\therefore i = 2.35$

$f_s = \frac{N}{J A_s i} = \frac{3000}{0.85 \times 23 \times 2.35} = 650$ K/cm²

$f_c = \frac{f_s}{n} \times \frac{K}{1-K} = \frac{650}{12} \times \frac{0.4}{0.6} = 36$ K/cm²

$f_s' = 2 f_s \times \frac{K - \frac{d'}{d}}{1-K} = 1{,}300 \times \frac{0.235}{0.600} = 510$ K/cm²

section ok

Circular Beam

Vertical loads

	Cover Dome	106 000 kgs
	Wall	375,000 kgs
	Bott + water 2×995	1990,000 kgs
		2,471,000 kgs

Diameter = 11.30 m, Radius = 5.65 M

Perimeter = πD = 3.14 × 11.30 = 35.5 mt.

D. Load = 2,000 × 35.50 = 71000 kgs

Total load = 2471 + 71 = 2542 Tons

for 12 Columns

$M(-ve) = -0.00365 \times \overset{W}{2542} \times \overset{r}{5.62} = 52{,}500$ KMt

$M(+ve) = +0.00190 \times$ " × " = 27,400 " "

$M(\text{torsion}) = +0.000185 \times$ " × " = 2,670 Km.

Max M_T @ 6°21′ from ℄ of column.

shear :- $\omega = 2542/35.50 = 72$ T/Mt

angle between two columns = 30^{0}

Length of beam between two columns

$L = 35.50/12 = 2.95$ mts

$V = 72 \times 2.95/2 = 106$ Ton @ face for 60 Cm column.

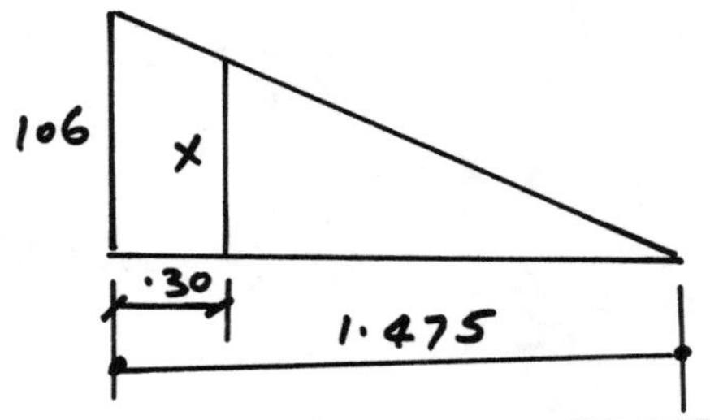

$\frac{x}{1.175} = \frac{106}{1.475}$

$x = 84.5$ TONS.

Flexure $d = \sqrt{5250000/12 \times 60} = 85.7$ Cm

shear max $v = 14$ K/cm^2

$bd = 84500/0.875 \times 14 = 6890$ Cm^2

make beam 60×140, $d = 130$ Cm.

At support

$A_s = 52500/11.3 \times 130 = 35.7$ cm^2

$\Sigma_o = 84500/7 \times .9 \times 130 = 103.5$ CmS use 14-ϕ1" in two rows

At center

$A_s = 27400/11.3 \times 130 = 18.7$ Cm^2

$A_{s_{min}} = 0.005 \times 60 \times 130 = 3.9$ Cm^2 8 ϕ1"

Shear

a) for flexure

$v_b = 84500/60 \times .875 \times 130 = 12.4$ K/cm^2

b) for torsion

$v_t = \frac{M_t}{hb^2}\left(3 + 1.8\frac{b}{h}\right) = \frac{267000}{140 \times 60^2}\left(3 + 1.8\frac{60}{140}\right) = 4.1$ K/cm^2

$v_{total} = 12.4 + 4.1 = 16.5$ K/cm^2

shear taken by Concrete $v_c = 5.3$ K/cm^2

Balance shear = 16.5 - 5.3 = 11.2 k/cm²

Total equivalent shear

V = 16.5 × 60 × 0.875 × 130 = 112,500 kg

Uniform eq. Load

$w = 2V/L = 2 \times 112500/(2.95-0.60) = 95.8$ T/ML

Point where no stirrups are req'd

$$x_1 = \frac{l}{2} - \frac{V_c b J d}{w} = 1.17 - \frac{5.3 \times 60 \times 0.9 \times 130}{95800} = 0.78 \text{ mts}$$

for ½"φ stirrups

$$S = \frac{A_v f_v}{b(V - V_c)} = \frac{2 \times 1.26 \times 1260}{0.60 \times 11.2} = 4.73 \text{ cms}$$

½ @ 4.73 cm.

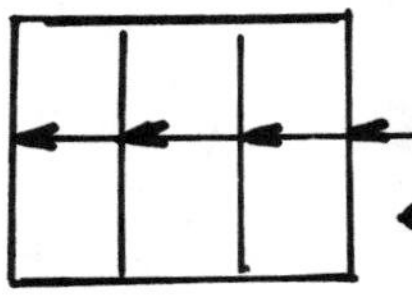

other ½" @ 50 cm.

Columns (12)

Load per column = $\frac{2542}{12}$ = 212 Tons

H = 13 mts

wind pressure = 100 k/M²

Area = 16.80 × 14.50 = 245 M²

Total pressure W = 80% (245 × 100) = 19600 kgs

Horizontal Load per col. = $\frac{19600}{12}$ = 1640 kg = $\frac{W}{n}$

Moments @ top $M = 2M_t + \frac{W}{n} \cdot \frac{h}{3}$

= 2 × 2670 + 1640 × 4.32

= 12,400 KM

Moments @ bottom

= 12,400 KM

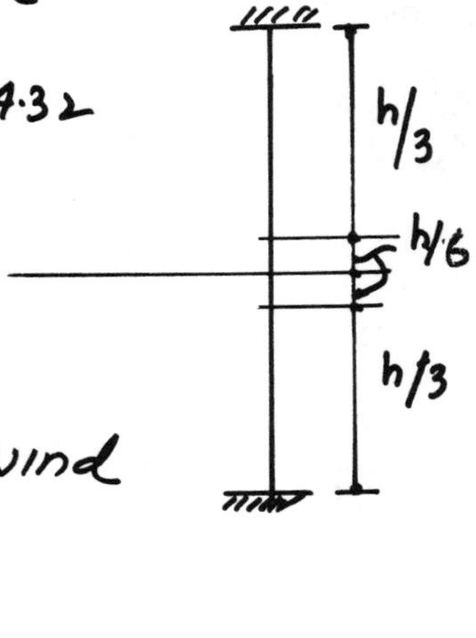

Axial Loads 212 Tons

Additional compression due to wind

$$N_{max} = \frac{r}{\Sigma y^2}(wh - Vx)$$

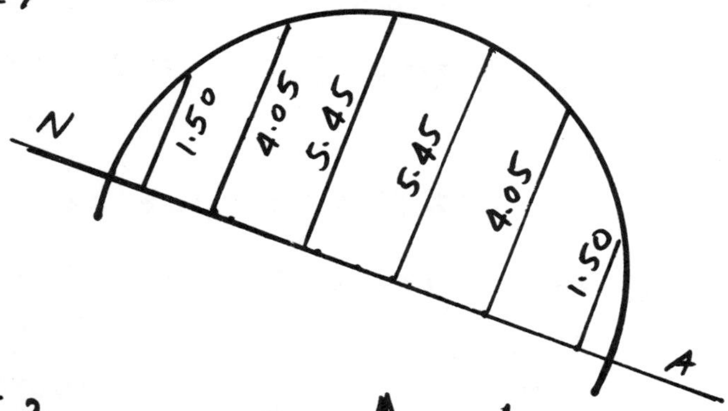

$y_1 = 1.5$ $\quad \bar{y}_1^2 = 2.25$ $\quad$ ↑wind

$y_2 = 4.05$ $\quad \bar{y}_2^2 = 16.40$ $\qquad h = 13 + \frac{14.50}{2} = 20.25\ mt$

$y_3 = 5.45$ $\quad \bar{y}_3^2 = 29.75$

$y_4 = 5.45$ $\quad \bar{y}_4^2 = 29.75$

$y_5 = 4.05$ $\quad \bar{y}_5^2 = 16.40$

$y_6 = 1.50$ $\quad \bar{y}_6^2 = 2.25$

$\Sigma \bar{y}^2 = 96.80$

$$N_{max} = \frac{5.65}{96.80}(19600 \times 20.25 - 1640 \times 4.32) = 23T$$

$P_{Total} = 212 + 23 = 235$ Tons.

Column design:-

$M = 12.4\ Tmt$, $N = 235\ T$

for such a small moment, we add 20% of the load and design as an axial load

$N = 283\ T$

Col. Load $= 12\ T$

295 Tons

$P/A_g = 0.225 f_c' + f_s P_g$

$A_g = \frac{\pi d^2}{4} = 2800\ Cm^2$, $f_c' = 2500\ Psi = 175\ ^k/Cm^2$

f_s = 16000 Psi. = 1125 kg/cm²

$29500/2800 = 0.225 \times 175 + 1125\, P_g$

$P_g = 5.85\%$.

$A_s = 0.585 \times 2800 = 164$ cm² 33-1"φ or 22-1¼"φ

spirals

diameter for steel = 48 cm.

$L = \pi d = \pi \times 48 = 151$ cm

Space between bars $151/22 = 6.86$ cm

free space $= 6.86 - 3.2 = 3.66$ cm.

$p' = 0.45\left(\frac{A_g'}{A_c} - 1\right)\frac{f_c'}{f_s'}$; $A_g/A_c = \frac{60^2}{55^2} = 1.20$

$\frac{f_c'}{f_c'} = \frac{175}{2250} = 0.078$

$p' = 0.45 \times 0.20 \times 0.078 = 0.007 = .7\%$

3/8"@ 2¾" (7 cm c/c) gives 0.73%. CRSI Pg 251

Moment.

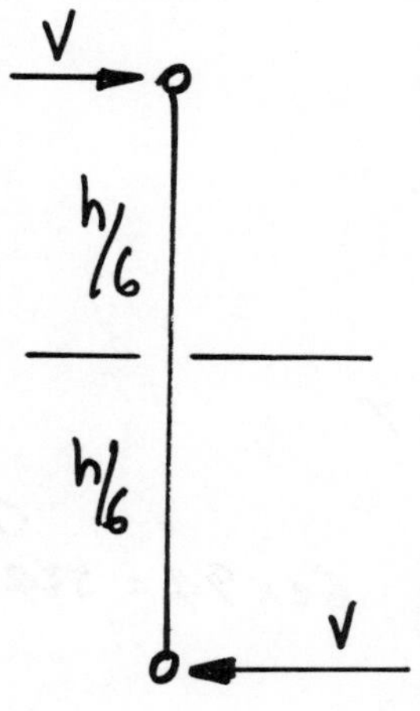

At columns:

$M = V\left(\frac{h}{6} + \frac{h}{6}\right) = \frac{Vh}{3}$

for each brace: $M_1 = M/2 = \frac{Vh}{6}$

$= 1640 \times \frac{13}{6} = 3550$ Km

Length of each brace $= \frac{35.5}{12} = 2.95$ mt.

moment due to own wt.

for 45×45 $w = 500$ K/mt

$M = \frac{wl^2}{10} = \frac{500 \times 2.95^2}{10} = 450$ Km.

Moment at support.

$M = 3550 + 450 = 4000$ Km.

$$d = \sqrt{40000/12 \times 40} = 29\ cm, \quad d = 32\ cm$$

$M_T = 0$

$$A_s = \frac{4000}{11.3 \times 32} = 11.0\ cm^2 \quad 4\ \phi\ 3/4" \text{ top \& bottom.}$$

$$V = \frac{wl}{2} = \frac{500 \times 2.95}{2} = 740\ kg$$

$v = 0.7\ k/cm^2$ ok

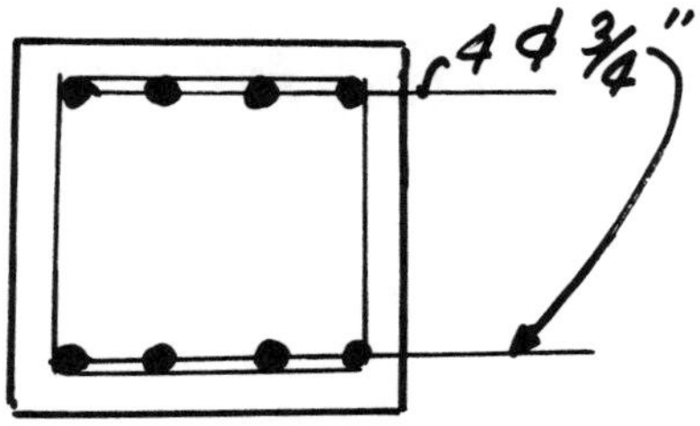

Footing

Loads

Tank full	=	2,542,000 kgs
12 Cols x 9000 kg	=	108,000 "
footing 10 T/ml x 35.5 ml	=	355,000 "
		3,005,000 kgs.

Moments in circular beam

$M(-) = -0.00365 \times 3005000 \times 5.65 = -62,000$ km

$M(+) = 0.00190 \times$ " $\times$ " $= 32,300$ "

$M(+) = 0.00185 \times$ " $\times$ " $= 3,120$ "

uniform load

$w = 3005000/35.5 = 84.3\ T/ml.$

@ support

$V = 84.3 \times 2.95/2 = 125\ T$

@ face of Col:- $V = \frac{1.15}{1.50} \times 125 = 96\ T$

Area for moment

$d = \sqrt{6200000/12 \times 60} = 94\ cm, \quad 60 \times 94 = 5640\ cm^2$

Area for shear

$A = 96000/0.875 \times 14 = 7850\ cm^2$

$b = 75\ cm,\ d = 105\ cm$

75 x 115

At Support

$A_s = 62000/11.3 \times 106 = 52.5\ \text{Cm}^2$

$\mathcal{E}_o = 96000/7 \times 0.9 \times 105 = 145\ \text{Cm}$

use 18 - ϕ1" two rows bottom.

At Center

$A_s = 32300/11.3 \times 105 = 27.3\ \text{Cm}^2$

$A_{s_{min}} = 0.005 \times 75 \times 105 = 39.5\ \text{Cm}^2$

8 ϕ1" one row above

Shear:-

a) for flexure : $\frac{v}{b} = \frac{96000}{75 \times 0.875 \times 105} = 13.9\ \text{k/cm}^2$

b) for torsion

$v_T = \frac{312000}{115 \times 75^2}\left(3 + 1.8\frac{75}{115}\right) = 2.0\ \text{k/cm}^2$

Total v = $13.9 + 2 = 15.9\ \text{k/cm}^2$

Concrete takes $-\ 5.3\ \text{k/cm}^2$

Stirrups take $10.6\ \text{k/cm}^2$

$V_{total} = 15.9 \times 75 \times 0.875 \times 105 = 109\ \text{Ton}$

$w = 2 \times 109/2.35 = 93\ \text{T/M}'$

$x_1 = 1.17 - \frac{5.3 \times 75 \times .9 \times 105}{93000} = 0.77\ \text{Mts}.$

½ ϕ Stirrups

$S = \frac{2 \times 1.26 \times 1260}{75 \times 10.6} = 4\ \text{Cm}.$

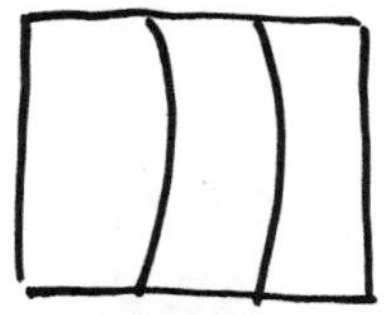

½"ϕ@ 8 Cm c/c in 85 Cms.
rest ½"@ 50 Cm c/c

Slab.

Total Load = 300 5000 kgs

Bearing f = 20 T/M2

Area reqd = $3005/20 = 150.3\ M^2$

Diameter circular slab

$d = \sqrt{150.3 \times 4/\pi} = 13.5$ mts

net pressure $w = \dfrac{(2542 + 108)}{150.3} = 17.5\ T/M^2$

We must have a cantilever of

$13.50 - 11.30/2 = 1.10$ Mts.

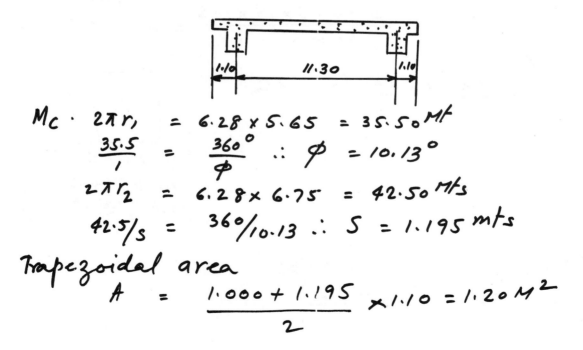

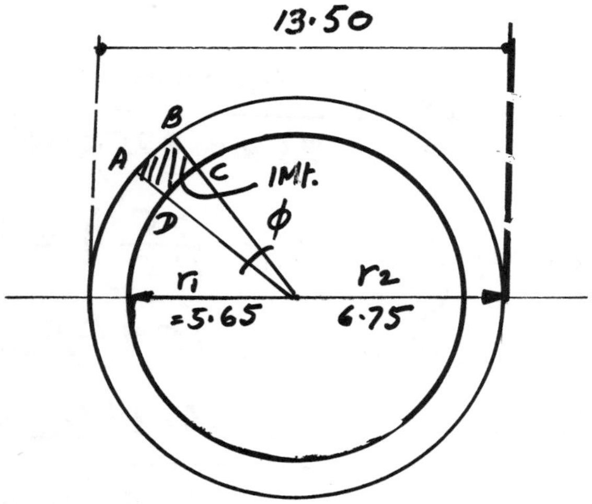

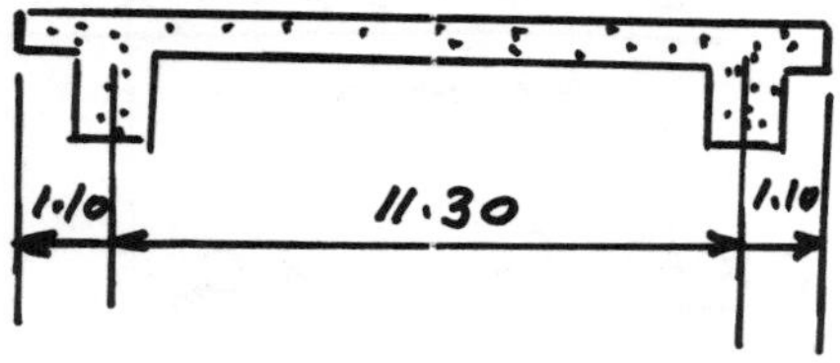

$M_C \cdot\ 2\pi r_1 = 6.28 \times 5.65 = 35.50$ Mt

$\dfrac{35.5}{1} = \dfrac{360^\circ}{\phi} \therefore \phi = 10.13^\circ$

$2\pi r_2 = 6.28 \times 6.75 = 42.50$ Mts

$42.5/S = 360/10.13 \therefore S = 1.195$ mts

Trapezoidal area

$A = \dfrac{1.000 + 1.195}{2} \times 1.10 = 1.20\ M^2$

total load $\omega = 1.20 \times 1.75 = 21$ Ton

C.C from base CD

$$C = \frac{1.10(2 \times 1.195 + 1.000)}{3(1.195 + 1.000)} = 0.57^{Mt}$$

$M_c = 21 \times 0.57 = 12$ T. Mts

from the coefficients for free slab we must deduct $\frac{M_c}{pR^2} = \frac{12.0}{17.5 \times 32} = 0.021$

$pR^2 = 560$ T

$M_{max} = 100.2$ TMt

$d = \sqrt{100200/14} = 85$ Cm $h = 115, d = 100$

Radial, reinforcement.

$M_{max} = 72.7$ TM/Mt @ 0.5R

$L = 2\pi \times 0.5 \times 5.65 = 17.70$ Mts @ 0.5R

then $M = 72.2 \times 17.7 = 1280$ TM

$A_s = 1280000/11.3 \times 100 = 1140$ Cm²

144 $\phi 1\frac{1}{4}$" @ 12.3 cm C/c on a circle of R = 2.82 @ top of slab.

Point	·0R	·1R	·2R	·3R	·4R	·5R	·6R	·7R	·8R	·9R	1.0R	
km/m Fixed +0.125 = Mr	·075	·073	·067	·057	·043	·025	·003	-·023	-·053	-0.087	-·125	
km/m Free −0.121 = Mr	·200	·198	·192	·182	0.168	0.150	0.128	0.102	·072	0.038	0	
KM/M Center	·179	·177	·171	·161	0.147	0.129	·107	·081	·051	·017	−·021	
coeff. × 560 = Mr TM/m T-m / Segment	100.24 0	99.12 9.9	95.76 19.2	90.16 27.0	82.33 33.00	72.26 36.2	59.92 36.0	45.36 31.7	28.56 22.8	9.53 8.6	−11.78 −11.8	
Mt fixed T-m/M Mt free +.125 −0.021 = Mt center	0.075 ·200 ·179	0.074 0.199 0.178	0.071 0.196 ·175	0.066 0.191 0.171	0.059 0.184 0.163	0.050 0.175 0.154	·039 ·164 ·143	·026 ·151 ·130	·011 ·136 ·115	−·006 ·119 ·098	−0.025 ·100 ·079	
coeff × 560 Mt T-m/Mt	100.2	99.7	98	95.2	91.3	86.2	80.1	72.8	64.4	54.9	44.2	

@ 0.8R M = 28.6 T-m/M

L = 2π × 0.8 × 5.65 = 28.4 Mts

M = 28.6 × 28.4 = 813 TM

As = 813000/11.3 × 100 = 720 Cm² 90 - $1\frac{1}{4}$"φ

M(-Ve)

@ 1.0R M(-) = 11.8 T.M

L = 2π × 5.65 = 35.5 Mt

M = 11.8 × 35.5 = 420 TMt

As = 42000/11.3×100 = 370 Cm² 47 φ $1\frac{1}{4}$φ.

on top of a circle of r = 5.65 mts

These bars are located at bottom of slab in 2 rows

Tangential reinforcement:- on top of slab

at Center M = 100.2 T-M/mt

As = 100200/11.3×100 = 89 Cm²/Mt

= φ $1\frac{1}{4}$ @ 9 Cm c/c

from Center to 0.8R = 4.52 mts

from 0.8R to 1.0R use $1\frac{1}{4}$"φ @ 14 Cm c/c

M = 64.4 T.m As = 64400/11.3 = 57 Cm²/Mt.

@ Cantilever use 1"φ @ 10 Cm c/c.

Bottom hole for water entrance φ = 1.20 meters.

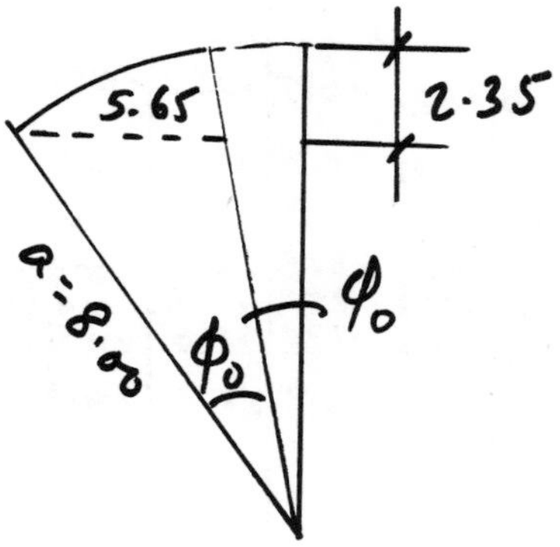

$\phi_1 = 45°$

$\sin\phi_1 = 0.707$

$\sin^2\phi_1 = 0.50$

$\sin\phi_0 = \frac{0.60}{8.00} = 0.0750$

$\sin^2\phi_0 = 0.0056$

$\cos\phi_0 = 0.9972$

assume a load of 10 ton uniformly distributed along the circumference of the hole

$$W = 10000 \text{ kgs}$$

Compression in ring

$$S = \frac{W \cos\phi_0}{2\pi \sin\phi_0} = \frac{10 \times \cdot 9972}{6{\cdot}28 \times \cdot 075} = 21T$$

Section 20X35 1% steel 29 Ton.

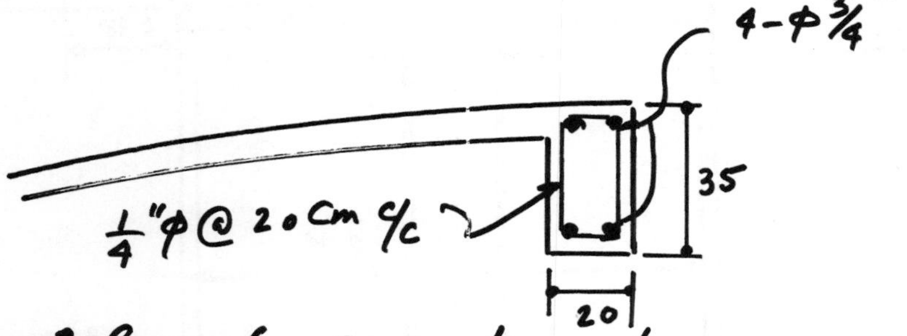

check of fcw for concrete when assumptions are based on A.W.W.A recommendations of wind $87.8\ ^{k}/m^2 = 18\ ^{\#}/sq\,ft = 108$ miles/HRS.

Assume the hollow column of support of Tank more or less like R.C chimney with no opening in the wall.

Max stresses due to combined action of wind & Dead load (Gaylord, Gaylord Str. H/Book)

$$f_{cw}' = \frac{W(1-\cos\alpha)}{2rt\left[(1-P)(\sin\alpha - \alpha\cos\alpha) - np\pi\cos\alpha\right]}$$

$$f_{cw} = f_{cw}'\left[1 + \frac{t}{2r(1-\cos\alpha)}\right]$$

$$f_{sw} = n f_{cw}' \frac{1+\cos\alpha}{1-\cos\alpha}.$$

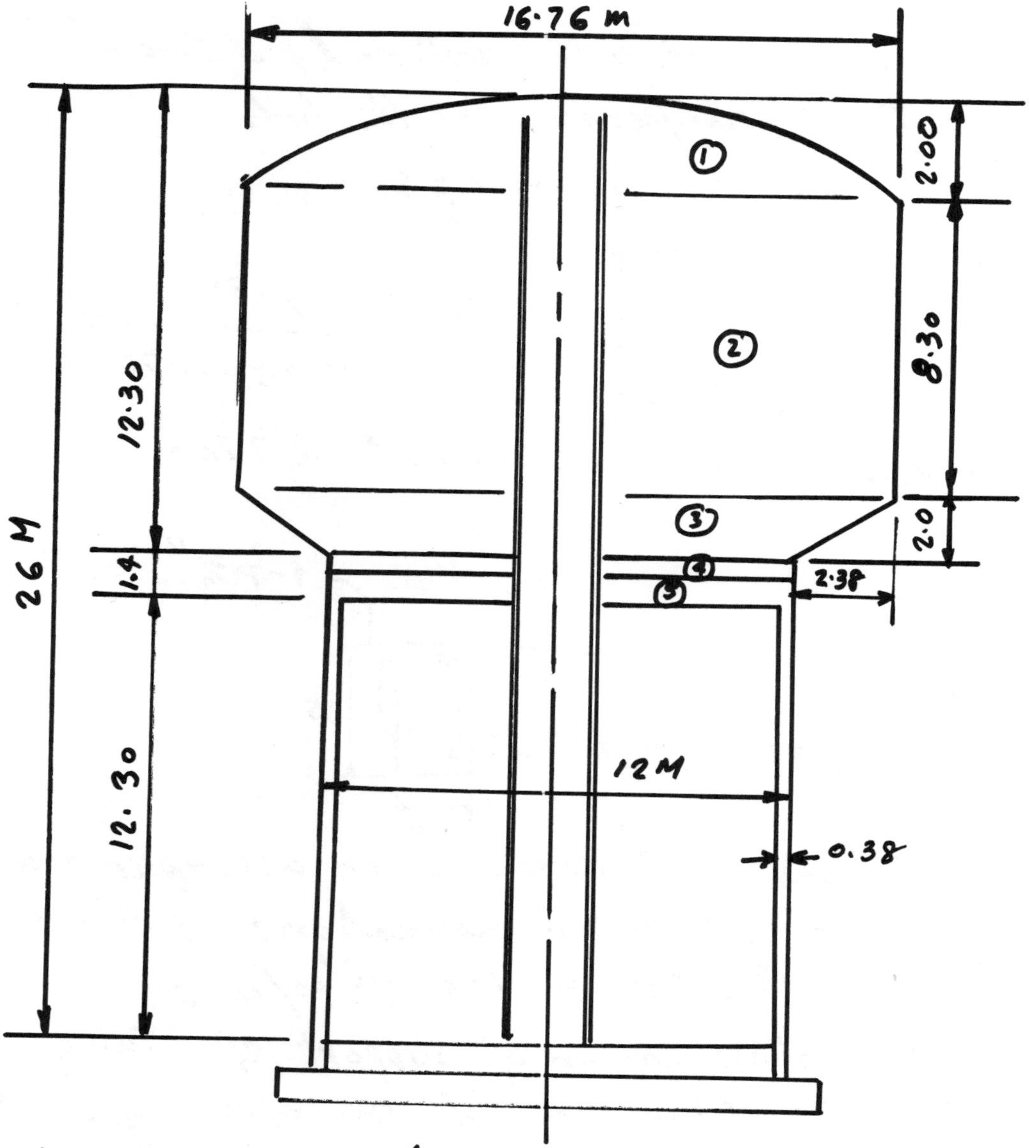

where W = Dead load
r = mean radius @ trial section
t = thickness of wall
p = ratio of vert. steel to area of Conc.
$\eta = \frac{E_s}{E_c} = 9.2$
α = one half the central angle between eccentricity as a chord on circle of radius r and centroid

W = 1,995500 kg

wind force H_1 = $60 \times 12.30 \times 16.76 = 12\,368$ kgm.

$H_2 = 60 \times 13.70 \times 12.70 = 10439$ kgm

Overturning moment $= 12368 \times 22.85 + 10439 \times 9.85$

$= 385433$ kgm.

$$e = \frac{M}{W} = \frac{385433}{1995500} = 0.1931\,m.$$

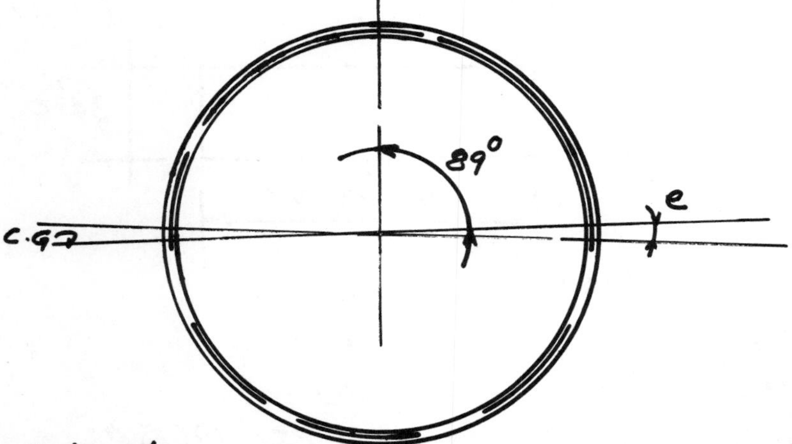

worst situation is when tank is empty & wind load max.

$$f_{cw}' = \frac{1995500\,(1 - \cos 89^\circ)}{2 \times 5.81 \times 0.38\left[(1 - 0.01)(\sin 89 - 89 \cos 89) - 10 \times .01 \times \pi \cos 89^\circ\right]}$$

$= 463789.83$ kg/m²

$$f_{cw} = f_{cw}'\left[1 + \frac{t}{2r(1 - \cos\alpha)}\right]$$

$$= 463789.83\left[1 + \frac{0.38}{2 \times 5.81(1 - .0175)}\right] = 479187.65 \text{ kg/m}^2$$

$$f_{sw} = n f_{cw}' \frac{1 + \cos\alpha}{1 - \cos\alpha}$$

$$= 9.2 \times 463789.83 \times \frac{1 + 0.0175}{1 - 0.0175} = 6285.72 \text{ \#/□''}$$

$= 4418866.77$ kgm/m² < 12500 ok

$$\frac{f_{sw}}{n} = \frac{6285.72}{9.2} = 682 \text{ P.si} < 750 \text{ ok.}$$

EXAMPLE 9-03

Given:- Design of 114'-0" O.D. x 34'-0" deaerator for Graver Water Company, West Virginia.

Design pressure 75 PSI @ 450°F
15 PSI @ 450°F

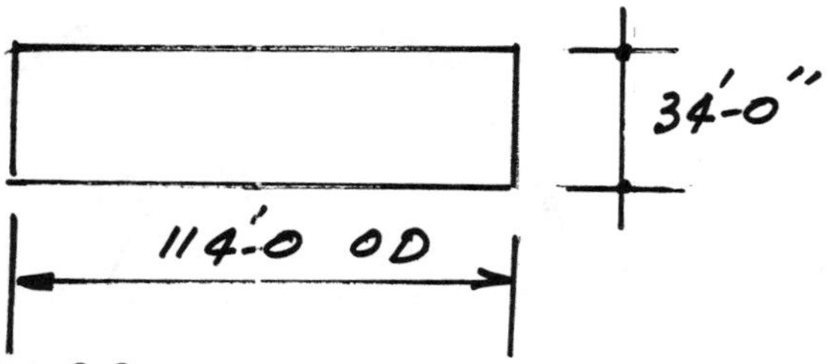

Corrosion allowance 0
Radiograph spot
Heat treatment NO
Hydrostatic Test 113 PSI @ TOP
MATERIAL A-285 C FLG Q.
Code A.S.M.E SECTION VIII

Shell

$$t_s = \frac{75 \times 56.5}{11687 - 45} = 0.364''$$

$$\frac{L}{D_o} = \frac{141}{114} = 1.24, \quad \frac{D_o}{t} = \frac{114}{0.50} = 228$$

$$P_{allow} = \frac{4500}{228} = 19.7 \text{ Psi} \quad \text{use } t = \frac{1}{2}''$$

ASME Head F & D

$$\frac{L}{r} = \frac{108}{6.875} = 15.75$$

$$t_h = \frac{75 \times 108 \times 1.74}{27500 - 15} = 0.514''$$

$$\frac{L_1}{100 t_h} = \frac{108}{40} = 2.7$$

$$P_{all} = \frac{5900}{.270} = 20$$

Shell stiffening ring, Assume 5" I @ 14.75#

$A = 4.29$, $I = 15.00$

$$B = \frac{15 \times 114}{0.5 \times \frac{8.44}{141}} = 3050$$

$W = 1.10\sqrt{114 \times 0.5} = 8.3$

$NA = \dfrac{4.15 \times 0.25 + 4.29 \times 3}{8.44}$

$= 1.65''$

$I = 15 + 4.29(1.35)^2$
$+ 0 + 4.15(1.4)^2 = 30.96$

$I = \dfrac{114^2 \times 141 \times 0.56 \times 0.00023 \times 1.3}{14}$

$= 21.5 \text{ IN}^4$

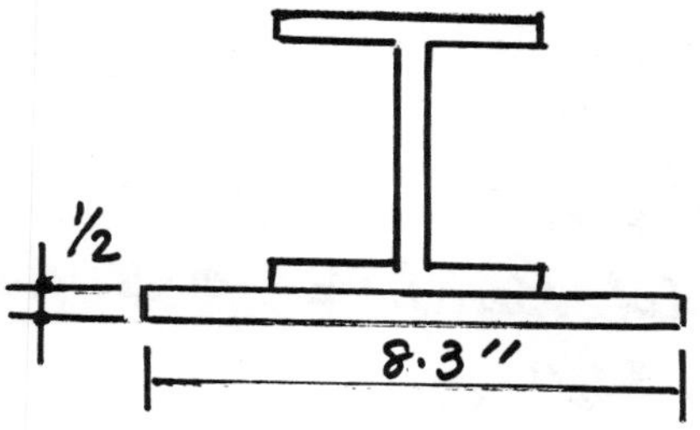

use 5" I @ 14.75#, INTERMEDIATE weld - ¼" Fillet - 4" LG on 8" centers.

for Nozzle Reinforcement.

Shell $t_r = \dfrac{75 \times 56.5}{13750 - 45} = 0.310$ interior

$t_r = 0.50$ Exterior

Head $t_r = 0.295$ Int. $t > 2t_r$
$t_r = 0.400$ Ext $t > 1\frac{1}{2} t_r$ } Hence no reinforcmt.

24" M. HOLE IN HEAD.

$R_1 = 2(56.375 - 6.875 + 3.36) = 52.86$

from I.D of M.H To Knuckle Head

$= 52.86 - (33 + 11.5) = 8.36$

$t_r^n = \dfrac{75 \times 11.5}{13750 \times 0.85 - 45} = 0.074''$

$A_{R\,INT} = 0.310 \times 23 = 7.13\square''$

$A_S = 16.72(0.625 - 0.310) = 5.26\square''$

$A_N = 5 \times 0.5 \times (0.5 - 0.074) = 1.06\square''$

$A_{N\,INT} = 2 \times 0.5 \times 0.5 = 0.50\square''$

$\frac{1}{2}''$ F.W. Int & Ext $2 \times \frac{1}{2} \times \frac{1}{2} = 0.50\square''$

$7.32\square''$

$A_{R\,Ext} = \frac{1}{2} \times 0.400 \times 23$ — $4.6\square''$

$A_S = 16.72(0.625 - 0.4)$ — $3.76\square''$

$A_{N\,INT}$ & A_{FW} — 1.00

$4.76\square''$

Hence no additional Reinforcement.

20" Nozzle in shell (3/8" wall thick)

$A_{R\,int}$ = 0.310 × 19.25 = 5.96 □"

$A_{s\,int}$ = 19.25(0.5 − 0.310) = 3.66 □"

Add Reinf: = 0.5 (26 − 20) = 3.00

4 − 3/8" FW = 0.28

6.94 + Nozzle

AR Ext = $\frac{1}{2}$ × 0.5 × 19.25 = 4.31

Excess A in shell = 0

A_{noz} = 5 × 0.5 (0.375 − 0.10) = 0.69

Added Reinf: 0.5 (26 − 20) = 3.00

$A_{Noz.\,Int}$ = 2 × 0.5 × 0.375 = 0.37

A weld = 0.28

4.34 □"

Add 26"φ × $\frac{1}{2}$" thick Plate.

4" Nozzle in shell

4 Sch. 40 Pipe 0.237" thick wall.

A_R = $\frac{1}{2}$ × 0.5 × 4.026 = 1.07 □"

Ext_{Noz} = 5 × 0.237 (0.237 − 0.1) = 0.16 □"

Int_{Noz} = 5 × 0.237 (0.237) = 0.28 □"

Add Noz Reinforcement 2 × 2 × 3/8 = 1.50 □"

1.94 □"

Add Reinforcing 3/8" thick × 8$\frac{1}{2}$"φ

EXAMPLE 9-04

Given:-Design a stripper measuring 30" O.D. X 85'-6" long for Ashland Oil and Refining Company.

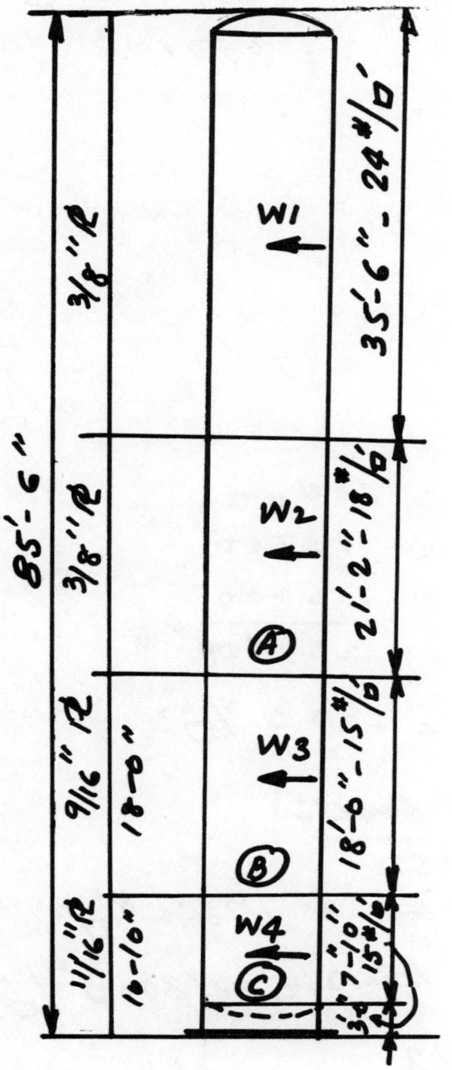

Shell @ (A)

D.L Top Head = 120#

3/8" Shell 56x119 = 6670#

52 Trays @ 70#/Tray = 3640#

1-360 FLG = 2000#

Connections = 2500#

14930#

1/16" Corrosion − 2930

Corrected Wt:- 12000#

Liquid 44x52 2300#

Insulation 5000#

Corrected Wt 19300#

$Eff.\ D = (2.5+1.0)1.20$

$= 4.2'$

$W_1 = (24 \times 4.2 \times 35.5) \times 38.92$

$= 139000\#$

$W_2 = (18 \times 4.2 \times 21.17) \times 10.59$

$= 17000\#$

$\Sigma W = 3570 + 1600 = 5170\#$

$M@A = 139000 + 17000$

$= 156000'\#$

$\frac{5}{16}$" thick PL $A = 29.68 \times \pi \times 0.312 = 29.0□"$

$S = 14.84 \times \pi \times 0.312 = 215.5\ IN^3$

$\text{Longitudinal stress} = \frac{15 \times 14.84}{2 \times 0.312} = -360\#/□"$

$\text{Max } f_c = -360 - 665 - 8700 = -9725\#/□"$

$\frac{L}{100t} = \frac{14.63}{100 \times .3125} = 0.47$ Allow = 12000#/□"

Shell @ (B)

New D.L at (A) = 14930

9/16" Shell 18 @ 17.7 = 3200

17 tray @ 70. = 1200

Connection = 600.

19900

1/16 corrosion 3800

Corrected Wt:- 16100

Liquid 70x44 3100

INSULATION 6100

Corrected Wt 25300 #

$A = 29.875 \times \pi \times \frac{1}{2}$

$= 46.9 \square''$

$S = 14.93 \times \pi \times \frac{1}{2}$

$= 350 IN3.$

$W_3 = 4.2 \times 18 \times 15 = 1150 \times 9 = 10400$

$5170 \times 18 = 93200.$

6320 156000

259600 '#

$\text{Long. stress (Vac)} = \frac{-15 \times 14.84}{2 \times 0.50} = -223 \#/\square''$

$\text{Max fc} = -223 - \frac{25300}{46.9} - \frac{259600 \times 12}{350}$

$= -223 - 539 - 8900 = -9662 \#/\square''$

$\frac{L}{100t} = \frac{14.63}{50} = 0.293 \quad \text{Allow fc} = 13000 \#/\square''$

$\text{Long. stress (Pr)} = \frac{+75 \times 14.93}{2 \times 0.50} = 1120 \#/\square''$

$\text{Max. ft} = +1120 - 475 + 8900 = 9522 \#/\square''$

$\text{Long. stress (Pr)} = \frac{75 \times 14.84}{2 \times 0.312} = +1780$

$ft = 1780 + (-665) + 8700 = 9815 \#/\square''$

Shell @ (C)

" DL = 19900

11/16 Shell 7.83x216 = 1700

Conn	700
New	22300
$\frac{1}{16}$" Corr	4000
	18300
INS.	6600
Liquid	3100.
Corrected Wt	28000 #

$W_4 = 4.2 \times 7.83 \times 15 = 500 \times 3.92 = 1960$

$6320 \times 7.83 = 49580$

682_0 259600

311140

$\frac{5}{8}$" Shell $A = 30 \times \pi \times 0.625 = 58.9$

$S = 15^2 \times \pi \times 0.625 = 442 \text{ IN}^3$

Long. stress (Vac) $= \dfrac{-15 \times 15}{2 \times 0.625} = -180 \text{ \#/□}''$

max $f_c = -180 - \dfrac{28000}{58.9} - \dfrac{311140 \times 12}{442}$

$= -180 - 475 - 8447 = -9102 \text{ \#/□}''$

Long stress (Pr) $= \dfrac{75 \times 15}{2 \times 0.625} = 900 \text{ \#/□}''$

Max $f_t = +900 - 475 + 8447 = 8872$

$\dfrac{L}{100t} = \dfrac{14.63}{62.5} = 0.234$, f_c allow $= 13500 \text{ \#/□}''$

Skirt @ base

D.L	=	22300
Bott. HD	=	300
$\frac{1}{16}$ ℄ 3x216	=	650
Conn	=	350
		23600
$\frac{1}{16}$" corrosion		4100
		19500 #
Liquid		4300 #
Insulation		6800 #
		30600 #

flooded (New D.L) = 23600

3000 gal @ 8.33 = 25000

Flooded   48600

$W_5 = 4.2 \times 3 \times 15 = 190 \times 1.5 = 300$

$6820 \times 3 = 20500$

7010 311140

331940

$\frac{11}{16}$" skirt

$A = 22.94 \times \pi \times 0.687 = 64.5 \text{ IN}^2$

$S = 14.97^2 \times \pi \times 0.687 = 484 \text{ IN}^3$

$f_c = -\dfrac{48600}{64.5} - \dfrac{331940 \times 12}{484} = -8985 \text{ \#/□}''$

ANCHOR BOLT operative condition.

$W = 30600\#, \quad M = 332000'\#$

Assume $K = 0.250$

$C_c = 1.37, \quad C_t = 2.551, \quad Z = 0.448, \quad J = 0.779$

$$F_t = \frac{332000 - 30600 \times 0.448 \times 3.42}{0.779 \times 3.42} = 106975\#$$

$$f_s = \frac{106975}{0.162 \times 20.5 \times 2.551} = 12645\#/\square''$$

$$F_c = 106975 + 30600 = 137575\#$$

$$f_c = \frac{137575}{12.45 \times 20.5 \times 1.37} = 394\#/\square''$$

$$\text{Check } K = \frac{1.0}{1.0 + \frac{12650}{3940}} = 0.238$$

Base Plate

$$P = 394 \times \frac{12.45}{11.0} = 445\#/\square'$$

$$b = 48 \times \pi \times \frac{1}{12} = 12.55$$

$$\frac{L}{b} = \frac{11}{12.55} = 0.878$$

$$M_x = 0.085 \times 445 \times 12.55^2 = 5960'\#$$

$$M_y = 0.115 \times 445 \times 11.00 = 6200'\#$$

$$t^2 = \frac{6 \times 6200}{22500} = 1.65$$

$$t = 1.28 \text{ Min.}$$

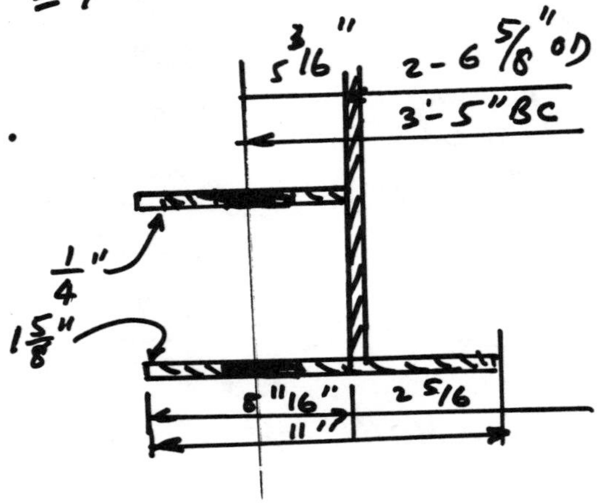

EXAMPLE 9-05

<u>Given:</u>-Design a structural steel pressure bin for a PHILLIP CAREY Company of size 20'x32'-8". Material to be A-283 Gr.C and Structural Steel be A-36.

Design contents = 20 #/cft

Roof. SL = 25 #/□'

w.L = 30 #/□'

Cap = $\pi \times r^2 \times 32.67 = 10250$

$\frac{3.14 \times 9.33}{12}(20^2 + 20\times8 + 8^2) = 1520$

50 x 1 = 50

11820 c.f

Weight contents

= 11820 x 20 = 236400 #

Pressure @ knuckle

= 33 x 0.434 x 0.32

= 4.6 #/□'

Assume 1/4" shell

$f_t = \frac{4.6 \times 120}{0.25} = 2210$ #/□"

$\tan\alpha = \frac{6.0}{9.3} = 0.643$

$\alpha = 32°45$

Load/inch shell = $\frac{23640}{\pi \times 240}$ = 314 #/IN

Comp. Load

= 314 x 0.643

= 202 #/"

Ring Compression

= 202 x 120

= 24300 #

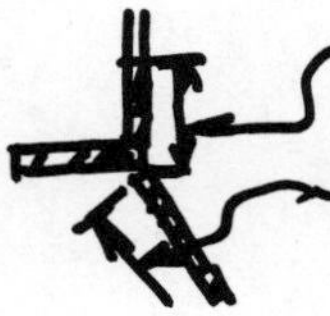

0.60 x $\sqrt{120 \times 0.25}$ = 3.38

0.60 x $\sqrt{142 \times 0.25}$ = 3.48

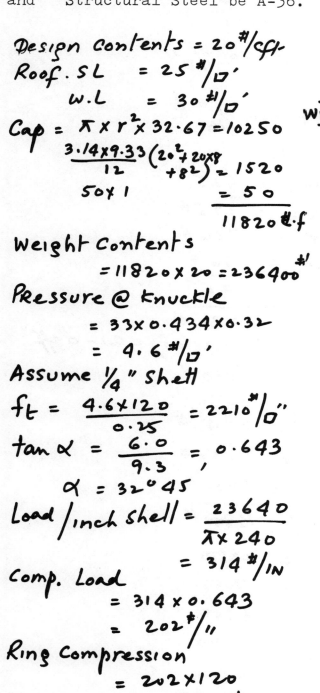

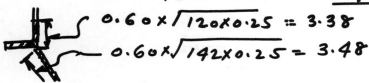

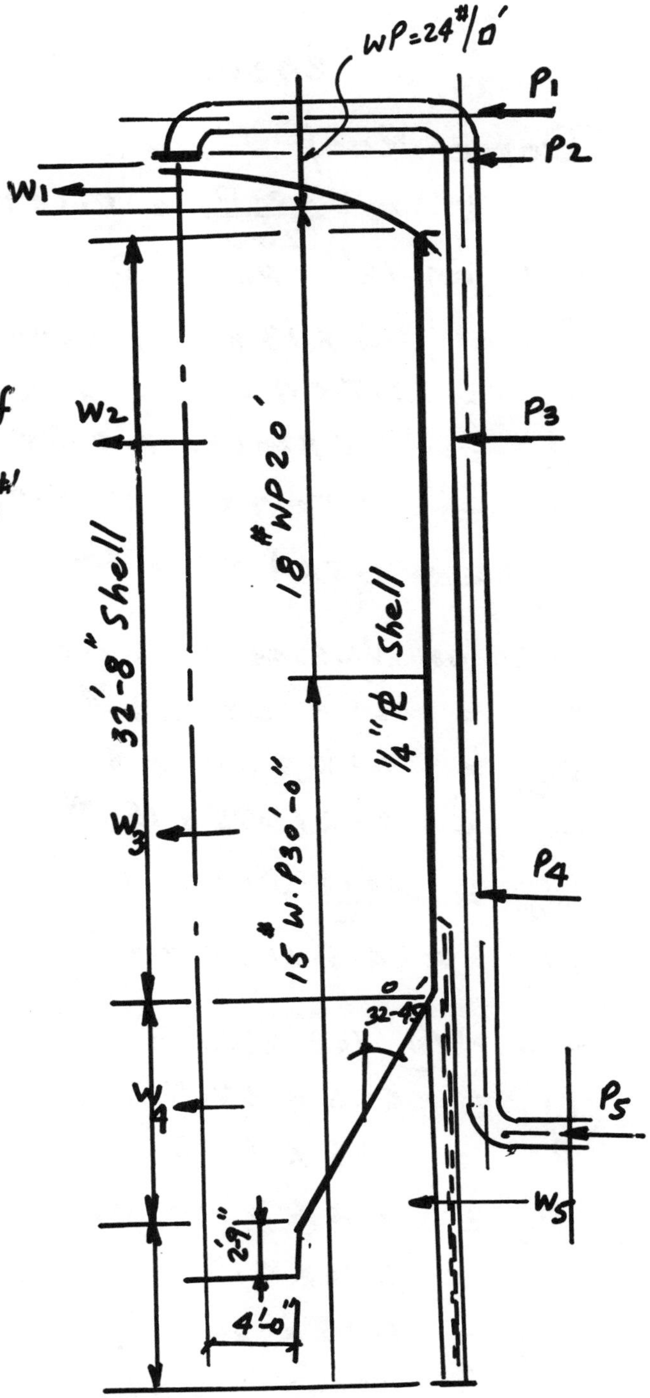

$A = 3.30 \times 0.25 = 0.82$

$3.48 \times 0.25 = 0.87$

$4 \times 3/8''$ FLT $= 1.50$

3.19 □''

$f_c = 24300 \div 3.19 = 7600$ #/□''

Dome Roof:-

$t = \dfrac{20.0}{200} = 0.100$ use $3/16''$ PL

W.L on 12'' Pipe, $D_{eff} = 1.5''$

$P_1 = 1.5 \times 13 \times 40 \times 0.80 = 625$#

$P_2 = 1.5 \times 4 \times 40 \times 0.80 = 195$#

$P_3 = 1.5 \times 20 \times 30 \times 0.80 = 720$#

$P_4 = 1.5 \times 19 \times 25 \times 0.80 = 570$#

$P_5 = 1.5 \times 4 \times 25 \times 0.80 = 120$#

2230 #

W.L ON Vessel = 20.0 + 1.0 (Ladder) = 21'-0'' eff.

$W_1 = 21 \times 2 \times 24$# $= 1010$#

$W_2 = 21 \times 20 \times 18$# $= 7560$#

$W_3 = 21 \times 13.75 \times 15$# $= 4340$#

$W_4 = \dfrac{20+8}{2} \times 9.92 \times 15$# $= 2090$#

$W_5 = 4.5 \times 16 \times 25$# $= 1800$#

16800 #

W.L M @ TOP of CONE

$P_1 = 625 \times 37.5 = 23500$

$P_2 = 195 \times 35.5 = 7000$

$P_3 = 720 \times 23.5 = 16900$

$P_4 = 570 \times 4.5 = 2600$

$W_1 = 1010 \times 34.3 = 34600$

$W_2 = 7560 \times 24.0 = 182000$

$W_3 = 4340 \times 7.0 = 30400.$

29700

$P_5 = -120 \times 5.75 = -700$

$W_4 = -2170 \times 4.5 = -9800$

-10500

Net moment @ top of cone = 297000
10500
286500 F#

Load

D.L Roof	350 x 7.65	= 2700
Shell	62.8 x 3.27 @ 10.2 =	20900
M.H & CONN.		= 500
12" Pipe	60 x 55 #	= 3300
Ladder	53 x 25 #	= 1400
Curb & HR		= 1300
		30100 #

1/4" shell $A = 240 \times \pi \times \frac{1}{4} = 188.5 \square''$

$S = 120^2 \times \pi \times \frac{1}{4} = 11,150\ IN^3$

$fc_{max} = \frac{30100}{188} + \frac{286500 \times 12}{11150} = 470\ \#/\square''$

$\frac{L_1}{100t} = \frac{120}{25} = 4.8 \quad fc_{all.} = 3500\ \#/\square'$

Column & Bracing .

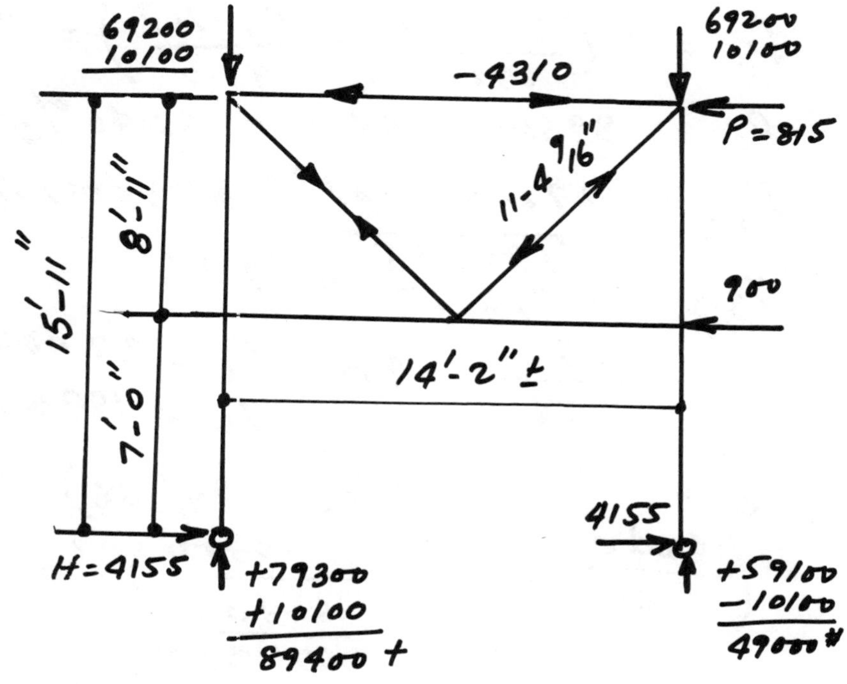

D.L from above = 30100

Cone 515 @ 10.2 = 5300

Supports = 4900

40300 #

Contents 236400 #

276700 #

$$Load/Col = \frac{276700}{4} = 69800^{\#}$$

Wind Load P = 2230

16800 - 1800 = 15000

$$\frac{17230}{2} = 8615^{\#}$$

W.L/Col

$$T.L = \frac{286500}{2 \times 14.2} = \pm 10100$$

V @ base = ± 8615 × 15.92 = 137300

900 × 7.0 = 6300

$$\frac{143600}{14.2} = \pm 10100^{\#}$$

Col Mom @ strut = 4155 × 84 = 400,000 ″#

Assume W10×49

$$f_b = M\left(\frac{5 \times .707}{272.9} + \frac{5 \times .707}{93.0}\right) = 20400 \,^{\#}/\square''$$

$$f_a = 89600 \div 14400 = 6240 \,^{\#}/\square''$$

$$I_{3\cdot3} = 272 \times 0.707^2 + 93 \times 0.707^2 = 182.45$$

$$r_{3\text{-}3} = \sqrt{\frac{182.45}{14.4}} = 3.56$$

$$\frac{L}{r} = \frac{107}{3.56} = 300, \quad F_b = 22000 \times 1.33 = 29400 \,^{\#}/\square''$$

$$F_a = 19940 \times 1.33 = 26600 \,^{\#}/\square''$$

$$F_e' = 149000,00/(2 \times 84/3.56) = 67100$$

$$\therefore \left(\frac{6240}{26600}\right) + \left(\frac{0.85 \times 20400}{\left(1 - \frac{6240}{67100}\right) 29400}\right) = 0.829 < 1.0$$

ok.

Also $\frac{6240}{29400} + \frac{20400}{29400} = 0.907 < 1.0$ ok

Diagonal strut assume $3\frac{1}{2} \times 3\frac{1}{2} \times \frac{5}{16}$" ∠.

$C = 4310 \times \frac{11.38}{7.10} = 6900$

$f_a = \frac{6900}{2.09} = 3300$ #/□"

$\frac{L}{r} = \frac{11 \times 12}{0.67} = 192$, $F_a = 6330 \times 1\frac{1}{3} = 8450$ #/□"

Horizontal Strut. C = 4760. Assume W 4×13

$\frac{L}{r} = \frac{170}{0.99} = 172$, $f_a = 4760 \div 3.82 = 1250$ #/□"

WIND at 90°

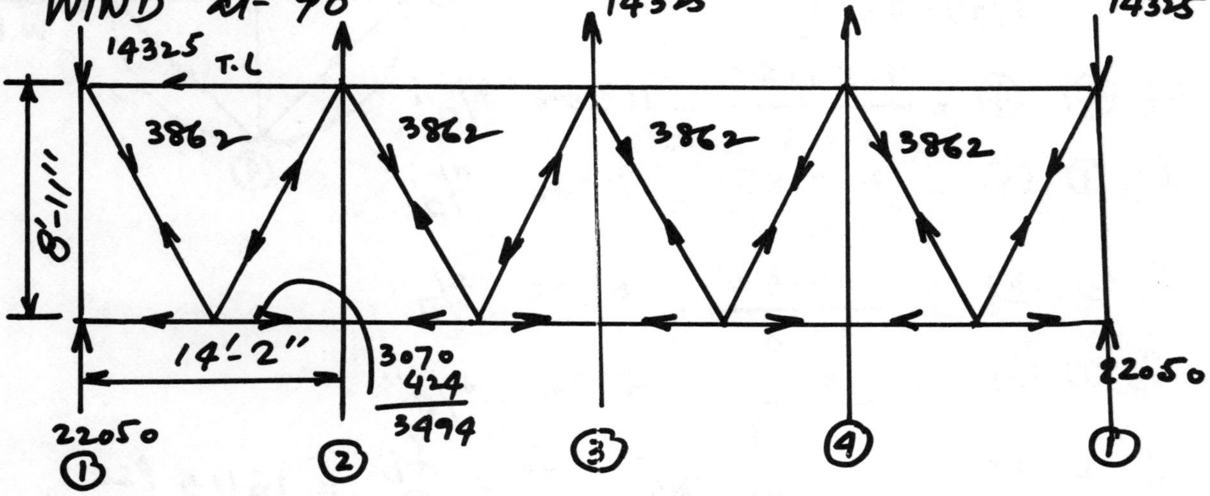

V @ T.L = $\frac{286500}{20} = 14325$ #

M @ strut = 286500

$17310 \times 8.92 = 154500$

441000 #

V @ strut = $441000 \div 20 = 22050$ #

V @ Bott. Strut = $3863 \times \frac{7.1}{8.92} = 3070$

$\left(\frac{1800}{3}\right) \div 2 \times 1.414 = 424$

3494

M @ base = 286500

$17310 \times 15.92 = 276000$

$1800 \times 7 = 12600$

575100

$$V_{max} = \frac{575100}{20} = 28750^{\#}$$

Max Col ① Comp = 28750 WL
69200 DL+LL
97950

Assume Horizontal Load on Columns

$$H = 6988 \times 0.707 \times 4 = 19800$$

② ④ $\frac{19800}{2(272.9+93)} \times 272.9 = 7350^{\#}$

① ③ $\frac{19800}{2(272.9+93)} \times 93.0 = 2500^{\#}$

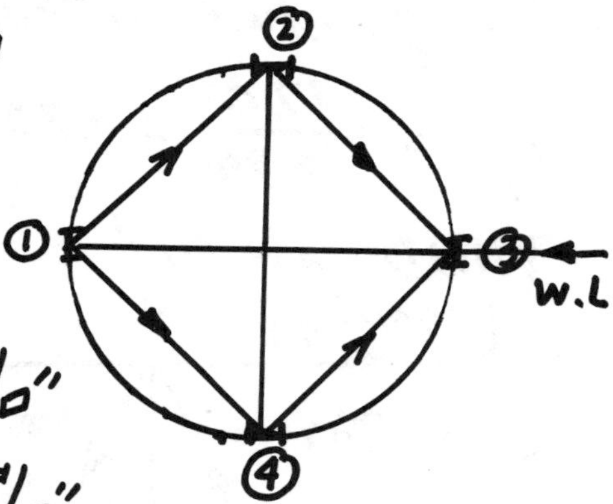

f_b ②, ④ $= \frac{7350 \times 84}{54.6} = 11300$ #/□"

f_b ①, ③ $= \frac{2500 \times 84}{18.6} = 11300$ #/□"

f_a ②, ④ $= \frac{97950}{14.4} = 6800$ #/□"

f_a ①, ③ $= \frac{69200}{14.4} = 4810$ #/□"

f_a ②④ + f_b ②④ = 18100 Psi ; f_a ①③ + f_b ①③ = 16110 Psi

Base Plate. Assume 12" × 7"

$p = \frac{97260}{204} = 480$ #/□" ; $n = \frac{12-8}{2} = 2$

$M = 480 \times \frac{3.75^2}{2} = 3480$ "# , $m = \frac{17-9.5}{2} = 3.75$

$t = \sqrt{\frac{6 \times 3460}{22000}} = 0.945 \therefore t = 0.97''$ use $t = 1''$

Max W.L = $29060^{\#}$
D.L = -2530
26530

$A_{bolt} = \frac{26530}{20000} = 1.33$

Use 2-$1\frac{1}{4}$"ϕ (1.78□")

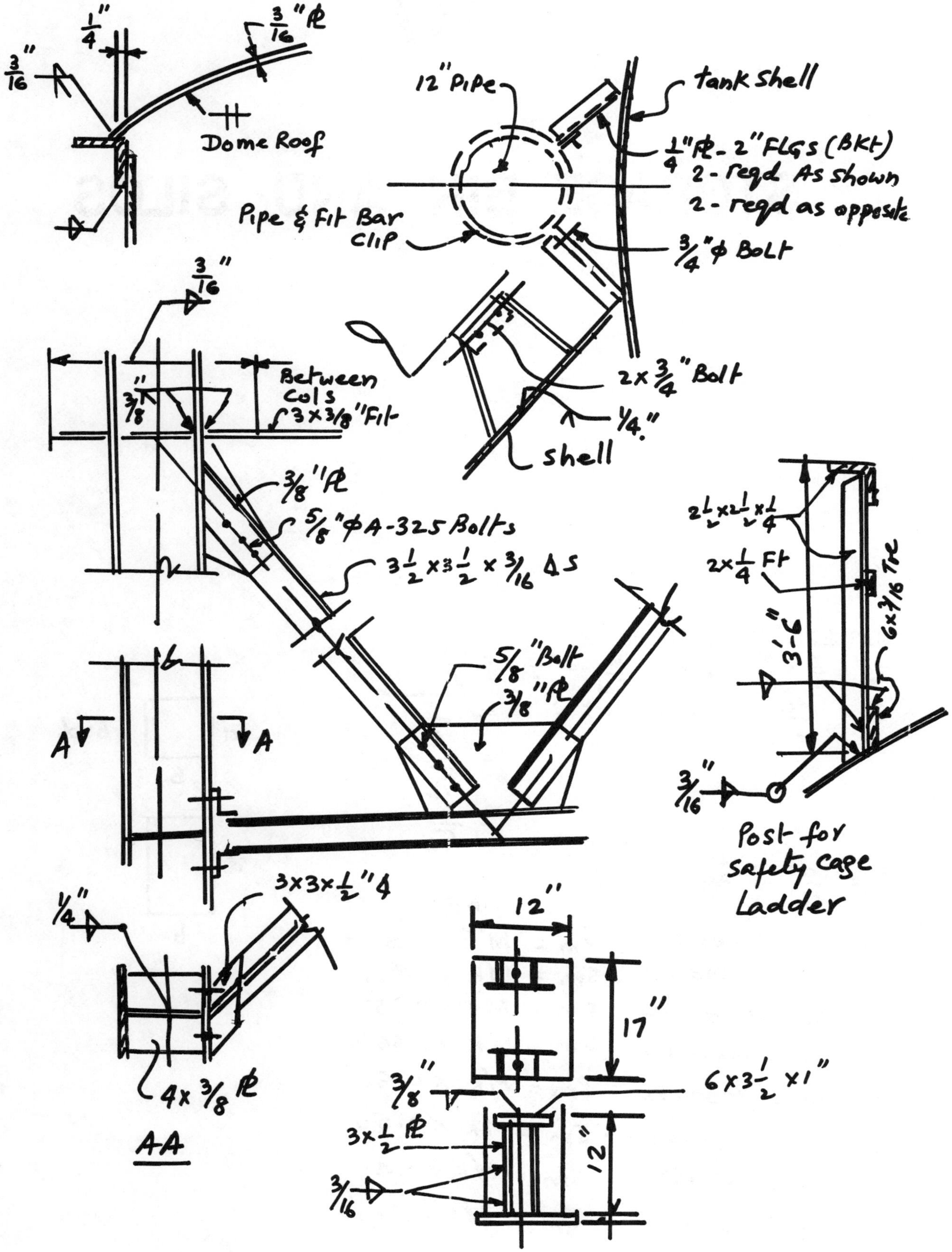
1/4"
3/16" ℞
3/16"
Dome Roof
12" Pipe
tank Shell
1/4" ℞ - 2" FLGS (BKt)
2 - reqd As shown
2 - reqd as opposite
Pipe & Fit Bar Clip
3/4" φ Bolt
2 x 3/4" Bolt
1/4"
shell
3/16"
Between Cols
3/8"
3 x 3/8" Fit
3/8" ℞
5/8" φ A-325 Bolts
3 1/2 x 3 1/2 x 3/16 ∠s
5/8" Bolt
3/8" ℞
A
A
2 1/2 x 2 1/2 x 1/4
2 x 1/4 Ft
3'-6"
6 x 7/16 Tie
3/16"
Post for safety cage Ladder
3 x 3 x 1/2" ∠
1/4"
4 x 3/8 ℞
AA
12"
17"
3/8"
6 x 3 1/2 x 1"
3 x 1/2 ℞
3/16
12"

10

STORAGE BIN AND SILOS

MISCELLANEOUS FORMULAES

$S_m = \frac{I}{c} = \frac{M}{f}$; $f = \frac{M}{S_m} = \frac{Mc}{I} = \frac{My}{I}$

$I = \frac{Mc}{f}$; $I = Ar^2$; $r = \sqrt{\frac{I}{A}}$

$= \frac{d}{\sqrt{12}}$

$= \frac{b}{\sqrt{12}}$

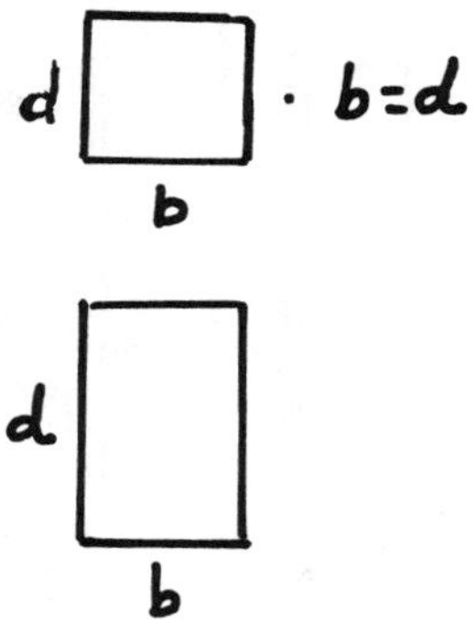

$I = \frac{bd^3}{12}$; $S_m = \frac{bd^2}{6}$; $F = \frac{6M}{bd^2}$

for f_s = 12000 P.si ; $S_m = M'K \times 1.0$
f_s = 14000 P.si ; $S_m = M'K \times 0.86$
f_s = 16000 psi ; $S_m = M'K \times 0.75$
f_s = 18000 Psi ; $S_m = M'K \times 0.667$
f_s = 20000 Psi ; $S_m = M'K \times 0.60$
f_s = 24000 Psi ; $S_m = M'K \times 0.50$
f_s = 26667 Psi, $S_m = M'K \times 0.45$
f_s = 32000 Psi; $S_m = M'K \times 0.375$

$$M_R = f\frac{I}{c} = f \times S_m$$

$$w = \frac{8M}{L^2} \quad \text{or} \quad L^2 = \frac{8M}{w}$$

$$E = \frac{f}{\delta}L^2 = \frac{P}{A} \div \frac{\Delta}{f} \quad \& \quad \Delta = \frac{f\delta}{E} \text{ where } \delta \text{ is in Inches}$$

$$\frac{M}{EI} = \frac{d^2y}{dx^2} \quad \text{Slope \& Deflection at any point}$$

$$M = EI\frac{d^2y}{dx^2}$$

Avg Vert. shear $= v = \frac{V}{A} = \frac{V}{dt}$ (girders)

Horizontal shearing stress at any section, $v = \frac{VQ}{Ib}$

Vertical & Horizontal shears are equal at the same point and are usually maximum at mid Height of beam.

EQUIVALENT $V = \frac{M}{83.3} L \times \frac{d}{bt}$ where L is in feet, M in 'k & V is shear.

$$I = \frac{\pi r_1^4}{4}; \; A = \pi r_1^2; \; r = \frac{r_1}{2}$$

where r = least radius of gyration

$$I = \frac{\pi}{4}\left(r_0^4 - r_1^4\right); \; A = \pi\left(r_0^2 - r_1^2\right)$$

$$r = \sqrt{\frac{I}{A}} = \frac{1}{2}\sqrt{r_0^2 + r_1^2}$$

Silos are deep bins.
Bunkers are shallow bins.
If H $> 1.5\sqrt{A}$ or H > 1.5 D ,then it is Circular silo.
If H > 1.5 a ,then it is R3ctangular silo.
Equation for bin pressures

$$L = \frac{wR}{\mu'}\left[1 - e^{-k\mu' h/R}\right]$$

If depth is more than $2\frac{1}{2}$x diameter,the last term may be omitted.
w=Weight of material; R = Hydraulic radius = area/wetted perimeter
L=Lateral pressure ; $\mu' = \tan\phi$:Coefficient of Friction on walls.
v= Vertical pressure ; k = Constant for particular mass.

$$P = \frac{wR}{\mu'}\left[h - \frac{R}{k\mu'} + \frac{R}{k\mu'}\left(1 - e^{-k\mu' h/R}\right)\right] \quad \& \quad v = L/k$$

If h = $2\frac{1}{2}$diameter,last term may be omitted.
P= Total lateral pressure at depth h per unit of length of cir-

-cumference.

P_v'= Total load per lin.ft. carried by side walls.

P_v'x circumference = Total load on the entire bin wall.

P_v'x πD+ Weight of contents = Total load on bottom of bin.

Note: For pressure in a rectangular bins, calculate pressures in a circular or a square bin that has the same hydraulic radius.

EXAMPLE 10-1 (using tables)

Given:-Design a 20' diameter x 100' deep concrete bin containing wheat of 50 pcf.

$H/D = 100/20 = 5$. From table $L/D = 29.8$, $V/D = 49.66$

$V = 49.66 \times 20 = 9932$ #/□'

$L = 29.80 \times 20 = 596$ #/□'

Horizontal reinforcement $A_s = \dfrac{L \times rad}{f_s} = \dfrac{596 \times 10}{16000} = 0.372$ □"

use #5 bars, spacing $= \dfrac{12 \times \text{Area of bar}}{\text{Area req'd}} = \dfrac{12 \times 0.3068}{0.372} = 10$" c/c

Vert. reinforcement

Assume $n = 12$, $A_c = 72$ □", $W_c = 7500$ #/ft

$P_v' = 50 \times 4.96 \left[100 - \dfrac{4.96}{0.25}\right] = 19{,}900$ #/ft.

use #5 @ 18"

EXAMPLE 10-02

Given: Same as example 10-01 except use column B of tables.

assume 20'-0" dia; 100'-0" high and 6" conc. walls. wheat @ 50#/cft

Total weight of bin filled $= 314$ □' $\times 50 \times 100 = 1.57 \times 10^6$ #

$H/D = \dfrac{100}{20} = 5$; $\dfrac{L}{D} = 29.80$ #□'; $\dfrac{V}{D} = 49.66$ #□'

$L = 29.80 \times 20 = 596$ #/□', $V = 49.66 \times 20 = 993$ #/□'

Lateral reinforcing

Area of steel required to resist bursting pressure

$A_s = \dfrac{L \times radius}{f_s} = \dfrac{596 \times 10}{16000} = 0.372$ □"

using #5 bars, then spacing $= \dfrac{12 \times \text{Area of bar}}{\text{Area reqd}} = \dfrac{12 \times 0.3068}{0.372}$

$= 10$"

for reinforcing at various depths, use new H/D for example at $\frac{1}{2}$ Height.

Vertical reinforcement.
The vertical steel is required to carry the load in bending between horizontal bands of steel.

$M = wL^2/12$

There will be -ve moment M at the horizontal reinforcement and +ve bending moment M midway between the horizontal reinforcement. This vertical steel also takes its shape of vertical wall load.
Vertical load on wall
The grain carried by the bin walls will be equal to the total weight of grain in the bin minus the total pressure on the bottom of the bin.

Total weight: = 1570,000 #
Total pressure on bottom of bin = 993 x 314 = = - 312,000 #
1,258,000 #
Load per foot of wall: = 1258000/20.5x3.14 = 20000 #/ft

To this add weight of concrete in wall, then deduct opening through the wall, and determine the thickness of the wall by the allowable bearing on the foundation slab.

The total vertical load per lin.ft. of wall = 20000 #
the weight of the concrete = 7500
Total weight/Lin. ft of wall = 27500 #

Bearing at bottom of wall $= \frac{27500}{12 \times 6} = 382 \#/\square''$

(assuming no area is lost by the opening in walls)
Assume vert, steel #5φ @ 18" o/c As V. = 0.134; n = 10
stress in steel = 382 #/□" x 10 = 3820 #/□"
Note: For pressure in rectangular bin, determine the pressure in a circular bin that has the same hydraulic radius.
R (Hydraulic Radius) It is the ratio of area to the perimeter of horizontal cross section of bin

$$R = D/4$$

EXAMPLE 10-03
Given: wheat @ 50 PcF in Concrete Bin.
Bin 18'-0' x 20'-0" x 70'-0" Deep
Area = 360 □ft
Perimeter = 72'

$R = \frac{360}{72} = 5$

$D = 5 \times 4 = 20'$ DIA. Bin

$\frac{H}{D} = \frac{70}{20} = 3.5$

$\frac{L}{D} = 29.09$

$L = 29.09 \times 20 = 581.8 \#/\square'$

$\frac{V}{D} = 48.48$

$V = 48.48 \times 20 = 969.6 \#/\square'$

Pressure in Lbs Per Sq. Foot in diameter in deep Conc. bins

H/D	A L/D	A V/D	B L/D	B V/D	C L/D	C V/D	D L/D	D V/D	E L/D	E V/D
0.1	4.05	9.65	2.85	4.75	2.90	9.68	2.88	9.60	0.88	4.88
0.2	7.74	18.42	5.43	9.05	5.58	18.59	5.62	18.72	1.71	9.58
0.3	11.24	26.75	7.77	12.94	7.92	26.40	8.16	27.20	2.51	13.93
0.4	14.56	34.65	9.90	16.49	10.16	33.88	10.61	35.36	3.26	18.13
0.5	17.42	41.46	11.80	19.67	12.18	40.59	12.82	42.78	3.98	22.12
0.6	20.15	47.96	13.54	22.56	13.99	46.64	14.98	49.92	4.67	25.92
0.7	22.93	54.57	15.10	25.17	15.71	52.36	16.99	56.64	5.32	29.53
0.8	25.35	60.33	16.53	27.54	17.16	57.20	18.86	62.88	5.94	32.87
0.9	27.54	65.55	17.81	29.67	18.55	61.82	20.64	68.80	6.52	36.24
1.0	29.56	70.35	18.97	31.67	19.87	66.22	22.27	72.24	7.08	39.35
1.1	31.47	74.19	20.02	33.36	20.99	69.96	23.86	79.52	7.61	42.30
1.2	33.27	79.18	20.97	34.94	22.06	73.54	25.39	84.64	8.12	45.12
1.3	34.98	83.25	21.83	36.38	23.00	76.67	26.69	88.96	8.60	47.80
1.4	36.47	86.80	22.60	37.07	23.91	79.70	27.94	93.12	9.06	50.34
1.5	37.90	90.20	23.31	38.85	24.68	82.28	29.18	97.28	9.49	52.76
1.6	39.83	93.37	23.95	39.91	25.41	84.70	30.89	100.96	9.91	55.07
1.7	40.46	96.30	24.52	40.87	26.07	86.19	31.39	104.64	10.31	57.86
1.8	41.54	98.87	25.04	41.73	26.73	89.10	32.40	108.00	10.68	59.34
1.9	42.63	101.46	25.56	42.52	27.26	90.86	33.31	111.04	11.04	61.33
2.0	43.61	103.79	25.74	43.24	27.76	92.53	34.18	113.92	11.38	63.27
2.1	44.51	105.93	26.33	43.88	28.22	94.05	35.02	116.72	11.69	64.93
2.2	45.36	107.96	26.67	44.45	28.63	95.43	35.85	119.49	12.01	66.71
2.3	46.14	109.81	27.00	45.00	29.04	96.80	36.55	121.84	12.29	68.30
2.4	46.57	111.55	27.28	45.47	29.37	97.96	37.27	124.24	12.58	69.88
2.5	47.55	113.17	27.54	45.90	29.70	99.00	37.92	126.40	12.84	71.35
2.6	48.10	114.48	27.77	46.24	29.99	99.95	38.61	128.70	13.09	72.75
2.7	48.75	116.03	27.99	46.64	30.24	100.79	39.07	130.94	13.34	74.05
2.8	49.28	117.23	28.18	46.96	30.50	101.66	39.63	132.10	13.56	75.34
2.9	49.55	118.71	28.35	47.25	30.11	102.38	40.13	133.76	13.78	76.57
3.0	50.24	119.57	28.51	47.51	30.91	103.04	40.61	135.36	13.98	77.69
3.2	51.07	121.55	28.78	47.96	31.25	104.18	41.48	138.27	14.37	79.81
3.4	51.75	123.24	29.00	48.33	31.56	105.20	42.24	140.80	14.71	81.70
3.6	52.39	124.69	29.18	48.64	31.80	105.99	42.92	143.06	15.03	83.47
3.8	52.93	125.97	29.33	48.88	31.99	106.65	43.51	145.04	15.30	85.00
4.0	53.35	127.04	29.45	49.09	32.17	107.23	44.45	146.82	15.52	86.47
4.5	54.26	129.14	29.66	49.43	32.47	108.24	45.11	150.35	16.10	89.46
5.0	54.86	130.57	29.80	49.66	32.67	108.90	45.88	152.93	16.52	91.79
6.0	55.57	132.26	29.93	49.88	32.87	109.56	46.86	156.21	17.10	95.02
8.0	56.06	133.47	29.97	49.88	32.98	109.93	47.65	158.83	17.67	98.70
10.0	56.17	133.69	30.00	50.00	33.00	109.99	47.91	159.70	17.88	99.33

Values of Constants & Pressures

Material	W	K	μ'	L/D & V/D
Cement	100	0.42	0.445	Col. A.
Raw MIX	75	0.42	0.445	75% Col A
Anthricite	52	0.42	0.445	52% Col A
Wheat	50	0.60	0.4167	Col. B
Stone	100	0.38	0.767	Col. C
Sand	100	0.30	0.52	Col. D
Gravel	100	0.30	0.52	Col. D
Bituminous	50	0.18	0.695	Col. E

V = Vert. pressure in #/□'

L = Lat. Pressure " "

D = Dia. of bin in Feet

K = Ratio of $\frac{\text{Lateral pressure}}{\text{Vert. pressure}}$

μ' = Tang of ∠ of friction

W = weight of material in PCF

H = Depth in ft from top surface of material to Point L & V are req'd.

SUSPENDED STORAGE BIN

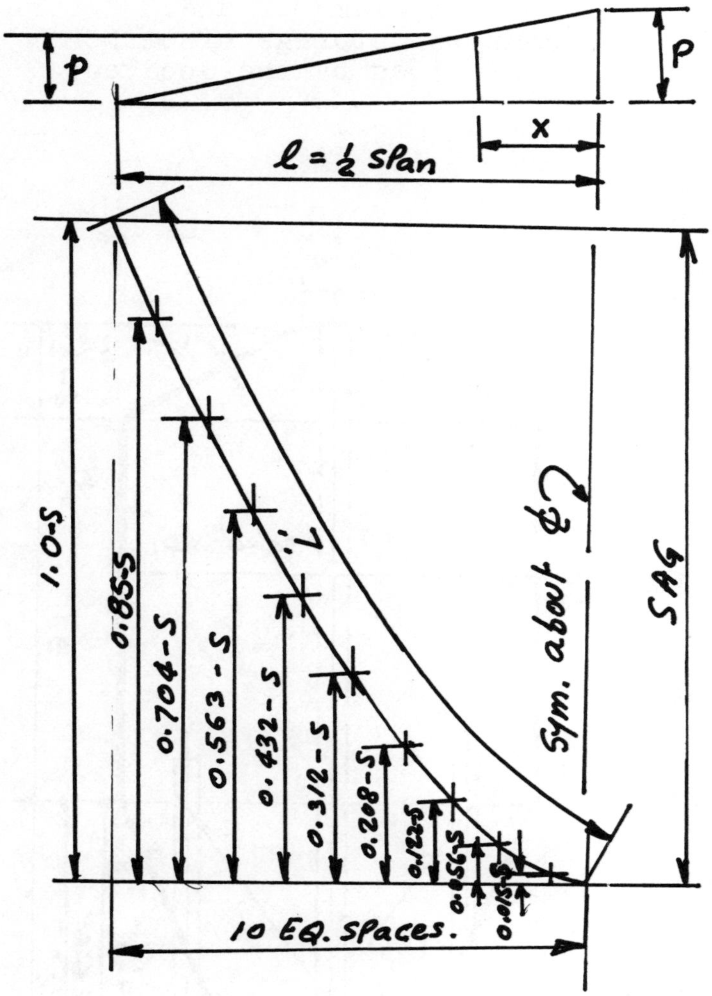

Curve Equation of the Bin.

$$Y = \frac{1}{2}\frac{S}{l^2}\left(3x^2 - \frac{x^3}{2}\right)$$

$$C = \frac{5}{4} l S$$

$$P = \frac{Cw}{2}$$

$$p = \frac{5}{4} S w$$

$$H = \frac{C w l}{3S}$$

$$V = \frac{1}{2} C w$$

$$= \frac{5}{8} S l w \text{ for bin level full.}$$

$$T = C w \sqrt{\frac{1}{4} + \frac{l^2}{9S^2}}$$

Note:
Loading of bin is represented by the lar loading diagram varying from "p" zero. At each support to a max. "P" at the center. To provide for best conditions of cleaning bin, the sag should be made not less than the total span. Under special conditions a shallow bin be approved.

l = ½ span in feet, S sag in feet.
H = horizontal component of stress in plates in lbs/ft of bin.
w = weight of bin filling lbs/cft.
T = Max. tension in plates lbs/ft of bin
r = reaction of bin lbs/ft of bin.
C = capacity of bin cft/ft of bin.

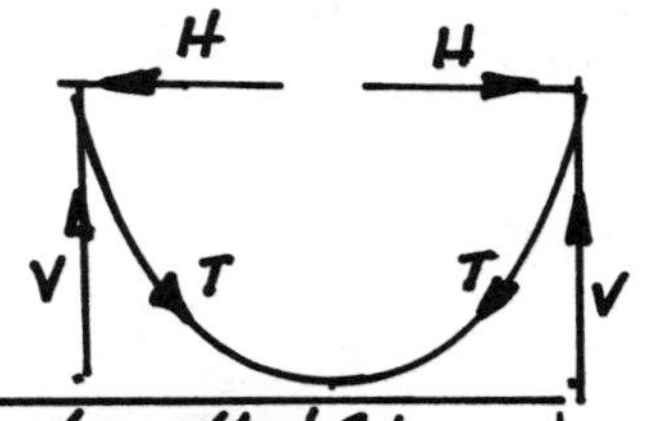

Length of Curve

Sag Ratio S/l	Length 'l'	Sag Ratio S/l	length 'l'
1/4	1.06378	1	1.45722 l
1/2	1.13686 l	6/5	1.61131 l
1/3	1.22992 l	4/3	1.71906 l
3/4	1.28307 l	3/2	1.85815 l
7/8	1.36651		

EXAMPLE 10-04

Given:- Design a steel storage bin 34' in diameter and 33' straight shell height supported on columns for storage of carbon black to be used for the manufacture of tires by the Goodyear Tire and Rubber Company.

Weight of 1 cft Carbon black

content = 20#/cft

design = 35#/cft

Contents:-

Top cone frustum (4' filled)

$V = 0.2618 \times 4(34^2 + 34 \times 6 + 6^2)$

$= 1383.35$

Shell,

$V = \frac{\pi \times 34^2}{4} \times 33 = 30003.92$

Bottom Cone,

$V = 0.2618 \times 29.25(34^2 + 34 \times 9 + 9^2)$

$= 12172.46$

Total $V = 1383.35 + 30003.92 + 12172.46$

$= 43559.73$ cft

Less 4'φ Pipe

$V = \frac{\pi \times 4^2}{4} \times 70.37 = -884.00$

Net-Volume $V = 42675.73$ cft

Contents = 42675 × 20

= 85350#

Wind:-

Shell $36 \times 33 \times 18\#/\square' = 21384\#$

Bottom cone $\frac{36+9}{2} \times 29.25 \times 15\#/\square' = 9750\#$

Roof $\frac{36+6}{2} \times 8.12 \times 18\#/\square' = 3069\#$

34203#

Wind on Bin:- = 34203#

Wind on one Panel = 17102#.

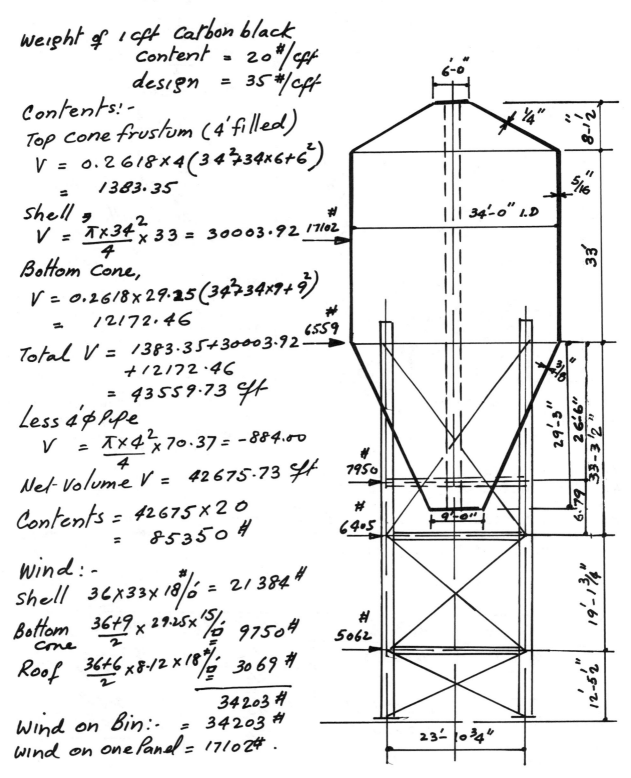

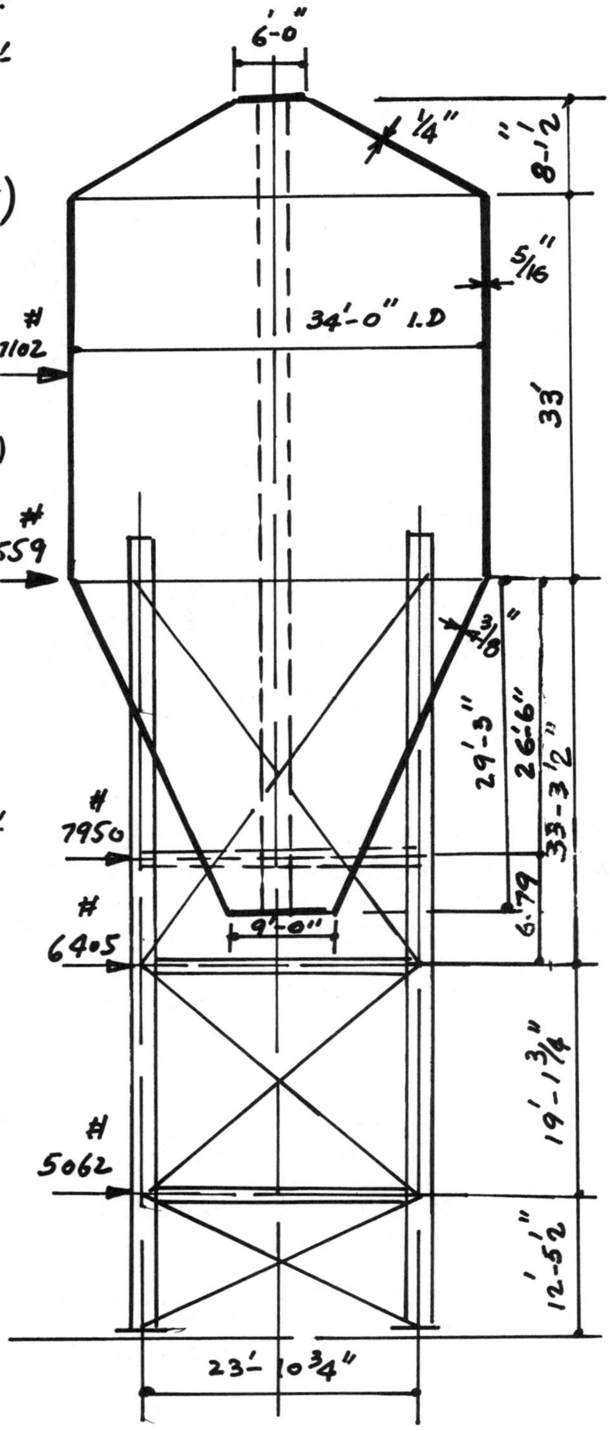

$\frac{26.5}{2} \times 33 \times 30\ \#/\square' = \frac{13118}{2} = 6559\#$

$\left(\frac{6.79+26.5}{2}\right) \times 33 \times 30\ \#/\square' = \frac{15900}{2} = 7950\#$

$\left(\frac{6.79+19.14}{2}\right) \times 33 \times 30\ \#/\square' = \frac{12810}{2} = 6405\#$

$\left.\begin{array}{l} \frac{19.14}{2} \times 33 \times 30\ \#/\square' = \frac{9540}{2} = 4750\# \\ \frac{12.5}{2} \times 50 \times 2 = \frac{625}{2} = 312\# \end{array}\right\} 5062$

$M.W = \left\{17102\,(64.88+16.5+2.7) + \left[(33 \times 52.36)30\right]\left[12.5 + \frac{52.36}{2}\right] + \left[(12.5)^2 \times \frac{4 \times 50}{2}\right]\right\} / 23.88\sqrt{2}$

$= 48800\#$ Say 50 K

Column Design

Wt. of contents	= 42000 x 35	=	1,470,000 #
wt. of Col & Bracing =		=	25,000 #
wt. of Tare Bin		=	70,000 #
wt of Equip		=	10,000 #
		Total	1575,000 #

wt./column $= \frac{1575K}{4} = 393^K$ Say 395^K

wind Load $50K$

Total Load/Col. $= 445^K$

Try 20" O.D (0.344" thick wall)

$A = 0.7854(20^2 - 19.312^2) = 22\ \square''$

$S = 0.098175(d^2 + d_1^2)/4 = 107.99\ in^3$

$r = \frac{\sqrt{d^2 + d_1^2}}{4} = 6.95''$

$l_u = 33' - 3\frac{1}{2}'' = 399.5''$

$\frac{l}{r} = \frac{399.5}{6.95} = 57.5$

$F_a = 17.67 + \frac{1}{3}$ due to wind $= 23.56^{ksi}$

Load allowable $= 23.56 \times 22 = 518.32 > 445$ ok

Use 20" O.D (0.344" Thick wall) Tubing str. Grade.

Col. base Plate.

$F_p = 0.75Ksi$, concrete 3000 #/□" 28 days.

$P = 445$

$F_b = 27Ksi$ For A36 steel.

$$A = \frac{P}{Fp} = \frac{445}{0.75} = 590 \, \square''$$

Try $25 \times 25 = 625 > 590$ ok

$$m = \frac{25 - 0.95 \times 20}{2} = 3$$

$$n = \frac{25 - 0.8 \times 20}{2} = 4.5 \quad \text{use} \leftarrow$$

$$Fp (actual) = \frac{445}{625} = 0.712 \, KSI$$

$$t = \sqrt{3 \, Fp \, n^2 / Fb} = \sqrt{\frac{3 \times 0.712 \times 4.5^2}{27}} = 1.262$$

use $t = 1\frac{1}{2}''$ thick

Size of the base $\mathcal{P}\!L$ $25'' \times 25'' \times 1\frac{1}{2}''$

Anchor $\mathcal{P}\!L$ Bolts

Max w.L $= 50,000^{\#}$

$- D.L = \frac{105000 - 25'}{4} \doteq 19,560^{\#}$

$\overline{30440^{\#}}$

A Bolt Req'd $= \frac{30440}{20000} = 1.52 \, \square''$

Use $4 - 1\frac{1}{4} \, \phi$ Bolts $(3.56 \, \square'')$ w/ $5''$ Proj above Pier.

Bin walls :- Design for liquid sp. Gravity $= \frac{62.4}{35} = 1.78$

Shell :- Per U.G 27(c) A.S.M.E Code $\underline{VIII}$

$$t = \frac{PR}{SE + 0.4P}$$

for simplification we can use

$$t = \frac{PR}{SE}, \quad P = 0.433 \times 33 \times 1.78 = 25.43 \, \text{pcf}$$

$$R = 204'', \, S = 22000 \, psi, \, E = 0.85$$

$$t = \frac{25.43 \times 204}{22000 \times 0.85} = 0.277$$

use $t = \frac{5}{16}'' \, \mathcal{P}\!L$

Roof :- $t = \frac{D}{200} = \frac{34}{200} = 0.17''$ use $t = \frac{1}{4}'' \, \mathcal{P}\!L$

CONe :- Head $= 33 + 9.75 = 42.75$

$$P = 0.433 \times 42.75 \times 1.78 = 33.23$$

$$t = \frac{33.23 \times 204}{22000 \times 0.85} = 0.362$$

Use $t = 3/8''$ Plate

Check by alternate formula

$$T_1\,(\text{Lat. Arc}) = \frac{R_3}{2\cos\alpha}\left(P + \frac{(W_w + W_s)}{A}\right)$$

where R_3 = radius at junction of cone & shell = 204''

$\alpha = 23^\circ$, $P = 25.43$ Psi

$W_w = 1470{,}000\#$, W_s (bottom of cone) $= 426{,}000\#$

Total $A = \pi R_3^2 = 130741\ \square''$

$\cos\alpha = 0.61$

$$T_1 = \frac{204}{2\times 0.61}\left(25.43 + \frac{1470000+426000}{130741}\right) = 6070\#/''$$

$3/8''$ PL $= 16184\ \#/\square'' < 22000$ Psi ok

Use $3/8''$ PL.

Design of Compression Ring

Shell at Knuckle

weight contents $= 840{,}000\#$

P @ knuckle $= (33+8.12)\,0.434\times 0.32 = 5.7\ \#/\square''$

Thickness of shell $= 5/16''$

$$f_t = \frac{5.7\times 405}{0.313} = 7420\ \#/\square''$$

$\tan\alpha = \tan 23^\circ = 0.4245$

$$\text{Load }\#/\text{inch shell} = \frac{840{,}000}{408\times\pi} = 655\ \#/''$$

Comp. Load $= 655\times 0.4245 = 278\ \#/''$ ⊙℄

Ring Compression $= 278\times 204 = 56700\#$

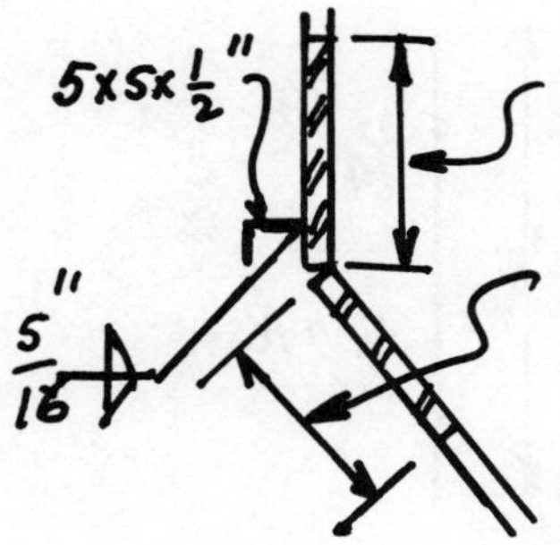

$0.60\sqrt{204\times 0.313} = 4.05$

$0.60\sqrt{256\times 0.375} = 6.00$

A =	4.05×0.313	$= 1.267$
	6.00×0.375	$= 2.250$
	∠ $5\times5\times\frac{1}{2}''$	$= 5.750$
		$9.267\ \square''$

$$M = \frac{2.88}{12} \times 78 \times 5834 = 109000 \text{ "\#}$$

$$S = \frac{109{,}000}{20000} = 5.45 \text{ in}^3$$

Try $5 \times 3 \times \frac{1}{4}$ L; $I = 5.1 \text{ in}^4$, $A = 1.94 \square''$

$$(1.94 + 3.75)\bar{x} = 3.75 \times .19 + .194 \times 4.72$$

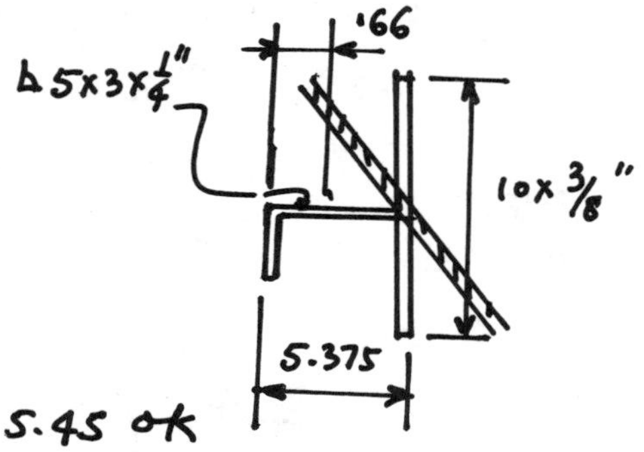

$$\bar{x} = 1.54$$

$$I = 5.1$$

$$Ad^2 \quad (3.75) \times (1.35)^2 = 6.82$$

$$\overline{11.92}$$

$$S = \frac{11.92}{1.54} = 7.76 > 5.45 \text{ ok}$$

use L $5 \times 3 \times \frac{1}{4}$ upto D'

@ 26' below knuckle

$$V = \frac{5}{4} \times 35 \times 11.77 \left(1 - e^{-0.8 \frac{59}{11.77}}\right) = 507 \#/\square' = 3.52 \#/\square'$$

$$p_E' = 3.52 \times \left(\frac{1.92}{0.842 \times 2.37}\right) = 1.59 \#/\square''$$

$$M = \frac{1.59}{12} \times 78 \times \frac{100^3 + 100^3}{100 + 100} = 103000 \text{ "\#}$$

$$S = \frac{103000}{20000} = 5.15$$

$$Ph_A = Ph \tan^2(45 - \theta/2) = 35 \times 33 \tan^2\left(45 - \frac{35}{2}\right)$$

$$= 384.62 \#/\square' = 2.67 \#/\square''$$

Partition Plate thickness

$$f = 0.141\left(\frac{w l^2}{t^2}\right)$$

$$t = \sqrt{\frac{0.141 \times 2.67 \times 60 \times 60}{24000}} = 0.24 \quad \text{use } 5/16\text{" thick PL}$$

$$Ph_E = 35 \times 17 \times 0.5774^2 = 198 \#/\square' = 1.37 \#/\square''$$

$$t = \sqrt{\frac{0.141 \times 1.37 \times 60^2}{24000}} = .175$$

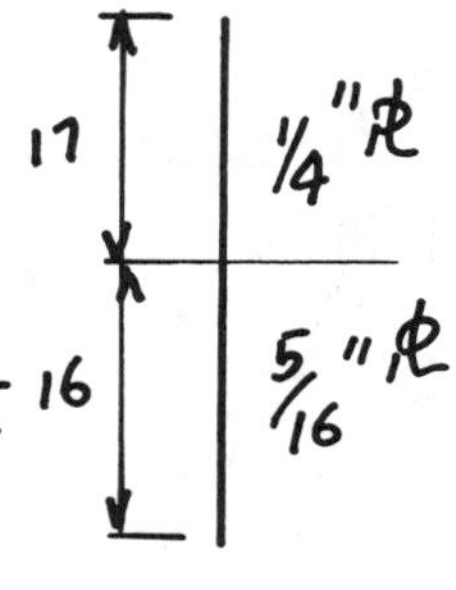

use $t = 1/4''$

Design of stiffener for Partition Plate

$$P = 354.62 \#/\square', \quad w = 1923 \#/ft$$

$$fc = \frac{56700}{9.267} = 6130 \#/\square'' < 22000 \text{ Psi OK}$$

Judging from experience, place compression ring @ 5 ft from knuckle in shell & then @ 7'-0 spacing

∠ 5x3x5/16"

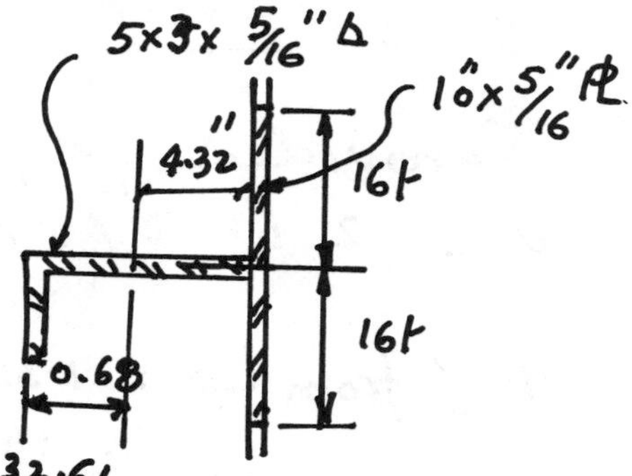

$I = 6.3 \text{ in}^4, \; A = 2.4 \square''$

$(2.4 + 3.13)\bar{x} = 3.125 \times \frac{165}{32} + 2.40 \times 0.68$

$\bar{x} = 3.22''$

$I = 6.3 + 2.4(2.47)^2 + 3.125(1.94)^2$

$= 32.61 \text{ in}^4$

$S_1 = \frac{32.61}{3.22} = 10.15 \text{ in}^3, \quad S_2 = \frac{32.61}{2.09} = 15.6$

$fc = \frac{56700}{5.53} = 10220 \#/\square'' \text{ ok}$

use 5x3x5/16 ∠.

Provide compression ring in the cone @ 6'-6" from knuckle.

∠ of repose 30°

$\Theta = 67°$

$p_{B'} = \frac{r \sin^2(\Theta + \phi)}{\sin^3\Theta \left(1 + \frac{\sin\phi}{\sin\Theta}\right)^2}$

&

$V = \frac{5}{4} wd \left(1 - e^{-0.8\frac{h}{d}}\right)$

$= \frac{5}{4} \times 35 \times 28.43 \left(1 - e^{-0.8\frac{39.5}{28.43}}\right)$

$= 6.42 \#/\square'$

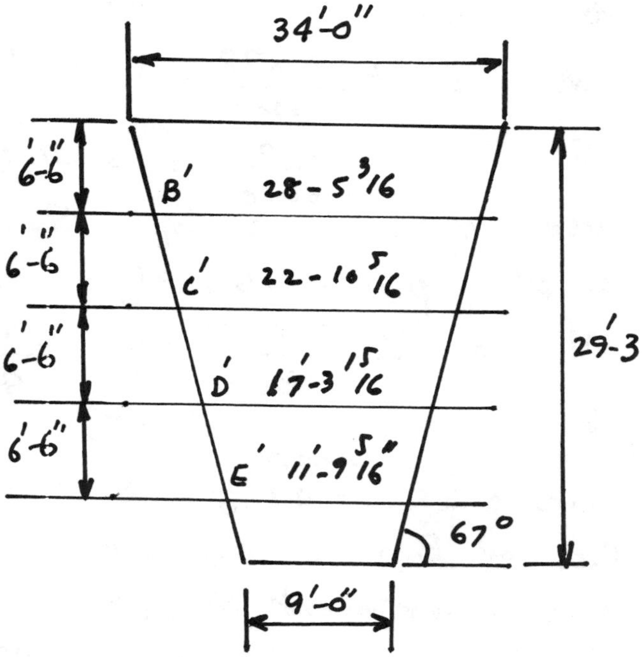

$p_{B'} = \frac{6.42 \sin^2(67 + 30)}{\sin^3 67 \left(1 + \frac{\sin 30}{\sin 67}\right)^2}$

$= 2.88 \#/\square''$

6'-6" below knuckle

Can be taken as square side $= \frac{341}{\sqrt{2}} = 240.5''$

$\frac{L^3 + B^3}{L + B} = \frac{240.5^3 + 240.5^3}{240.5 + 240.5} = 5834$

Span 15'

$$M = \frac{wl^2}{10} = \frac{1923 \times 15 \times 15 \times 12}{10} = 496{,}000''\#$$

$$\sigma = 24000 \text{ psi}$$

$$S = \frac{496000}{24000} = 20.7 \text{ in}^3$$

$S_{provided} = 33.4 \text{ in}^3$

Use 2 ∟s $8'' \times 8'' \times \frac{1}{2}''$

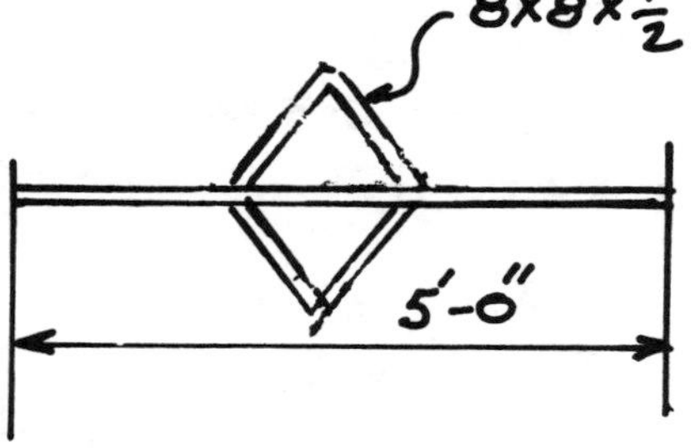

$$p_{18'} \text{ from top} = 1.35 \times 144$$
$$= 195 \#/\square'$$

$$M = \frac{wl^2}{10} = \frac{5 \times 195 \times 15 \times 15 \times 12}{10} = 263{,}000$$

$$S = \frac{263000}{24000} = 10.95$$

Provide 2∟ $6 \times 6 \times \frac{5}{8}''$, $S = 15.8 \text{ in}^3$.

$$p_{13'} \text{ from top} = 2.88 \#/\square'$$

$$M = \frac{2.88 \times 78}{12} \times \pi \times \frac{(341.1)^2}{4} \times \frac{1}{9} = 602000$$

$$S = \frac{60200}{20000} = 3.01 \text{ in}^3$$

Use 2∟s $4 \times 4 \times \frac{3}{8}''$ $S_x = 3.00 \text{ in}^3$

At E', $p_{E'} = 1.59 \#/\square''$

$$M = \frac{1.59 \times 78}{12} \times \pi \times \frac{(141.3)^2}{4} \times \frac{1}{9} = 15100$$

$$S = \frac{15100}{20000} = 0.75$$

Use 2∟s $4 \times 4 \times \frac{1}{4}$ $S = 2.00 \text{ in}^3$.

Dia of Bin = 34' I.D.

6 compartment @ 60°

Length of arc of one compartment

$$a = \frac{A}{R}$$

$$A = aR$$

$$\text{Log } A = \log a + \log R = 0.02003 + 1.23045$$
$$= 1.25048$$

$$A = 17'\text{-}9\tfrac{13}{16}''$$

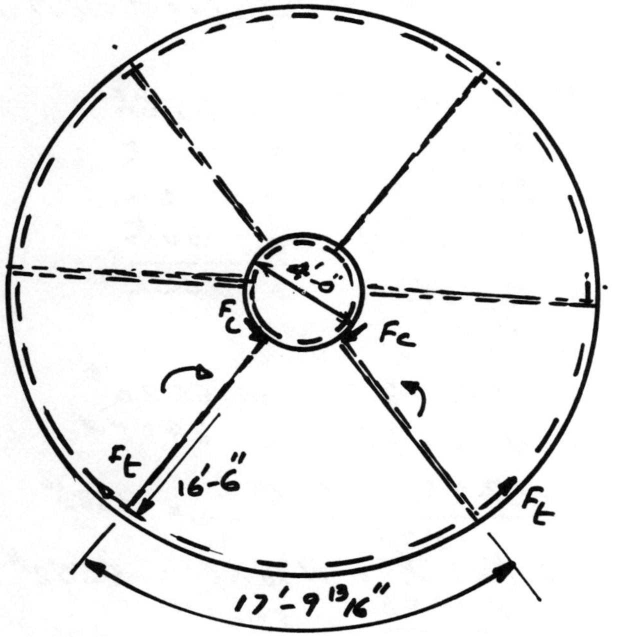

A of inner pipe $= \frac{\pi(4\times12)}{6} = 25.14''$

$$M = \frac{\sigma t_f b_f^2}{r_i 8}$$

$$S = \frac{M}{\sigma} = \frac{t_f b_f^2}{r_i 8}$$

Let partition wall be 1/4" thick

then $S = \frac{bd^3}{12} = \frac{186}{12} \times \frac{1}{4} \times \frac{1}{4} \times \frac{1}{4} = 0.248$

$$\therefore 0.248 = \frac{t_f \times 25.14^2}{24 \times 8}$$

$$t_f = \frac{0.248 \times 24 \times 8}{(25.14)^2} = 0.01904''$$

say $= 0.125''$ say 1/8"

EXAMPLE 10-05

Given:- Design a Ferric Sulphate Bin of size 21' x 18' and 14.5' in height supported on columns.

Weight of 1 cft Fe_2SO_4 = 60#

weight of Bin contents

Vol. Rectangle = 21x18x14.5 = 5481 = 5481

Bottom = $2 \times \frac{11.92}{3}(10.55\times18 + 1\times18 + \sqrt{189}\times18)$ = 2120

7601 cft

weight = 7601x60 = 456k

wt. Top of Bin = = 6k

wt. col & Bracing = 10k

wt. Bin (Self wt) = 30k

Load on 4 cols. 502k

Wind = 25 #/□'

End: 18x14.5x25 = 6520#

9.5x11.92x25 = 2835#

$V_{w1} = \frac{3260\times7.25 - 1417\times4}{15.75} = 1138\#$

Wind on one Panel = 1138x4 = 4552#

$V_{w2} = \frac{4552\times19.92}{15.75} = 5800\#$

Side:- 21x14.5x25 = 7600#

10x11.92x25 = 2980#

$V_{w1} = \frac{7600\times7.25 - 2980\times4}{2\times19.0} = 1490\#$

Wind on one Panel = 3800+1490 = 5290#

$V_{w2} = \frac{5290\times19.92}{19.0} = 5550$

Max. Wind Load = 5800+1138 = 6.938 Say 7K.

Load on 1 Col. = 125k (DL+L.L)

Wind Load = 7K

Max. M_{col} = $\frac{P}{2}(C-e) = \frac{5290}{2}(19.92-11.92)$

= 21160 Ft# = 21.160k

Try 12"x12"x1/4" structural tube

S = 43.48 in^3; A = 11.48 in^2, r = 4.77 in

$f_b = M/S = \frac{21.16\times12}{43.48} = 5.84$ ksi

$f_a = \frac{132}{11.48} = 11.50^k/\square''$ with wind

$\frac{l}{r} = \frac{96}{4.77} = 20.5$

$F_a = 20.570 \times 1\frac{1}{3} = 27.427^{ksi}$ for wind

$F_b = 22^{ksi}$ use 29.33 ksi for wind

$F_e' = \frac{149000}{(20.5)^2} = 355^{ksi}$

$= 355 \times 1\frac{1}{3} = 473.33^{ksi}$ for wind

$$\frac{f_a}{F_a} + \frac{C_m f_b}{\left(1-\frac{f_a}{F_e'}\right)F_b} \leq 1$$

$$\frac{11.5}{27.427} + \frac{0.85 \times 5.84}{\left(1-\frac{11.5}{473.3}\right)29.33} = 0.601 \leq 1 \text{ ok}$$

$$\frac{f_a}{22} + \frac{f_b}{F_b} \leq 1$$

$$\frac{11.5}{22} + \frac{5.84}{29.3} \leq 1$$

$0.523 + 0.199 = 0.722 \leq 1$ ok.

$\frac{L}{r} = \frac{(11.92-2.63)\times 12}{4.77} = 23.4$

$F_a = 20.38$, $\therefore P = 20.38 \times 11.48 = 234^k > 132$ ok

Use $12'' \times 12'' \times \frac{1}{4}''$ structural tube.

Column base Plate

$F_p = 0.750$ ksi, Concrete $3000^{\#}/\square''$ 28 days, $P = 132^k$, $F_b = 27^{ksi}$

$A = \frac{P}{F_p} = \frac{132}{0.75} = 175\ \square''$

Size Approximate $13.33'' \times 13.33''$, use $14'' \times 21''$

$m = \frac{21 - 0.95 \times 12}{2} = 4.8$ ← use

$n = \frac{14 - 0.95 \times 12}{2} = 1.3$

$F_{p\,actual} = \frac{140}{294} = 0.475^{ksi}$

$t = \sqrt{\frac{3 F_p m^2}{F_b}} = \sqrt{\frac{3 \times 0.475 \times 4.8^2}{27}} = 1.1$ use $1\frac{1}{8}''$

$\therefore$ Size of Base Plate $21 \times 14 \times 1\frac{1}{8}''$

1) For 18'-0" Inside dimension

$L_d = 18'\text{-}4'' = 220''$

Stress in DD' $= \frac{4552 \times 19.92}{9.29 \times 2} = 4875^{\#}\ (+)$

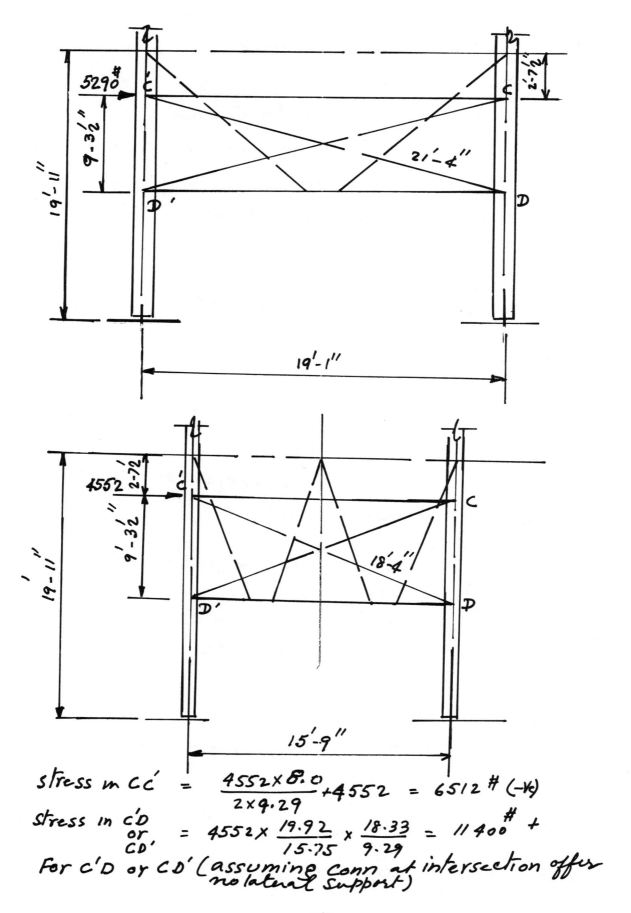

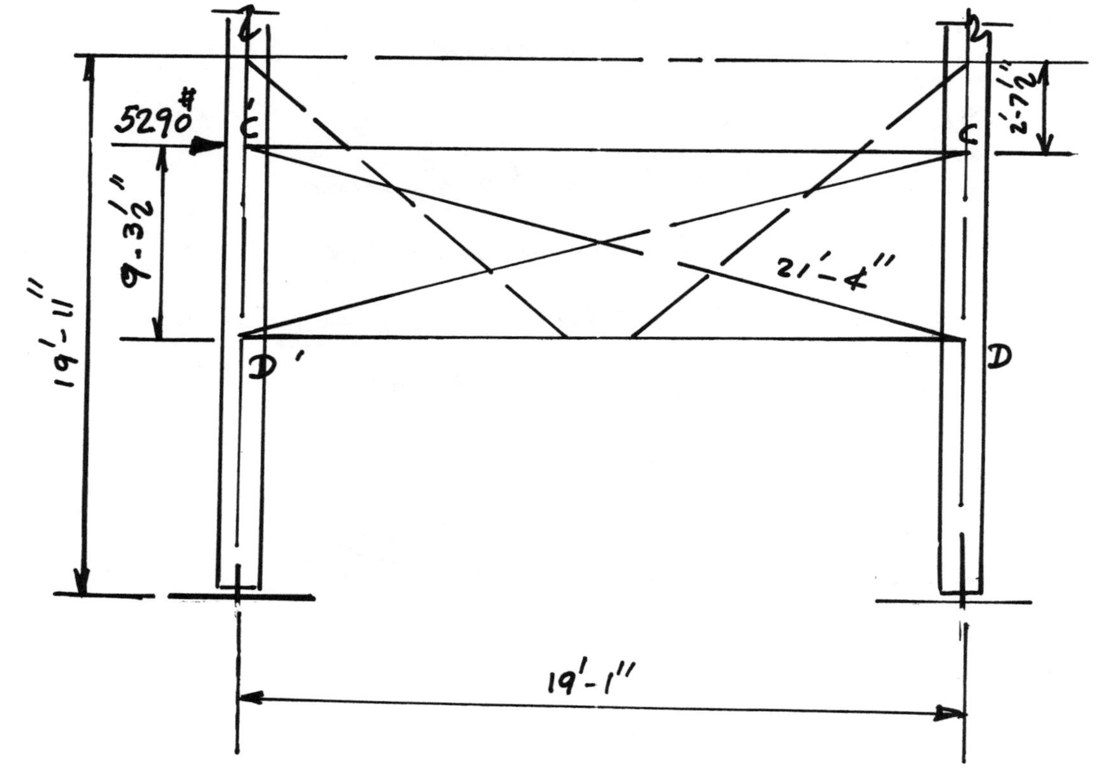

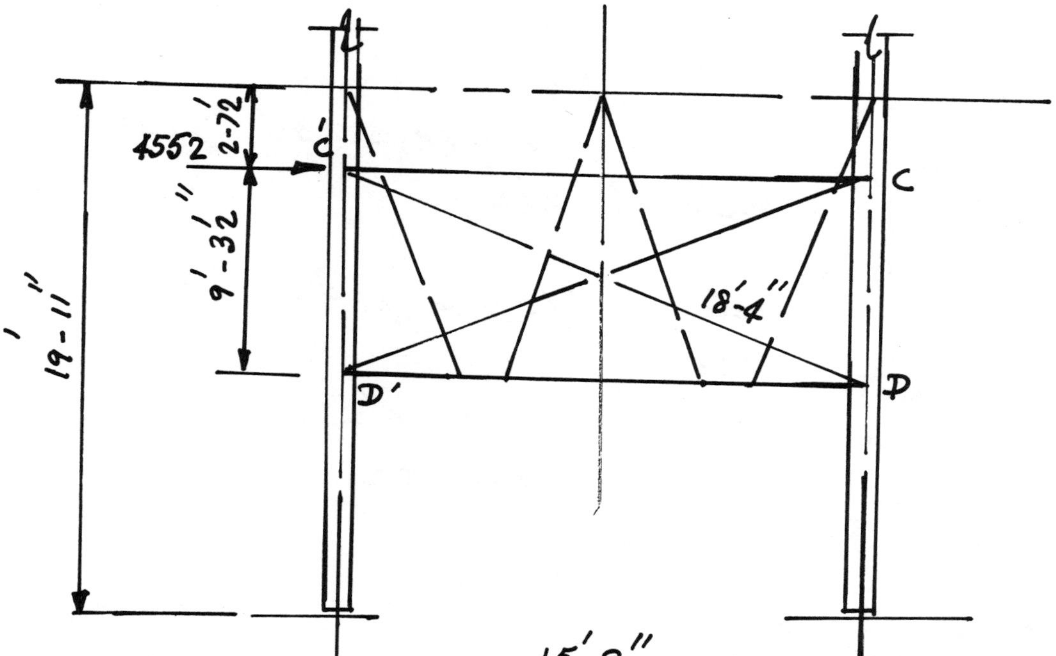

stress in CC' $= \dfrac{4552 \times 8.0}{2 \times 9.29} + 4552 = 6512^{\#}$ (−ve)

stress in C'D or CD' $= 4552 \times \dfrac{19.92}{15.75} \times \dfrac{18.33}{9.29} = 11400^{\#}$ +

For C'D or CD' (assuming conn at intersection offers no lateral support)

Max. $\frac{L}{r}$ for tension member = 300

min r = $\frac{220}{300}$ = 0.73"

For back to back ∠

r_{min} = 0.85"

Pallow = 2.38 × 22

= 62.36 K > 11.4 ok

Use 2- ╥ 3" × 2" × $\frac{1}{4}$" b to b 3/8"

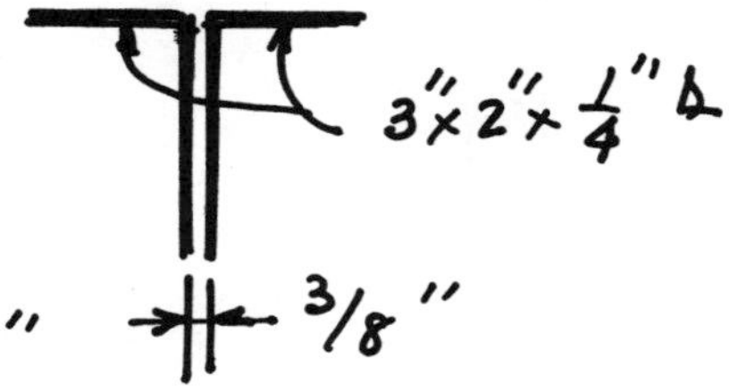

For 21'-0" Inside dimension

Ld = 21'-4" = 256"

Stress in DD' = $\frac{5290 \times 19.92}{2 \times 9.29}$ = 5400# (+)

stress in CC = $\frac{5290 \times 8.0}{2 \times 9.29}$ + 5290 = 7570 (−)

stress in C'D or CD' = $5290 \times \frac{19.92}{19.08} \times \frac{21.33}{9.29}$ = 13275# (+)

For C'D or CD' assuming conn at intersection offer no lateral support.

Max $\frac{L}{r}$ for tension member = 300

Min r = $\frac{256}{300}$ = 0.85"

Use 2 - ╥ 3 × 2 × $\frac{1}{4}$ B to B 3/8", r = 0.85"

Pall = 2.38 × 22 = 62.36 > 13.2 ok

Member DD' for 18' side tension = 4.88 K, L = 15.75'

" " For 21' side tension = 5.4 K, L = 19.08'

$\frac{L}{r}$ = 300 for tension

$r_{18'}$ = $\frac{189}{300}$ = 0.66", r_{21} = $\frac{229}{300}$ = 0.77"

Use 2- $2\frac{1}{2}$ × 2 × $\frac{1}{4}$" ╥ b to b 1/4", r = 0.78"

Pallowable = 2.12 × 22 = 46.64 > 4.88 > 5.4 ok

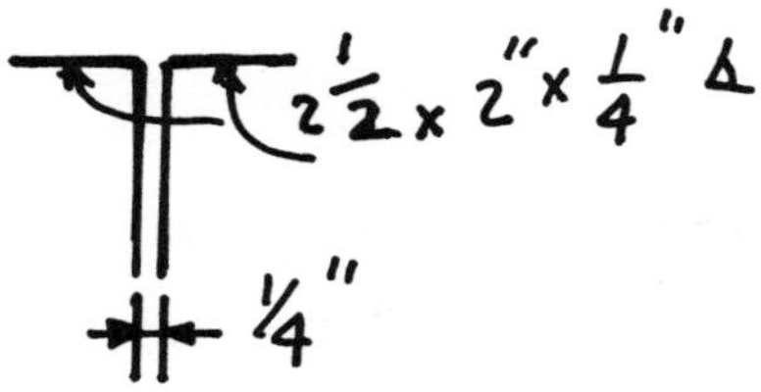

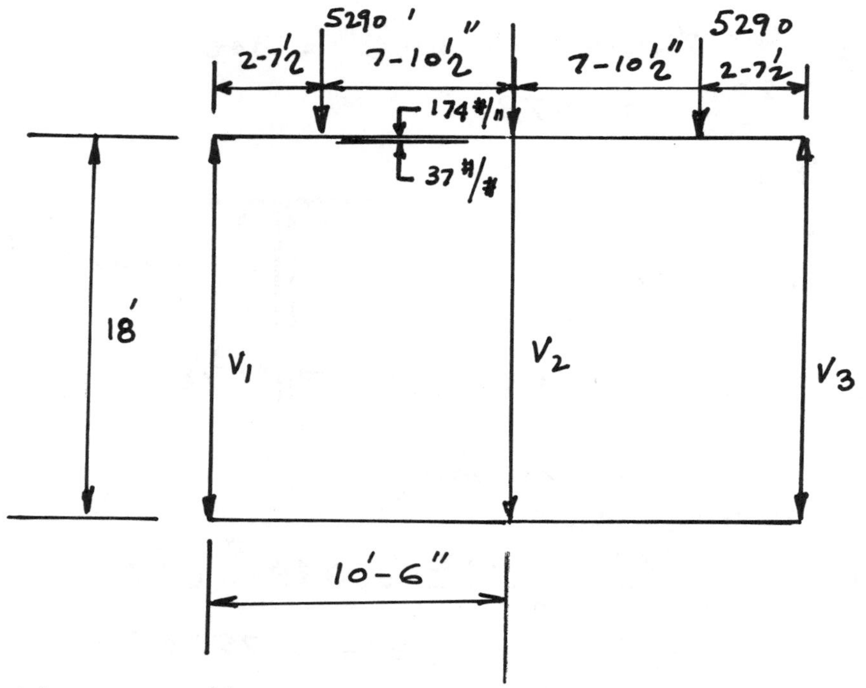

$M = M_{SS} - M_1$

$M_{SS} = \frac{137 \times 126^2}{8} = 271000''\# \; ; \; k = \frac{216}{126} = 1.71$

$-M_1 = \frac{137}{12} \times \frac{\{126^2 + (2 \times 216^2 \times 1.71)\}}{1 + 2 \times 1.71} = 455600''\#$

$M = 4556000 - 271000 = 184600$

M_{max} @ Load $= \frac{Pab}{4l^3}\left(4l^2 - a(l+a)\right) - \frac{Pab}{4l^3}a(l+a)$

$= \frac{Pab}{4l^3}\left(4l^2 - 2al - 2a^2\right)$

$= \frac{5290 \times 31.5 \times 94.5 \times 2}{4 \times 126^3}\left(31600 - 3970 - 990\right)$

$= 104300''\#$

$\Sigma M = 184600 + 104300 = 288900$

$S = \frac{288.9}{16} = 18.05 \text{ IN}^3$

Use 12 ⊔ 20.7, S = 21.4, plus shell gives S = 25.9 which will take care of compression.

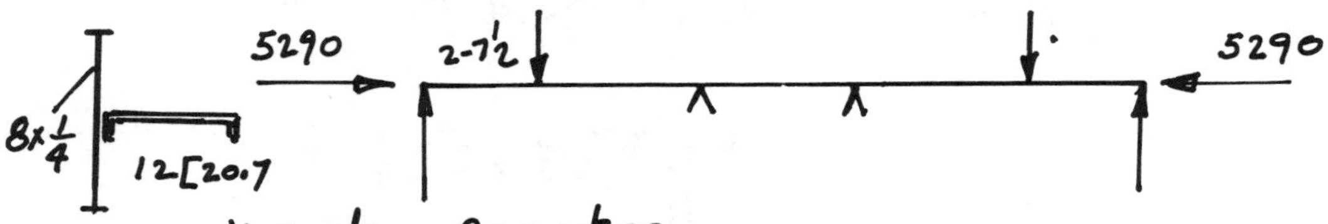

X-section Properties

$A = 6.03 + 2 = 8.03$

$$8.03 \times x = 6.03 \times 6 + 2 \times 12.125 = 36.18 + 24.25 = 60.43$$

$$x = 7.5$$

$$I = 128.1 + 6.03(1.5)^2 = 141.3$$

$$2 \times (5.625)^2 = \underline{61.6}$$

$$202.9$$

$$\frac{S}{2} = \frac{202.9}{7.5} = 25.9 \, in3$$

Section is compact   use $Fb = 24 ksi$

$$fa = \frac{5.290}{6.03} = 0.88$$

$$\frac{L}{ry} = \frac{57.25}{0.81} = 72.8$$

$$Fa = 16.13, \quad Fe' = 27.41 \text{ for } \frac{L}{r} = 72.8$$

$$1 - \frac{fa}{Fe'} = 1 - \frac{0.88}{27.41} = 0.97$$

for outside span $Cm = 1 + \psi \dfrac{fa}{Fe}$

$$\psi = -0.3$$

$$Cm = 1 - 0.3\left(\frac{0.88}{27.41}\right) = 0.91$$

$$\frac{fa}{Fa} + \frac{Cm \, fb}{\left(1 - \frac{fa}{Fe'}\right)Fb} \leq 1 \qquad \text{where } fb = \frac{531}{25.9} = 20.5$$

$$\frac{0.88}{16.13} + \frac{0.91 \times 20.5}{0.97 \times 24} = 0.854 \leq 1.0 \text{ ok}$$

Stiffener Design

$$P_h = 60 \, h \tan^2\left(45 - \frac{25}{2}\right)$$

$$= 340 \, \#/\square' = 2.38 \, \#/_{''}$$

$$P_A = 2.38 \times 30 = 71.4$$

$$k = \frac{b}{L} = \frac{216}{126} = 1.72$$

$$M = \frac{71.4}{12}\left(\frac{126^2 + 2(216)^2 1.72}{1 + 2(1.72)}\right)$$

$$= 232200 \, ''\#$$

$$S = \frac{232200}{22000} = 10.55 \, ^{in3}$$

$$P_B = 65.1$$

$0.82 \times 54 = 44.2 \, \#/_{''}$

$1.48 \times 42 = 62.1 \, \#/_{''}$

$1.97 \times 33 = 65.1 \, \#/_{''}$

$2.38 \times 30 = 71.4 \, \#/_{'}$

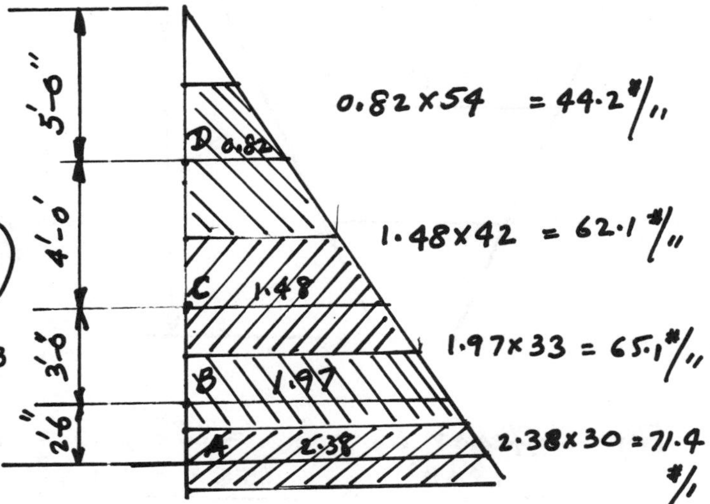

$$k = \frac{18}{21} = 0.859$$

$$M = \frac{65.1}{12}\left(\frac{252^2+(216^2)2\times 0.859}{1+2(0.859)}\right) = 313\,k''$$

$$M_{ss} = \frac{65.1}{8}\times(252)^2 = 515^{k''}$$

$$+M = 515-313 = 202\,k/''$$

$$S = \frac{313}{22} = 14.23\ in^3$$

Use 10" ⊔ 20#

$$P_C = 62.1\ \#/''$$

$$-M_1 = \frac{62.1}{12}\times\frac{107200}{1.859} = 300\ k\,in$$

$$S = \frac{300}{22} = 13.64\ in^3$$

Use 10 ⊔ 20

$$P_D = 44.2\ \#/''$$

$$-M_1 = \frac{44.2}{12}\times\frac{107200}{1.859} = 210\,k''$$

$$S = \frac{210}{22} = 9.54\,in^3$$

Use 9" ⊔ 13.4

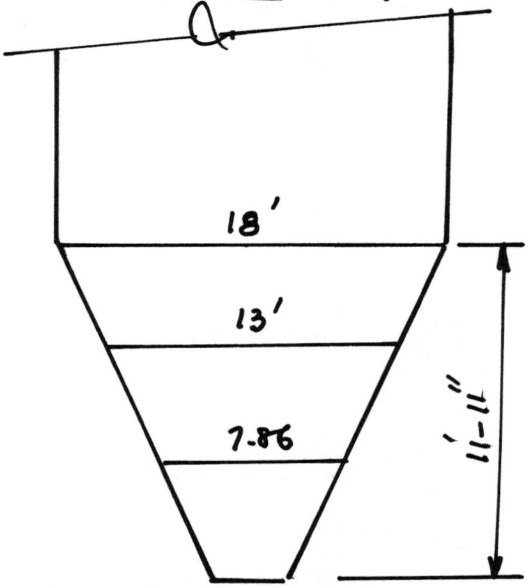

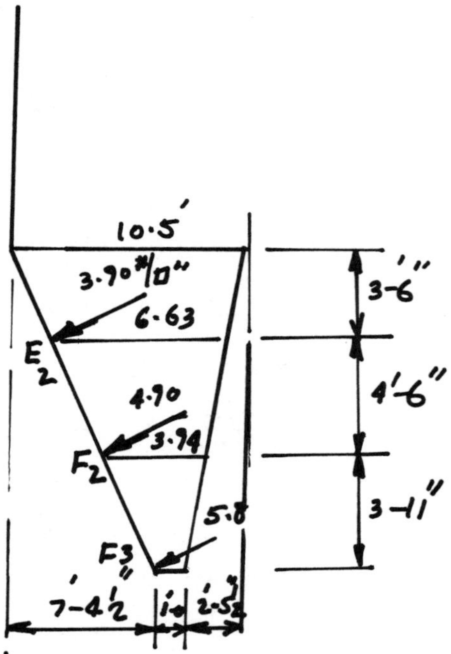

For stiffener E_2, $L = 156''$, $B = 79.5''$

$$\frac{L^3+B^3}{L+B} = \frac{156^3+79.5^3}{156+79.5} = 16850\ in^2$$

$W = 3.98 \times 48 = 187.5 \text{ \#/}''$

$M = \dfrac{187.5}{12} \times 16850 = 263000''\#$

$S = \dfrac{263000}{20000} = 13.1 \text{ in}^3$

$\tan\theta = \dfrac{11'-11''}{7'-4\frac{1}{2}''} \therefore \theta = 58^\circ\text{-}20'$

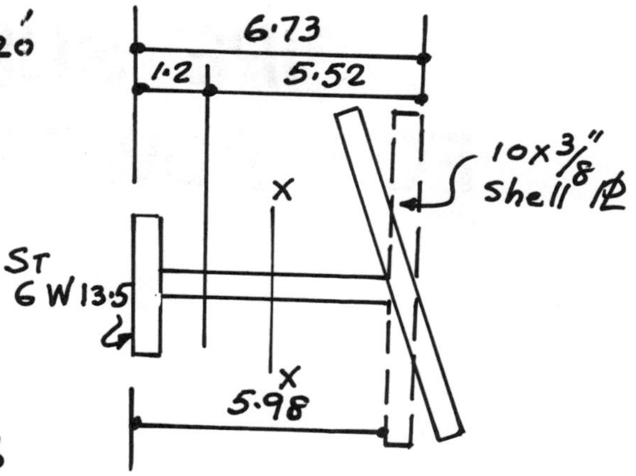

To find C.G

$(3.75 + 3.99)x = 3.75 \times 0.19 + 3.99 \times 5.15$

$7.74x = 21.33$

$x = 2.76$

I built up Section w/16t shell PL

$I_{ST6W13.5} = 11.4$

$Ad^2 = 3.75 \times (2.57)^2 = 24.8$

36.7

$\therefore S = \dfrac{36.7}{2.76} = 13.67 > 13.1 \text{ in}^3 \text{ ok}$

Use ST 6 W 13.5 & weld stem end to shell.

Similarly stiffener @ F_2, ST 5 W 10.5 Can be used.

In the same manner, the stiffener @ B, C & D can be made of 10 ⊔ 15.3, 10 ⊔ 15.3 & 8 ⊔ 11.5 with 16t shell PL.

11

PIPE SUPPORTS FOR POWER PLANTS

General Criteria

All new supports and modifications to existing supports shall be in accordance with the technical design guides prepared for the project.
Calculation lead sheets shall be prepared and attached to all supporting calculations.
Calculations shall be prepared for all pipe supports.

Design

Pipe supports shall be made of standard hardware whenever possible.
Pipe insulation protection saddles and/or pipe shoes shall be provided on insulated piping to protect insulation from crushing.
All welding attachments to stainless steel pipe shall be stainless steel.
For stainless steel pipe with an operating temperature greater than 200 F, spacers shall be provided on all pipe clamps.
A minimum of 1/16" clearance shall be provided between pipe and structural members of any box type restraint.
All U-Bolts shall have the notation "allow to slide" to prevent possible lock up of the pipe at time of installation.

Technical

Load summary sheets showing thermal, seismic and dynamic loads

should be available.Dead weight loads should also be cosidered. Proper isometric sketch for the piping supports shall be prepared.
Proper thermal displacements must be availble for all points.

EXAMPLE 11-01
Given:- Design a pipe support for the worst case of the followings loading conditions.

Load Type		Pounds			Pounds-Ft		
		Fx	Fy	Fz	Mx	My	Mz
Thermal		-177	-	-			
Dead Weight		-4	-	-			
Dynamic Loads	Normal	±12	-	-			
	Emerg.	-	-	-			
	Faulted	-	-	-			
Total Load	Normal	+12 -193	-	-			
	Emerg	-	-	-			
	faulted	-	-	-			
original Support design Load if any.	Normal						
	Emerg.						
	faulted						

$F_z = 177 \times 0.3 = 53.1^{\#}$ Frictional Force

$F_y = 53.1^{\#}$

Moments acting on wall Plates. Worst Case:- Seismic, frictional forces & weight of frame all acting at the same time.

Moment_y due to $F_z = 53.1^{\#} \times 31.75'' = 1685.93''^{\#}$

Moment_z due to $F_y = 53.1^{\#} \times 24'' = 1274.4''^{\#}$

Moment_z due to seismic normal $= 199/2 \times 10'' = 995''^{\#}$

Moment_z due to frame $= 75^{\#} \times 24'' = 1800''^{\#}$

Frame Wt.
$2 \times 3 \times 16.84 = 101.04$
$2 \times 1.33 \times 8.8 = 23.41$
$+$ Misc $= 25.00$
$\} = 149.45$ Say $150^{\#}$ or $75^{\#}$ Per Pl.

Total moments on each Plate

$= 1685.93 + 1274.4 + 995 + 1800 = 5755.33''\#$

$M_y = 1685.93''\#$; $M_z = 1274.4 + 995 + 1800 = 4069.4''\#$

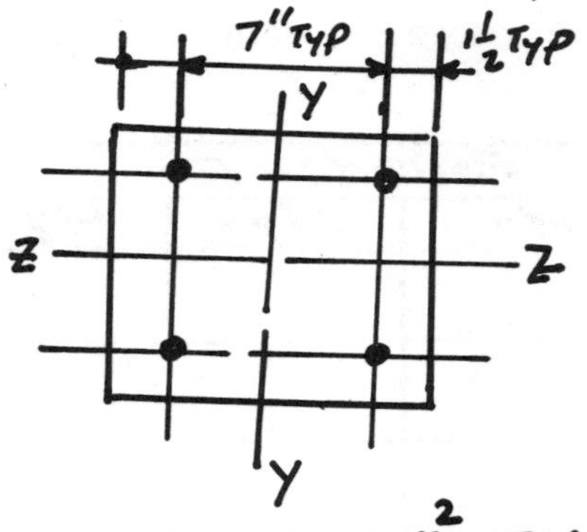

$$\Sigma T_x = \frac{199}{2} + \frac{1685.93}{7} + \frac{4069.4}{7} = 922$$

$$\Sigma V_y = \frac{53}{2} + \frac{1685.93}{49} = 61.4$$

$$\Sigma V_z = \frac{53}{2} + \frac{4069.4}{49} = 110$$

$I_z = 1 \times 2 \times 3.5^2 = 24.5$

$S_z = \frac{24.5}{3.5} = 7$

$I_y = 24.5 \quad S_y = 7$

$I_p = 24.5 + 24.5 = 49$

$$\Sigma V_y + V_z = (61.4^2 + 110^2)^{1/2} = 126$$

Try ½"φ Phillips Red Head Anchors

$$\frac{922}{1720} + \frac{110}{1750} = 0.599 < 1.0 \text{ o.K}$$

Thickness of PL

$$t = \frac{6M}{f_{all} \times b} \quad \text{where } M = (M_y^2 + M_z^2)^{1/2} = 4405''\#$$

$$= \frac{6 \times 4405}{21600 \times 10} = 0.122 \text{ use } 3/4''$$

∴ Size of wall Plates $10 \times 10 \times 3/4''$

Weld of Ts 4x4 to wall PL.

Total moment per Plate $= 5755.33''\#$

$$S_w = bd + \frac{d^2}{3} = 4 \times 4 + 4^2/3 = 21.33$$

$$f_w = \frac{5755.33}{21.33} = 270$$

$$\text{Req'd weld size} = \frac{270}{14400 \times 0.707} = 0.027'' \text{ use } 1/4'' \text{ all-around.}$$

Use ¼" fillet welds for all remaining welds By inspection.

Standard Trunion work sheet.

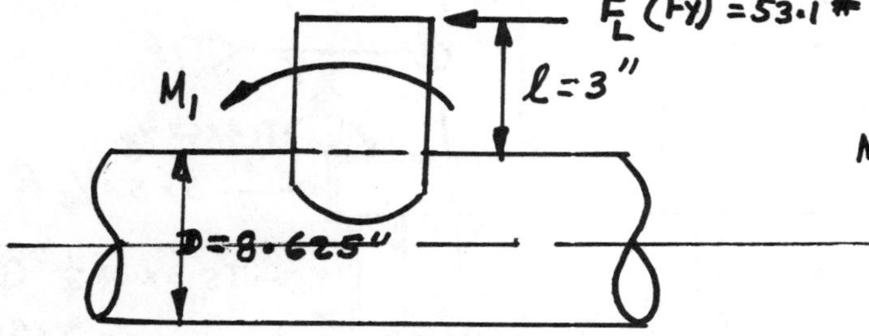

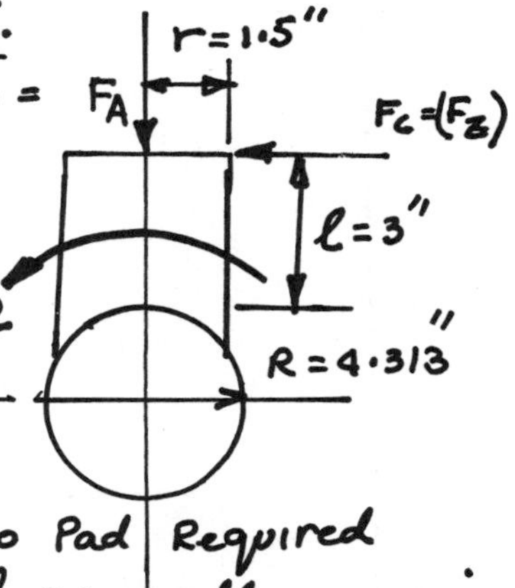

Design Pressure $= P = 75$ Psi

Pipe O.D $= D = 8.625$ in

$R = D/2 = 4.313$ in

$l = 4.313$ in (IF $l < R$, use $l - R$)

$r = 1.5$ in

$x = \pi r^2 = 7.07 \text{ in}^2$

$y = 2\pi r = 9.42$ in

$$Q_1 = \frac{PR}{2t_0} = \frac{75 \times 4.313}{2 \times 0.242} = 668.34 \text{ Psi}$$

$$Q_2 = \frac{PR}{t_0} = \frac{75 \times 4.313}{0.242} = 1336.7 \text{ Psi}$$

Use Q_1 for Load Combination 1

Use Q_2 for Load Combination 2

t = Nominal pipe wall − corrosion allowance = 0.24 in

t_0 = Nominal pipe wall − corrosion allowance

$= 0.322 - 0.08 = 0.242''$

Corrosion Allowance = 0.08"

carbon st O.D stainless steel.

$$M = 1.17\sqrt{R}/t_0^{1.5} = \frac{1.17\sqrt{4.313}}{(0.242)^{1.5}} = 20.4$$

Load Table 1

Load type	F_L	F_C	F_A	$M_L = F_L(l) + M_1$	$M_C = F_C(l) + M_2$	$f_L = M_L/x$	$f_C = M_C/x$	$f_A = F_A/y$	$f_R = \sqrt{f_L^2 + f_C^2}$
Dead weight	1.2			5.18		0.73			0.73
Thermal	53.1			229		32.39			32.39
DW + Normal	53.1	53.1	193	229	229	32.39	32.39	20.49	32.39
DW + Emer.									
Total faulted									

Load table 2

Load Type	1	2	3
	$f = f_L + 1.5 f_A$	$f = 1.5(f_C + f_A)$	$f = 1.5(f_R + f_A)$
Dead weight	0.73	–	1.10
DW + Normal	63.13	79.32	79.32
DW + Emerg.			
Total faulted			

Load table 3

Load type	1	2	3
	$f = f_L + 1.5 f_A$	$f = f_C + 1.5 f_A$	$f = f_R + 1.5 f_A$
thermal	32.39	–	32.39

Load table 4

Load type	f	$(f)(M) + Q_1$ or Q_2	$[(f)(M) + Q]$ max
Dead weight	1.10	1359.14	15000 ok
Dead weight + Normal	79.32	2954.83	10000 ok
Themal + Dead Wt + Normal	111.71	3615.58	17500 ok

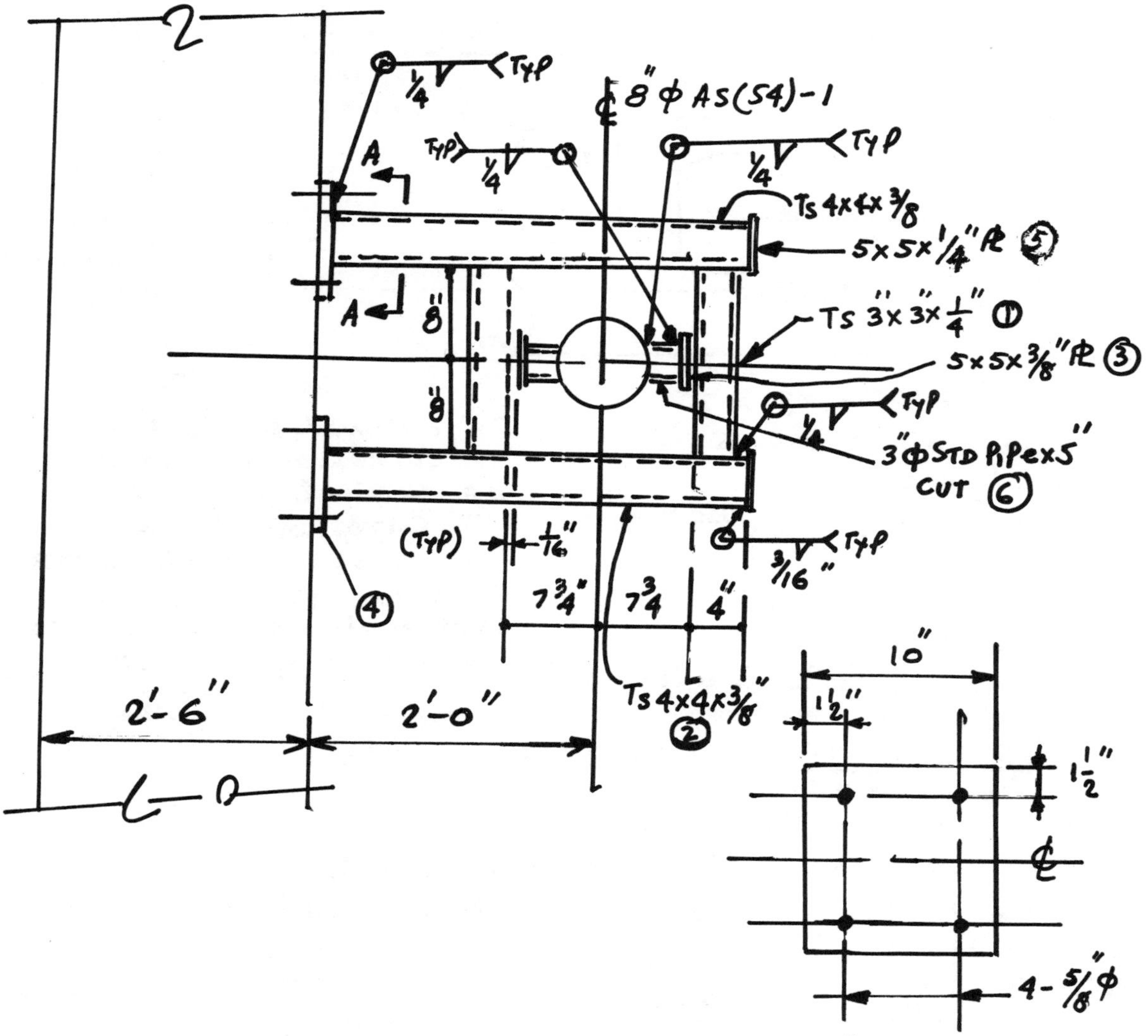

1 1/4" LG. Bolts for R.H. ANCHORS. Field to furnish 8-1/2" Phillips R.H. Anchors.

EXAMPLE 11-02

Given:- Design a pipe support for the following loading Conditions.

Loading condition:-

ANCHOR	Operating	Seismic	Thermal	Total
Fx	±9	±1103	-146	-1240#
Fy	+1415	±1072	+753	+3240
Fz	-15	±1303	-281	-1599
Mxx	+2067	±4305	+1397	+7769x12=+93228"#
Myy	-141	±1186	+290	+1335x12=+16020"#
Mzz	4110	±2010	+221	+3331x12=+15972"#

$$\bar{M_y} = \overset{M_y}{16022} + \overset{F_z}{1599 \times 6''} = 25616''\#$$

$$P_1 = 1599 + \frac{25616}{21} = 2819\#$$

$$\bar{M_z} = \overset{M_z}{15972} + \overset{F_y}{3240 \times 9} = 45132''\#$$

$$P_2 = 3240 + \frac{45132}{18} = 5747$$

$$\bar{M_x} = \overset{M_x}{93228}''\#$$

ATTACHMENT ① ℞ and bolt design.

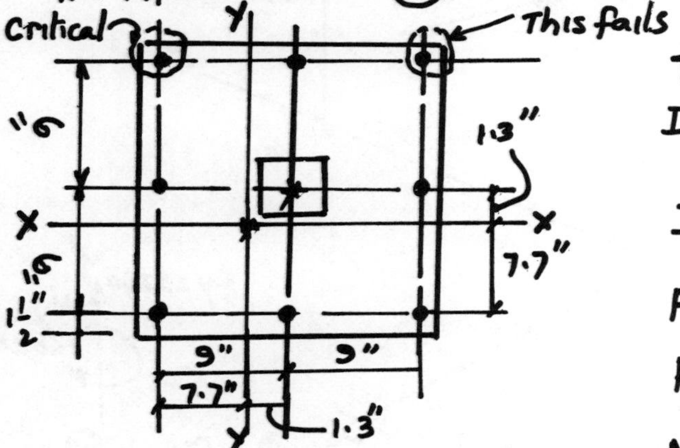

SECT 1-1
1"×21"×21" ℞
8-7/8"φ R.H

Try 8-7/8"φ R.H ONE Fails

$$I_x = I_y = 2(1.3^2 + 10.3^2) + 3(7.7)^2 = 393$$

$$I_p = I_x + I_y = 786$$

$$F_T = 1628 + 1240 = 2868$$

$$F_{sy} = 2507\#, \quad F_{sx} = 1220\#$$

$$M_p = 93228 + 1.3(2507 + 1220) = 98073''\#$$

$$f_t = \frac{2866}{7} + \frac{2868 \times 1.3 \times 10.3}{393} - \frac{2868 \times 1.3 \times 7.7}{393} = 434\#$$

$$f_{sx} = \frac{1220}{7} + \frac{98073 \times 10.7}{786} = 1509\#$$

$$f_{sy} = \frac{2507}{7} + \frac{98073 \times 7.7}{786} = 1319\#$$

$$f_s = (f_{sx}^2 + f_{sy}^2)^{1/2} = 2004$$

$$\frac{434}{2900} + \frac{2004}{2800} = 0.865 < 1.0 \text{ ok. use } 8\text{-}7/8\phi$$

$$M℞ = 3 \times 434 \times 6 = 7812''$$

$$t = \left(\frac{7812 \times 6}{32400 \times 18}\right)^{1/2} = 0.28'' \text{ use } 1''$$

Hence use 1"×21"×21" ℞ + 8-7/8φ R.H

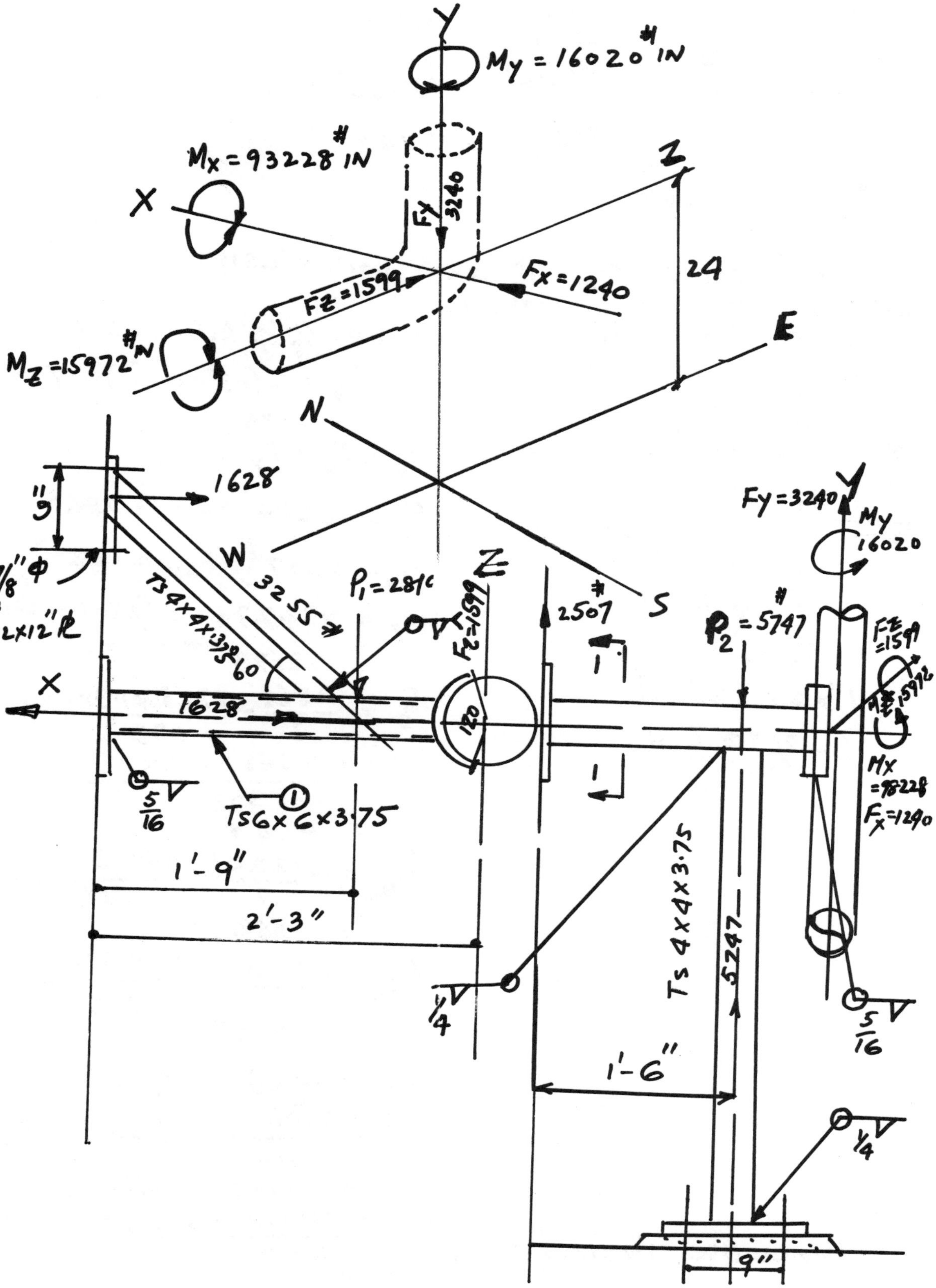
Y
My = 16020 # IN
Mx = 93228 # IN
X
Z
Fy 3240
24
FZ = 1599
Fx = 1240
E
MZ = 15972 # IN
N
1628
6"
W
4-7/8" Φ RH 1X12X12" PL
3255 #
TS 4X4X.3125
60
P1 = 2810
Fz = 1599
2507 #
S
P2 = 5747
Fy = 3240
My 16020
Fz = 1599
Mz 15972
Mx = 93228
Fx = 1240
X
1628
120
1
5/16
TS 6X6X3.75
1'-9"
2'-3"
1/4
TS 4X4X3.75
5247
1'-6"
5/16
1/4
9"

TRUNION Design:-

$M_L = M_Z = 45132$

$M_C = M_Y = 25616$

$F_A = F_X = -1240\#$

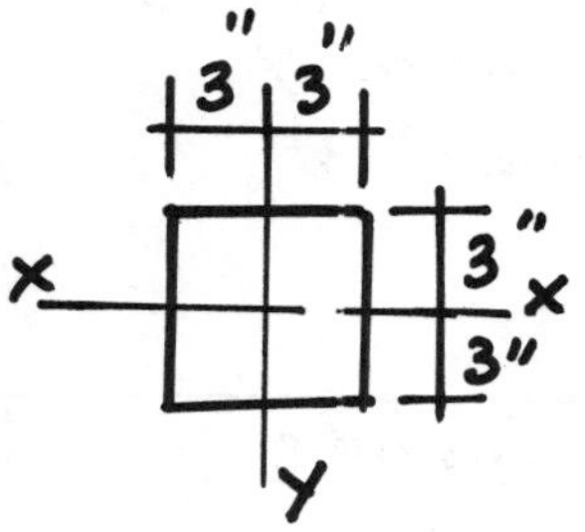

Pipe Data

8"φ Pipe STD

Material A106 Gr.B

Temp = 100°F

Press = 100 Psi

$t = 0.322 - 0.08 = 0.242''$

Try Ts 6×6×0.375

$I_X = I_Y = 2 \times 6 \times 3^2 + 2 \times \frac{1}{12} \times 6 = 144$

$Z_L = Z_C = \frac{144}{3} = 48$

$L = 4 \times 6 = 24''$

$f_L = \frac{M_L}{Z_L} = \frac{45132}{48} = 940\#$

$f_C = \frac{M_C}{Z_C} = \frac{25616}{48} = 533\#$

$f_R = (940^2 + 533^2)^{1/2} = 1080\#$

$f_A = \frac{1240}{L} = \frac{1240}{24} = 26\#$ } 1106#

$f_1 = 1.5(f_R + f_A)$

$= 1.5(1080 + 26) = 1659 < 4582\#$

$S_B = 15000(1.2) - \frac{100(4.3125)}{0.242}$

$= 16218$ Psi

$f_m = \frac{16218 \times (0.242)^{1.5}}{1.17\sqrt{4.3125}}$

$= 795\#/\text{IN} < 1106$ N.G.

Try ½" thick Pad.

$t = 0.242 + 0.5 = 0.742''$

$S_B = 18000 - \frac{100(4.3125)}{0.742}$

$= 17419$ Psi

$f_m = \frac{17419\ (0.742)^{1.5}}{1.17\sqrt{4.3125}}$

$= 4582\#/\text{IN} > 1106$

ok ✓

EXAMPLE 11-03

Given:- Design a pipe support for the followind loading condition, tabulated on the next sheet.

From the computer output & Joint (5); member △5 to member △6.

$A_W = \pi \times 3.5'' = 10.996 \simeq 11''$

Axial	-708 #	Torsion Moment	-8297.996	$S_w = \frac{\pi d^2}{4}$ for θ
Shear Y	1330 #	Moment Y	5774.996	$S_w = \frac{\pi \times 3.5^2}{4}$
Shear Z	-846 #	Moment Z	16409.00	= 9.62

$J_w = \frac{\pi d^3}{4} = 33.67$

Loading Condition

Load Type		Pounds			Pounds INCHES		
		Fx	FY	FZ	Mx	My	MZ
Thermal		0	-634	-49	-540	0	0
Dead Weight		0	-167	-6	6	0	0
Dynamic Load ±	Normal	708	529	791	7752	276	7764
	Emerg.	97	277	197	1788	216	1152
	Faulted	868	659	973	9528	348	9528
Total Load	normal	708 -708	362 -1330	785 -846	7746 -8298	276 -276	7764 -7764
	Emerg.	+97 -97	-524 -1078	191 -252	1782 -2334	216 -216	1152 -1152
	faulted	868 -868	492 -826	967 -979	9522 -9534	348 -348	9528 -9528

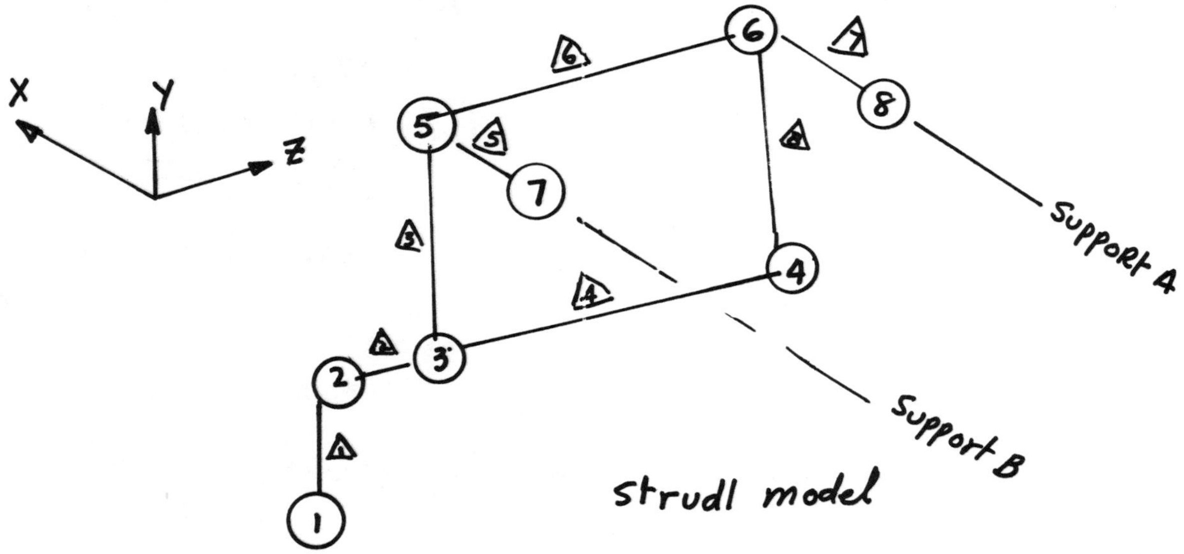

strudl model

T_x $\qquad$ V_y $\qquad$ V_z

$708/11 = 64.4$ $\qquad$ $1330/11 = 121$ $\qquad$ $846/11 = 77$

Conservatively figuring Tension as Shear

$$\left[\frac{T}{A_W} + \frac{M_1+M_2}{S_W}\right] + \left[\left(\frac{M_{Torsion} \times C}{J_W} + \frac{V_{max}}{A_W}\right)^2 + \left(\frac{V_{min}}{A_W}\right)^2\right]^{1/2}$$

$$\left(\frac{708}{11} + \frac{5775+16409}{9.62}\right) + \left[\left(\frac{8298 \times \frac{3.5}{2}}{33.67} + \frac{1330}{11}\right)^2 + \left(\frac{846}{11}\right)^2\right]^{1/2}$$

$$64 + 2306 + 557 = 2927$$

$$\frac{2927}{14400 \times 0.707} = 0.288''$$

Use full penetration weld for welding △5 to △6.

Joint ⑦ member anchor △5 to pipe.

$A_w = 11''$, $S_w = 9.62$, $J_w = 33.67$

Axial $= 708^{\#}$ $\qquad$ Torsion $= 8298''^{\#}$

$F_y = -1330^{\#}$ $\qquad$ Moment Y $= -276''^{\#}$

$F_z = 846^{\#}$ $\qquad$ Moment Z $= -7764''^{\#}$

$$\left[\frac{708}{11} + \frac{276+7764}{9.62}\right] + \left[\left(\frac{8298 \times 1.75}{33.67} + \frac{1330}{11}\right)^2 + \left(\frac{846}{11}\right)^2\right]^{1/2}$$

$$= 64 + 836 + 557 = 145$$

$$\frac{1457}{14400 \times 0.707} = 0.143 \text{ use } 1/4'' \text{ weld.}$$

Joint ⑧, member anchor △7 to pipe.

Axial T $= 569^{\#}$ $\qquad$ Torsion $= 8631''^{\#}$ $\qquad$ $A_w = 11$

$F_y = -723^{\#}$ $\qquad$ Moment y $= -1716''^{\#}$ $\qquad$ $S_w = 9.62$

$F_z = 752^{\#}$ $\qquad$ Moment Z $= -5724''^{\#}$ $\qquad$ $J_w = 33.67$

$$\left[\frac{569}{11} + \frac{1716+5724}{9.62}\right] + \left[\left(\frac{8631 \times 1.75}{33.67} + \frac{752}{11}\right)^2 + \left(\frac{723}{11}\right)^2\right]^{1/2}$$

$$= 52 + 773 + 521 = 1346; \quad \frac{1346}{14400 \times 0.707} = 0.132'' \text{ use } 1/4'' \text{ weld.}$$

Similarly Joint (6) member $\triangle A$ to member $\triangle 6$

$A_w = 11''$, $S_w = 9.62$, $J_w = 33.67$

Axial	= −569#	Torsion	−8630
F_y	= 723 #	Moment y	6604
F_z	= −752 #	Moment z	10424

$$\left[\frac{569}{11} + \frac{6604+10424}{9.62}\right] + \left[\left(\frac{8631*1.75}{33.67} + \frac{7.52}{11}\right)^2 + \left(\frac{723}{11}\right)^2\right]^{1/2}$$

$$= 52 + 1770 + 521 = 2343$$

$$\frac{2343}{14400 \times 0.707} = 0.230''$$

Use full penetration weld for welding Anchor member $\triangle A$ to member $\triangle 6$.

Joint (5) member $\triangle 6$ to member $\triangle 3$; member $\triangle 3$ to Joint (5)

Axial	= 3400#	Torsion	6396"#
F_y	= −587	Moment y	2912"#
F_z	= −1214	Moment z	17999"#

$\triangle 6$ Ts 5×5×3/8

$\triangle 3$ Ts 4×4×3/8

Use 4×4 = 16 = A_w

S_w for Ts 4×4 $= bd + \frac{d^2}{3} = 21.3$

J_w for Ts 4×4 $\frac{(b+d)^3}{6} = 85.33$

$$\left[\frac{3400}{16} + \frac{2912+17999}{21.33}\right] + \left[\left(\frac{6396 \times 2}{85.33} + \frac{1214}{16}\right)^2 + \left(\frac{6396 \times 2}{85.33} + \frac{587}{16}\right)^2\right]^{1/2} = 0$$

$$213 + 980 + 293 = 1486$$

$$\frac{1486}{14400 \times 0.707} = 0.146'' \text{ use } 1/4'' \text{ weld.}$$

Similarly Joint (6) & Joint (4) use 1/4" weld. Also for Joint (3), use 1/4" weld.

Joint (1) Global $F_x = 1277$#, $F_y = 2053$#, $F_z = 1598$#

$M_x = 25318$"#, $M_y = 24766$"#, $M_z = 47903$"#

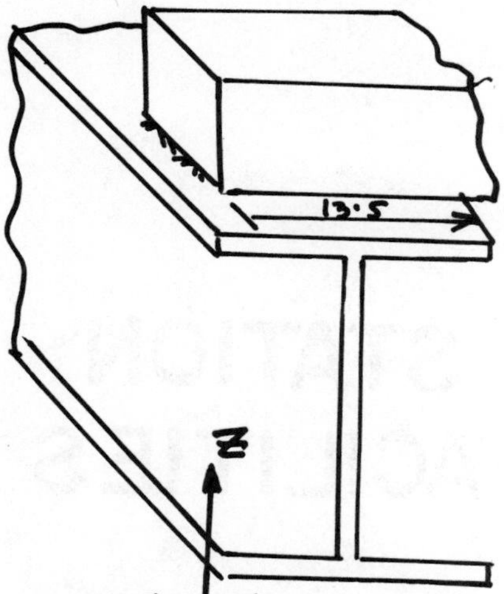

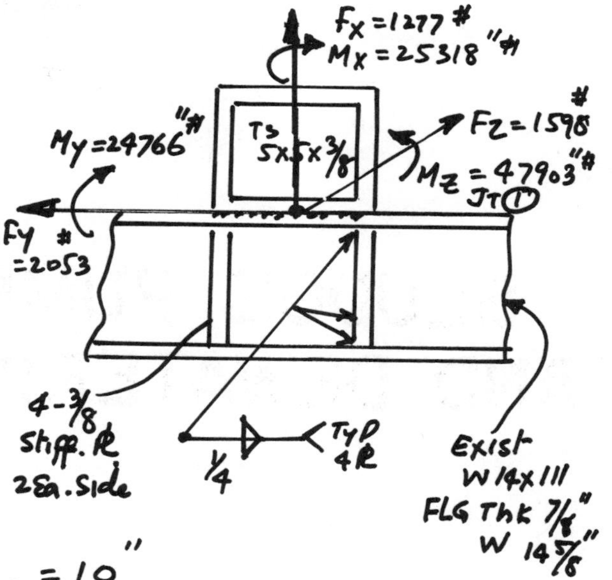

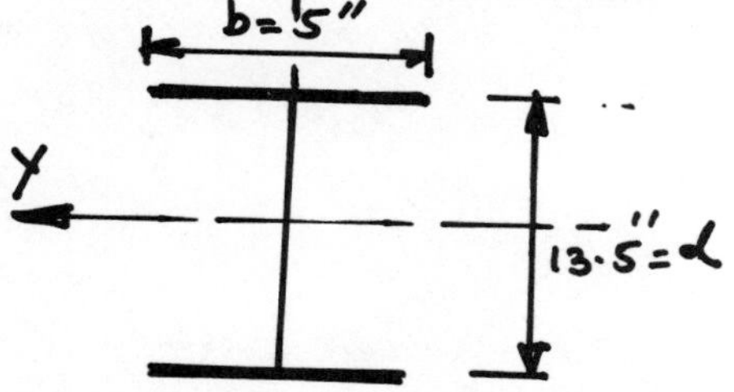

$A_w = 10''$

$S_{wy} = bd = 13.5 \times 5 = 67.5$

$S_{wz} = \frac{d^2}{3} = \frac{13.5^2}{3} = 60.75$

J_{wy} for M_x $= \frac{b^3 + 3bd^2}{6} = \frac{5^3 + 3 \times 5 \times 13.5^2}{6} = 476.5$

$$\left[\frac{M_y}{S_{wy}} + \frac{M_z}{S_{wz}} + \frac{F_x}{A_w}\right] + \left[\left(\frac{M_x \cdot b/2}{J_w} + \frac{F_y}{A_w}\right)^2 + \left(\frac{F_z}{A_w}\right)^2\right]^{1/2}$$

$$= \frac{247.66}{67.5} + \frac{47903}{60.75} + \frac{1277}{10} + \left[\left(\frac{25318 \times 2.5}{476.5} + \frac{2053}{10}\right)^2 + \left(\frac{1598}{10}\right)^2\right]^{1/2}$$

$$= 367 + 789 + 128 + 374 = 1658$$

$$\frac{1658}{14400} \times \frac{1}{0.707} = 0.163''$$ use 1/4 weld.

Checking Existing W14x111

$M_y = 24766''\#$

Force acting as couple on FLG. $= \frac{24766}{14.37 - .873} = 1839\#$

Worst Case when FLG Loading @ Center

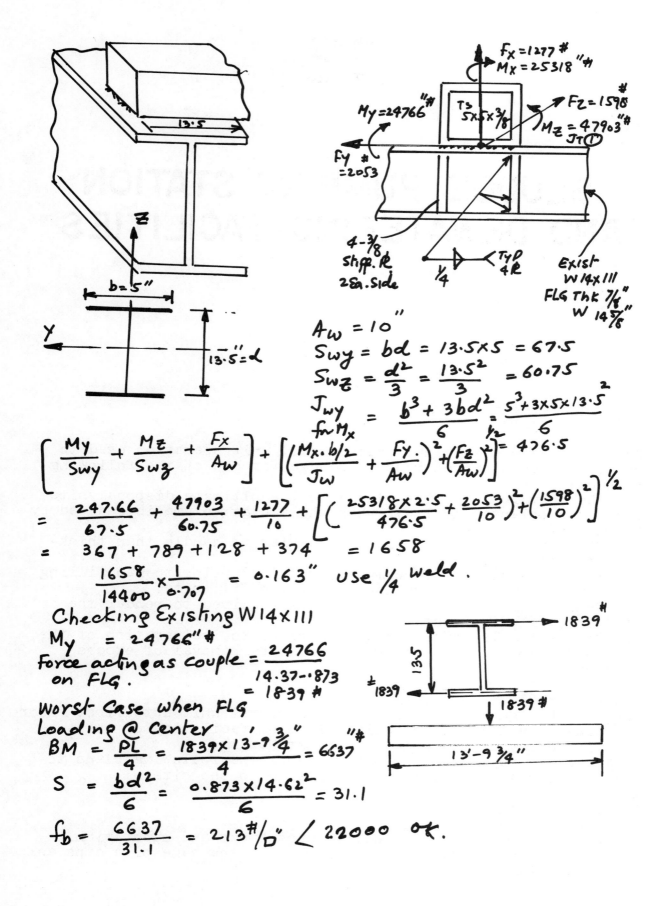

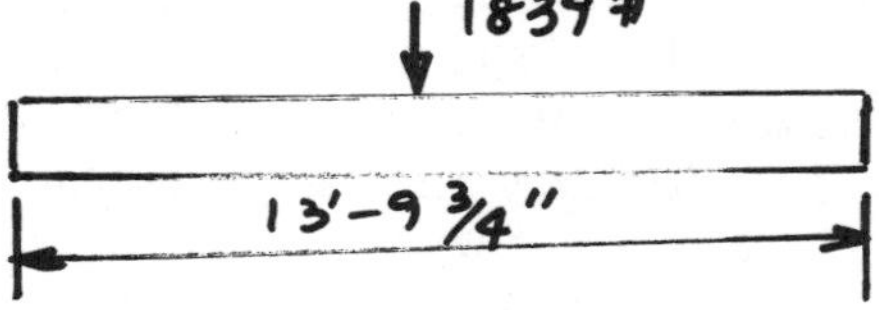

$BM = \frac{PL}{4} = \frac{1839 \times 13'\text{-}9\frac{3}{4}''}{4} = 6637''\#$

$S = \frac{bd^2}{6} = \frac{0.873 \times 14.62^2}{6} = 31.1$

$f_b = \frac{6637}{31.1} = 213\#/\square'' < 22000$ ok.

12

SLUDGE PUMPING STATION AND DEWATERING FACILITIES

Deawatering is a physical (mechanical) unit operation used to reduce the moisture content of sludge for one of the following reasons:

1. The cost for trucking sludge to the ultimate disposal site becomes substantially lower when the sludge volume is reduced by dewatering.
2. Dewatered sludge is generally easier to handle than thickened or liquid sludge.
3. Sludge dewatering is commonly required prior to landfilling to reduce leachate production at the landfill site.
4. Removal of excess moisture may be required to render the sludge totally odorless.
5. Dewatering is usually required prior to incineration of the sludge to increase the Calorific Value by removal of excess moisture.

EXAMPLE 12-01

Given:- Design a foundation and structural unit upto first floor for sludge dewatering and solids loading facilities of the Passaic Valley Sewage Commisioners at Newark.
Design is to be based upon the study of the following plans to make the design economical and suitable to the site:-

1) Site plan,grading.
2) Site plan,outside piping.
3) Site details
4) Plans and profiles of electric duct banks and substation.
5) The filterate line may be supported on the same pile caps as the parrallel duct bank.

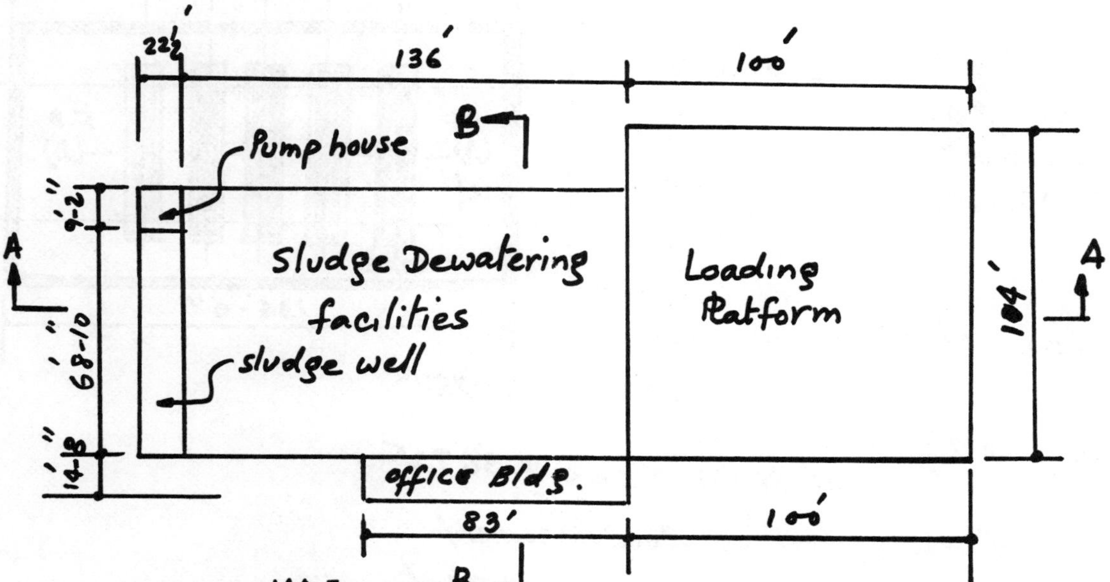
22½'
136'
100'
B
Pump house
9'-2"
A
Sludge Dewatering facilities
sludge well
68'-10"
14'-8"
Loading Platform
104'
A
office Bldg.
83'
100'
B

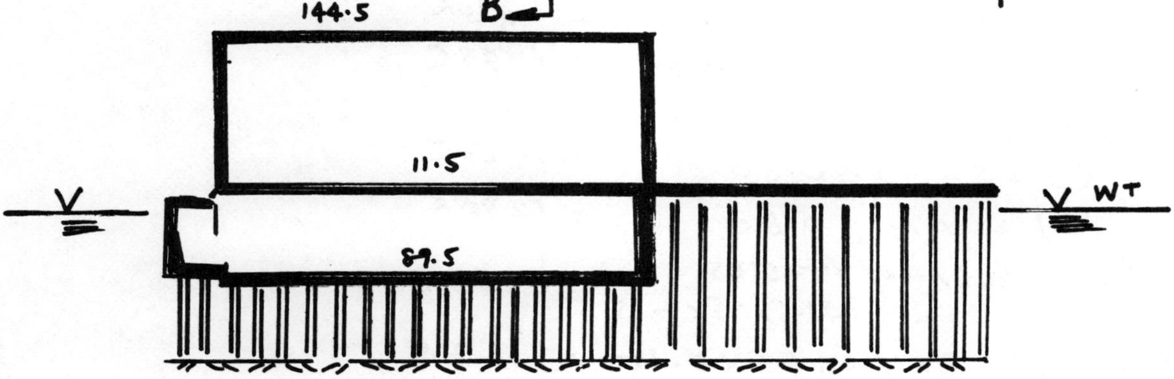
144.5
11.5
89.5
WT

SEC A-A

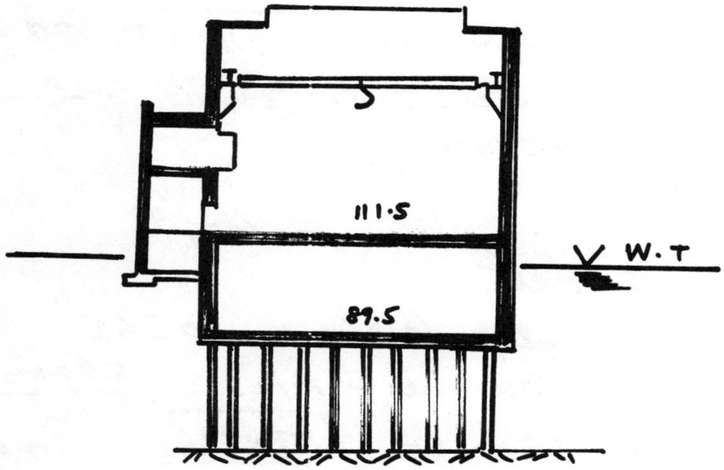
111.5
89.5
W.T

SEC B-B

Design of Basement.

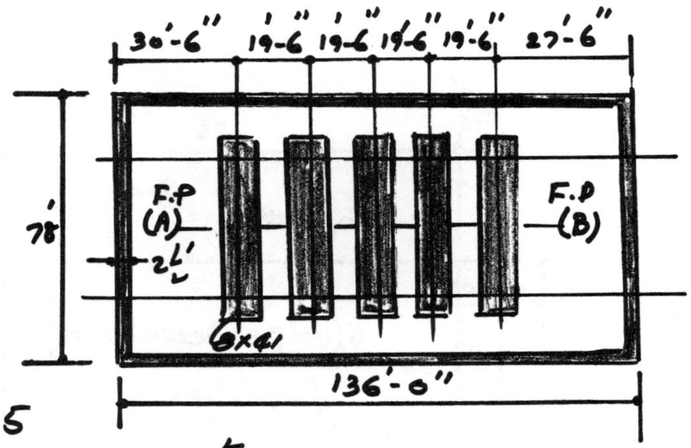

Loading

1, Load of Ea. Press = 567^k

Load of 4 cols supporting

$4 \times 2 \times 1 \times 23 \times 0.15 = 28^k$

595^k

∴ Load of 5 Press = 595×5

$= 2975 \qquad = 2975^k$

2, D.L. of $2\frac{1}{2}'$ thick wall

$2.5 \times (136+78) 2 \times 23 \times 0.15 = 3692^k$

3, D.L of Main floor or Roof Basement

$1.5 \times 136 \times 78 \times 0.150 = 2390^k$

L.L @ 300#/□' $89 \times 73 \times 0.300 = 1949^k$

4, Filter area F.P

(A) $25 \times 73 \times 0.80 = 1460^k$

(B) $22 \times 73 \times 0.80 = 1285^k$

Less opening of Presses

$5 \times 8 \times 41.6 \times 1.5 \times 0.15 = -374^k$

5, STAIRS $2 \times 16 \times 6.75 \times 0.100 = 22^k$

6, Live load Basement Floor

$136 \times 78 \times 0.300 = 3182^k$

7, Piping & Col. Loads Say $= 1202^k$

Total Load of Foundation $= 17873^k$ Say 20000^k

Using closed end Piles driven to rock filled with Concrete

Effective depth = 31'

Size = $10\frac{3}{4}''\phi$

capacity = 60 T

Pile pipe thickness = 0.365"

∴ Required number of Piles = $\frac{20000}{120} = 167$

Spacing $S = \sqrt{\frac{78 \times 136}{167}} = 7.96'$

For group action, spacing of Piles should be greater

than 3d & less than 6'-0" & Also min. edge distance should be 15".

Actual Piles provided = 399 > 167 ok

Actual design load per pile $= \frac{20000}{399} = 51 < 120$ ok

Compressive stress $= \frac{51000}{90.71} = 562$ psi < 4500 being rock

Hence no lagging req'd.

Actual bearing capacity P = mental friction R_f of Pile + Pile Tip ressistance R_t

$$R_f = \frac{1}{2} L_c^2 \pi d \tan\phi \, k_p$$

$$= \frac{1}{2} \times 31^2 \times \pi \times \frac{10.75}{\times 12} \times 0.577 \times 100 = 38.99T$$

$$R_t = \frac{\pi}{4} \frac{r L_c d^2 \tan(\alpha + \phi_1)}{\tan\alpha}$$ where $\alpha = \text{Arctan} \frac{d/2}{h}$

$= \text{Arctan} \frac{5.37}{9.25}$

$= \text{Arctan } 0.58$

$$= \frac{\pi}{4} \times 100 \times 31.5 \times \frac{10.75^2}{144} \times \frac{\tan 60}{\tan 30} = 5.96K \text{ or } 3T$$

$$P = R_f + R_t = 38.99 + 3 = 41.99 > 25.5 \text{ Ton.}$$

Check for upLift Pressure

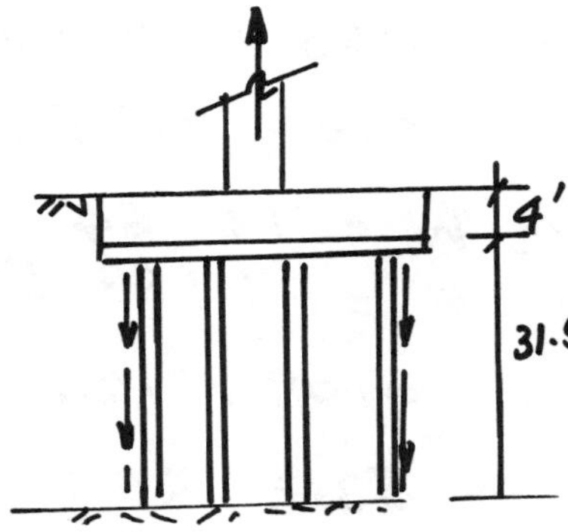

$p = (78 + 136)2 = 428'$

$A = 78 \times 136 = 10608^{\square}$

weight acting downward

Wt. of Pile Cap + Wt of soil above pilecap + Wt. of block of soil + Frictional resistance of Pile.

$= \frac{24}{12} \times 78 \times 36 \times 0.150 + 4 \times 78 \times 136 \times 0.100 + 0.100 \times 31.5 \times 10608 + 0.848 \times 428 (31.5 + 4)$ where $S = c + \sigma \tan\phi$

$= 300 + \frac{1}{2} \times 1.9 \times 5.77$

$= 0.848$

$= 50543$

uplift pressure due to G.W

$P_U = r_w B h = 62.4 \times 136 \times 78 \times 46 = 30449^K.$

$$F.S = \frac{50543}{30449} = 1.65 > 1 \text{ ok}$$

Pile supported mat foundation.

Assumption:-

1) horizontal load not to exceed 10% of vert. load capacity

2) may increase pile load by 1/3 for load of short duration.

Pile cap design

$f'_c = 3000$ Psi, $f_s = 24000$ Psi

Total load on Panel 'W'

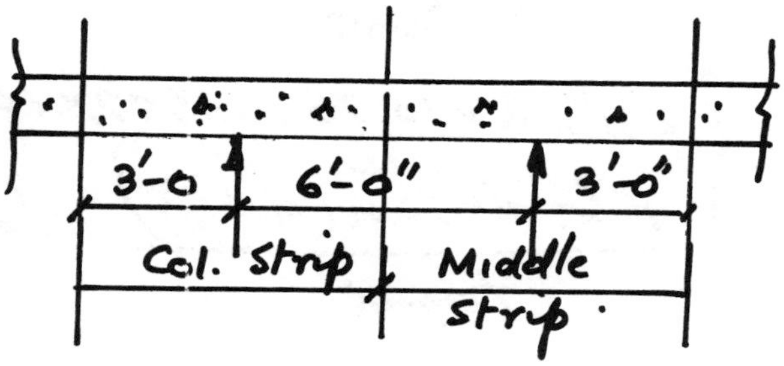

Superimposed Load

$$= \frac{20000}{10608} \times (6.0)^2$$

$$= 67.68 = 67.68^k$$

$$\text{Pile cap} = \frac{24}{12} \times 6^2 \times 0.15 = 10.80^k$$

$$78.48^k$$

$$W_u = 1.55 \times 78.48 = 121.64^k$$

$$M_o = 0.09\, WLF \left(1 - \frac{2c}{3L}\right)^2$$

where $W = 121.64$, $L = 6'\text{-}0$, $c = 10.75''$

$$F = 1.15 - \frac{c}{L} = 1.15 - \frac{0.89}{6.0} = 1.002 > 1 \text{ use } 1$$

$$\therefore M_o = 0.09 \times 121.64 \times 6 \times 1 \left(1 - \frac{2 \times 0.89}{3 \times 6.0}\right)^2$$

$$= 53.33'^k$$

For interrior panel w/o drop panel.

Col. strip $= +M = 0.22 M_o = 11.73'^k$

$-M = -0.46 M_o = -24.53'^k$

Mid. strip $= \pm M = 0.16 M_o = 8.53'^k$

Check for thickness

$$t_1 = 0.028 L \left(1 - \frac{2c}{3L}\right) \sqrt{\frac{w'}{f'_c/2000}} + 1.5$$

Check shear

$$v = \frac{V}{b_o d}$$

$$v_{allow} = 2\phi\sqrt{f_c'} = 94$$

$$b = \pi(10.75 + 20) = 96.5$$

$$\therefore d = \frac{120000}{94 \times 96.5} = 13.22'' < 24 \text{ use } 24''$$

Check Punching Shear

$$\text{Area} = \pi r L - \pi \times 5 \times 5 \times 1.4 = \pi[(t+5)(1.4t+7) - 35]$$

$$= \pi[1.4t^2 + 14t]$$

Allowable Punching shear $4\phi\sqrt{f_c'} = 186.2$ Psi

$$\therefore \pi[1.4t^2 + 1.4t] \times 186.2 = 120000$$

$$t^2 + 10t - 146 = 0, \therefore t = -19.35, +8.07''$$

$$\therefore d = 8.07 + 6 = 14.07 < 24 \text{ ok Use } 24''$$

Design of Reinforcement

$$d_{eff} = 24 - 6 - 3 - \frac{0.5}{2} = 14.75$$

for $b_w = 12$, $d = 14.75$, $F = 0.225$

$$K_U = \frac{M_U}{F} = \frac{24.53}{0.225} = 109$$

$$A_s = \frac{24.53}{2.93 \times 14.75} = 0.57 \text{ Use } \#6@8'' \text{ \& } \#4@12''$$

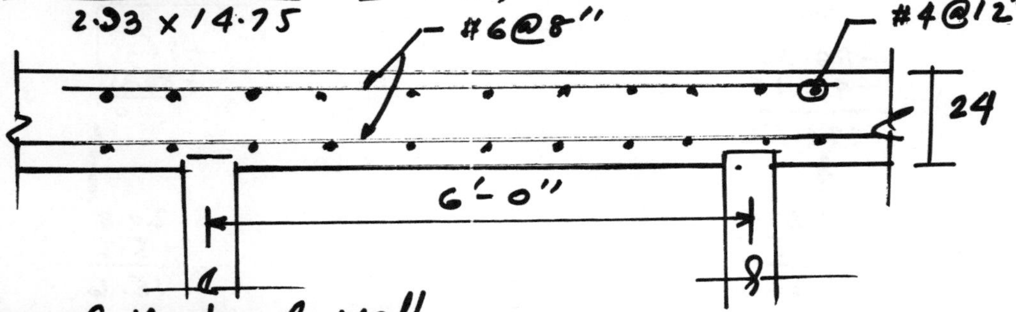

Design of Vertical wall

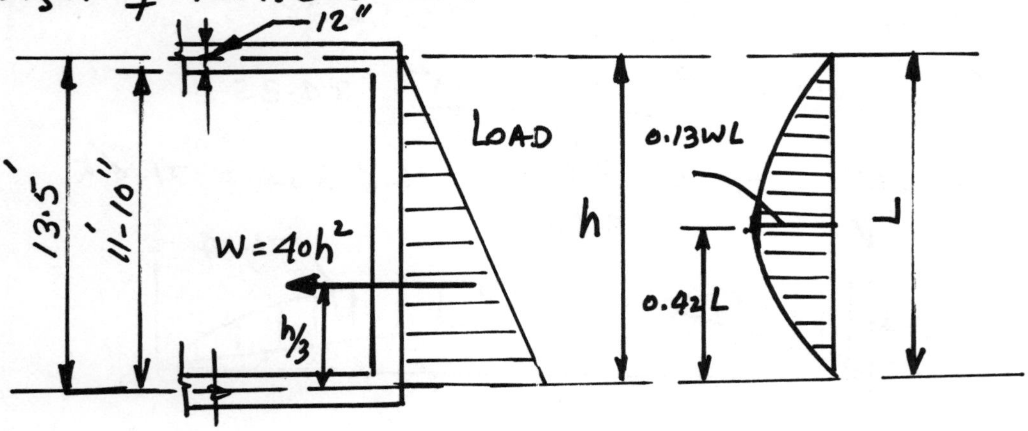

W = Hor. pressure $= 40h^2 = 40 \times 13.5^2 = 7204^{\#}$

$W_U = 1.4 \times 7204 = 10085^{\#}$

$M_U = 0.13\,WL = 0.13 \times 10.85 \times 13.42 = 17.6^{'k}$

$b = 12''$, $h = 18''$; $d_{eff} = 18 - 2.5 = 15.5''$

$F = 0.24$, $K_U = \dfrac{17.6}{0.24} = 73$, $a_U = 4.45$

$$A_s = \frac{17.6}{4.45 \times 15.5} = 0.25\,\square''$$

But Min $A_s = 0.0033 \times 12 \times 15.5 = 0.61$

Use #6 @ 8"

$A_{s\,temp} = 0.0018 \times 12 \times 18 = 0.39\,\square''$

Use #5 @ 9"

Design of slab (portion fixed at one end & supported at other end) $h = 20''$

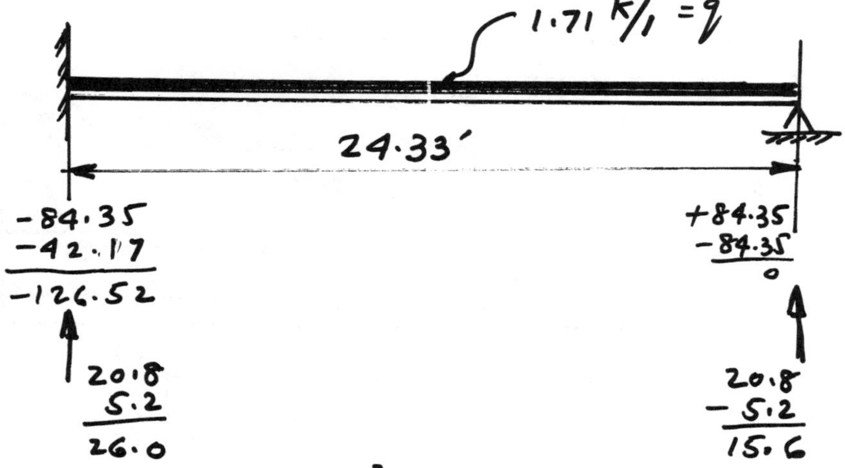

$$M = \frac{wl^2}{8} = \frac{1.71 \times 24.33^2}{8} = 126.52^{'K}$$

$$F.E.M = \frac{wl^2}{12} = \frac{1.71 \times 24.33^2}{12} = 84.35$$

$$+M = \frac{R^2}{2q} - M = \frac{26.0^2}{2 \times 1.71} - 126.52 = 71.14^{'k}$$

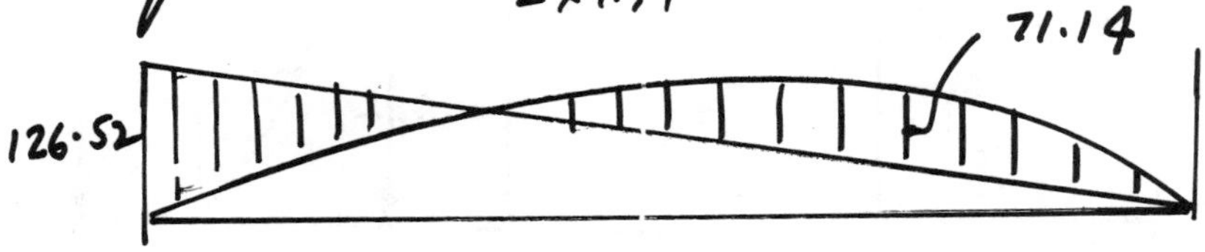

Reinforcement $+M = 71.14'^{k}$

$F = \dfrac{71.14}{0.28} = 254 \quad a_u = 4.31, \; A_s = \dfrac{71.14}{4.31 \times 16.75} = 0.98\,\square''$

#7 @ 6"

$-M = 126.52'^{k}, \; F = \dfrac{126.52}{0.28} = 451.85$

$a_u = 4.15, \; A_s = \dfrac{126.52}{4.15 \times 16.75} = 1.82\,\square''$ use #8 @ 5"

$A_{s\,temp} = 0.0018 \times 12 \times 18.5 = 0.40$
use #5 @ 9"

Design of Basement wall

wall is acting as simple beam with waterpressure on the side plus with col. Load of 150k @ eccentricity of 5"

Free body diagram of two actions.

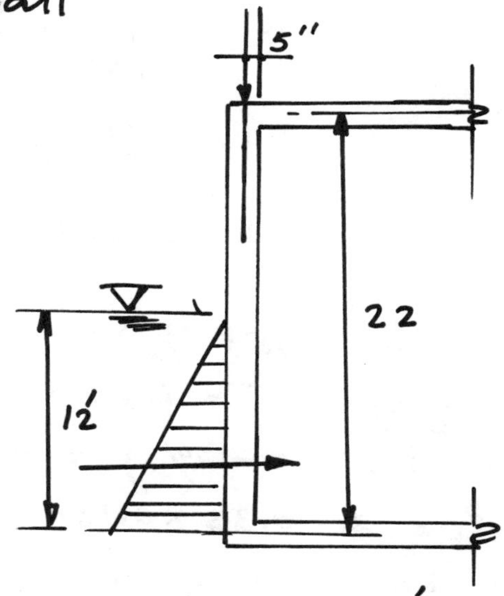

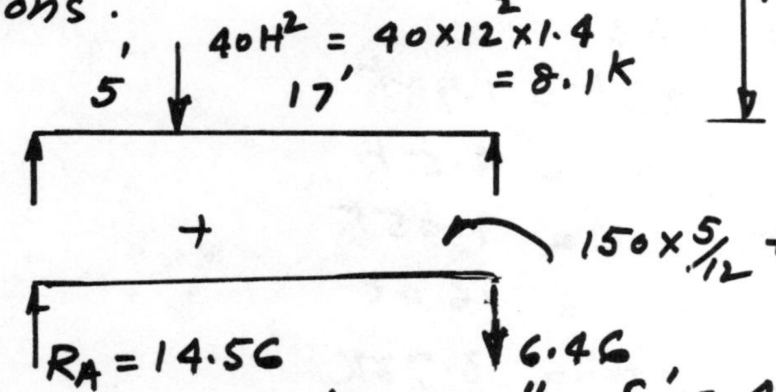

$b = 12''$, $h = 30''$, $f_c' = 4000$ Psi, $f_y = 60000$ Psi

$d_{eff} = 27''$, $F = 0.727$

$K_u = \dfrac{182.5}{0.729} = 250.3, \; a_u = 4.3$

$A_s = \dfrac{182.5}{4.3 \times 27} = 1.57\,\square''$, use #7 @ 4"

$A_{s\,temp}$ = #4 @ 6"

Check for bearing stress $= P/A \pm M/S$

P from Col = 150
from BM = 120.5
$270.5 \times 1.4 = 330.5^k$

$= \dfrac{330500}{30 \times 12} \pm \dfrac{182.5 \times 12}{\frac{12 \times 30^2}{6}}$

$= 2134 < 0.85\phi f_c' = 2380$ ok

Design of sludge retaining wall.

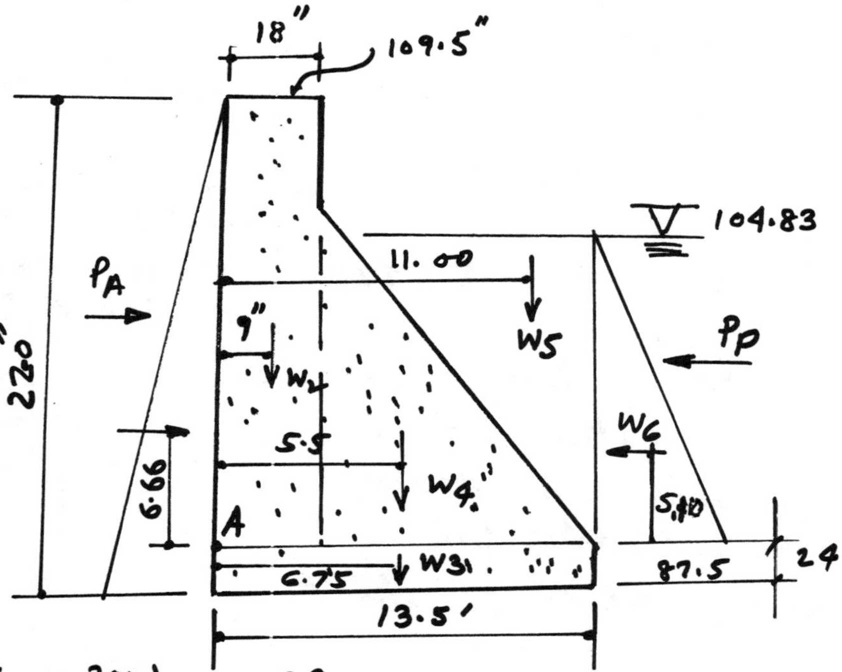

$$k_p = \tan^2(45 + 30/2) = 2.99$$

$$W_6 = P_p = \tfrac{1}{2} K_p w h^2 = \tfrac{1}{2} \times 2.99 \times 0.068 \times 15^2 = 22.8k$$

$$K_A = \tan^2(45 - 30/2) = 0.33$$

$$W_1 = P_A = \tfrac{1}{2} \times 0.33 \times 0.100 \times 22^2 = 7.98k$$

$$W_2 = 20 \times 1.5 \times 1 \times 0.150 = 4.5k$$

$$W_3 = 13.5 \times 2 \times 1 \times 0.150 = 4.05k$$

$$W_4 = \tfrac{1}{2} \times 12 \times 17.75 \times 0.150 = 16.0k$$

$$W_5 = \tfrac{1}{2} \times 15 \times 0.068 \times 7.43 = 3.78k$$

Taking moment about A

Force	Arm ft	Moment Ft K	
$W_1 = 7.98$	5.33	+ 48.53	OT
$W_2 = 4.5$	0.75	+ 3.37	
$W_3 = 4.05$	6.75	+ 27.00	
$W_4 = 16.0$	5.50	+ 82.50	
$W_5 = 3.78$	11.00	+ 41.58	
$W_6 = 22.8$	5.10	− 116.28	

$R_V = 28.33$ $R_H = 30.78$

$X = \frac{154.45}{28.33} = 5.45'$

$e = 6.75 - 5.45 = 1.31 < \frac{b}{6}$ ∴ Safe

F.S against overturning $= \frac{154.45}{73.75} = 2.09 > 1.5$ ok

$f = \frac{P}{A}\left(1 \pm \frac{6ex}{dx} \pm \frac{6ey}{dy}\right)$

$= \frac{28330}{13.5 \times 1}\left(1 \pm \frac{6 \times 1.31}{13.5}\right)$

$= 3.290$ ksf

Max resistance to sliding $= 0.6 \times 28.33 = 16.98^k$

F.S against sliding $= \frac{16.98}{5.46} = 3.09$ Safe ok

Pump house

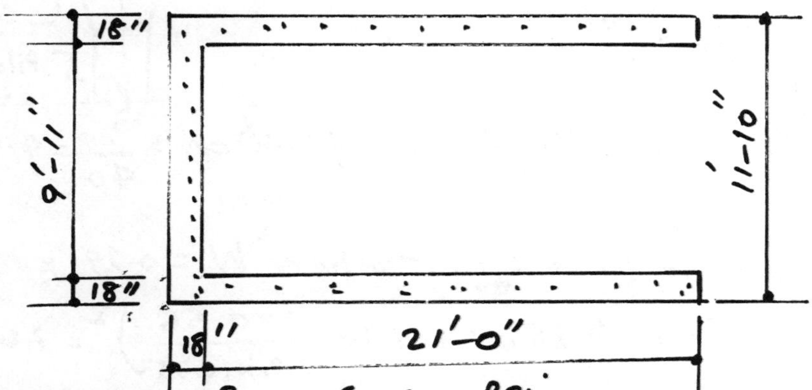

$f_c' = 4000$ Psi, $f_y = 60000$ Psi

Min thickness of slab $= h = \frac{\ell}{20} = 6.85"$

Due to Earth D.L $= 1 \times 8.17 \times 0.12 = 0.98^k/_1$ } $1.13^k/_1$

" " Slab D.L $= 1 \times \frac{12}{12} \times 0.15 = 0.15^k/_1$

$W_U = 1.13 \times 1.4 = 1.58^k/_{12}$

$M_U = \frac{W_U L^2}{8} = \frac{1.58 \times 11.42^2}{8} = 25.74'^k/_1$

for $b = 12$, $d_{eff} = 10.9"$, $F = 0.121$, $K_U = \frac{25.74}{0.121} = 213$

$a_U = 4.34$ ∴ $A_s = \frac{25.74}{4.34 \times 10.9} = 0.55\,\square"$ use #6@8"

$A_{s\,temp} = 0.0018 \times 12 \times 12 = 0.26$ use #4@9"

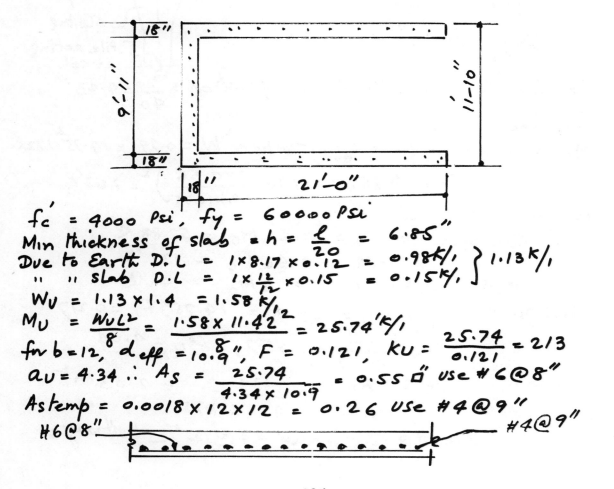

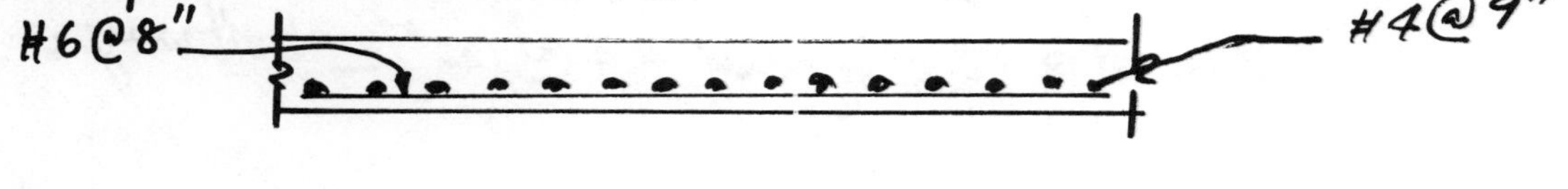

Loading Platform design.

Assume Sludge load distribution is in shape of Pyramid.

Unit weight of sludge = 68 #/cft

Volume of Pyramid = Area Base x $\frac{\text{Altitude}}{3}$

1, Load / sq.ft = $\left[100 \times 104 \times \frac{25}{3} \times 68\right] \frac{1}{100 \times 104}$ = 566 #/□'

2, L.P. Slab D.L = $\frac{18}{12} \times 150$ = 225 #/□'

3, Wt of 18" Pile Cap + Pedestal = 2.5×150 = 375 #/□'

Load on Pile Cap = 1166 #/□'

Load on Platform = 791 #/□'

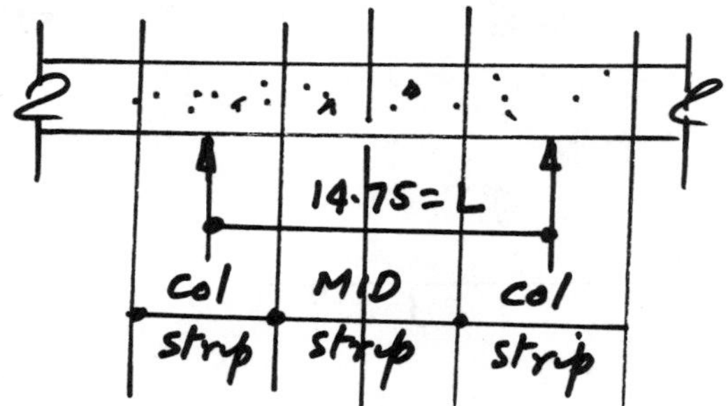

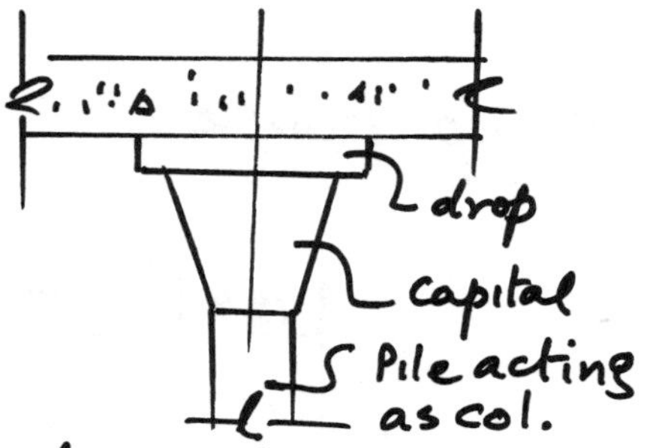

Min. Slab Thickness Req'd by deflection = $\frac{L}{40}$ = 4.43"

t provided = 18"

$M_o = 0.10\, WLF \left(1 - \frac{2c}{3L}\right)^2$ where $W = 0.791 \times 14.75^2 = 172^k$

$= 0.10 \times 172 \times 14.75 \times 1.10 \left(1 - \frac{2 \times 0.66}{3 \times 14.75}\right)^2 = 263'^k$

For Interior Panel.

Col. Strip = $+M = 0.22\, M_o = 57.88'^k$

$-M = 0.46\, M_o = 121'^k$

Mid Strip = $\pm M = 0.16\, M_o = 42'^k$

Design slab for bw = 12, d = 14.75, $F_1 = 0.217$

$K_u = \frac{121}{0.217} = 557$, $a_u = 4.04$

$A_s = \frac{M_u}{a_u d} = \frac{121}{4.04 \times 14.75} = 2.03\, in^2$

Use #8 @ 6" o/c and #4 @ 12 o/c bothways.

13

MATERIAL HANDLING

MATERIAL HANDLING SYSTEMS

Belt conveyor systems are used in the field of construction, where they provide most satisfactory and economical method of handling and transporting materials, such as earth, sand, gravel, crushed stone, cement, concrete etc. Because of the continuous flow of materials at relatively high speeds, belt conveyors have high capacities. The essential parts of a belt conveyor system include a continuous belt, idlers, a driving unit, driving and tail pulleys, take up equipment and supporting structures.

The belt is the moving and supporting surface on which the material is transported. Idler provides the supports for a belt conveyor.

The power required to drive a belt conveyor (empty):-

Power 'P' = E/33000 ; where E = LSCQ.

E = Energy ft lbs/minutes

L = Length of conveyor, ft.

S = Belt speed fpm.

C = Idler friction factor.

Q = Weight of moving parts per ft. of conveyor.

Power required to move a load horizontally.

P = LSCW/33000.

The above equation may be expressed in terms of the load moved in Tons per hour. Let T = tons material moved per hour.

SW = lbs material moved per min.

T = 60 SW/2000 = 3SW/100

SW = 100T/3

P = 100 LCT/3x33000 = LCT/990

Power required to move a load up an inclined belt conveyor:-

$P = 100\ TH/3x33000 = TH/990$

H = Net change in elevations;

Horse Power 'P' = $DT_eN/33000$

D = dia. of pulley, ft.

T_e = effective force between pulley and belt, lbs.

N = number RPM.

EXAMPLE 13-01

Given: Design a belt conveyor to transport mixed size of crushed lime stone for the data given below:

Capacity = 350 ton/hr

Horizontal distance = 400 ft

Vertical lift = 50 ft.

Max size of stone = 6 in.

Weight of stone = 100 Pcf

Required belt width from manufacturer Cat. of Hewitt Robbins = 24"

Max speed = 400 f.p.m.

Capacity at 400 fpm = 100 x 4 = 400 Tons/hr.

Required belt speed $= \frac{400 \times 350}{400} = 350$ fpm.

Design speed of conveyor with margin of safety = 350 + 14.2% = 400 fpm

H. Power to operate empty belt $= \frac{400 \times 400 \times 0.036 \times 20.9}{33000}$

= 3.65 hP

H.P to move load horizontally $= \frac{LCT}{990} = \frac{400 \times 0.036 \times 400}{990}$

= 5.81 h.P.

H.P to lift Load $= \frac{TH}{990} = \frac{400 \times 50}{990} = 20.20$ h.P.

Sub Total = 3.65 + 5.81 + 20.20 = 29.66

Due to pulley friction 4% of 29.66 = 1.19

h.P. required by belt 30.85

h.P for drive add 10% to belt 3.09

Total Power Required 33.94

Say 35 H.P.

To find type, size & number of driving Pulleys for operation of belt which is to be driven by head pulley.

$$T_e = \frac{hp \times 33000}{\text{belt speed fpm}} = \frac{30.85 \times 33000}{400} = 2545^{lbs}.$$

T_1 = tight side Tension

T_2 = slack side Tension

$T_e = T_1 - T_2 = 2545^{lbs}$.

To find T_2 → tension at tail Pulley, basing on assumption of tension in belt at Loading point ≥ 20#/in of belt

= 20 × 24 + 50 × 6 = 780 #

∴ T_1 = 780 + 2545 = 3325 #

For single lagged drive, Arc of contact is 215°

ie 2545 × 1.38 = 3512 # > 3325 # ok.

From Hewitt Robins literature, allowable working tension & Pulley diameter for 24" belt.

3 plies, 42 oz/Ply belt has a tension = 3840# > 3325 ok

hence minimum pulley dia. head = 24 in

tail take up & snub = 20 in

bend = 16 in

troughing idler 5" φ & 5'-0" spaced apart, with max. spacing of 1'-6" at the Loading Point. The return idlers should be 5" φ and spaced 10'-0 apart.

EXAMPLE 13-02

Given:-Find the stresses in 18"x48" bucket elevator;s casing for the following data:-

wind pressure w = 40#/□'

w on side = 4×40 = 160#/Ft

w on ends = 1.86×40 = 74#/Ft.

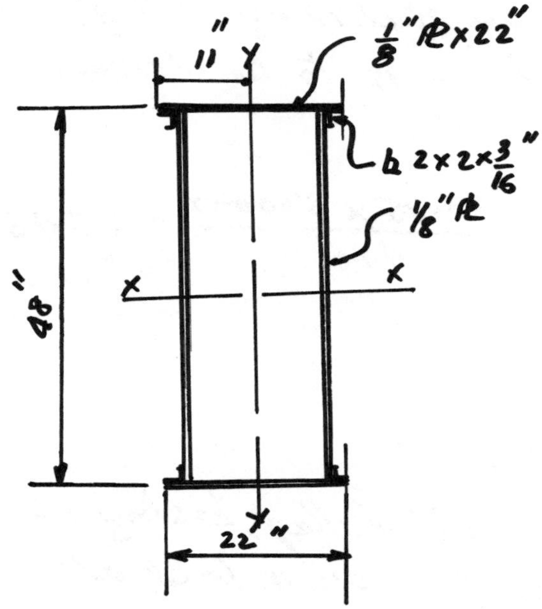

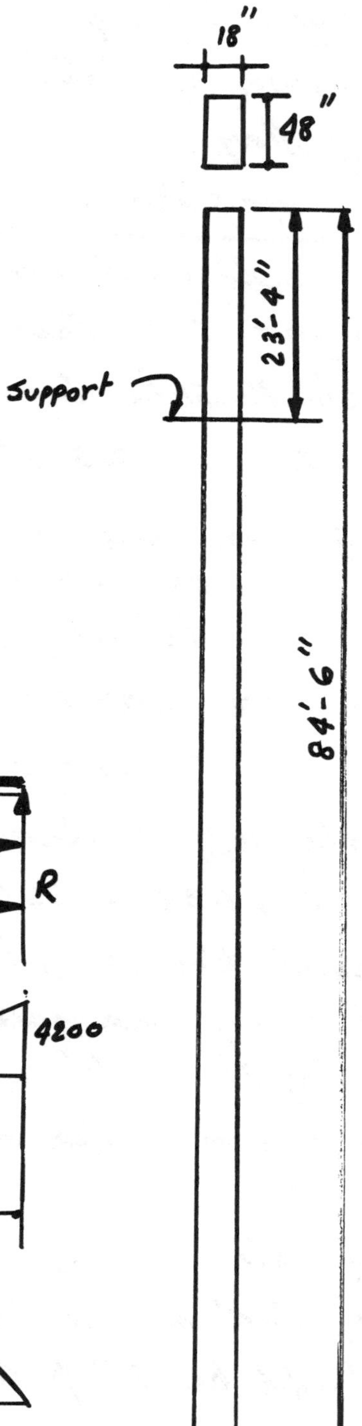

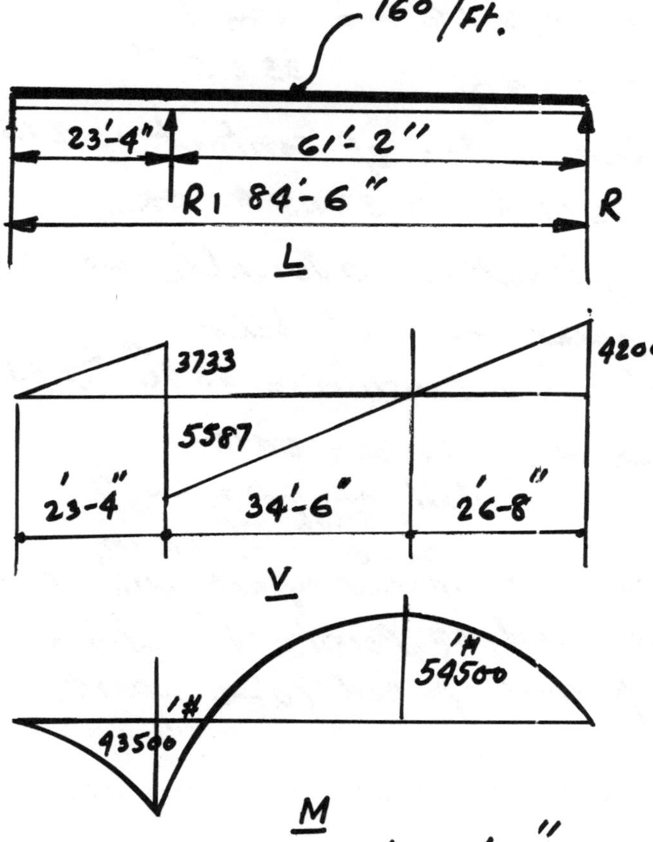

$$R_1 = \frac{160 \times 84'\text{-}6'' \times 42'\text{-}3''}{61'\text{-}2''} = 9300^{\#}$$

$$R = 13500 - 9300 = 4200^{\#}$$

Point zero V $= \frac{5587}{160} = 34'\text{-}6''$

$-ve\ M = \frac{160 \times 23'\text{-}4''^2}{2} = 43.5'^K$

$+ve\ M = 4200 \times 26'\text{-}8'' - \left(\frac{160 \times 26\text{-}8^2}{2}\right) = 54.5'^K$

Moment of Inertia about X–X

SECTION	A_0	Y	AY^2	I_0	I_{Total}
2 PL 1/8 x 22	5.5	24			3175
4 L 2x2x 3/16"	2.84	23			1500
2 PL 1/8 x 48	12.0				2304
Σ	20.34				6979

$r = \sqrt{\frac{6979}{20.34}} = 18 \qquad S_m = \frac{6979}{24} = 290$

$\frac{l}{r} = \frac{361 \times 12}{18} = 41, \quad f_{allow} = 16.17$

$\omega = 1.84 \times 40 = 74\ \#/Ft.$ for ends.

then $R_1 = \frac{74 \times 84.5 \times 42.17}{61.17} = 4350\#$

$R = 74 \times 84.5 - 4350 = 1900\#$

Pt of zero shero $= \frac{2650}{74} = 36'$

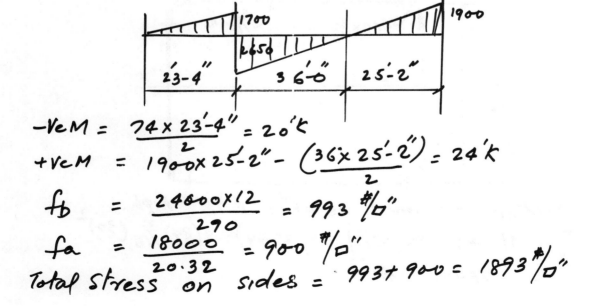

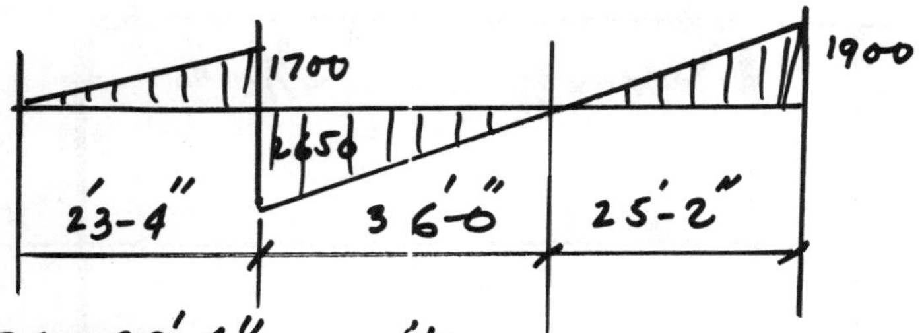

$-Ve\,M = \frac{74 \times 23'\text{-}4''}{2} = 20'^k$

$+Ve\,M = 1900 \times 25'\text{-}2'' - \left(\frac{36 \times 25'\text{-}2''}{2}\right) = 24'^k$

$f_b = \frac{24600 \times 12}{290} = 993\ \#/\square''$

$f_a = \frac{18000}{20.32} = 900\ \#/\square''$

Total Stress on sides $= 993 + 900 = 1893\ \#/\square''$

Moment of Inertia about YY axis.

Section	A □"	x_{in}	Ax^2	I_o	I_{yy}
2 PL 1/8×48	12.00	9.0	972		972
4 ∠ 2"×2"×3/16"	2.84	9.6	-	1.08	266
2 PL 1/8×22"	5.00			222	222

$\Sigma 20.34$ $\Sigma I_y = 1460$

$$r = \sqrt{\frac{1460}{20.34}} = 8.5''$$

$$\frac{l}{r} = \frac{61.17\times 12}{8.5} = 86, \quad f_{all} = 13.41 \text{ ksi}$$

$$S_M = \frac{1460}{7.5} = 154$$

$$f_a = \frac{18000}{20.32} = 900 \#/\square'', \quad f_b = \frac{54.5\times 12}{154} = 4.25 \text{ K}/\square''$$

$$\therefore f = 0.900 + 4.250 = 5.150 \text{ K}/\square''$$

EXAMPLE 13-03

Given:- Design a bucket elevator to carry a cement at a rate of 1195 tons per hour at the speed of 700 ft.p.m. in a seismic zone #1.

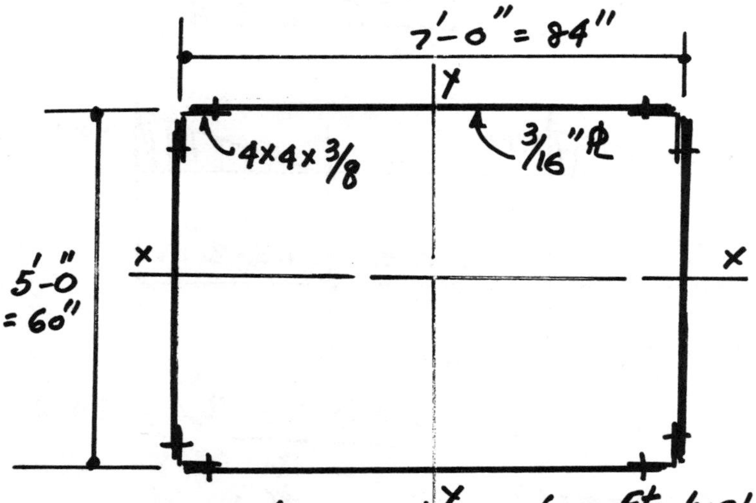

Section assumed as above & 78 ft. high.

$$I_x = 4\left[4.4 + 2.86(28)^2\right] + 2(2744) + 4(84)\tfrac{3}{16}(30)^2$$

$$= 74936 \text{ in}^4$$

$A = 4 \times 2.86 + 2 \times 84 \times \frac{3}{16} + 57.28 \times \frac{3}{16} \times 2$

$= 53.68$

$r = \sqrt{\frac{74936}{53.68}} = 37.2''$

$\frac{L}{r} = \frac{78 \times 12}{37.2} = 25.3$

Since Col/Elevator is fixed at base & free to rotate at top.

$k = 2.1$

$\frac{kL}{r} = 2.1 \times 25.5 = 53.55$

$F_a = 18.04$ ksi

$\therefore P_a = 18.04 \times 56.68 = 1022.5^k$

Load on Bucket Elevator.

D.L	3/16" PL	7.6' × 24#/□'	= 182.4#/'
	L 4×4×3/8"	4' × 9.8#/□'	= 39.2#/'
	L 3×3×1/4"	2' × 4.9 "	= 9.9#/'
	FLG @ Every 10'		= 21.3#/'
	2×[2(5+7)+2]×1/10×4.1		
	stiffeners		= 5.2#/'
		Total =	258.0#/'

D. Load for 78' high $= 78 \times 258 = 20.2^k$

Live Load $= 57 \times 78 = 4.4^k$

$\left(\frac{1195 \times 200}{60 \times 700}\right) = 57$#/ft

Earth quake Load $= 49.0 HD^2$

(Zone #1, $K_e = 0.0375$) $= 49 \times 78 \times 8.62^2 = 284^k$

Total Load $= 309.6 = 310^k$

< 1022.5 ok

1st 50' Section from top

$$M_e = W K_e h''\left(1 + \frac{h'}{100}\right)$$

$$= 258 \times 50 \times 0.0375 \times \frac{50}{2}\left(1 + \frac{15.6}{100}\right)$$

$$= 14000^{\#'}$$

where $h' = \frac{1}{5}$ height (basic design section)

h'' = C.G. of Section Considered.

$$I/c = \frac{74936}{30} = 2498 \text{ in}^3.$$

$$f = \frac{W}{A} + \frac{Mc}{I}$$

$$= \left[\frac{258 \times 50}{53.68} + \frac{57 \times 50}{53.68}\right] + \frac{14000 \times 12}{2498}$$

$$= 981 \text{ Psi}$$

$$F_a = \frac{2,400,000}{549} = 4360 \text{ Psi} \quad \because \frac{d}{t} = \frac{8.62 \times 12}{3/16} = 549$$

ok

Hence trial section assumed ok

Check section at base

$$M_e = 258 \times 78 \times 0.0375 \times 39'\text{-}0 = 29500'^{\#}$$

$$f = \left(\frac{258 \times 78}{53.68} + \frac{57 \times 78}{53.68}\right) + \frac{29500 \times 12}{2498}$$

$$= 1878^{psi} < 4360 \text{ Psi} \quad \text{ok}$$

$$\therefore F_s = \frac{4360}{1878} = 2.32 \quad \text{AMPLE.}$$

EXAMPLE 13-04

Given:- Check the support and rail of Tripper designed for the Public Service Indiana, Wabash Station.

The rails on which tripper wheels runs alongside of Conveyor are supported rigidly on external support in order to maintain alignement.

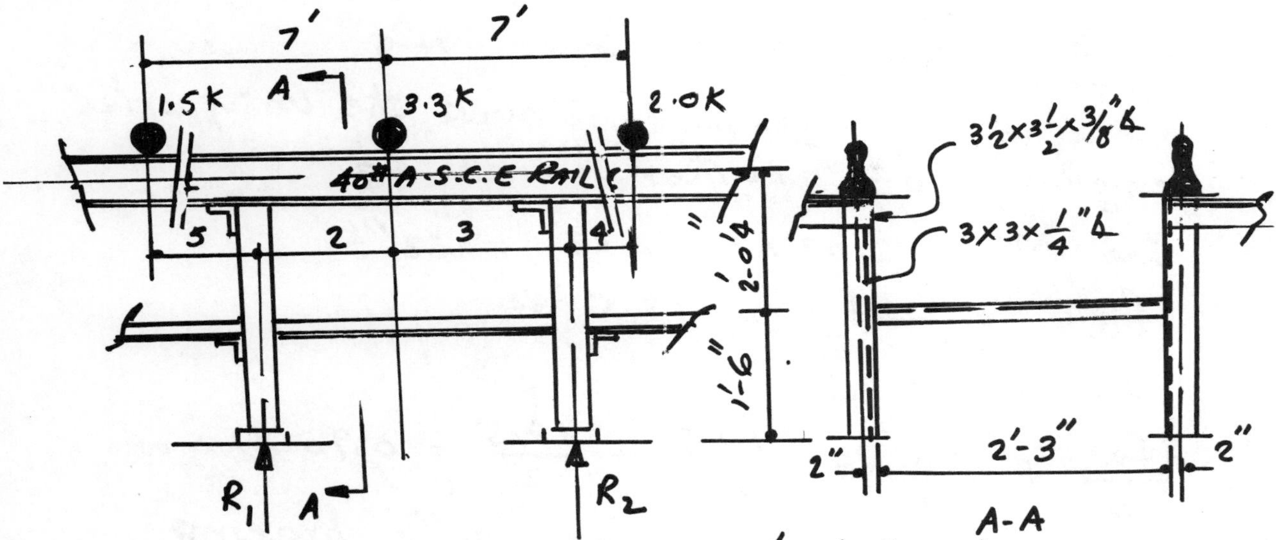

Lateral Load = 20% of max. Load Capacity

$= 0.20(1.5+3.3+2.0)2\times\frac{1}{2} = 1.36^K$

Longitudenal force (due to starting & stopping of tripper)

$= 25\%$ wheel load

$R_2 \times 5 = 2\times9 + 3.3\times2 - 1.5\times5 = 17.1$

$R_2 = 3.42^K$

Due to D.L of rail used 40# A.S.C.E

$R_2 \times 5 = 560\times2 = 1.12^K$

$R_2 = \frac{1.12}{5} = 0.23^K$

$R_{2\,max} = 3.42 + 0.23 = 3.65^K$

Hence Vert. Load $= 3.65 + 25\% = 4.56^K$

Lat. Load $= 1.36^K$

support height $= 3'\text{-}8'' - 0'\text{-}1\frac{3}{4}'' = 3'\text{-}6\frac{1}{4}'' = 3.52'$

Moment due to lateral Load $= 1.36\times3.52\times12 = 57.5^{"K}$

$F_b = M/S$.

S L $3\times3\times\frac{1}{4} = 0.58\ in^3$

L $3\frac{1}{2}\times3\frac{1}{2}\times\frac{3}{8} = 1.20\ in^3$

$1.78\ in^3$

$f_b = \frac{57.5}{1.78} = 32.2$ ksi

$f_a = \frac{4.56}{2.48+1.44} = 1.16$

$\therefore \frac{f_a}{F_a} + \frac{f_b}{F_b} \le 1$

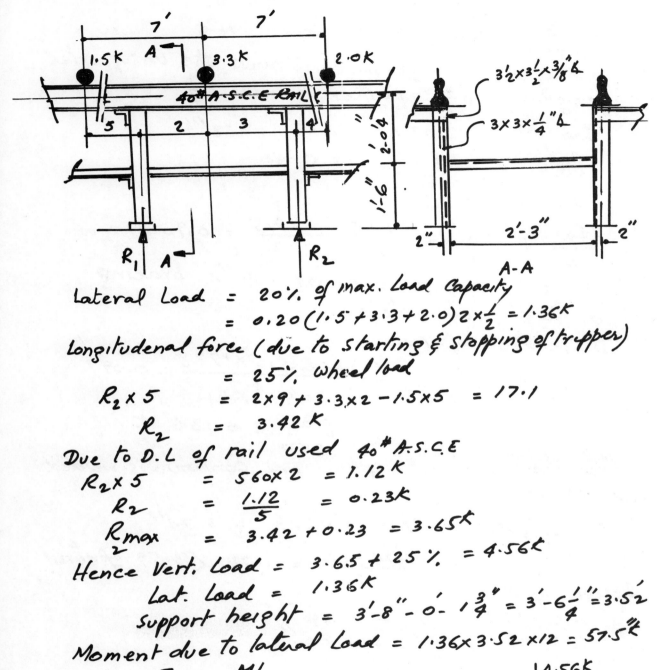

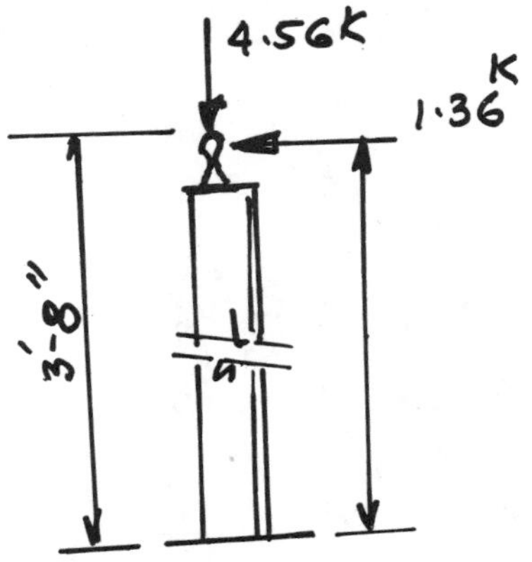

$$\frac{1.16}{22} + \frac{32.2}{22} = 1.51 > 1 \quad N.G.$$

Hence it is suggested to make the unsupported length $2'-0\frac{1}{4}''$ rather than $3'-6\frac{1}{4}''$

then $M = 2.02 \times 1.36 \times 12 = 33''k$

$$f_b = \frac{33}{1.78} = 18.5 \text{ ksi}$$

$$f_a = 1.16$$

$$\frac{f_a}{F_a} + \frac{f_b}{F_b} = \frac{1.16}{22} + \frac{18.5}{2} = 0.90 < 1.0 \text{ ok.}$$

Hence supports are ok with bracing at $1'-6''$ from bottom.

Deflection of rail.

$$\Delta = \frac{Pl^3}{48EI} = \frac{4.56 \times 5 \times 5 \times 5 \times 1728}{48 \times 30 \times 10^6 \times 6.54} = 0.097''$$

$$< \frac{\text{Span}}{450} = 0.136'' \text{ ok}$$

Even then rail at splice are continuous welded and spliced

$$\text{Max. } M_{@\,center} = 2 \times 7 - 3.42 \times 3 = 3.74'k$$

$$S = \frac{3.74 \times 12}{25} = 1.78 < 3.59 \text{ of } 40^{\#} \text{ rail}$$

Design of Pin

W 6 x 15.5 $t_w = 0.24''$

[6 x 8.2 $t_w = 0.20''$

$$M = 2 \times 14 = 28''k$$

$$F_b = 0.9 \times F_y = 0.9 \times 36 = 32.4 \text{ ksi}$$

$$d = \sqrt[3]{\frac{32M}{\pi F_b}} = \sqrt[3]{\frac{32 \times 28}{\pi \times 32.4}} = 2.04''$$

Use $2\frac{3}{16}''\phi$ S.A.E 1045

Shoe & Pin Plates.

$$\text{Bearing} = F_p = 0.90 \times 36 = 32.4 \text{ ksi}$$

$$t = \frac{2}{32.4 \times 2.188} = 0.028'' \text{ use } 1'' \text{ PL.}$$

Check of Link Connection

$$\frac{M}{P} \cdot \frac{P_e}{M_e} = \frac{3P \times bc^2 \sigma_e}{P \times \frac{2}{3} b c^2 \sigma_c} = \frac{4.5}{3} = 1.5$$

$$\frac{M}{M_e} = 0.6 \;\&\; \frac{P}{P_e} = 0.4$$

$$\therefore P = 0.4 P_e = 0.4 \times 4.62 \times 36000$$

$$= 66800^{\#} \quad \text{ok}$$

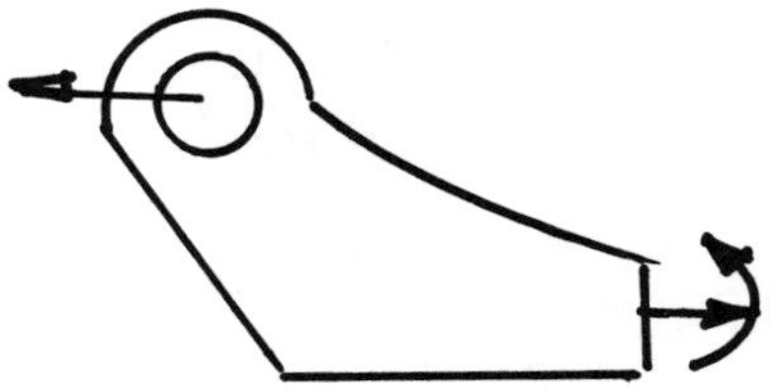

Hence link of W 6x15.5 can resist tensile load of 66.8^k which is far more than what we need.

Beam W 6x15.5 is actually just supporting D.L and proposed for Lateral Supports.

for 6'-3" span of W 6x15.5

$$\Delta = \frac{0.02276 L^2}{d} = \frac{0.02276 \times 6.25^2}{6}$$

$$= 0.148'' < \frac{6.25 \times 12}{360} = 0.2 \quad \text{ok}.$$

EXAMPLE 13-05

Given:- Design a belt conveyor truss (continuous) to carry rubber material for the Good Year Tire Company for a span of 86'.

Loading

Wind $= 20^{\#}/\text{sft}$

transfer to lower chord

$$\Sigma M_a = \frac{20}{2.96}(6 + 4.8 + 3.5) = 100^{\#}/\text{ft} \text{ vertical}.$$

DL + Mat'L.

Belt + Mat'l	=	$10^{\#}/_1$
Conv. HSG	=	$50^{\#}/_1$
Truss	=	$60^{\#}/_1$
		$120^{\#}/_1$

Snow Load (Ice) $\quad 10^{\#}/_1$

$$R = \frac{60 \times 4.25 + 200 \times 1.45}{2.95} = 185^{\#}/_1$$

$$A_s = \frac{43}{29.3} = 1.47\square'' < 2.20\square'' \text{ ok}$$

Hence use ∟ $4 \times 3 \times \frac{3}{8}''$

Stress in bottom. chord Try $4 \times 3 \times \frac{3}{8}$ ∟ $A = 2.48\square''$

Hor. wind $= \frac{61}{3} = 20\text{ k}$

(Vert. wind + DL + MAT'L + SL) $= \frac{216}{5} = 43\text{ k}$

63 k

$l_x = 80''$, $r_x = 1.26$, $l_{zz} = 40''$, $r_{zz} = 0.64$

$$\frac{l}{r} = \frac{80}{1.26} = 63.5; \quad Fa = 17.1 + \tfrac{1}{3}(17.1) = 22.8$$

$$fa = \frac{63}{2.48} = 25.4 > 22.8 \quad \text{N.G.}$$

To reduce fa (actual) to Fa (allowable), Reinforce bott. chord at support with corbel angle, extended 8' on either side of support where $M = 0.06wl^2$

$$M = 0.06 \times 0.285 \times 87^2 \div 5 = 26$$

$$0.06 \times 0.08 \times 87^2 \div 3 = 12$$

$$38\text{K}$$

$$fa \text{ @ } 8' \text{ away} = \frac{38}{2.48} = 15.3 < 22.8 \text{ ok with}$$

1 corbel angle.

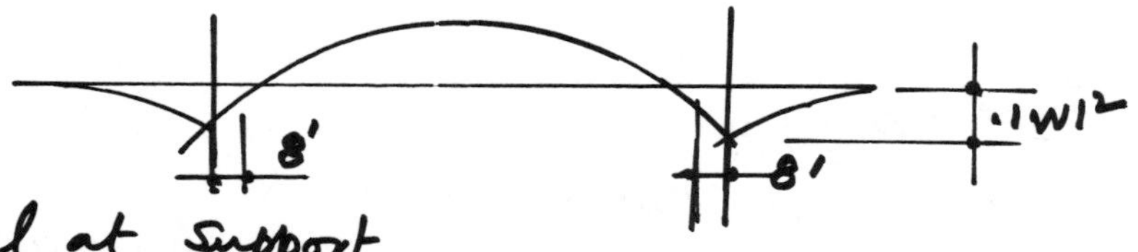

check corbel at support

$$M = \frac{PL}{4} = \frac{9.4 \times 6.67}{4} = 15.3'\text{k}$$

$$S = \frac{15.3 \times 12}{22} = 8.4 \text{ in}^3 \quad \text{use } 2 \text{ ∟s } 7 \times 4 \times \tfrac{3}{8}'', S_x = 8.97\text{r}$$

Span 2nd corbel ∟ between points over supports.

Diagonal stress in member (a)

Try $2\frac{1}{2} \times 2\frac{1}{2} \times \frac{1}{4}$ ∟, $A = 1.19$, $r_{zz} = 0.49$, $V_{max} = (9.4 + 4.79)\frac{2}{3}$
$= 9.46$

Compressive Load in member (a) $= 9.5 \times \frac{6}{5} = 11.4$

$l_{zz} = 4'6''$, $\frac{l}{r} = \frac{54}{0.49} = 110$, $Fa = 11.67 + \frac{1}{3}W = 15.56\text{ Ksi}$

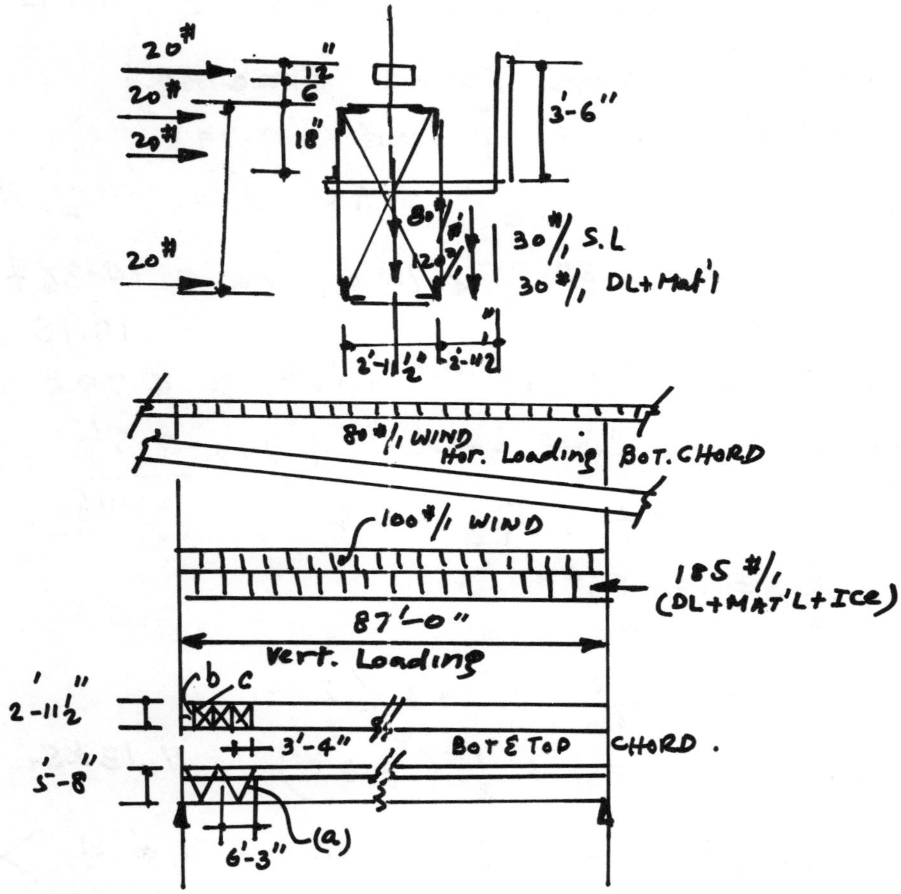

Assuming continueous truss

$M_{support}$ Due to (S.L + Mat'l + Dead Load)

$$= \frac{0.185 \times 87^2}{10} = 140'^{K}$$

$M_{support}$ Horz. Load wind

$$= \frac{0.080 \times 87^2}{10} = 61'^{K}$$

$M_{support}$ vert. wind Load

$$= \frac{0.100 \times 87^2}{10} = 76'^{K}$$

$$R_{support}\ (\text{vert. wind}) = \frac{1.1 \times 0.1 \times 87}{2} = 4.9K$$

$$R_{support}\ (DL + Mat'L + S.L) = \frac{1.1 \times 0.185 \times 87}{2} = 9.4K$$

STRESS in top chord (vert. wind + D.L + MAT'L + S.L) Try $\llcorner 4 \times 3 \times \frac{3}{8}$, $A_N = 2.20\,\square''$

$$(140 + 76)\frac{1}{5} = 43K$$

$$F_b = 22 + \frac{22}{3} = 29.3\,KSi$$

$$A_s = \frac{11.4}{15.56} = 0.735 \square'' < 1.19 \square''$$

Bottom & Top chord (Wind Bracing)

MBR(b) Max. Comp. Load $= 4.79K$

Try $\angle$ $2\times2\times\frac{1}{4}$, $r_{zz} = 0.40$, $l = 2'\text{-}11\frac{1}{2}''$, $A = 0.94\square''$

$$\frac{l}{r} = \frac{35.5}{0.40} = 88.75 < 140, \quad Fa = 14.36 + \frac{1}{3}(14.36) = 19.15$$

$$P_{allowable} = 19.15 \times 0.94 = 18K > 4.79K \text{ ok}$$

MBR C Max Comp Load $= 4.79 \times \frac{4\text{-}5\frac{1}{2}}{2'\text{-}11\frac{1}{2}} = 7.3K$

Try $\angle$ $2\times2\times\frac{1}{4}$, $r_{zz} = 0.4$,

$l = 4'\text{-}5\frac{1}{2}''$

$A = 0.94$

$$\frac{l}{r} = \frac{53.5}{0.40} = 133 < 200$$

$$Fa = 8.35 + \frac{1}{3}(8.35) = 11.13 ksi$$

$$P_{allowable} = 11.13 \times 0.94 = 10.4 > 7.3 \text{ ok.}$$

EXAMPLE 13-06

Given: Design the conveyor #2E Gallary, Junction Tower #2E/3E with its foundation and Track Hopper Pit for DONNER HANNA COKE CORP. of Buffalo, New York. to carry coke of unit weight 35 Lbs pcf.

Conveyor #2E Gallary.

Dead Load :-

Roof	5x11	= 55#
Siding	4x16	= 64#
Bott. SH	3x11	= 33#
Truss	50x2	= 100#
Conc. slab	40x11	= 440#
Conveyor	35	= 35#
		727# Say 730#

D.L Per truss $= \frac{730}{2} = 365\#/ft$

Live Load

Coke		= 35
Snow	40x11	= 440
L.L on floor	50x6	= 300
		775#

L.L / TRUSS = 390#/FT.

Wind = 30#/□'

P = 30×12 = 360#/ft

$M_{max} = \frac{0.36 \times 45^2}{8} = 92'^k$

Forces on chord = $\frac{92}{11} = 8.4^k$

Max. Shear = 0.36 × 22.5 = 8k

Design $M_{max} = (0.365 + 0.39)\frac{45^2}{8} = 192'^k$

Force in chord = $\frac{192}{8} = 24^k$

Max. End Reaction = 0.755 × 22.5 = 17k

Panel Loading = $\frac{34}{4} = 8.5^k$

Bottom chord $A_{req'd} = \frac{24}{20} = 1.2$ □" use ST W6×13.5

Top chord l_{max} = 9'-0", Try St W6×13.5

$\frac{l}{r} = \frac{12 \times 9}{1.36} = 80 \therefore F_a = 15.36 < 22$

$P_{all.} = 15.36 \times 3.76 = 58^k$ ok

Vert. $P_{max} = 17^k$, l = 10'-0", Try 2 ∟s 3×3×5/16 TT

$l/r = \frac{120}{0.94} = 128$, $F_{all} = 9.11$ ksi

$P_{all} = 9.11 \times 3.24 = 29.5$ K ok.

Diagonal $P = 17 \times \frac{17}{4} = 21^k$

$A_{req'd} = \frac{21}{20} = 1$□", $r = \frac{17.5 \times 12}{240} = 0.88$

Use ∟ 3½×3½×¼"

Bott. Bracing & top Bracing Max. Wind Reaction = 4^k

$\frac{l}{r} = 200$, $r = \frac{12 \times 14}{200} = 0.84$, Use 4×3×5/16"

JUNCTION TOWER. 2E/3E

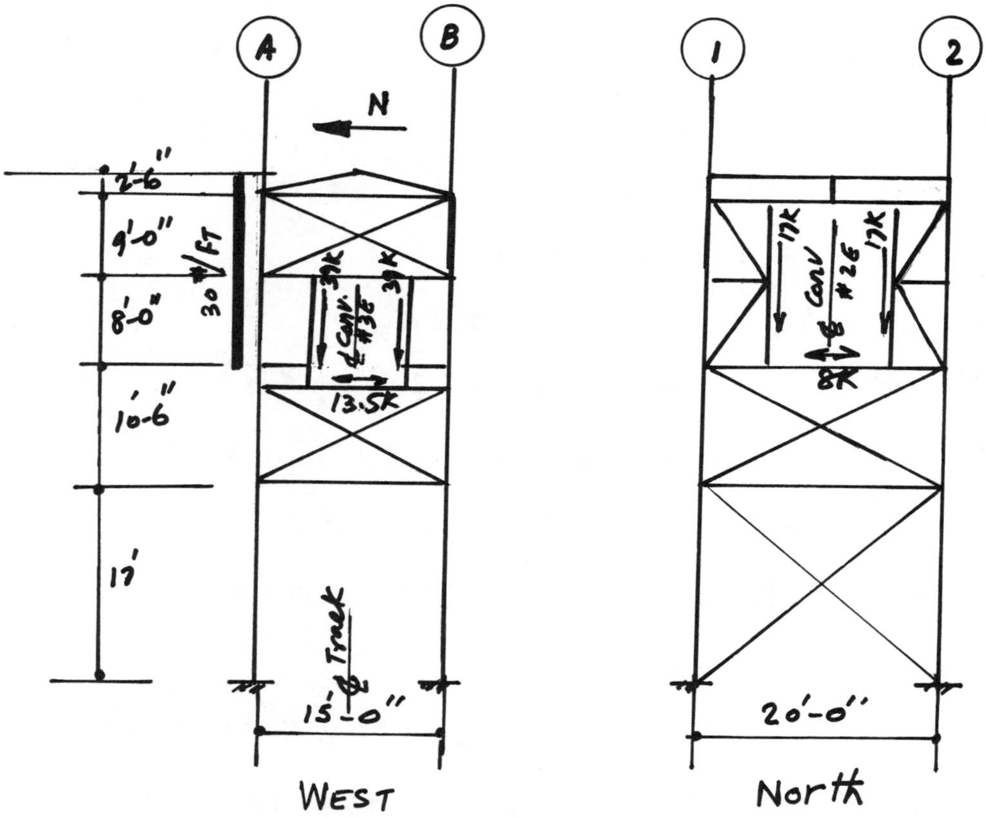

Col. Reaction from Tower

Roof:- Snow $40^{\#}/\square^2 = \frac{16 \times 21 \times 0.40}{4} = 3.35^K/\text{col.}$

D.L $10^{\#}/\square^2 = \frac{16 \times 21 \times 0.01}{4} = 0.85^K/\text{col.}$

3rd & 2nd floor

L.L $50^{\#}/ft^2 = \frac{15 \times 20 \times 0.05}{4} = 3.75^K/\text{col.}$

D.L $75^{\#}/ft^2 = \frac{15 \times 20 \times 0.07}{4} = 5.6^K/c$

1st floor

LL $= 1.5^K/\text{col.}$

DL $= 1^K/\text{col}$

Siding & Bracing $DL = 6^{\#}/\square^2 = (42+32)28 \times 0.06 = \frac{9.8}{4} = 2.45^K/\text{col.}$

Wind Load

Wind on gallary #3E Neglected Due to stablizing effect of 2E.

WIND Direction East-West.

Load on Col. $= \frac{1}{2}\left[\frac{(0.03 \times 20 \times 16) \times 37.5}{20} + \frac{8 \times 37.5}{20}\right] = 16.5^K/\text{col.}$

Wind direction North South.

Load on col. $\frac{1}{2}\left(\frac{0.03 \times 20 \times 21 \times 37.5}{20}\right) = 11.8^k/\text{col.}$

Resultant forces on Columns.

		A_1	A_2	B_1	B_2
FROM CONV. 2E	DL / LL	19 / 8	19 / 8		
" " 3E	DL / LL		22 / 17		22 / 17
" TOWER	DL / LL	15.5 / 12.35	15.5 / 12.35	15.5 / 12.35	15.5 / 12.35
WIND E.W ON TOWER		∓ 9	∓ 9	∓ 9	∓ 9
" " ON GALLARY 2E		∓ 7.5	± 7.5	∓ 7.5	± 7.5
" N.S ON TOWER		∓ 11.8	∓ 11.8	± 11.8	± 11.8

Max. Load on column A-2 $\quad 46.5 + 37.35 + 16.5 = 100.35$

or $\quad 46.5 + 37.35 = 83.85$

Min. Load on col B1 $\quad = 15.5 - 16.5 = 1^k$ uplift

Design Case 1 (Max. DL + LL), $P = 83.85^k$

Try 8 WF 31 $\quad \frac{l}{r_x} = \frac{17 \times 12}{3.47} = 59, \quad \frac{l}{r_y} = \frac{8.5 \times 12}{2.01} = 51$

$F_a = 17.53\ \text{ksi}, \quad f_a = \frac{83.85}{9.12} = 9.2\ \text{ksi}$

Case 2. (Max DL + LL + WNS) $P = 100.35$,

$M = 3.15 \times 9 = 28.3^k\text{ft}$ - Say $30^{k\text{ft}}$

$F_b = 22\ \text{ksi}, \quad f_b = \frac{30 \times 12}{27.4} = 13.13$

$f_a = \frac{100.35}{9.12} = 11\ \text{ksi}$

$\frac{f_a}{F_a} + \frac{f_b}{F_b} = \frac{11}{17.53} + \frac{13.13}{22} = 1.22 < 1.33$ ok.

Foundation:-

M @ Top Piles $= 30 + 3.2 \times 5 = 46'^k$

Load on Piles $= 101 + 5.5^2 \times 4.5 \times 0.12 = 118^k$

$S_{pile} = \frac{2 \times 1.5^2 \times 2}{1.5} = 6\ \text{ft}^3$

Max/Min Load on pile $= \frac{118}{4} \pm \frac{46}{6} = 41^k, 21.83^k$

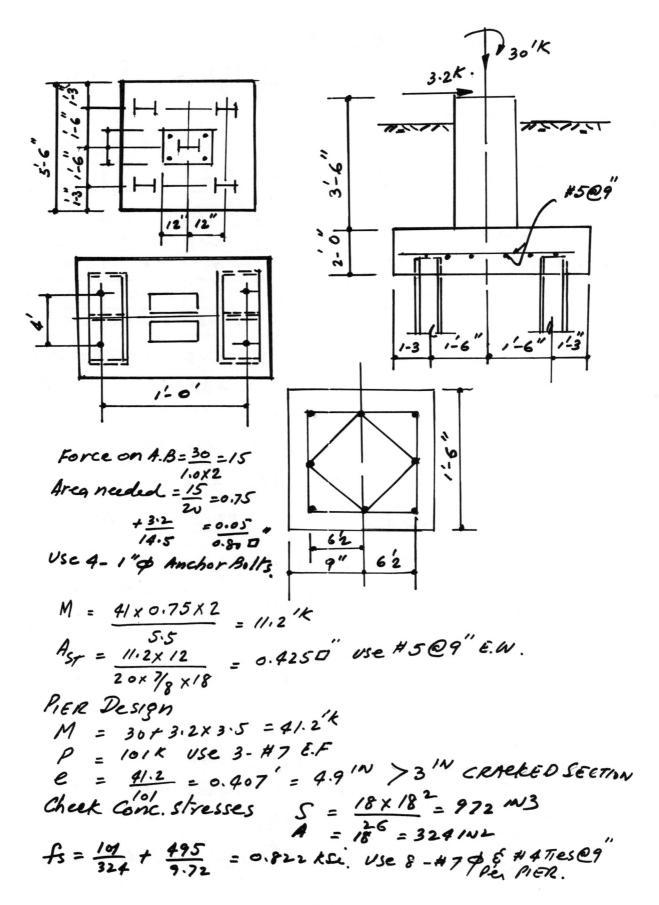

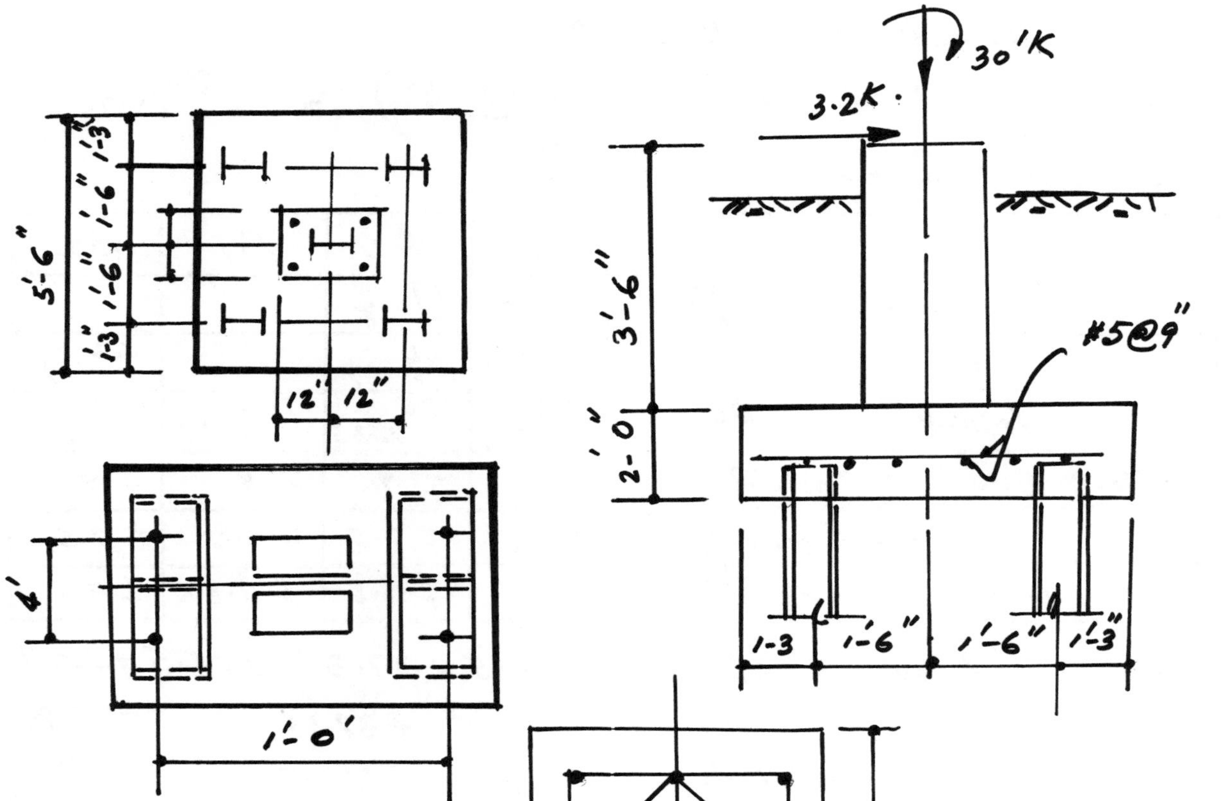

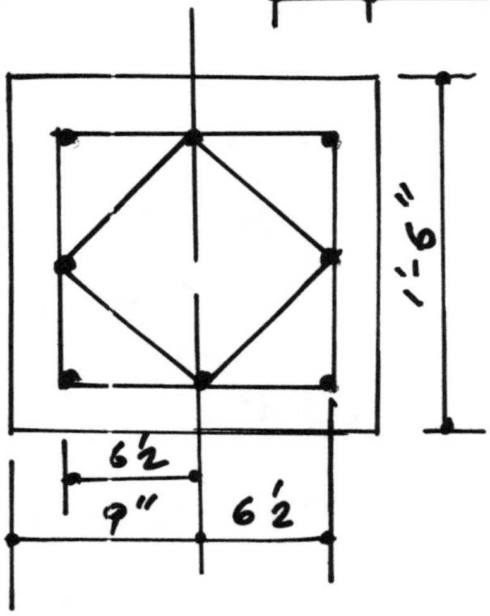

Force on A.B $= \frac{30}{1.0 \times 2} = 15$

Area needed $= \frac{15}{20} = 0.75$

$+ \frac{3.2}{14.5} = \frac{0.05}{0.80 \square''}$

Use 4- 1"φ Anchor Bolts.

$$M = \frac{41 \times 0.75 \times 2}{5.5} = 11.2'^{K}$$

$$A_{ST} = \frac{11.2 \times 12}{20 \times 7/8 \times 18} = 0.425 \square''$$ use #5@9" E.W.

PIER Design

$M = 30 + 3.2 \times 3.5 = 41.2'^{K}$

$P = 101^{K}$ use 3- #7 E.F

$e = \frac{41.2}{101} = 0.407' = 4.9^{IN} > 3^{IN}$ CRACKED SECTION

Check Conc. stresses $S = \frac{18 \times 18^2}{6} = 972\ IN^3$

$A = 18^2 = 324\ IN^2$

$f_s = \frac{101}{324} + \frac{495}{9.72} = 0.822$ ksi. Use 8 - #7φ & #4 Ties @9" Per PIER.

TRACK HOPPER

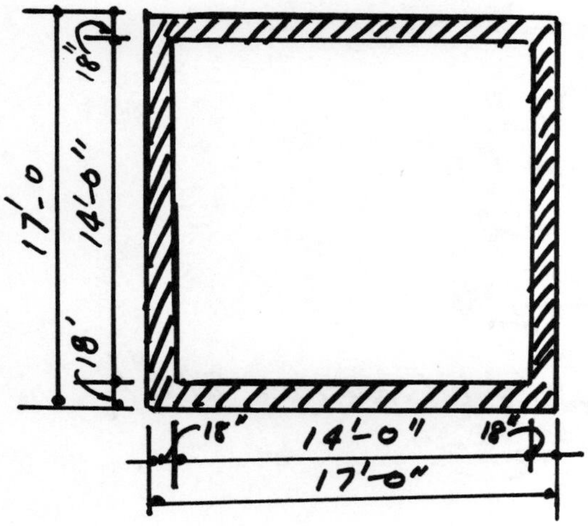

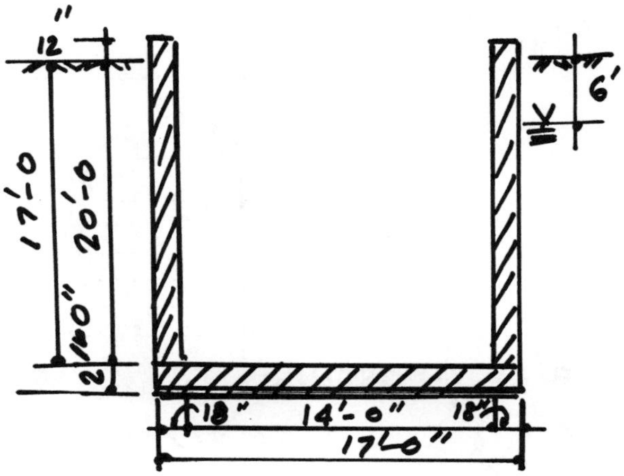

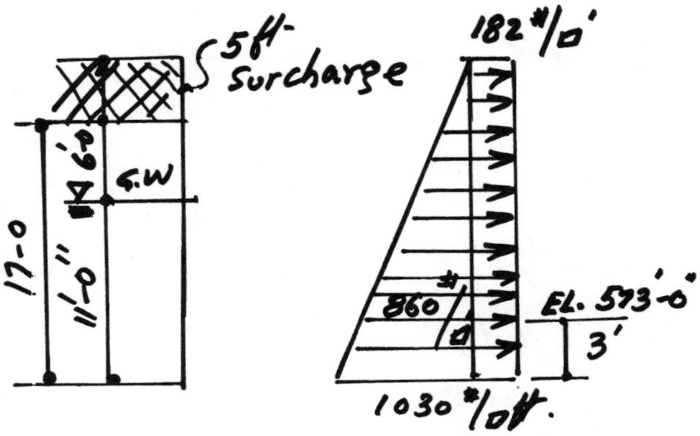

Soil pressure on wall.

Assumption

5'-0" Surcharge

$\gamma_{soil} = 110 \text{ \#/cft}, \ \phi = 30^\circ, \ \lambda = 0.33$

$C = 0$

$P = \gamma h \lambda = 36.3h \text{ \#/ft}$

$P = (\gamma + 62.4) h \lambda = 56.9h \text{ \#/ft}$

$P_{soil} = 0.86 \text{ k/□'}$

$M_{span} = \frac{0.86 \times 16^2}{24} = 9.2 \text{ 'k}$

$A_{st} = \frac{9.2 \times 12}{20 \times 7/8 \times 15} = 0.42 \text{ □"/ft.}$ use #6@12"

$M_{support} = \frac{0.86 \times 16^2}{12} = 18.4 \text{ 'k}$

$M@edge = 18.4 + \frac{0.86 \times 1^2}{2} - 0.86 \times 8 \times 1 = 11.87 \text{ 'k}$

A_s edge $= \dfrac{11.87 \times 12}{20 \times 7/8 \times 15} = 0.542\ \square''/ft$ use #6@9"

Bott. slab.

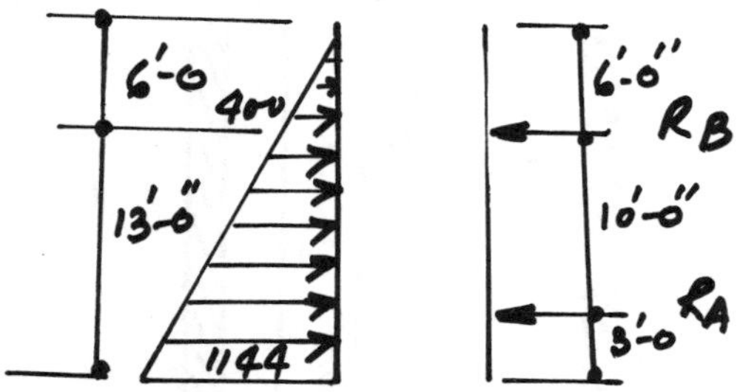

Water pressure @ EL 569'-0" $= 62.4 \times 13 = 812\ \#/\square'$

$M_{slab} = \dfrac{0.812 \times 15^2}{18} = 10.2'^k$

A_{st} slab $= \dfrac{10.2 \times 12}{20 \times 7/8 \times 21} = 0.332\ \square''/'$ use #5@12"

$M_{edge} = \dfrac{0.812 \times 15^2}{12} = 15.3'^k$

A_{st} edge $= \dfrac{15.3 \times 12}{20 \times 7/8 \times 15} = 0.7\ \square''/ft$ use #7@9"

Sheet pile

$R_A = 0.182 \times 19 \times \dfrac{3.5}{10} - \dfrac{1}{2} \times 0.218 \times 6 \times \dfrac{1}{10} + 0.218 \times 13 \times \dfrac{6.5}{10}$
$+ 0.744 \times \dfrac{1}{2} \times 13 \times \dfrac{8.66}{10} = 7.23\ ^k/ft$

$R_B = 0.182 \times 19 + \dfrac{1}{2} \times 0.218 \times 6 + 0.218 \times 13 + 0.744 \times \dfrac{1}{2} \times 13 - 7.23$
$= 4.56\ ^k/'$

Temp sheet piling supporting beam EL. 573'-0"

$W = 7.23\ ^k/'$, $M = 7.23 \times \dfrac{7.5^2}{8} = 51'^k$

$S_{req'd} = \dfrac{51 \times 12}{24} = 25.5\ IN^3$, use W10×25 $S = 26.4$

$Q = 7.23 \times \dfrac{7.5}{2} + \dfrac{51}{7.5} = 33.9$, $q = \dfrac{33.9}{10 \times 0.252} = 13.45^{ksi}$

$4.56 = 0.182 \times 6 + 0.182x + \frac{1}{2} \times 0.218 \times 6 + 0.218 \times 6 + 0.218x$
$+ 0.057 \times \frac{1}{2} x$ or $x^2 + 14x - 9.85 = 0 \therefore x = 5.15$

$M = 4.56 \times 6.15 - 1.1 \times 8.15 - 0.93 \times 7.15 - 0.65 \times 5.15$
$- 1.12 \times 2.57 - 0.755 \times 1.71 = 4.9'^k$

$S = \dfrac{4.9 \times 12}{20} = 2.94$ Use U.S.S Sheet Piling MP-115

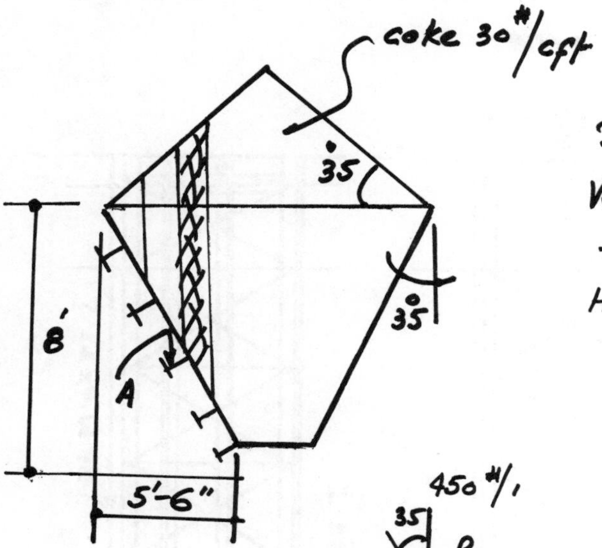

Design a beam A

Vert. Load $= 1.5 \times 8 \times 30 = 360^{\#}/'$

+ Impact $= 25\%$

Hor. Pressure, $\phi = 35$

$$\lambda = \frac{1 - \sin\phi}{1 + \sin\phi} = 0.293$$

$$P = \gamma \lambda h = 30 \times 0.293 h = 8.8h$$

$$= 8.8 \times 8 = 70.5^{\#}/ft$$

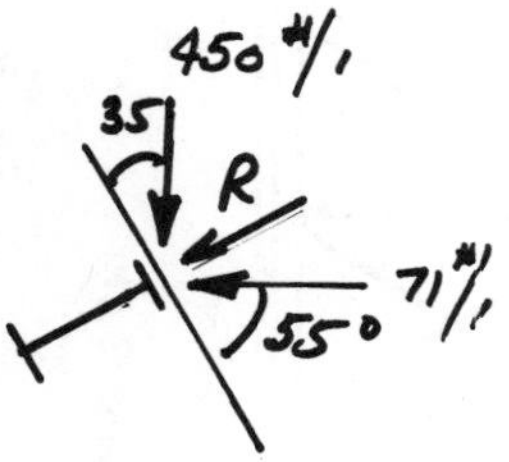

$$R = 450 \sin 35 + 71 \sin 55$$

$$= 318^{\#}/'$$

$$M_{max} = \frac{0.318 \times 10^2}{8} = 4'k$$

$$S_{reqd} = \frac{4 \times 12}{20} = 2.2 \text{ use B8x10}$$

Wt. Per ft support

	$3 \times 3 \times 8 \times 30$	$= 2160$
	$\frac{1}{3} \times 11^2 \times 8 \times 30$	$= 9700$
	$\frac{1}{3} \times 14^2 \times 5 \times 30$	$= 9800$
		$\frac{21660}{56} = 388^{\#}/'$
D. W =		$= 200^{\#}/'$
		$588^{\#}/'$
		Say $600^{\#}/ft$.

EXAMPLE 13-07

<u>Given</u>:- Design an uncovered truss gallary 14'-6"x 8'-4"x120' along with necessary bents to support the conveyor system.

Gallary Loads	D.L/'	L.L/'
Gallery	170.0	
Deck & framing	93.0	
Siding - Girts	36.0	
Walkway Concrete/GRATING	45.0	
Material		106.00
BELT	40.0	

Uncovered TRUSS FOR Public Service Co of INDIANA

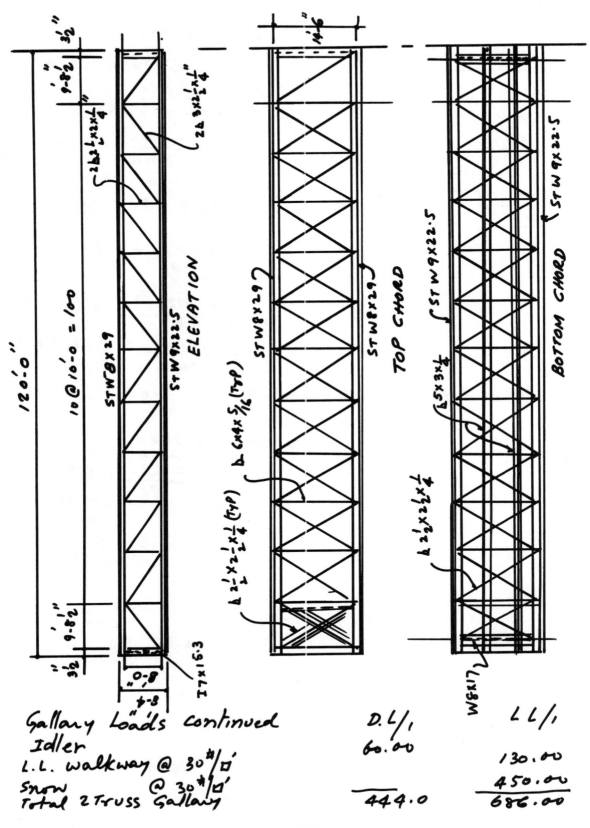

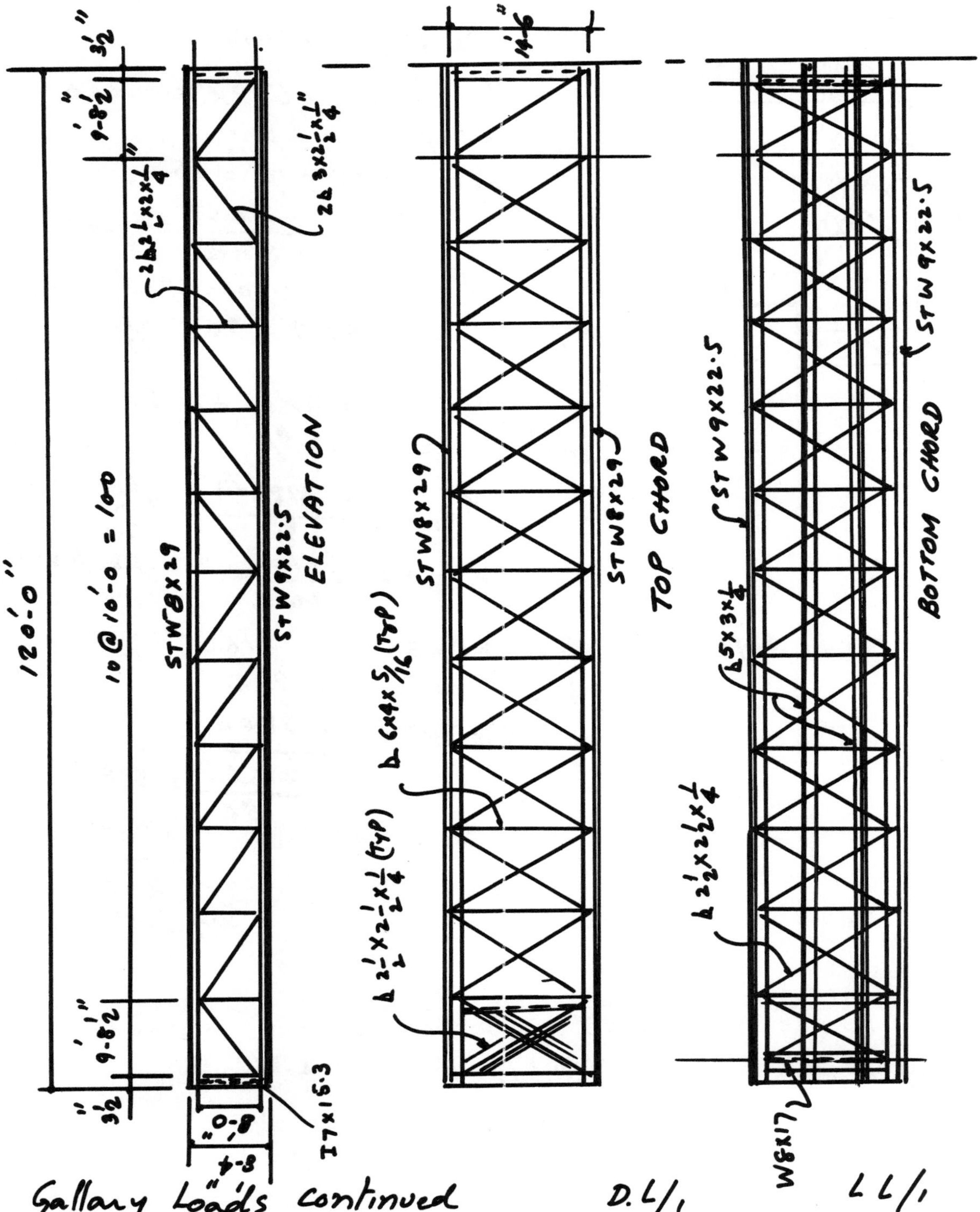

Gallary Loads continued	D.L/1	L L/1
Idler	60.00	
L.L. walkway @ 30#/□'		130.00
Snow @ 30#/□'		450.00
Total 2Truss Gallary	444.0	686.00

UNCOVERED TRUSS

TOP CHORD							BOTT. CHORD						
MBR	DL+LL +SL +MAT'L	DL+LL +SL	WIND	DL+LL+SL + WIND	3/4(DL+LL +SL+W)	DESIGN STRESS	MBR	DL+LL+SL +MAT'L	DL+LL +SL	WIND	DL+LL+SL +WIND	3/4(DL+LL +SL·W)	Design Stress
2N	37.8	34.4	4.6	39.0	29.2	-37.8	1A	8.5	7.7	9.2	16.9	12.7	+12.7
4N	69.0	62.6	8.4	71.0	53.2	-69.0	3B	31.1	28.2	16.8	45.0	33.8	+33.8
6N	93.5	84.6	11.2	95.8	71.8	-93.5	5C	63.5	57.6	22.4	80.0	60.0	+63.5
8N	111.0	100.0	13.3	113.3	85.0	-111.0	7D	89.5	80.1	26.6	106.7	80.0	+89.5
10N	121.0	110.0	14.5	124.5	93.4	-121.0	9E	108.1	98.4	29.0	127.4	95.5	+108.1
12N	125.0	113.2	14.9	128.1	96.1	-125	11F	120.0	109.0	29.8	138.8	104.0	+120.0

Total Load per Truss = $\frac{1130}{2}$ = 565 #/'

D.L + LL + S.L = 512 #/'

Ratio = $\frac{512}{565}$ = 0.906

Total wind = 360 #/' Gallery

Top chord = $\frac{1}{3}(360)$ = 120 #/'

Bott. chord = $\frac{2}{3}(360)$ = 240 #/'

STRESS Ratio for Top chord = $\frac{120}{200}$ = 0.6

stress ratio for bott. chord = $\frac{240}{200}$ = 1.2

Top Chord Stress = 125 K (Comp)

Try ST W8X29 $r = 1.88$, $A = 8.52\ IN^2$

Ded A. = 1.62 × 0.645 = 1.05 IN^2

Net A = 8.52 − 1.05 = 7.47 IN^2

$\frac{l}{r} = \frac{10 \times 12}{1.88} = 63.8$

Fa = 17.06

STRESS = 17.06 × 7.47 = 127.5 K > 125 ok.

USE ST W8X29

Bottom chord

Stress = 122.0 K (comp)

Area required = $\frac{122}{22}$ = 5.55 IN^2

Try ST W9 × 22.5, A = 6.62, Anet = 6.62 − 1.62 × 0.499 = 5.81 IN^2

STRESS = 5.81 × 22 = 128 > 122 ok

USE ST W9X22.5

Verticals Stress = 30K

l = 8.0', Try 2L 3×2½ × 5/16 ⟶ A = 3.24, A_n = 3.24 − 1.62 × 5/16 = 2.73

$\frac{l}{r} = \frac{8 \times 12}{0.94} = 102$

Fa = 12.72 Ksi

Stress = 12.72 × 2.73 = 34.8 K > 30 kips

Use 2 L 3×2½ × 5/16 ⊤⊤

Diagonals Max stress 48.4K

use 2 ∠ 3x $2\frac{1}{2}$ x $\frac{5}{16}$.

Top or Bot Chord Bracing

Diagonals use 1 ∠ 4x$3\frac{1}{2}$x$\frac{1}{4}$ LLV

Top Bracing horizontal $l_u = 14.5$

$r_{min} = \frac{14.5 \times 12}{200} = 0.87$ IN, use 1 ∠ 6x4x$\frac{1}{4}$ LLV

Bott. Bracing Horiz.

use B 6x12

Bent #1

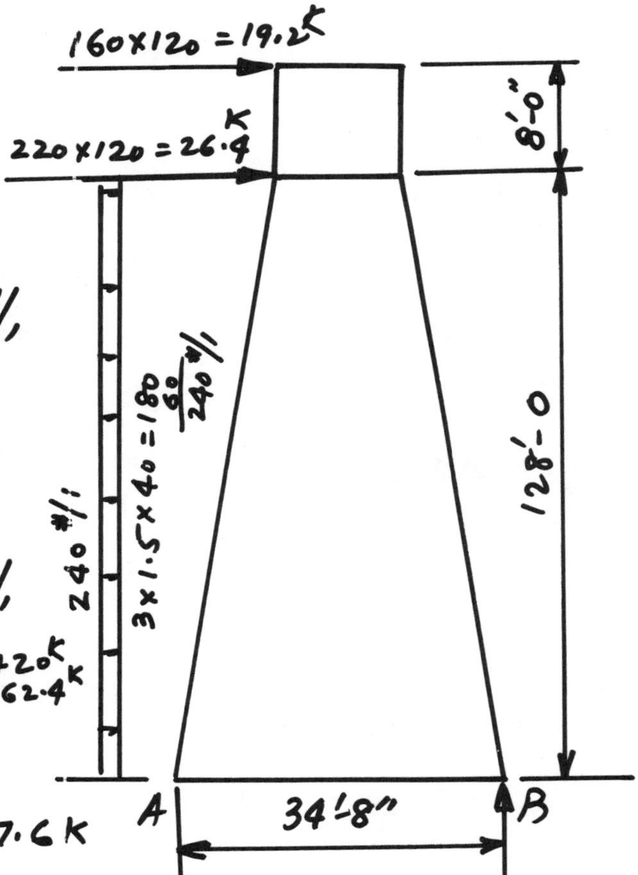

$D.L = \frac{222+483}{2} = \frac{705}{2}$

$= 353$ #/1

$L.L = \frac{343+343}{2} = 343$ #/1

WIND = Top chord

$= \frac{120+200}{2} = 160$ #/1

WIND = BOT. CHORD

$= \frac{240+200}{2} = 220$ #/1

$D.L = 353 \times 120 = 42.4^k + 20^k = 62.4^k$

$LL = 343 \times 120 = 41.2k$

$WL = 230k$

uplift = 230 + 62.4 = 167.6 K

$R_B (34.67) = 19.2 \times 136 + 26.4 \times 128 + \frac{240 \times 128 \times 64}{1000} = 7955$

$R_B = \frac{7955}{34.67} = 230k$

$Horz = (26.4 + 19.2 + 30.7)\frac{1}{2} = 38.2k$

$l_u = 128'-0$

Design load $= (260)\frac{3}{4} = 195^k$

$r_x = \frac{128 \times 12}{200} = 7.67$ IN
$r_y = \frac{24 \times 12}{200} = 1.44$ IN
} Min. Req'd

Try W18X64 WITH Increment Pl.

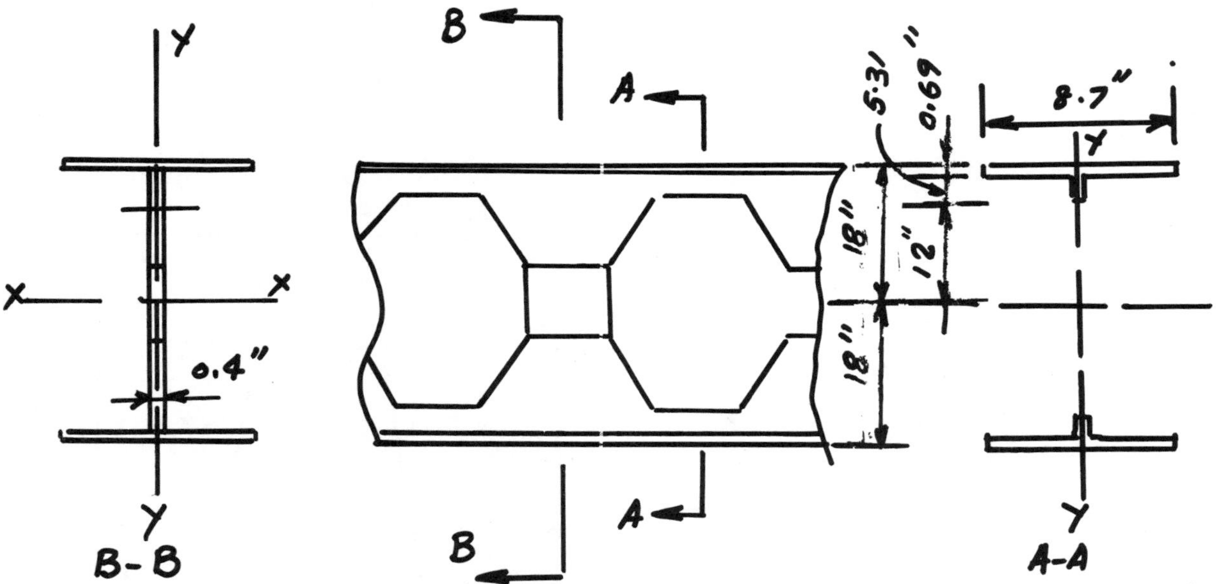

Working with section A-A (hole)

$\frac{1}{2}(I_x) = \frac{1}{12}(0.4)(5.31)^3 + 0.4(5.31)(14.65)^2 + \frac{1}{12}(8.7)(0.69)^3$
$+ 8.7(0.69)(17.65)^2 = 2331.24$ IN^4

$I_x = 4662.48$ IN^4

Similarly $I_y = 2\left[\frac{1}{12}(0.69)(8.7)^3 + \frac{1}{12}(5.31)(0.4)^3\right] = 61.2$

$\frac{1}{2}$ Area (Section A-A) $= 0.4 \times 5.31 + 8.7 \times 0.69 = 8.12$

$\therefore$ Area $= 16.24$ IN^2

$r_x = \sqrt{\frac{4662.48}{16.24}} = 16.95$ IN

$r_y = \sqrt{\frac{61.2}{16.24}} = 1.94$ IN.

Working with Section B-B (SOLID)

$I_x = \frac{1}{12}(0.4)(34.62)^3 + 2[0.24 + 1870.0]$
$= 5123.48 \ IN^4$

Similarly $I_y = \frac{1}{12}(34.62)(0.4)^3 + \frac{1}{12}(0.69)(8.7)^3 2$
$= 77.18$

Area (Section B-B) $= 0.4 \times 34.62 + 0.69 \times 8.7 \times 2$
$= 25.70 \ IN^2$

$r_x = \sqrt{\frac{5123.48}{25.7}} = 14.12 \ IN$

$r_y = \sqrt{\frac{77.18}{25.7}} = 1.73 \ IN$

$\frac{l_x}{r_x} = \frac{128 \times 12}{14.12} = 108.7$

$\frac{l_y}{r_y} = \frac{17 \times 12}{1.73} = 105.0$ $\qquad F_a = 12.33 \ ksi$

Net area $= 16.2 \ IN^2$
$\therefore$ Stress $= 16.2 \times 12.33 = 200 > 195$ ok.

EXAMPLE 13-08
GIVEN:- Design a roof truss for a span of 35' over the Sampler house for Public Service of Indiana.

Girt design:-
For 35' span
Girt spacing = 8'-0"
Sag rods @ 1/3 point.

Wind Loading:- (use 25 PSF)
$25 \times 8 = 200$ PLF
$w_{x-x} = 200$ PLF
$M_{xx} = \frac{(200) \times (35)^2}{8} = 30,620$ Ft.lb

Assume Wt. of siding $= (8)(3.0) = 24$ PLF
Assume Wt. of girt $= 21$ PLF
$w_{yy} = 45$ PLF.

$$M_{yy} = \frac{(167)^2(45)}{10} = 612.8 \text{ Ft Lb}$$

Try [12×20.7 – $S_{xx} = 21.4 \text{ IN}^3$, $S_{yy} = 1.7$

Also assume siding offers lateral Resistance

$$f_b = \frac{(12)(30.62)}{21.4} + \frac{12(0.613)}{1.7} = 21.49 \text{ ksi}$$

$F_b = (0.6)(36) = 21.6 \text{ ksi} > 21.49$ ok.

(Donot use [12×20.7 because of 12" girt Line)

Try W 8×24, $S_{xx} = 20.8$, $S_{yy} = 5.6 \text{ IN}^3$

$$f_b = \frac{12 \times 30.62}{20.8} + \frac{12 \times 0.613}{5.60} = 19.21 < 22 \text{ ok}$$

Use W 8×24

Sag Rods

Total weight of girt & siding = 60 kips

Load per ft = 0.43k/ft

$P = (1.10)(0.43)(11.68) = 5.5 \text{ kips}$

$$\text{Area Req'd} = \frac{5.5}{22} = 0.25 \text{ IN}^2$$ use 5/8" ϕ sag rod.

Max spacing for sag rods.

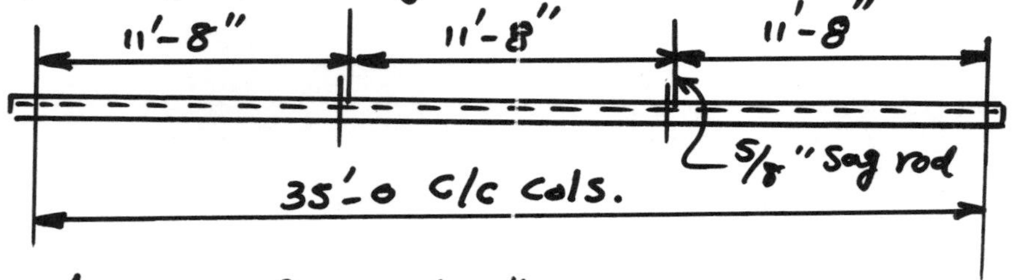

Purlin design for 17'-6" span.

Assume purlin spacing @ 4'-0"

Sag rods @ 1/3 Points

			Load per foot
Snow loads	=	30 PSF	Snow = 30×4×0.95 = 114
Roofing	=	25 PSF	Roofing = 25×4×0.95 = 9.5
Purlin	=	15 PLF	Purlin = 15.0
			Total = 138.5

Use 138 PLF.

$$M_x = \frac{(0.135)(17.5)^2}{8} = 5.28 \text{ ftk}$$

$$M_y = \frac{(0.044)(6.0)^2}{10} = 0.10 \text{ ftk}$$

Try [8 × 11.5, $S_x = 8.1$, $S_y = 0.79$

$$f_b = \frac{12 \times 5.28}{8.1} + \frac{12 \times 0.16}{0.79} = 10.3 < 22 \text{ ok}$$

Hold purlin deflection to 1"

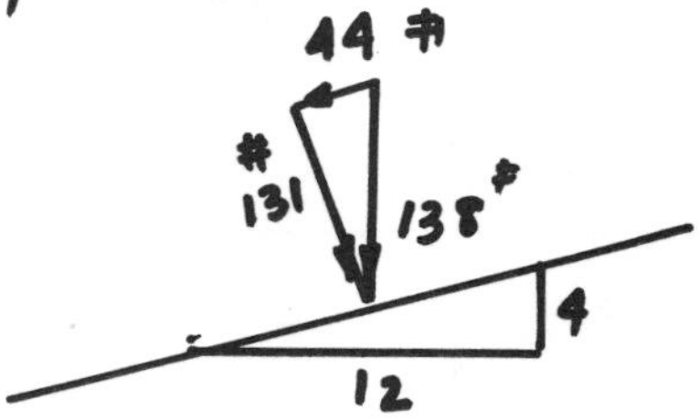

$$d = \frac{0.02276\,(17.5)^2}{1.0}$$

Min Beam Depth = 7"

Deflection controls use [8X11.5

Roof TRUSS.

DL + SNOW LOAD

Check Middle TRUSS

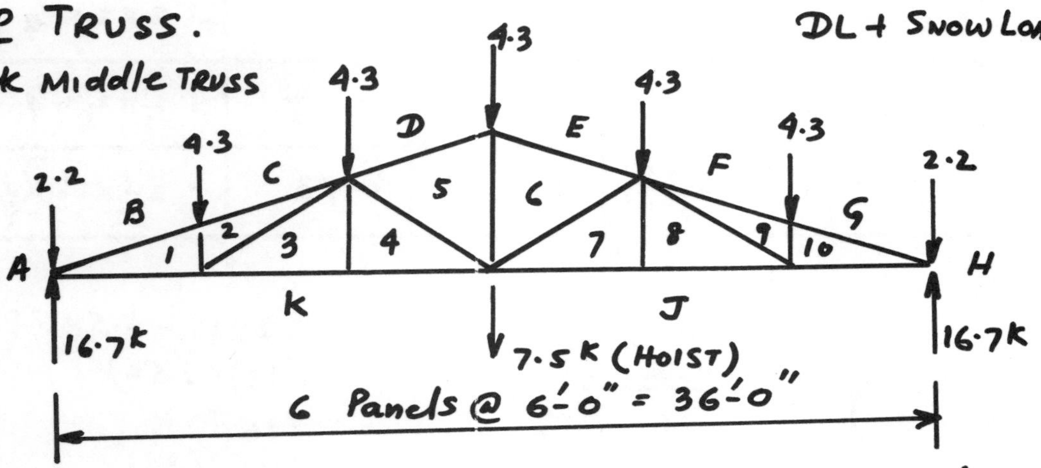

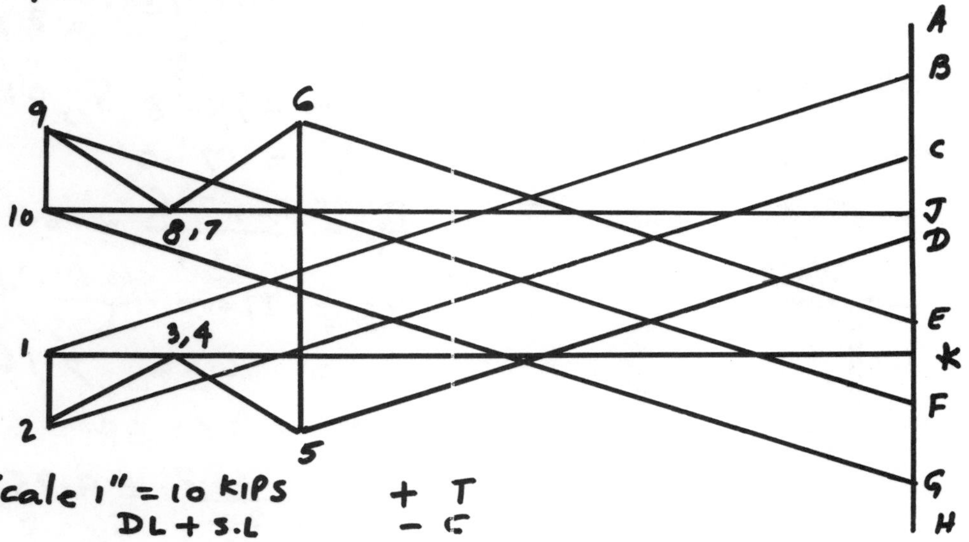

Scale 1" = 10 KIPS
DL + S.L

+ T
− C

$(2)(2.2) = 4.4$
$(5)(4.3) = 21.5$
7.5

$\frac{33.4}{2} = 16.7 = R_A = R_H$

Assume 3 Ton Hoist
6×1.2 (IMPACT) = 7.2
7.2 + 0.3 (HOIST WT) = 7.5

MEMBER	STRESS	MIN. r	Area Req'd	SELECTION
TOP CHD	−46K	0.65	4.48	7Γ 3½×3½×3/8"
BOT. CHD.	+44K	0.30	2.00	JL 2×2½×¼ SLV
1−2	−5K	0.20	0.49	J 2×2×¼
2−3	+8K	0.35	0.37	J 2×2×¼
3−4	0	0.20	−	J 2×2×¼
4−5	−8K	0.42	0.78	J 2½×2½×¼
5−6	+16K	0.30	0.73	J 2½×2½×¼

Eave Strut.

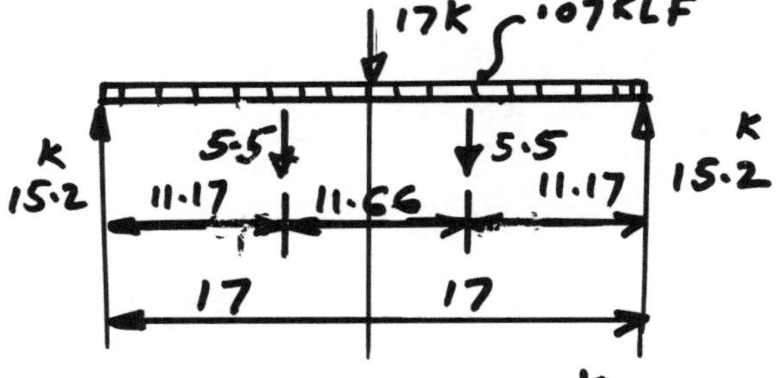

$0.07 \times 34 = 2.38^K$

$M_x = 15.2 \times 17 - 5.5 \times 5.83 - (1.19)(8.50) = 216$ FTK

$M_y = \frac{(.06)(34)^2}{8} = 8.7^{1K}$ (WIND)

Try W 24×68, $S_{xx} = 153.1$
$L_u = 17'\text{-}0''$

$f_b = \frac{12 \times 216}{153.1} = 16.93$ KSi

$F_b = 22000 - \left(\frac{0.679}{1.75}\right)\left(\frac{12 \times 17.0}{1.79}\right)^2 = 16.96 > 16.93$ ok

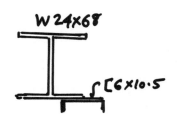

Use W 24×68

$S_{yy} = \frac{12 \times 8.7}{22} = 4.75 \text{ IN}^3$

use [6×10.5, $S_x = 5.0$

14

MISCELLANEOUS

EXAMPLE 14-01

Given:-Design a trial batch report for a concrete mix to be used for the Project of Campus Core West (SUCF-31-028) SUNY @ Old Westbury,Long Island,N.Y.

Contractor A.D.Herman Construction Co.
Supplier Astro Ready Mix -Westbury,N.Y.

Material

cement-	Atlantic	Type 1	cal.no.	401-62 SM
F.agg.-	Natural Sand		c.agg.	Crushed Dolomite Stone.
source.-	West Hills,L.I.		source	N.y.Traprock,Co.
admixture	-		cal.no	-

series no.IJH 100

AGGREGATE TESTS

SIEVE	100	50	30	16	8	4	3/8	1/2	3/4	1	1 1/2	SP.GR	WT. PCF	F.M		
F.A	2.0	10.7	41.1	66.48	82.6	95.3	100					2.63	98.1	3.02		
C.A						3.7	24.7	60.3	91.6	100		2.81	99.7	6.80		

CUBIC YARD PROPORTIONS

S.No	SACKS	Cement	F.AGG	C.AGG	Water GAL.	Slump	WT.Pcf	W/C Ratio	AIR %
1	4.01	377	1651	1799	36.3	5.0"	152.4	9.05	0.5
2	5.00	470	1548	1801	36.7	4 1/2	152.9	7.34	0.0
3	6.00	564	1445	1801	37.7	5"	153.2	6.28	0.5
4	7.00	658	1337	1807	38.5	5.0"	153.7	5.50	0.5

COMPRESSION TESTS

	7 Days Results	AVG.	28 Days Results	AVG.
1	1405, 1590	1540	2405, 2335, 2440, 2305	2370
2	2230, 2160	2195	3220, 3075, 3150, 3115	3140
3	2900, 2970	2935	3995, 4035, 4035, 4140	4050
4	3890, 3995	3945	5025, 5165, 5130, 5060	5095

RECOMMENDED MIXTURE

	3000 PSI.	4000 PSI.
cement lbs	564 (6.0 SKS)	658 (7.0 SKS)
f.agg. lbs	1450	1350
c.agg. lbs	1800	1800
water gals	37.7	38.5

	3000 PSi	4000 PSi
Slump	5" max	5" max
W/c Ratio	6.28	5.50

Aggregates comply with A.S.T.M C-33.

Cement Cube Strength 4650 PSi - 28 days.

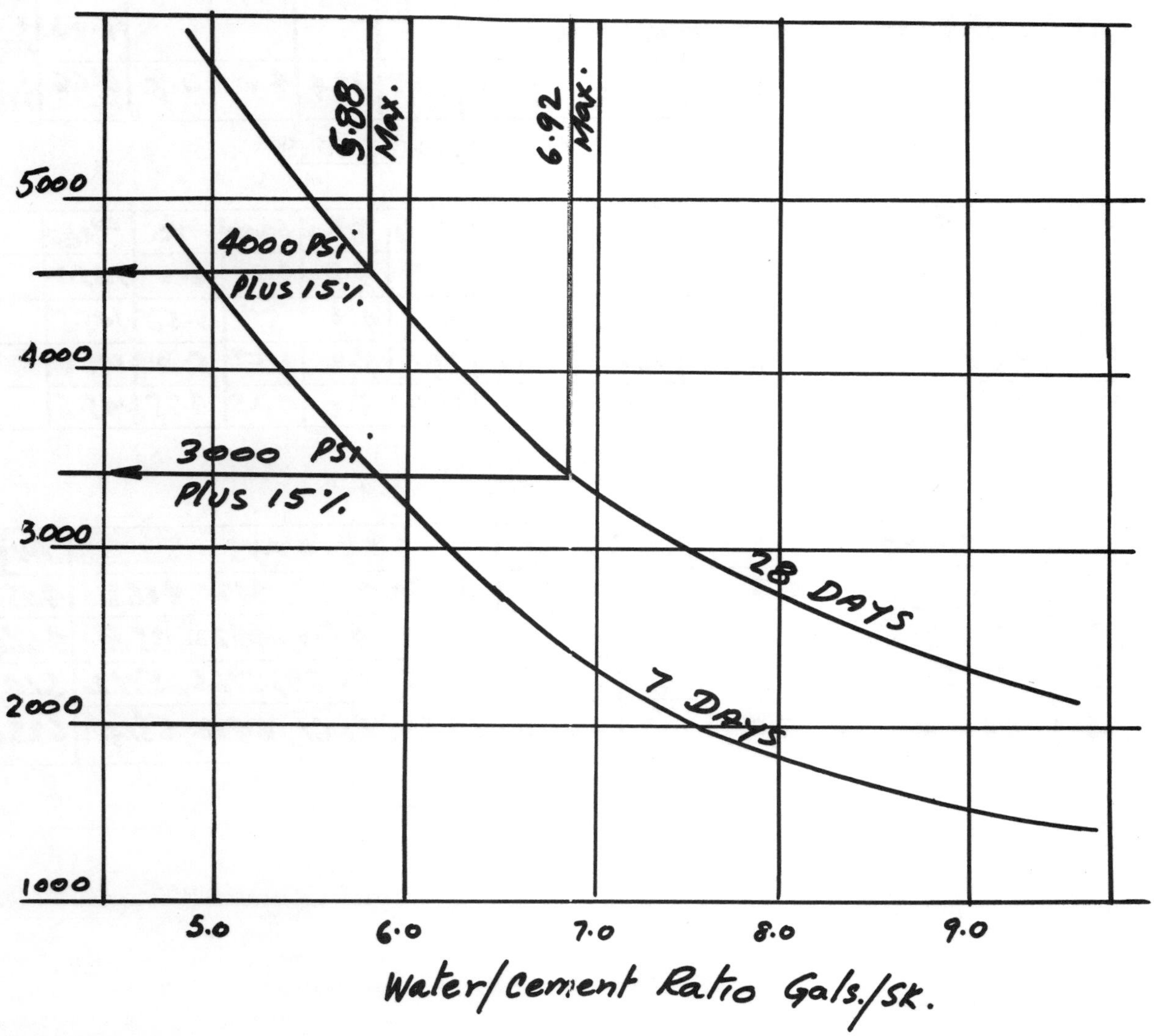

EXAMPLE 14-02

Given:-Design a trial batch concrete mix (Pump Concrete) of 3000 p.s.i 25% at 28 days for Dental Science Building of New York University, N.Y.

Project: Dental Science Building at 421 Ist Ave.New York for New York University.
Client : Grand Metro Ready Mix,Brooklyn,N.Y.

Material

cement- Hudson type I
sand - Long Island Natural
coarse aggregate 3/4" stone-New York Trap rock,dolomite
admixture_ Sika air Cal.229-63 SM.

GRADATION TESTS

SIEVE	100	50	30	16	8	4	3/8	1	3/4	3/8	#4	#8	F.M	SPG / Y
F.A	2.1	17.9	46.2	70.9	84.8	96.1	100						2.82	2.64 / 102.7
C.A								100	92.8	39.4	4.1	0.8	6.66	2.80 / 103.6

DRY CUBIC YARD PROPORTIONS

MIX #	Cement	Sack	SAND	STONE	Adm oz	water gal	AIR %	Slump	w/c	w PCF
1	541	5.75	1265	1825	4.3	35.8	4.8	4.75"	6.0	145.2
2	611	6.50	1190	1825	4.9	36.3	4.9	5"	5.58	145.5
3	658	7.0	1150	1825	5.25	37.1	5.2	3.5"	5.3	146.0
4	752	8.0	1035	1825	6.0	38.0	5.0	4.25	4.75	145.5

COMPRESSION TESTS

	7 days	Avg	28 days	Avg
1	2936, 2865	2900	3980, 4051, 4121, 4068	4055
2	3343, 3255	3299	4386, 4510, 4422, 4546	4466
3	3767, 3679	3723	5218, 5049, 5165, 5112	5147
4	4404, 4528	4466	6367, 6261, 6402, 6314	6336

RECOMMENDED MIXTURE

Mix #3 for 3500 p.S.I

cement- 658 lbs

f.agg - 1150 lbs

c.agg.- 1825 lbs

adm Sika oz/yd 5.25

water 37.1 gal.

air contents 5.2 %

slump. - 3.5"

w/c ratio. 5.3

unit wt. 146.0 pcf

EXAMPLE 14-03

Given: -Find the maximum spacing of studs for 1" nominal thickness planks when the form for a concrete wall be filled at the rate of 4'-6" per hour and the temperature of concrete is 70 degrees F. The maximum deflection of planking is 1/8".

Consider a horizontal strip of planking 12" wide

$b = 12''$

$h = \frac{25}{32}''$

max. pressure in P.S.f exerted by concrete when vibrated 'w' = $150 \times 4.5 = 675$ psf.

Also for Douglas fir, whose $E = 1600{,}000$ psi

$I = \frac{bh^3}{12}$, $\delta = 1/8''$

$$l = 62.6 \sqrt[4]{\frac{bh^3}{w}}$$

$$= 62.6 \sqrt[4]{\frac{12\left(\frac{25}{32}\right)^3}{675}} = 62.6 \times 0.3034 = 18.99'' \text{ say } 19''$$

Again also

$$l = 93.5 \sqrt[4]{\frac{12\left(\frac{25}{32}\right)^3}{675}} = 28.37 \text{ in}$$

when member is extended beyond several supports.

Use l the least value 19"

EXAMPLE 14-04

Given:-Design a false work for the construction of new bridge over L.I.R.R. on Parsons Boulevard in Queens, N.Y.

weight of 12" C.I Main for Gas = 55 #/ft

weight of 3 Cable (Electric) 3x15 #/ft = 45 #/ft

Total 100 #/ft

Consider a beam W 10x100, $I = 623$ IN4, $E = 29 \times 10^6$ Psi.

$$l = 4.464\, h \sqrt{\frac{F_b \times b}{w}}$$

spaning of planks between flanges of beam

span = 8.25′

then $w = 8.25 \times 100 = 825^{\#}$

Clear span after providing horizontal & vertical clearance to track

$$31 \times 12 = 4.464 \times 11.10 \sqrt{\frac{22000 \times b}{825}}$$

$b = 2.11$

use $b = 10.34''$

Again based on deflection of 1″ of Beam

$$l = 5.5 \sqrt[4]{\frac{EID}{w}}$$

$$31 \times 12 = 5.5 \sqrt[4]{\frac{29 \times 10^6 \times I \times 1}{825}}$$

$I = 595 \text{ IN}^4$

$I_{provided}$ $623 > 595 \text{ IN}^4$ ok.

use W 10×100 $S = 110 \text{ IN}^3$

for col base Pℓ. considering 1 ft wide form

$$P = \frac{8.25 \times 100}{2} = 41.25^{\#}/ft$$

$$\text{Reaction on col.} = \frac{41.25 \times 31}{2} + \frac{100 \times 8.25 \times 31}{4}$$

$= 12798^{\#}$

use $P_{\text{on col max}} = 20^K$

$$A = \frac{20}{0.750} = 26.6 \quad \text{size } 5.15 \times 5.15$$

Use 14×14

$$m = \frac{14 - 0.95 \times 11.1}{2} = 1.72, \quad n = \frac{14 - 0.80 \times 10.34}{2} = 2.86$$

↑ use

$$f_p = \frac{20}{14 \times 14} = 0.102$$

$$t = \sqrt{\frac{3 F_p n^2}{F_b}} = \sqrt{\frac{3 \times 0.102 \times 2.86^2}{27}} = 0.30 \text{ say } 3/8''$$

size of col Base Pℓ $14'' \times 14'' \times 3/8''$

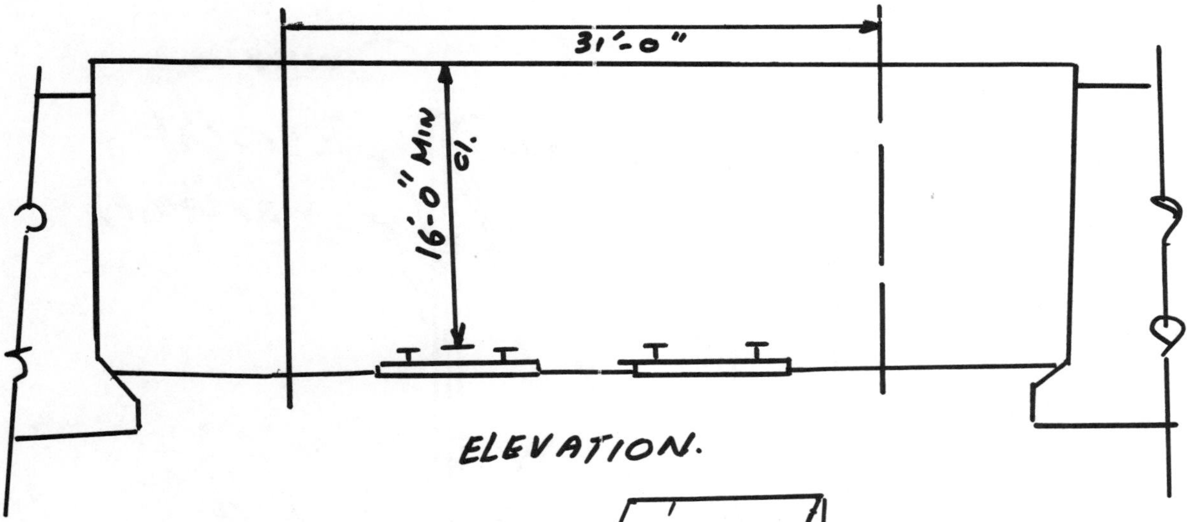

ELEVATION.

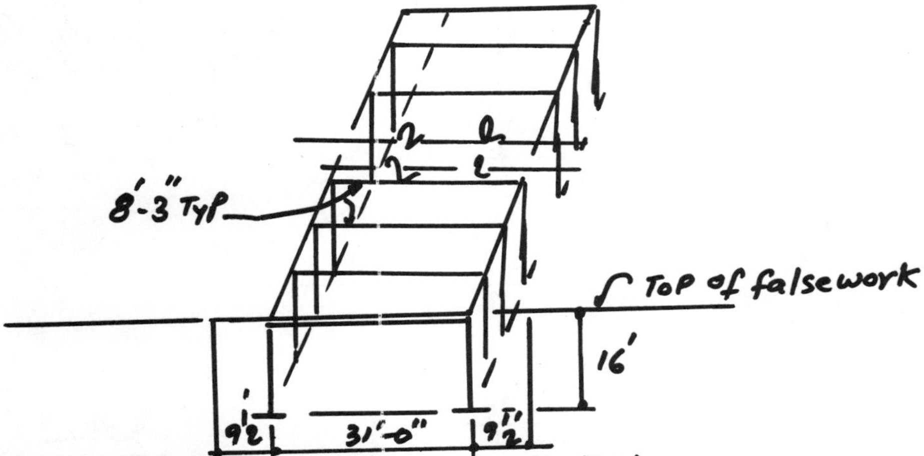

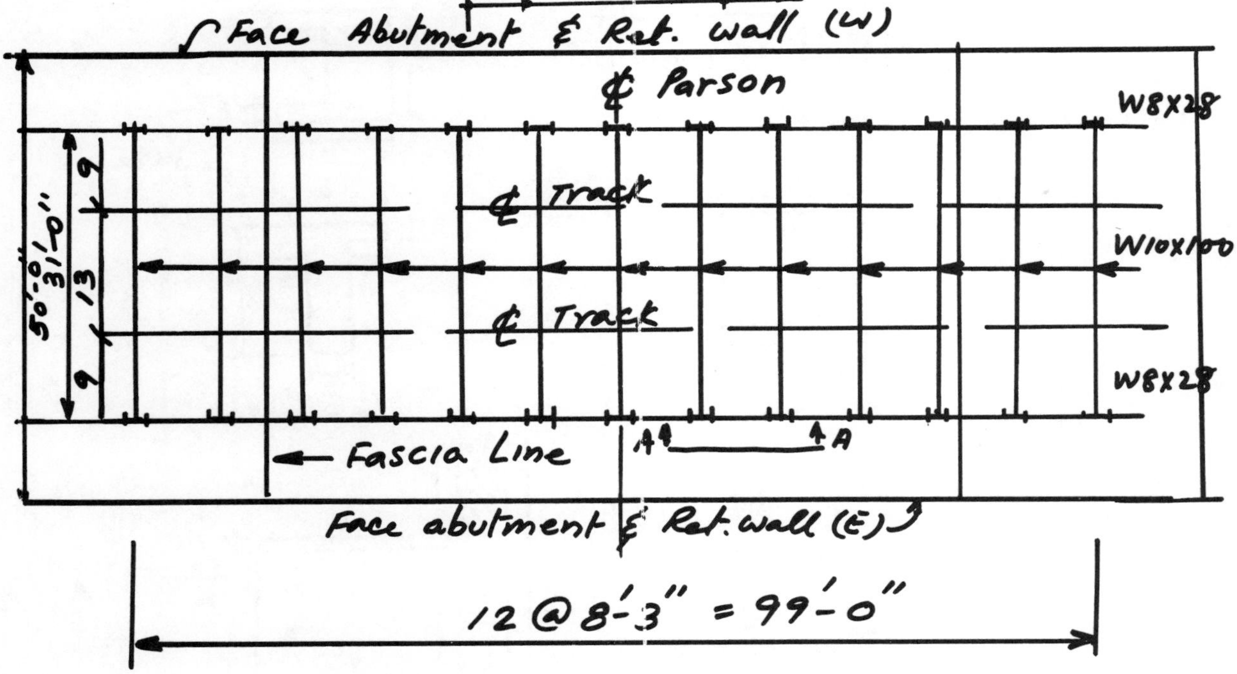

PLAN

LAYOUT OF PROPOSED FALSE WORK

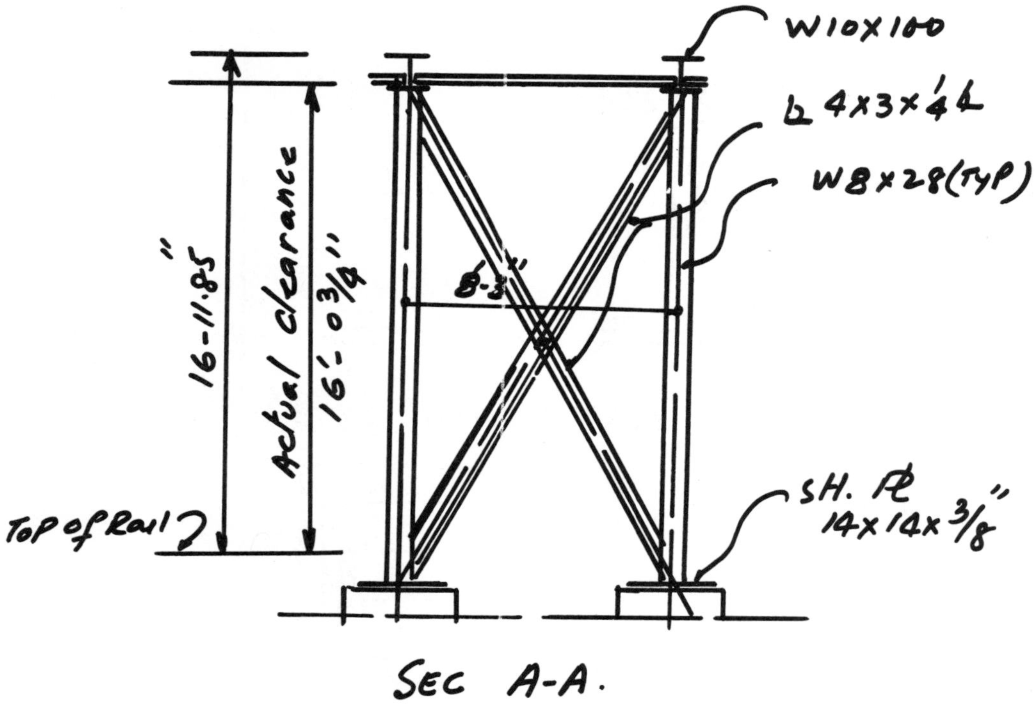

Fig.1.Equivalent flange width b for use in converting various cross sections into an equivalent L beam.

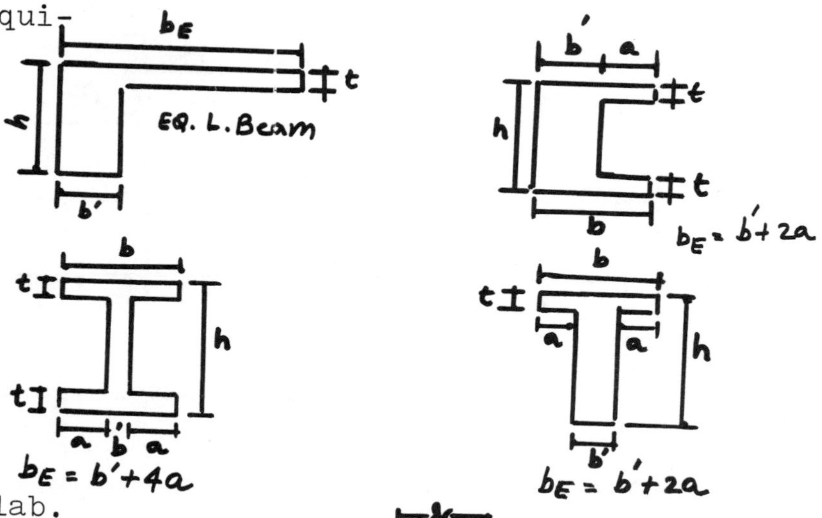

Fig.2.Cantilever slab.

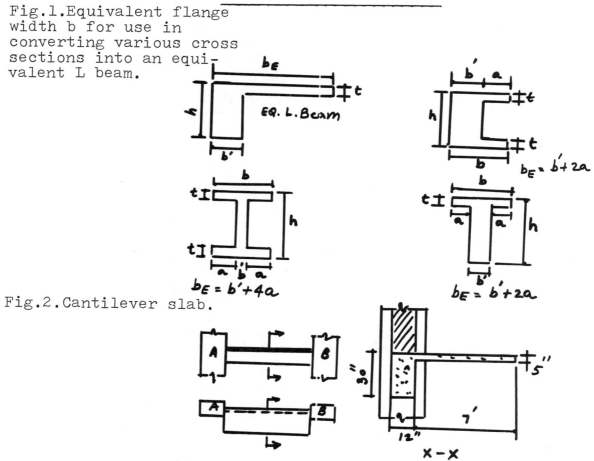

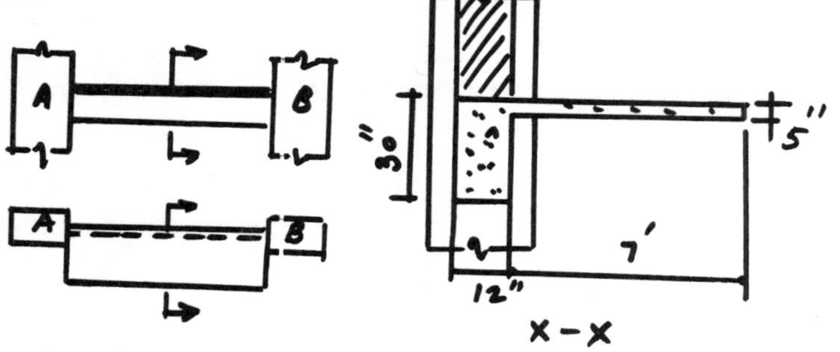

SHEAR IN CONCRETE BEAM DUE TO CONCRETE FLOOR SLAB

Reasearch has indicated that the static theory is not entirely satisfactory for accurately predicting the stresses in concrete due to torsion. The plastic sand heap analogy was utilized to develop a basic equation for torsional stresses in L beams. It was found that the tosional shear stress eqation for any open end, flanged section can be transformed into the basic equation for an L beam.
Figs.* 1 illustrate the equivalent flange width b_E for use in converting various cross sections into an equivalent L beam. The relationship between ultimate tosional shear stress V_{tu} and ultimate torsional moment M_{tu} may be expressed as follows:

$$V_{tu} = \frac{M_{tu}}{[(b'^2/6)(3h-b') \div [(t^2/2)(b-b')]} = \frac{M_{tu}}{J_E} \quad \text{———} \quad (1)$$

where J_E = Equivalent polar moment of Inertia. $= C_t (b')^2 h^2$ — (2)

where C_t = torsional coefficient $= \left[(1/6)(3 - b'/h)\right] \div \left\{(1/2)(t/b')^2 \left[\left(\frac{b}{h} - \frac{b'}{h}\right)\right]\right\}$ ---- (2a)

(Note: Basic L beam equations can be used for rectangular sections by considering flange thickness to be zero.)
Longitudinal Steel
The presence of torsional shear stress in transverse direction gives rise to longitudinal tensile stresses. If this total torsional shear flow in transverse direction is assumed to be equal in magnitude to that of longitudinal direction, the longitudinal steel requirement for torsion is to met by the following:

$$A_L = \frac{6 M_{tu}[(1 + b'/h) - 4(d''/h)]}{(b'/h)[3 - b'/h] f_y h} \quad \text{———} \quad (3)$$

where A_L = Total area longitudinal steel for torsion, in in.
b' = Web width for flanged section, in inches
b_E = Equivalent width of flanges for transformating any flanged section into an equivalent L beam, in inches
h = Total depth of web for any section, in inches
C_T = Coefficient for obtaining the equivalent polar moment of Inertia for flanged or rectangular section
d'' = Distance from the center of stirrup leg to nearest face of concrete, in inches
J_E = Polar moment of Inertia for any section, in in.
M_t = Torsional moment at service load, in inch pounds
M_{tu} = Torsional moment at ultimate strength conditions, in inch pounds
t = Flange thickness, in inches
V_{tu} = Torsional shear stress, U.S.D.

EXAMPLE 14-05
Given:- The cantilever slab (see Fig.* 2) shown supports a roof dead load of 7.5 psf and and a live load of 20 psf. The wall over the beam is 10 ft.(3.0r) high and 50psf in weight of wall

* see Page 14-7

surface will use U.S.D. to propotion the section for shear due to direct load and torsion.

Assume:

1. torsion center of beam lies on the vertical centroidal axis of the web of L beam.

2. the beam is fully restrained against torsion at A and B. Use effective flange overhand of $6t$, $f_c' = 3$ k.s.i; $f_y = 50$ k.s.i.

The loads on slab are as follows:

Roof D.L = 7.5 psf

Slab D.L = 62.5 psf

Total $W_{D.L}$ = 70.0 psf ; W_{LL} = 20 psf

M_t due to service load for dead load = 7×70×(3.5+0.5) = 1960 #/,

M_t due to service load for Live load = 7×20×(3.5+0.5) = 560 #/,

Hence M_{tu} = 1.5(1960) + 1.8(560) = 3948 #/ft.

So M_{tu} @ face of either support = 10×3948 = 39480'#

Direct service load delivered to the beam for dead load

Slab & roof D.L = 7×70 = 490 #/, beam W_{DL} = 2.5×1×150 = 375 #/,

wall W_{DL} = 10×50 = 500 #/, ∴ Total w = 1365 #/, & L.load W_{LL} = 140 #/,

critical section for shear according to A.C.I. code occurs at a distance d from the face of support for direct shear. However, when torsion is present, the face of the support may be critical

R_{DL} = 10×1365 = 13650 #

R_{LL} = 10×140 = 1400 #

Total Shear V_u = 1.5×13650 + 1.8×1400 = 22995 #

v_u due to vertical load $= \frac{V_u}{bd} = \frac{22995}{12 \times 28} = 68$ psi

$b_E = b' + 6t = 12 + 30 = 42''$

using eqn 2a for C_t when $b = 42''$, $t = 5''$, $b' = 12$ & $h = 30''$

$C_t = 0.52$

$J_E = 0.52 \times 12^2 \times 30^2 = 67392$ in⁴

$v_{tu} = 39480 \times 12 \times 30 / 67392 = 211$ psi

Total shear stress on most highly stressed side of beam

$v_u = 68 + 211 = 279$ psi

v_{all} on concrete w/o web reinforcement $= 2\phi\sqrt{f_c'} = 92$ psi

Excess Shear $v_u' = 279 - 92 = 187$ psi which must be resisted by stirrups of closed type.

Assuming #3 stirrup $A_v = 2 \times 0.11 = 0.22$ in²/hoop

& for f_y = 50 ksi

$S = A_v f_y / (v_u')(b) = \frac{0.22 \times 50000}{187 \times 12} = 4.9''$

The spacing of stirrup should be variable as the torsional moment increases from the center of beam towards support and distance over which stirrups will be required can be found by

THRUST BLOCK NOMOGRAPH

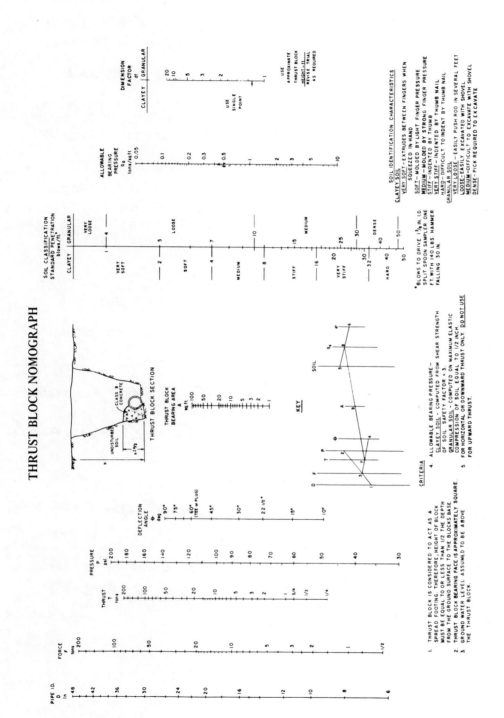

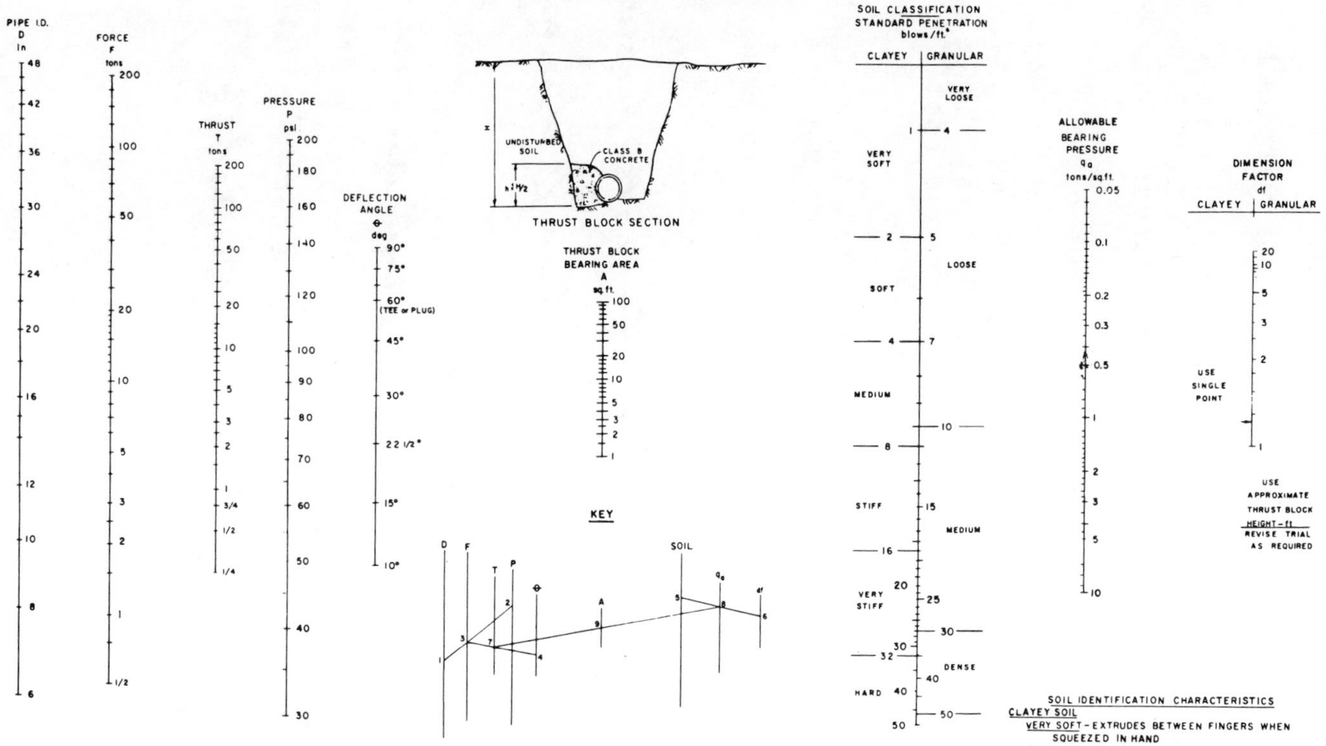

*BLOWS TO DRIVE 1 3/8 IN. I.D. SPLIT SPOON SAMPLER ONE FT. WITH 140 LBS. HAMMER FALLING 30 IN.

CRITERIA

1. THRUST BLOCK IS CONSIDERED TO ACT AS A SPREAD FOOTING. THEREFORE, HEIGHT OF BLOCK MUST BE EQUAL TO OR LESS THAN 1/2 THE DEPTH FROM THE GROUND SURFACE TO THE BLOCKS BASE.
2. THRUST BLOCK BEARING FACE IS APPROXIMATELY SQUARE.
3. GROUND WATER LEVEL ASSUMED TO BE ABOVE THE THRUST BLOCK.
4. ALLOWABLE BEARING PRESSURE –
   CLAYEY SOIL – COMPUTED FROM SHEAR STRENGTH OF SOIL. SAFETY FACTOR = 3.
   GRANULAR SOIL – COMPUTED ON MAXIMUM ELASTIC COMPRESSION OF SOIL EQUAL TO 1/2 INCH.
5. FOR HORIZONTAL OR DOWNWARD THRUST ONLY. DO NOT USE FOR UPWARD THRUST.

SOIL IDENTIFICATION CHARACTERISTICS

CLAYEY SOIL
- VERY SOFT – EXTRUDES BETWEEN FINGERS WHEN SQUEEZED IN HAND
- SOFT – MOLDED BY LIGHT FINGER PRESSURE
- MEDIUM – MOLDED BY STRONG FINGER PRESSURE
- STIFF – INDENTED BY THUMB
- VERY STIFF – INDENTED BY THUMB NAIL
- HARD – DIFFICULT TO INDENT BY THUMB NAIL

GRANULAR SOIL
- VERY LOOSE – EASILY PUSH ROD IN SEVERAL FEET
- LOOSE – EASILY EXCAVATED WITH SHOVEL
- MEDIUM – DIFFICULT TO EXCAVATE WITH SHOVEL
- DENSE – PICK REQUIRED TO EXCAVATE

Reprinted from article by Ed Morrison, Winslow, Maine with permission from the June 1969 issue of Civil Engineering ASCE official monthly publication of ASCE.

symmetrical triangles.

$x = 187 \times 10 \times 12/279 = 80.5''$

However, code requires that the stirrups be continued for a distance d beyond the theoretical stopping point.

$80.5 + 28 = 108.5$ Say 9'-1"

Ref.fig.note b'= 9", h=27" & d" = 1.5

& using eq.3

$A_L = 1.815^{in}$ for M_{tu}=39480"# @ support.

This must be added to reinforcement required for vertical bending.

The corner bars must be continued for full length of beam, but side and end bars may be discontinued at a distance d. Beyond that, they are not needed to resist torsional stress.

DESIGN OF THRUST BLOCKS

EXAMPLE 14-06

Given:- Determine the thrust block area required at a 30 degree bend in a 20-in. pipe under 120 psi pressure. The soil is a clean well graded sand with a blow count of 12 blows per foot. The pipe invert is 10 feet below the ground surface.

Assumption:

1) The block will be approximately square and that its height will be equal to one half the depth from the ground surface to the block base.

2) The allowable bearing pressure for granular soil are based upon a maximum compression of 1/2".

3) The thrust block is assumed to be below the ground water table.

Draw a line between 20" pipe size and the 120 Psi pressure on the nomograph scale (see next sheet)

Connect the resulting force of 19 Tons with the deflection angle of 30°.

Read the total thrust equal to 10 Tons.

Connect 12 blows/ft on granular side with an assumed height of block ie 4 ft.

Read allowable bearing pressure = 0.65 tsf.

Bearing area found to be 16 sft by connecting the thrust with allowable bearing pressure.

Hence size of thrust block 4'×4'.

EXAMPLE 14-07

Given:-Design of Harness clips at pipe flanges for tie bolts across Dresser Coupling for 48" Raw Water Line of Coagulation basins.

Design harness system for shut-off head of about 80 ft. (See Pump characteristics of raw water Pumps).

$p = 80 \times 0.0624 = 5.0^{k}/\square'$

Total thrust $= \frac{\pi \times 4.^2}{4} \times 5.0 = 63.0k$

Assume 4 harness bolts

Tension per bolt $= \frac{63}{4} = 15.76^{k}$

using allowable tension stress in bolts of $16000^{\#}/\square''$

Req'd area of bolt $= \frac{15760}{16000} = 0.983\ \square''$

use $1\frac{1}{8}$" bolt.

use $1\frac{1}{4}$" Pl $\times$ 4" wide.

check plate for bending

$M = 15.76 \times 1.0 = 15.76''k$

$S = 4 \cdot \frac{1.25^2}{6} = 1.04 in^3$

$f = \frac{15.76}{1.04} = 15.2^{\#}/\square'' < 16$ ok.

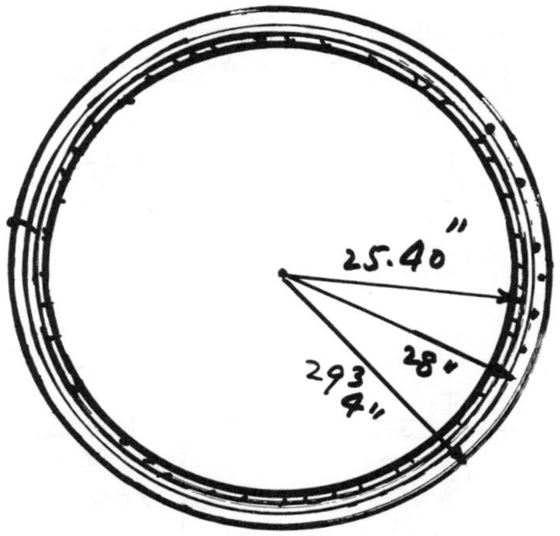

44- bolts

Bolt circle = 56" dia

Bolt Perimeter = 175.896"

℄ to ℄ Bolt = 3.9976" along arc.

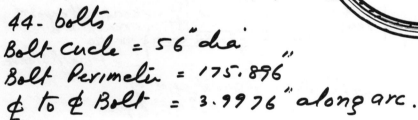

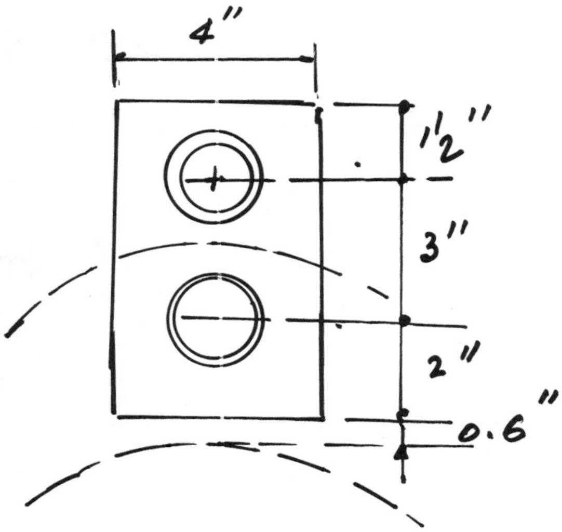

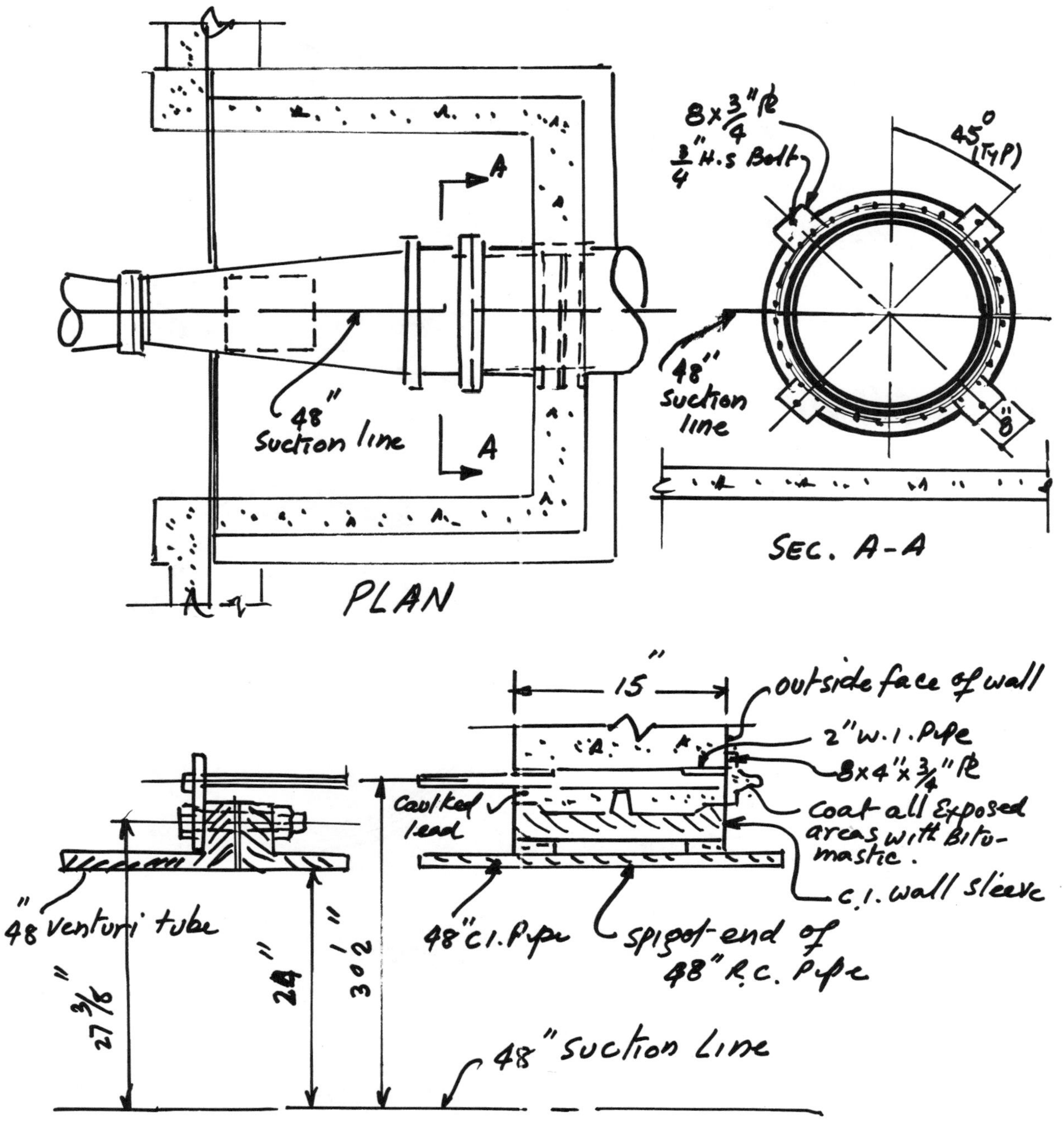

48" suction line Thrust Restraint

EXPANSION JOINTS

The design of a structure should be kept as uniform as its function allows, viz, when an expansion joint is required in building, the bay length on each side of the joint should be typical. Expansion joints are common in long span decks to avoid participation of floor system in chord stresses.

In all forms of building construction, metal in some form has played an important role. But I will attempt to cover metal or substitution as used in expansion joint.

Due to vast scale of manufacturing program, industrial plants have become larger and are carried under a single roof. Due to shortage of material, buildings are being constructed of R.C.C and Steel and are without roof monitors, flat or domed roofs. The large area of roof construction present a problem of expansion and contraction which are explained below.

In design of expansion joint:-Profile of the roof affects the location and design of expansion joint and also major importance in proper expansion joint design is height of roof above floor. Steel building usually expand 2-21/2" and temperature ranges effecting the building when occupied average from 30°-80°. In considering expansion and contraction we must also consider storey height of the building. The roof will expand or contract the same whether high or low.

Fig.a) Expansion at the roof is same whether the building is high or low, but the distortion is much greater for the low building. Lower fig. show expansion action for symmetrical building units of same construction.

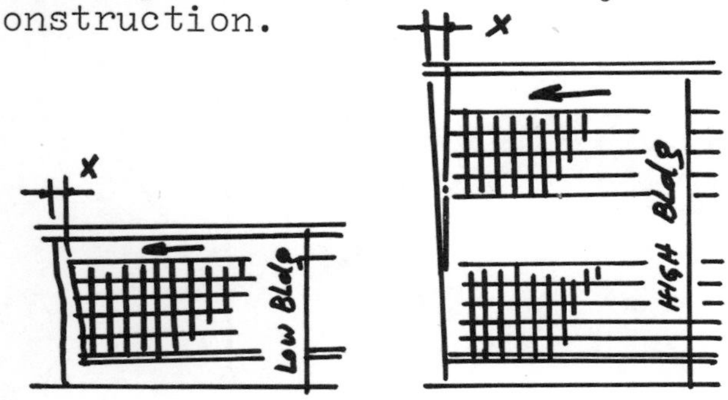

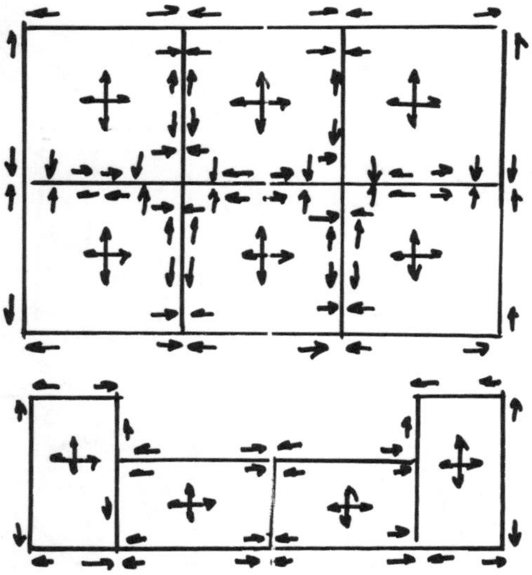

Fig.b) The V-type expansion joint for vertical side walls. Fig.b-1 shows expansion joint as mounted with concrete and brick facing.

Fig.c) the deck expansion joints of bridge.

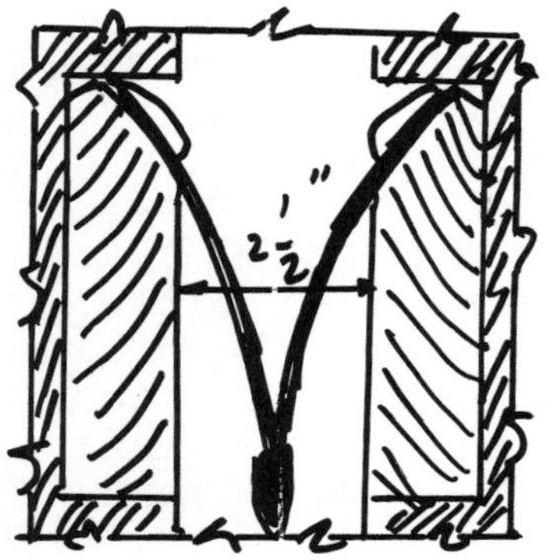

fig b.

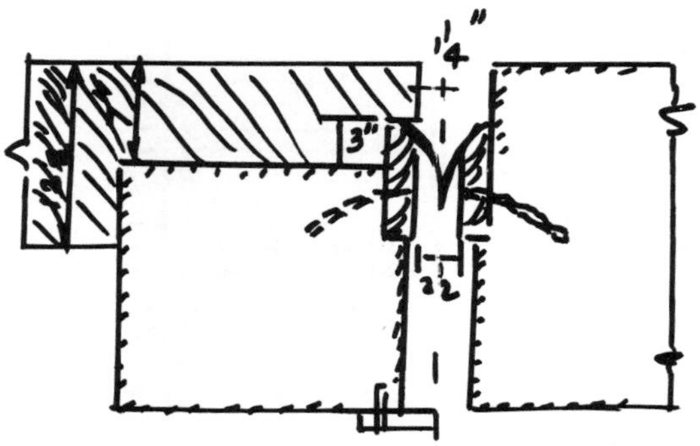

fig b-1

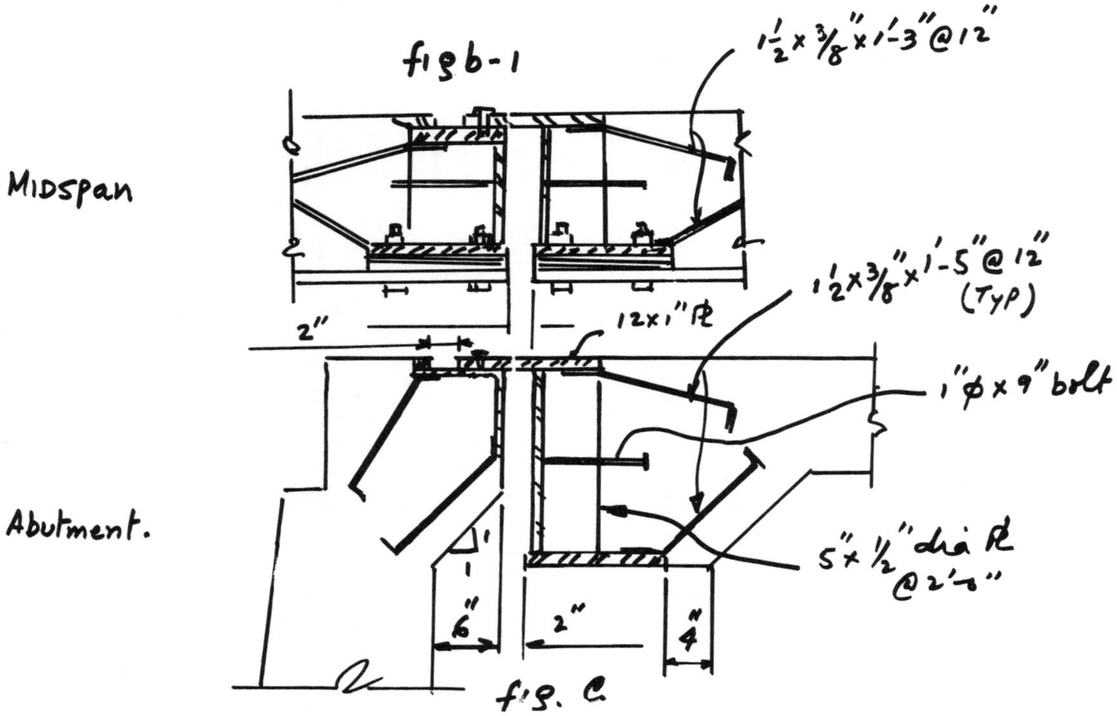

fig. c

EXAMPLE 14-08

Given:-Design a concrete masonry wall of light weight block for an industrial building 20'high and 100'wide consisting of 5 bays, as per uniform building code & 2 bays of 40' each long.

f'_m = approved ultimate compressive stress of masonry = 1350 Psi

f_s = stress in tensile reinforcement = 20000 Psi

$$n = \frac{E_s}{E_m} = \frac{30\times10^6}{500\times1350} = 44$$

Dead Load

5ply roofing,	=	2.0 #/□'
2×4 @ 24 o/c	=	0.8
Purlins	=	1.5 #/□'
MISC, Plywood etc	=	3.0
		7.3 #/□' say 7.5 #/□'
Live load	=	12 #/sqft

Design of masonry wall

assume 8", t = 7⅝"

$\frac{h}{t}$ for bearing wall = 25

then h_{max} = 25×8/12 = 16'-8" ie from floor to bond beam

Lateral force Wind = 15 #/□'

Moment simple span $= \frac{wl^2}{8} = \frac{15\times16.67^2}{8} = 520$ '#/ft

Place vertical steel @ 4' o/c

∴ Moment/vertical bar = 520×4 = 2080 '#/ vert: bar.

d_{eff} of 8" = 3.8"

then $K = \frac{M}{bd^2} = \frac{2080}{48\times3.8^2} = 36 < 44$ Balanced K

∴ from chart for n = 44, fm = 300 Psi & K < Balanced.

Hence steel governs.

$f_s = 26700$ Psi. $K = 36$

$p = 0.0015$ from chart of masonry H/Book.

$\therefore A_s = 0.0015 \times 3.8 \times 48 = 0.274$ Sq in

Use #5 @ 48" o/c. = 0.31

Horizontal steel $= 0.002\,bl = 0.002 \times 8 \times 12$

$= 0.192$

$= 0.192 - \frac{0.31}{4} = 0.115 \square''$

Use #5 @ 32" o/c.

STAIRS

Points to be kept in mind:

1. The maximum slope of stairs for comfort is about 1 on 2 (27) Exterior stairs generally range in slope from 20 -30 and interior stairs from 30°-35° .

2. Riser- Vertical face of step

$R = 9 - \sqrt{\frac{1}{7}(T-B)(T-2)}$ when T is fixed.

3. Tread- Horizontal face of step

$T = 5 + \sqrt{\frac{1}{7}(9-R)^2 + 9}$ when R is fixed

Average riser "R" equal to 7", is used and which is proportional to a tread of 11", a combination that produces a comfortable chair.

4. Width of Tread- Usually taken as the horizontal distance between risers. This is exclusive of a nosing which is the projection of a tread beyond the riser below.

5. Landing- (Platform) Is necessary where there is a turn or to break up long climbs. The landing should be as wide as the stairs and at least 44 in. long in the direction of travel.

6. Loading- The stairs and the landing should be designed for a live load of 100 psf or a concentrated load of 300 lbs. placed to produce maximum stress.

7. Railings- The handrails are set 2'6" to 2'10" above the intersections of the treads and risers at the front of the steps. Design for a horizontal load of 40 lbs./ft. and a vertical force of 50 lbs./ft. applied at the top of rail.

EXAMPLE 14-09

Given:- Design a stairway for a sludge dewatering facility for Passaic Valley Sewer Commisioners at Newark.

Stair slab BC.

Required thickness of slab $= \frac{l}{20} = \frac{12 \times 12}{20} = 7.2''$ Say 9"

$d_{effective} = 9'' - 2'' - 0.5 = 6.5$ inch.

Dead load on slab

Self wt of slab $= \frac{9}{12} \times \frac{12}{12} \times 0.150 = 0.1125\ ^{k}/_{1}$

$\frac{1}{2}$ riser wt $= \frac{1}{12} \times \frac{9}{12} \times \frac{12}{12} \times 0.150 = 0.056\ ^{k}/_{1}$

Total D.L $=$ $0.169\ ^{k}/_{1}$

$W_{U.DL} = 1.4 \times 0.168 = 0.235\ ^{k}/_{1}$

L.Load $= 1.7 \times 0.150 = 0.255\ ^{k}/_{1}$

$0.490\ ^{k}/_{1}$

$M_U = \frac{wl^2}{8} = \frac{0.49 \times 12^2}{8}$

$= 8.91\ 'k$

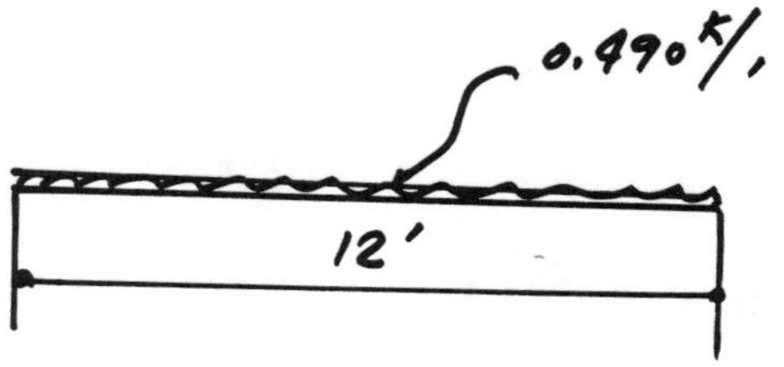

$V_c = \frac{Wl}{2} = \frac{0.49 \times 12}{2}$

$= 2.97^{k}$

thickness requirement by shear.

$V_c = 2 \times 0.85 \sqrt{4000} \times 12 \times d$

$d = \frac{2.97 \times 1000}{2 \times 0.85 \times 63.5 \times 12} = 2.29''$ $\therefore d_{eff}\ 6.5''$ ok.

$F = \frac{12 \times 6.5^2}{12000} = 0.042$

$K_U = \frac{M_U}{F} = \frac{8.91}{0.042} = 212$ $\therefore a_U = 4.31$

$A_s = \frac{8.91}{4.31 \times 6.5} = 0.318\ in^2$

$A_{s_{min}} = 0.0033 \times 12 \times 6.5 = 0.257\ in^2$

Use #6 @ 12''

$A_{s_{temp}} = 0.0014 \times 12 \times 6.5 = 0.109$

use #4 @ 12''

Slab CD & DE Similar

Slab AB

$D.L = \frac{9}{12} \times 0.150 = 0.112\ ^{k}/_{1}$

$W_U = 1.4 \times 0.112 = 0.157\ ^{k}/_{1}$

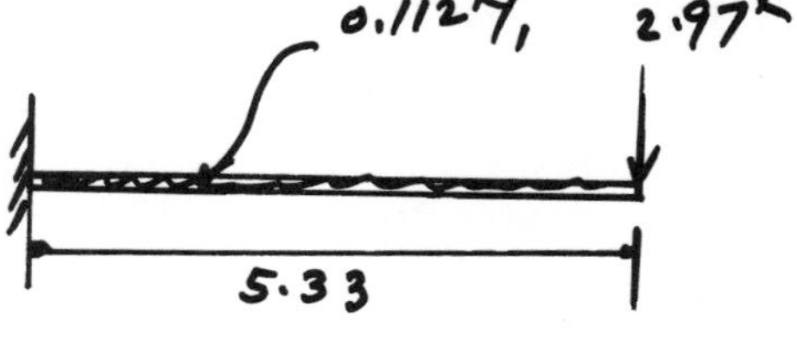

$$M_U = 2.97 \times 5.33 + \frac{0.157 \times 5.33^2}{2} = 15.83 + 2.23 = 18.06\ 'K$$

$$d = \frac{3.81 \times 1000}{2 \times 0.85 \times 63.5 \times 12} = 2.93 < 6.5''$$

use 6.5 deff $t = 9''$

$$K_U = \frac{M_U}{F} \ \& \ F = \frac{5.33 \times 6.5^2}{12000} = 0.019$$

$$\therefore K_U = \frac{18.06}{0.019} = 950$$

$$p = 0.029$$

$$A_s = 0.029 \times 12 \times 6.5 = 2.26 \quad \text{use } \#8@4''$$

Beam Assumed $10'' \times 12''$ Beam.

$$\text{Stair Load} = 6 \times \frac{9'' + 4.5}{12} \times 0.150 = 1.0\ K/ft$$

$$\text{slab load} = \frac{9''}{12} \times 4' \times 0.150 = 0.45\ K/,$$

$$1.45\ K/,$$

$$W_{UDL} = 1.4 \times 1.45 = 2.03\ K/,$$

$$\text{Live load} = 0.150 \times 8 = 1.2$$

$$W_{ULL} = 1.7 \times 1.2 = 2.04\ K/,$$

$$\text{Total } W_U = 2.04 + 2.03 = 4.07\ K/,$$

$$V = \frac{4.07}{2} \times 4 = 8.14\ K$$

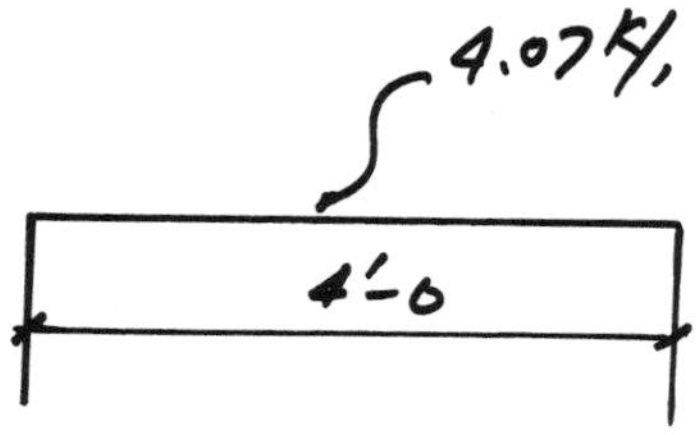

$$d_{\text{by Shear}} = \frac{8.14 \times 1000}{2 \times 0.85 \times 63.5 \times 8} = 9.42$$

Use $d = 9.5$

$h = 12''$

$$M = \frac{wl^2}{8} = \frac{4.07 \times 4^2}{8} = 8.14\ 'k$$

$$F = \frac{12 \times 9.5^2}{12000} = 0.09, \quad K_U = \frac{8.14}{0.09} = 90.0$$

$$A_s = \frac{8.14}{4.45 \times 9.5} = 0.192\ \square''$$ Use 2-#8 Top & BOTT.

#6@12" Stirrups

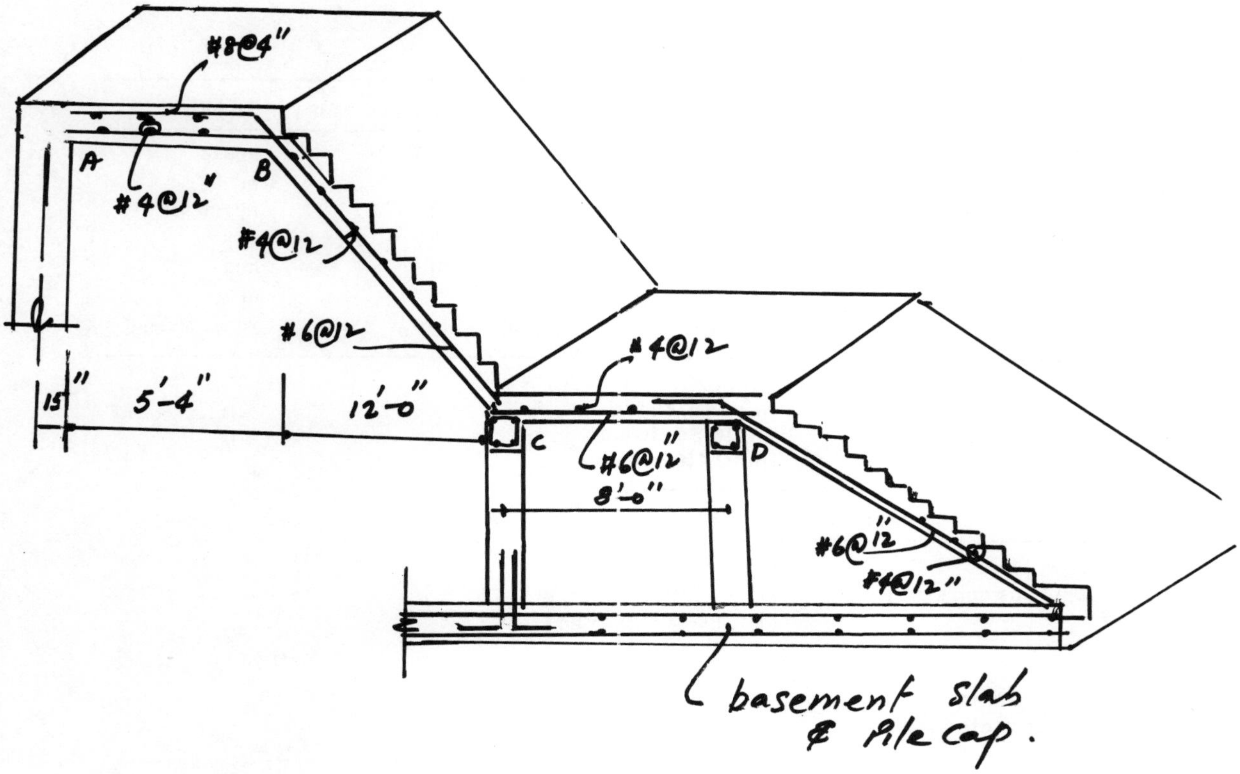
#8@4"
A
B
#4@12"
#4@12
#6@12
15"
5'-4"
12'-0"
#4@12
C
D
#6@12"
8'-0"
#6@12"
#4@12"
basement slab
& pile cap.

CONVERSION FACTORS, U.S. CUSTOMARY UNITS TO SI METRIC UNITS

Overall geometry			U.S. customary	SI metric
Spans	1 ft = 0.3048 m	Area	in^2	mm^2
Displacements	1 in = 25.4 mm		$ft.^2$	m^2
Surface area	1 ft^2 = 0.0929 m^2	Density	lb/ft^3	kg/m^3
Volume	1 ft^3 = 0.0283 m^3	Load	lb	N
	1 yd^3 = 0.765 m^3	Size	in	mm
			ft	m
Structural properties		Stress	lb/in^2	MPa = N/mm^2

Structural properties	
Cross-sectional dimensions	1 in = 25.4 mm
Area	1 in^2 = 645.2 mm^2
Section modulus	1 in^3 = 16.39×10^3 mm^3
Moment of inertia	1 in^4 = 0.4162×10^6 mm^4

Material properties	
Density	1 lb/ft^3 = 16.03 kg/m^3
Modulus and stress	1 lb/in^2 = 0.006895 MPa
	1 kip/in^2 = 6.895 MPa

Loadings	
Concentrated loads	1 lb = 4.448 N
	1 kip = 4.448 kN
Density	1 lb/ft^3 = 0.1571 kN/m^3
Linear loads	1 kip/ft = 14.59 kN/m
Surface loads	1 lb/ft^2 = 0.0479 kN/m^2
	1 kip/ft^2 = 47.9 kN/m^2

Stress and moments	
Stress	1 lb/in^2 = 0.006895 MPa
	1 kip/in^2 = 6.895 MPa
Moment or torque	1 ft-lb = 1.356 N-m
	1 ft·kip = 1.356 kN·m

REFERENCES

1.American Concrete Institute,Detroit,Michagon.Building Code requirement 318-71,77.
2.American Concrete Institute,Detroit,Michagon.Design Handbook.
3.American Insurance Association,New york.National Building Code.
4.American Institute of Steel Construction,Chicago,Ill.
a) Specification for design,fabrication and errection of Structural steel for buildings.
b) Manual of Steel Construction,7th Edition,
c) Plastic Design in Steel.
5.American Petroleum Institute,Standard Specifications for Petroleum Industry for Pressure Vessels.
6.American Society of Civil Engineers,New York.Transaction# 106. pages 1131-1156.
7.American Water Works Association Standards for tanks,reservoir.
8.Beedle,L.S. Plastic design of steel Frames.
9.Bressler,Borris.Design of steel structures.
10.Chellies,R.D. Pile foundations,John Wiley & Sons.
11.Dunham,Foundation of Concrete Structures.
12.Dunham,Theory and practice of Reinforced Cement Concrete.
13.Gaylor/Gaylord.Design of Steel Structures.
14.Gaylord/Gaylord.Structural Engineering Handbook.
15.Johnson,J.R. Design criteria for Hoppers & Bins.
16.Ketchem,M.S. Design of walls,Bins & Elevators.
17.Kleingoel.Rigid Frame Formulae.
18.Leonard,G.A. Foundation Engineering,McGraw Hill Co.
19.Metcalf & Eddy.Waste Water Engineering.
20.Merrit,Structural steel designer Hand Book.
21.Merrit,Civil Engineering Handbook.
22.Portland Cement Association's publication on cement concrete.
23.Terazaghi,Karl and Peck,Soil Mechanics in Engg.Practice.
24.Tall,L,Etall Structural Steel design,Ronald Press Co.
25.Handbook for Ultimate Strength by Structural Engineering Research Center,Roorkee,India.
26.Manual of Standard practice for detailing reinforced concrete Structures by A.C.I.
27.Steel designer's Manual.Published in London.
28. Indian Standard Institute code 456.Code of Practice for plain & Reinforced Concrete.
29.Indian Standard Practice for use of Structural Steel in General Building Construction I.S,800-1962.
30.Timoshenko,Theory of Elastic Stability.

INDEX